The Mössbauer Effect

Frontiers in Physics

A Lecture Note and Reprint Series

DAVID PINES, *Editor*

N. Bloembergen **NUCLEAR MAGNETIC RELAXATION:** *A Reprint Volume*

Geoffrey F. Chew **S-MATRIX THEORY OF STRONG INTERACTIONS:** *A Lecture Note and Reprint Volume*

R. P. Feynman **QUANTUM ELECTRODYNAMICS:** *A Lecture Note and Reprint Volume*

R. P. Feynman **THE THEORY OF FUNDAMENTAL PROCESSES:** *A Lecture Note Volume*

Hans Frauenfelder **THE MÖSSBAUER EFFECT:** *A Collection of Reprints with an Introduction*

David Pines **THE MANY-BODY PROBLEM:** *A Lecture Note and Reprint Volume*

L. Van Hove, N. M. Hugenholtz, and L. P. Howland **PROBLEMS IN THE QUANTUM THEORY OF MANY-PARTICLE SYSTEMS**

The Mössbauer Effect

A Review—with a Collection of Reprints

HANS FRAUENFELDER
University of Illinois

W. A. BENJAMIN, INC.
New York 1963

THE MÖSSBAUER EFFECT
A Review—with a Collection of Reprints

Library of Congress Catalog Card Number: 61-18181
Manufactured in the United States of America

First printing, March 1962
Second printing, with corrections and additions, October 1963

W. A. BENJAMIN, INC.
2465 Broadway, New York 25, New York

EDITOR'S FOREWORD

The problem of communicating in a coherent fashion the recent developments in the most exciting and active fields of physics seems particularly pressing today. The enormous growth in the number of physicists has tended to make the familiar channels of communication considerably less effective. It has become increasingly difficult for experts in a given field to keep up with the current literature; the novice can only be confused. What is needed is both a consistent account of a field and the presentation of a definite "point of view" concerning it. Formal monographs cannot meet such a need in a rapidly developing field, and, perhaps more important, the review article seems to have fallen into disfavor. Indeed, it would seem that the people most actively engaged in developing a given field are the people least likely to write at length about it.

"Frontiers in Physics" has been conceived in an effort to improve the situation in several ways. First, to take advantage of the fact that the leading physicists today frequently give a series of lectures, a graduate seminar, or a graduate course in their special fields of interest. Such lectures serve to summarize the present status of a rapidly developing field and may well constitute the only coherent account available at the time. Often, notes on lectures exist (prepared by the lecturer himself, by graduate students, or by postdoctoral fellows) and have been distributed in mimeographed form on a limited basis. One of the principal purposes of the "Frontiers in Physics" series is to make such notes available to a wider audience of physicists.

It should be emphasized that lecture notes are necessarily rough and informal, both in style and content, and those in the series will prove no exception. This is as it should be. The point of the series is to offer new, rapid, more informal, and, it is hoped, more effective ways for physicists to teach one another. The point is lost if only elegant notes qualify.

A second way to improve communication in very active fields of physics is by the publication of collections of reprints of recent articles. Such collections are themselves useful to people working in the field. The value of the reprints would, however, seem much enhanced if the collection would be accompanied by an introduction of moderate length, which would serve to tie the collection together and, necessarily, constitute a brief survey of the present status of the field. Again, it is appropriate that such an introduction be informal, in keeping with the active character of the field.

A third possibility for the series might be called an informal monograph, to connote the fact that it represents an intermediate step between lecture notes and formal monographs. It would offer the author an opportunity to present his views of a field that has developed to the point at which a summation might prove extraordinarily fruitful, but for which a formal monograph might not be feasible or desirable.

Fourth, there are the contemporary classics—papers or lectures which constitute a particularly valuable approach to the teaching and learning of physics today. Here one thinks of fields that lie at the heart of much of present-day research, but whose essentials are by now well understood, such as quantum electrodynamics or magnetic resonance. In such fields some of the best pedagogical material is not readily available, either because it consists of papers long out of print or lectures that have never been published.

"Frontiers in Physics" is designed to be flexible in editorial format. Authors are encouraged to use as many of the foregoing approaches as seem desirable for the project at hand. The publishing format for the series is in keeping with its intentions. Photo-offset printing is used throughout, and the books are paperbound, in order to speed publication and reduce costs. It is hoped that the books will thereby be within the financial reach of graduate students in this country and abroad.

Finally, because the series represents something of an experiment on the part of the editor and the publisher, suggestions from interested readers as to format, contributors, and contributions will be most welcome.

DAVID PINES

Urbana, Illinois
August 1961

PREFACE

Only four years ago, Rudolf Mössbauer discovered what is now known as the Mössbauer effect: Nuclei that are embedded in solids can emit and absorb low-energy gamma rays which display the natural line width and possess the full transition energy. No recoil energy is transferred to lattice vibrations. Mössbauer's experiment seemed at first to pass unnoticed, but within two years it was repeated and extended. Physicists soon realized that they had at hand a new and beautiful tool—simple in its basic ideas, requiring only a minimum of equipment, and allowing ingenious applications not only in nuclear physics, but also in relativity and in solid-state physics. The early trickle of publications became a stream. The rapidly growing body of knowledge was discussed and information exchanged in two international conferences in 1960 and 1961. In 1961, Rudolf Mössbauer received the Nobel prize.

In the present volume, a number of reprints on the Mössbauer effect are collected. I have tried to select those publications which are either essential to the understanding of the development of this field or which are useful as references for further work. As an introduction to these reprints, the first six chapters contain a review of the Mössbauer effect.

During the preparation of the introductory notes I have enjoyed many discussions with friends and colleagues. I should like to thank particularly K. Bleuler, J. D. Jackson, J. H. D. Jensen, W. E. Lamb, Jr., R. L. Mössbauer, D. E. Nagle, J. Petzold, D. G. Ravenhall, J. R. Schrieffer, and A. H. Taub for stimulating remarks. P. Debrunner, D. W. Hafemeister, S. Margulies, R. J. Morrison, and D. N. Pipkorn have read through many versions of the manuscript and I am grateful to make it more readable than it might otherwise have been. Finally, I should like to thank Mrs. M. Runkel for her unfailing help in the preparation of the manuscript.

HANS FRAUENFELDER

Urbana, Illinois
December 1961

ACKNOWLEDGMENTS

The publisher wishes to acknowledge the assistance of the following organizations in the preparation of this volume:

The American Institute of Physics, for permission to reprint the articles from the Physical Review, Physical Review Letters, Soviet Physics JETP, The Review of Scientific Instruments, and the Journal of Applied Physics.

Academic Press, Inc., for permission to reprint the articles from the Annals of Physics.

Gauthier-Villars Imprimeur-Libraire, for permission to reprint the articles from Comptes rendus hebdomadaires des séances de l'académie des sciences.

The Physical Society, for permission to reprint the articles from their Proceedings.

The Italian Physical Society, for permission to reprint the article from Il Nuovo cimento.

Springer Verlag, for permission to reprint the article from Zeitschrift für Physik.

Verlag der Zeitschrift für Naturforschung, for permission to reprint the article from Zeitschrift für Naturforschung.

North-Holland Publishing Co., for permission to reprint the article from Nuclear Instruments and Methods.

Macmillan & Co., Ltd., for permission to reprint the article from Nature.

CONTENTS

Reprints and Translations

THE MÖSSBAUER EFFECT

1 INTRODUCTION

1-1 RESONANCE FLUORESCENCE

The beauty and fascination of physics rarely becomes more apparent than when one follows a particular topic through the various stages of its development. The history of the neutrino, the most elusive of all particles, is an example. Another is the story of resonance fluorescence, the subject of the present volume. In this chapter, we outline briefly some phases in the history of atomic and nuclear resonance fluorescence and the Mössbauer effect, which begin with the mechanical interpretation of matter and end, hopefully only temporarily, with the Mössbauer effect.

The story of resonance fluorescence starts at the end of the last century with Lord Rayleigh, who suggested that resonance scattering should occur in atomic systems. Considerable time elapsed after this prediction before R. W. Wood discovered resonance radiation in 1904. The explanation of resonance scattering was then based entirely on mechanical analogies. The scattering resonators were assumed to be exactly in tune with the frequency of the incoming radiation. Wood's discovery led to other experiments, the techniques were rapidly improved, and a wealth of data was accumulated.[1-4] †

---

† References not directly connected with the Mössbauer effect are designated by superscripts and listed at the bottom of each page. References dealing specifically with the Mössbauer effect will be found listed in Chapter 7; they are indicated in the text by the name of the first author and the year of publication. Papers reprinted are denoted by "Reprint" and the name of the first author.

[1] R. W. Wood, "Physical Optics," Macmillan, New York, 1934, 3rd ed., Chap. XVIII.

[2] A. C. G. Mitchell and M. W. Zemansky, "Resonance Radiation

It is interesting to note that, in the mechanical picture underlying these early experiments, incoming and outgoing radiation maintain a fixed phase relation.

Resonance fluorescence fitted well into the Bohr theory, which superseded the earlier pictures: An atom, decaying from an excited state B to its ground state A, emits a photon of well-defined frequency ω_r. When such a photon passes through a gas consisting of the same element as the emitter, it can be absorbed and excite a target atom into the state B. After a short time, this excited target atom will in turn decay and emit a photon of frequency ω_r. Primary and secondary radiation thus have the same frequency, but the processes of absorption and reemission are independent and no fixed phase relation exists between them.

Many of the aspects of resonance radiation were correctly described by the Bohr theory and by the early quantum mechanics. However, problems connected with line width, radiation damping, and coherence were not easily explained. The Dirac theory of radiation, in the hands of Weisskopf and Wigner, finally provided a complete description of the processes of emission, absorption, and resonance fluorescence.[5,6] All the fundamental aspects of resonance radiation seemed to be solved, interest in basic investigations of atomic resonance fluorescence decreased, and research moved on to more complicated problems of fluorescence and phosphorescence.[3,4] (Incidentally it may be noted that atomic resonance has recently played an important role once more in the optical orientation of nuclei.)

Since atomic resonance radiation depends essentially on the existence of quantized levels and since quantized levels also occur in nuclei, the possibility of observing nuclear resonance fluorescence was obvious, and the search was started in 1929 by Kuhn.[7] However, even though problems in atomic and nuclear resonance seem very similar, there exist marked differences which render nuclear experiments much more difficult. In order to outline these difficulties, the process of resonance fluorescence must be discussed in more

---

and Excited Atoms," Cambridge University Press, Cambridge, 1934.

[3] P. Pringsheim, "Fluorescence and Phosphorescence," Interscience, New York, 1949.

[4] J. G. Winans and E. J. Seldin, Fluorescence and Phosphorescence, in E. U. Condon and H. Odishaw (eds.), "Handbook of Physics," McGraw-Hill, New York, 1958.

[5] V. Weisskopf, Ann. Physik, 9, 23 (1931). V. Weisskopf and E. Wigner, Z. Physik, 63, 54 (1930); 65, 18 (1930).

[6] W. Heitler, "Quantum Theory of Radiation," Clarendon Press, Oxford, 1949.

[7] W. Kuhn, Phil. Mag., 8, 625 (1929).

detail. Consider a free atomic or nuclear system, of mass M, with two levels A and B, separated by an energy E_r. If the system decays from B to A by emission of a photon of energy E_γ, momentum conservation demands that the momentum **p** of the photon and the momentum **P** of the recoiling system be equal and opposite. The recoiling system hence receives an energy R, given by

$$R = \frac{P^2}{2M} = \frac{p^2}{2M} = \frac{E_\gamma^2}{2Mc^2} \tag{1}$$

In this derivation, it is assumed that the recoiling system can be treated nonrelativistically—an assumption that is extremely well satisfied in atomic and nuclear spectroscopy. Actually, all gamma rays involved in atomic and nuclear resonance fluorescence have energies that are small compared to the rest energy Mc^2 of the emitting atomic or nuclear system. The recoil energy is thus very small compared to the gamma-ray energy.

Energy conservation connects E_r, E_γ, and R:

$$E_r = E_\gamma + R \tag{2}$$

Since R is very small compared to E_γ, and since, as will be obvious later, one needs to know R only to moderate accuracy, E_γ can be replaced by the transition energy E_r in (1):

$$R \cong E_r^2/2Mc^2 \tag{1'}$$

The recoil energy R is plotted in Fig. 1-1 as a function of the transition energy E_r for a quantum system of mass number 100.

One more feature now enters the discussion, namely, the width of the excited state B. Assume that the mean life against decay of the state B is τ. According to the Heisenberg uncertainty relation, the energy in state B then cannot be measured sharply, but only within an uncertainty given by

$$\tau \cdot \Gamma = \hbar \tag{3}$$

where $2\pi\hbar$ is Planck's constant. A detailed examination employing perturbation theory shows indeed that the decaying state B cannot be characterized by one well-defined energy E_r only, but that the energy E of the state is distributed about the center energy E_r as shown in Fig. 1-2a.[6] The energy of the stable ground state, according to (3), is sharp. Photons emitted in the transition from B to A thus show a distribution in energy E_γ, centered around $E_r - R$, and displaying a "natural line shape" of width Γ (Fig. 1-2b). To give an order of magnitude, the line width Γ corresponding to a mean life $\tau = 10^{-8}$

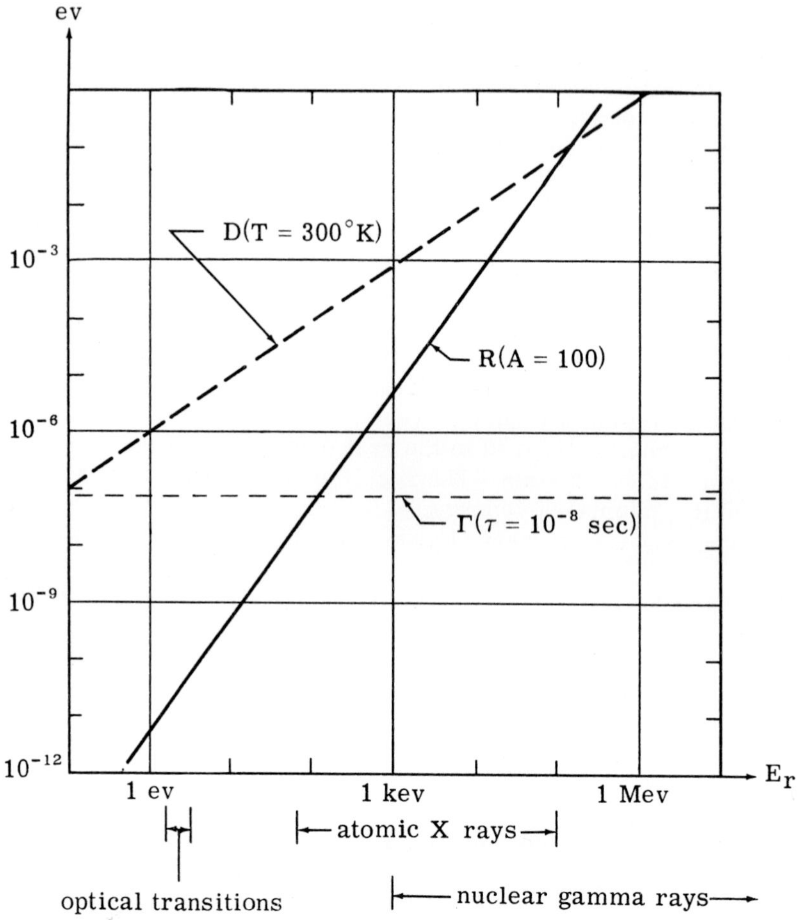

Fig. 1-1 Recoil energy R and Doppler broadening D (for a gas at 300°K) as a function of the transition energy E_r for a nucleus of mass number 100. For comparison, the natural line width Γ corresponding to a lifetime of 10^{-8} sec is shown also.

sec is shown in Fig. 1-1. Such a mean life is typical for atomic states and not unreasonable for low-lying nuclear levels.

Returning to resonance fluorescence again, when a photon of energy E_γ and momentum **p** strikes a target of mass M, which is initially at rest, the entire momentum **p** is transferred to the target. The target thus recoils and the energy of recoil R is again given by (1) or (1′). This energy must be supplied by the gamma ray. Thus

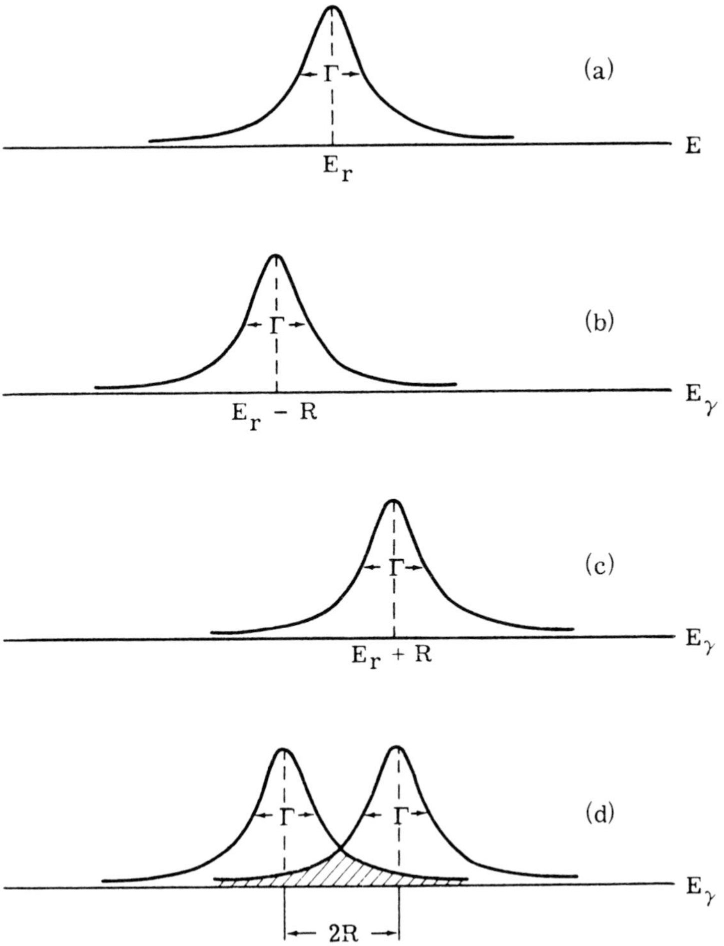

Fig. 1-2 Energy distributions involved in resonance fluorescence. (a) Energy distribution of excited state B. (b) Energy distribution of photons emitted in a transition B → A. (c) Energy spectrum required to excite state B in target *and* provide center-of-mass energy R. (d) Overlap of B and C.

only an energy $E_r - R$ is available for the excitation of internal degrees of freedom (Fig. 1-2b). In order to excite a level of energy E_r, the incoming gamma ray must have an energy $E_r + R$, as shown in Fig. 1-2c. Resonance fluorescence can occur only if some of the incoming photons possess enough energy to "reach" the state B and at the same time provide the energy R to recoiling system. Thus, only the overlapping part of the spectra 2b and 2c is responsible for resonance fluorescence (Fig. 1-2d). The condition for overlap is

$$2R \lesssim \Gamma \tag{4}$$

A glance at Fig. 1-1 shows that optical transitions fulfill condition (4), but that nuclear transitions are far from it.

In the discussion so far, the emitting and the absorbing system were assumed to be at rest. Actually, however, source and target atoms are in thermal motion, and this motion introduces an additional widening of the emission and absorption lines, called Doppler broadening. In order to see this effect qualitatively, consider a source with initial momentum $\mathbf{P}_i$, which emits a photon of momentum $\mathbf{p}$. The momentum of the source after the emission is given by $\mathbf{P}_i - \mathbf{p}$. The energy gained by the source and hence lost by the gamma ray is, in good approximation,†

$$R' = \frac{(\mathbf{P}_i - \mathbf{p})^2}{2M} - \frac{P_i^2}{2M} = \frac{p^2}{2M} - \frac{\mathbf{p} \cdot \mathbf{P}_i}{M} \tag{5}$$

The first term on the right-hand side of (5) is the recoil energy R [Eq. (1)] of the initially stationary system; the second term represents the Doppler broadening. Introducing the kinetic energy $\varepsilon = P_i^2/2M$ of the quantum system before the photon emission and a "Doppler energy"

$$D = 2(\varepsilon R)^{1/2} \tag{6}$$

this second term can be written

$$D \cos \varphi$$

where φ denotes the angle between $\mathbf{p}$ and $\mathbf{P}_i$. The photon energy then becomes

$$E_\gamma = E_r - R' = E_r - R + D \cos \varphi \tag{7}$$

where $E_r = E_B - E_A$ is the total energy released in the transition B → A. Generally the angle φ will vary from 0 to 2π and the Doppler term in (7) causes a spread in the photon energy E_γ of the order of D.

†In (5) it is assumed that the mass of the quantum system does not change during the emission. Actually, there is a very small change in mass, because the photon carries away energy. This effect has been observed experimentally (Sec. 5-4) but is unimportant in the present context.

In a source in which the velocities of the individual emitters are isotropic in direction and Maxwellian in magnitude, this additional broadening is of the order

$$\overline{D} \cong 2(\bar{\varepsilon}R)^{1/2} \tag{8}$$

where $\bar{\varepsilon}$ is the average value of the kinetic energy of the emitters. In Fig. 1-1 curve D represents such a Doppler broadening, corresponding roughly to that of a gaseous source at room temperature. Comparison of Fig. 1-2 and the three curves in Fig. 1-1 shows that the natural line width Γ is not always the dominant feature in resonance fluorescence; the Doppler broadening also plays an important role. For optical radiation, the recoil energy R is small compared to the Doppler broadening, emission and absorption lines overlap, and resonance conditions are obtained. For nuclear gamma rays, however, the recoil energy is comparable to, or greater than, the Doppler broadening, and the discussion of when to expect a measurable resonance fluorescence effect requires an investigation of the cross section for resonance fluorescence under various conditions.

1-2 CROSS SECTION FOR RESONANCE PROCESSES

Resonance experiments with gamma rays are usually performed by either measuring the scattered intensity (resonance fluorescence or resonance scattering) or by determining the attenuation of a beam due to resonance absorption. The cross sections for these two processes, for an incident gamma ray of energy E and wavelength $2\pi \lambda\!\!\!^{-2}$, can be calculated in a straightforward way[6,8] and, for thin absorbers, can be written

$$\sigma_{\text{scatt}}(E) = \sigma_0 \frac{\Gamma_\gamma^2}{4(E - E_r)^2 + \Gamma^2} \tag{9}$$

$$\sigma_{\text{abs}}(E) = \sigma_0 \frac{\Gamma \Gamma_\gamma}{4(E - E_r)^2 + \Gamma^2} \tag{10}$$

In these expressions, Γ is the total width of the absorption line, Γ_γ its gamma-ray width, and σ_0 the maximum resonance cross section given by

$$\sigma_0 = \frac{2I_B + 1}{2I_A + 1} 2\pi \lambda\!\!\!^{-2} \tag{11}$$

In (11) I_A is the spin of the ground state A and I_B the spin of the excited state B.

[8] J. D. Jackson, Can. J. Phys., 33, 575 (1955).

Scattering and absorption cross sections as given by (9) and (10) show a characteristic energy dependence of the form

$$I(E) = \frac{\Gamma}{2\pi} \frac{1}{(E - E_r)^2 + [(1/2)\Gamma]^2} \tag{12}$$

which is normalized to

$$\int_0^\infty I(E)\, dE = 1 \tag{12'}$$

Corresponding curves are sketched in Fig. 1-2. These distributions are said to show a Breit-Wigner or Lorentz shape. The parameter Γ gives the full width of the distribution at half maximum.

Since expressions (9) and (10) are fundamental for the Mössbauer effect, it is important to know that they are derived under the following assumptions:

a. Only one absorbing or scattering level exists. If more than one state appears at, or close to, the energy E_r, or if the state at E_r is split into sublevels, for instance by a strong magnetic field, then (9) and (10) must be modified (Margulies, 1962).

b. The width of the level is given entirely by decay processes. In nuclei, in all interesting cases, the two competing modes are gamma-ray emission and internal conversion. Total width and gamma-ray width are then related by the equation

$$\Gamma_\gamma = \frac{1}{1 + \alpha} \Gamma \tag{13}$$

where α is the coefficient of internal conversion. If the level is broadened by other influences, the line shape need not be Lorentzian.

c. The incoming photon is monoenergetic. An actual source, however, will possess an energy spectrum I(E), where I(E) dE denotes the number of gamma rays emitted with energies between E and E + dE. The observed cross sections for scattering and absorption then become integrals of the form

$$\sigma_{eff} = \frac{\int_0^\infty \sigma(E) I(E)\, dE}{\int_0^\infty I(E)\, dE} \tag{14}$$

Here in the introduction only two special cases of (14) will be treated. Further cases appear in the various reprints.

1. The incoming gamma ray possesses an energy E_r; its width is small compared to the width Γ, and the conversion coefficient α is zero. I(E) in this case is essentially a delta function $\delta(E_r)$, and from (9), (10), (13), and (14) one finds

$$\sigma_{\text{scatt}}(E_r) = \sigma_{\text{abs}}(E_r) = \sigma_0$$

This result explains the designation "maximum resonance cross section" for σ_0.

2. The incoming gamma ray has an energy spectrum I(E) described by a Lorentz shape [Eq. (12)], with a width Γ identical to the width of the absorbing state, and with its energy centered at E_r. In a resonance fluorescence experiment these assumptions mean that the recoil energy R is either negligible or has been compensated for, and that emitting and absorbing state are identical and are not broadened by external influences. With these assumptions, one finds from (10), (12), and (14) for the maximum cross section for the resonance absorption of a gamma ray with width Γ by a level with identical width,

$$\sigma_{\text{eff abs}} = \sigma_0 \frac{\Gamma_\gamma}{2\Gamma} = \frac{\sigma_0}{2(1+\alpha)} \tag{15}$$

One trivial remark must be added here. The actual width of the incoming gamma ray and of the absorbing level are both given by Γ and not by Γ_γ. Γ_γ is not a width that can be traced experimentally, but rather a quantity F which characterizes the fraction of decays proceeding by photon emission.

Equation (15) leads back to resonance fluorescence. In fact, it describes resonance absorption under the most ideal conditions, namely, (I) emission and absorption line possess the natural line width, and (II) emission and absorption line are centered at the same energy. If these two conditions are satisfied, the cross section for resonance absorption, given by (15), is very large provided the conversion coefficient is reasonably small. The effective maximum resonance cross section is plotted against photon energy in Fig. 1-3. It is obvious from the values in Fig. 1-3 that resonance experiments should yield large effects provided the two conditions I and II can be satisfied. Another glance at Fig. 1-1 shows that for optical resonance fluorescence, the second assumption is valid, but the first is not because Doppler broadening considerably widens the lines. The correct cross section for resonance scattering in the presence of Doppler broadening can be calculated easily. Even without calculation, one can make a good guess. Assume the target to be at rest and the incoming photons to have an energy spectrum characterized by a Doppler width D. Only a small part of the widened incoming spectrum overlaps with the resonance level. The fraction of incoming photons capable of undergoing resonance absorption is approximately equal to Γ/D. This fraction, however, is centered at the resonance energy E_r and hence enjoys approximately the maximum resonance cross section $\sigma_0 \Gamma_\gamma/\Gamma$ given by (10) for $E = E_r$. The effective absorption cross section thus becomes

$$\sigma_{abs}^{D} \cong \sigma_0 \frac{\Gamma_\gamma}{\Gamma} \frac{\Gamma}{D} \cong \sigma_0 \frac{\Gamma_\gamma}{D} \tag{16}$$

This estimate, which is borne out quite well by the exact calculation, shows that the maximum cross section is reduced by a factor

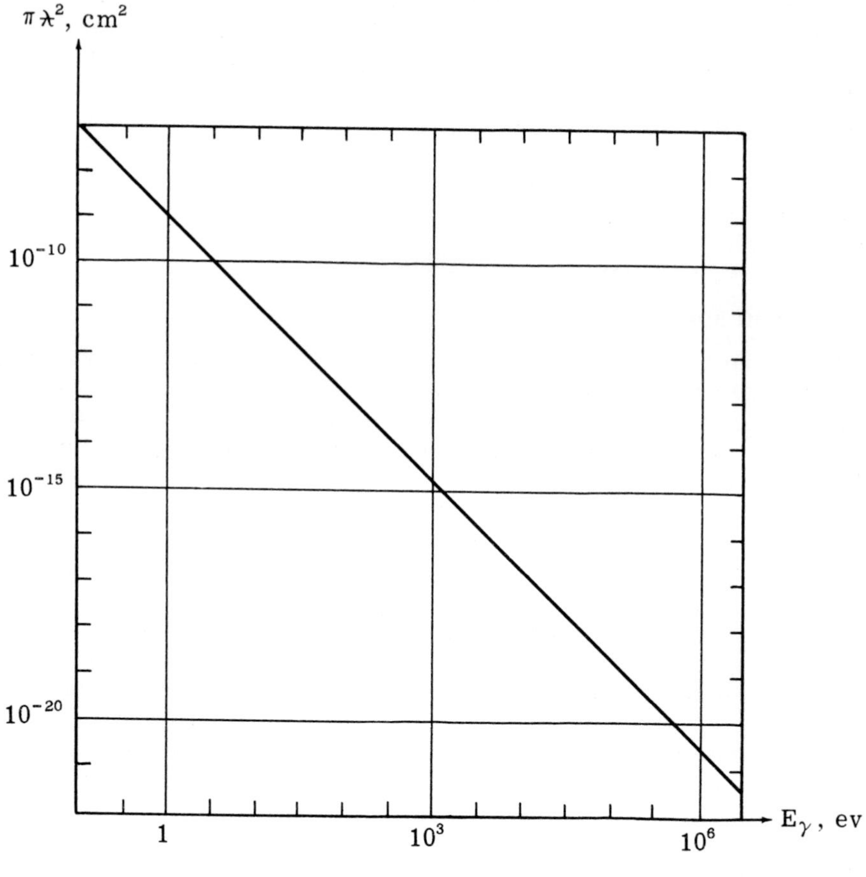

Fig. 1-3 Effective maximum resonance absorption cross section $\pi\lambda\!\!\!^{-2}$ as a function of photon energy. The curve is valid for vanishing conversion coefficient and for identical spins in the two states involved. To find the cross section for a decay with spins I_A, I_B, and with conversion coefficient α, multiply the value obtained from the curve by

$$\frac{2I_B + 1}{2I_A + 1} \frac{1}{1 + \alpha}$$

Γ_γ/D. For optical transitions, internal conversion is impossible, and $\Gamma_\gamma = \Gamma$. From Fig. 1-1 one can see that the maximum cross section is reduced only by one or two orders of magnitude and that experiments with optical transitions should be feasible—as indeed they are.

In nuclear experiments, both conditions are violated, but the second can be restored by several means. In 1950, Moon performed the first successful experiment by plating a source of Au^{198} onto the tips of a steel rotor and spinning the rotor up to tip speeds of 800 m/sec.[9] Gamma rays emitted tangentially thus gained additional energy sufficient to compensate for the recoil loss. Other possibilities of compensating for the recoil energy loss, for instance the use of the recoil from a transition preceding the gamma ray to be investigated, or the heating of source and absorber to increase the average kinetic energy, have also been used with positive results.

Despite these ingenious experiments, classical nuclear resonance fluorescence experiments are never easy, since condition (I) is not fulfilled. The ratio Γ_γ/D in (18) is much smaller for nuclear than for optical transitions. Figure 1-1 indicates that the maximum cross section is decreased by many orders of magnitude. Despite these difficulties many good experiments have been performed since 1950. These experiments and the underlying theory are discussed in a number of review articles.[10-12]

1-3 MÖSSBAUER'S DISCOVERY

Comparing (15) and (16) one is struck by the price one must pay for the effects of thermal motion. The question arises of whether there is a way to avoid the large decrease in cross section which is caused entirely by nonnuclear processes.

Dicke in 1952 theoretically studied the reduction of Doppler broadening by collisions in a dense gas[13] (Reprint Dicke). As a simple model he used a radiating atom enclosed in a one-dimensional well oscillating back and forth between the walls. Actually, such a model is more appropriate to the description of a solid. In any case, he found a normal Doppler distribution plus a sharp, non-Doppler broadened and unshifted line. Today, such a line would be

---

[9] P. B. Moon, Proc. Phys. Soc., **63**, 1189 (1950).

[10] K. G. Malmfors in K. Siegbahn (ed.), "Beta- and Gamma-Ray Spectroscopy," North-Holland, Amsterdam, 1955, Chap. XVIII(II).

[11] F. R. Metzger in O. R. Frisch (ed.), "Progress in Nuclear Physics," Pergamon, New York, 1959, Vol. 7.

[12] S. Devons in Fay Ajzenberg-Selove (ed.), "Nuclear Spectroscopy," Part A, Academic, New York, 1960, Chap. IV(B).

[13] R. H. Dicke, Phys. Rev., **89**, 472 (1953).

called a Mössbauer line. No successful experiments were carried out, however, before 1957 and Dicke's calculation had no influence on the later development.

R. L. Mössbauer, in 1957, started the dramatic next step from a completely different side, by an accidental discovery. (Reprint Mössbauer 1958, 1959) He investigated the nuclear resonance scattering of the 129-kev gamma ray from Ir^{191}. For this transition, the free recoil energy R is 0.05 ev, the Doppler broadening at room temperature about 0.1 ev. At room temperature emission and absorption spectrum thus overlap considerably, and resonance scattering can be observed. In order to reduce this residual scattering, Mössbauer cooled both source and absorber and expected a decrease in effect. Instead, the resonance scattering increased! After carefully ascertaining that this increase was not spurious, Mössbauer set out to investigate the nature of this surprising effect. Following a suggestion by Jensen, he found a paper by Lamb[14] (Reprint Lamb) in which the effect of lattice binding on the capture cross section of slow neutrons is discussed. The figures 2 and 3 in Lamb's paper already show peaks that could be called "Lamb-Mössbauer peaks." (Compare also reference 15.) By adapting Lamb's calculation to gamma rays, Mössbauer was able to explain his own experimental results. In one beautiful experiment, he had thus found the solution to both problems outlined in Sec. 1-2: A fraction of the 129-kev gamma rays, emitted by the cooled source, did not show a measurable recoil energy loss, and these same gamma rays also did not display a Doppler broadening. Their line width corresponded to the natural line width.

After Mössbauer's first publication (Reprint Mössbauer 1958), about a year elapsed before other laboratories, particularly Los Alamos and Argonne, began to repeat and extend his experiments. (As an amusing side remark, it may be told that the research at Los Alamos was started by a bet. Two physicists were discussing Mössbauer's discovery and one of the two did not believe it. The other bet a nickel that the effect was real and that he could repeat the experiment. He won.) All these early experiments, performed with Ir^{191}, were complicated by low-temperature requirements and by the smallness of the effect.

The next major advance came through the discovery of the Mössbauer effect in Fe^{57}, made independently at Harvard, Harwell, the University of Illinois, and Argonne. The ease with which the effect can be demonstrated with Fe^{57}, its very large size, its persistence up to temperatures of over 1000°C, and the very narrow natural line width, immediately changed this field of physics from one accessible

---

[14] W. E. Lamb, Jr., Phys. Rev., **55**, 190 (1939).

[15] H. Ott, Ann. Physik, **23**, 169 (1935).

to only a few laboratories to one in which even modestly equipped groups could compete. Moreover, the extremely narrow line width of Fe^{57} and the fantastically large value of E_r/Γ opened possibilities, such as the measurement of the red shift of photons in a terrestrial laboratory, which were thought to be impossible a short time earlier.

After these advances, more nuclei showing recoilless resonance absorption were found and many new and exciting experiments were performed. The various phases in the still young history of the Mössbauer effect are summarized in Table 1-1, due to H. J. Lipkin.

Table 1-1 History of the Mössbauer Effect[a]

Period	Date	Remarks
Prehistoric	Before 1958	Might have been discovered, but wasn't
Early iridium age	1958	Discovered, but not noticed
Middle iridium age	1958-1959	Noticed, but not believed
Late iridium age	1959	Believed, but not interesting
Iron age	1959-1960	Wow!!

[a]H. J. Lipkin, private communication.

1-4 LITERATURE AND REPRINTS

The description of resonance fluorescence in this chapter should give some of the background which is usually hard to find in research papers. Chapters 2 to 6 are more condensed, since they are intended mainly as guides to the collected reprints and to the literature. Only aspects that seem most important to the understanding of the physics of Mössbauer effect are given. Further details and summaries can be found in the review papers on recoilless emission of gamma rays, listed in Chapter 7.

The reprints collected in the back have been selected either because they have been essential in the development of the field or because they illustrate important aspects and are useful for contemplating new experiments or extensions of the theory. Any such selection is arbitrary and subject to Dyson's law: "If a book is to be published at a time T, and if it is supposed to be up-to-date to a time T − t, then it will inevitably be out-of-date at the time T + t."[16] However, it is hoped that within the limits of this law the selection and the introductory chapters will prove to be useful.

[16] F. J. Dyson, Physics Today, 8 (6), 27 (1955).

2 THEORY

2-1 PRELIMINARY REMARKS

Mössbauer, after his experimental discovery of recoilless gamma-ray emission and absorption, successfully explained these phenomena. He did so by adapting to gamma rays Lamb's theory of neutron capture by atoms bound in a crystal (Reprint Lamb, Reprint and Translation Mössbauer). Since then a number of theoretical papers have extended and elaborated the basic aspects. Despite the number of publications, however, some unsolved and unclear questions remain, as illustrated for instance by two quotes from recent papers: "It turns out that the existence of the Mössbauer line is a purely classical effect," and "The Mössbauer effect can only be understood quantum mechanically. The classical picture fails completely if one wants to understand the behavior of the emitter." A comparison between a classical treatment (Section 2-3) and the quantum mechanical theory (Section 2-5) shows that the former indeed yields some of the essential features, particularly the existence of an unshifted line and its correct intensity. Since the classical calculation assumes that the gamma rays are emitted without transfering recoil momentum to the emitter, the existence of an unshifted line is put into the theory and only the appearance of the correct expression for the intensity is surprising. The correct treatment of the Mössbauer effect must include recoil phenomena, and it can only be based on quantum mechanics.

Indeed, a complete treatment of the Mössbauer effect requires nearly all of quantum mechanics and it is then not surprising to observe that the apparent paradoxes of quantum theory, such as the famous double-slit experiment, appear again, in a somewhat changed form. In discussing the formulas describing recoilless emission and absorption, one must watch out not to quarrel about aspects that cannot be measured in principle. No better warning can be given than Pauli's:[17] "It is essential to observe that a statement, according to

---

[17] W. Pauli, Die allgemeinen Prinzipien der Wellenmechanik, "Encylopedia of Physics," Springer, Berlin, 1958, Vol. V, Part 1, p. 69 (note also page 136).

which a system, independent of a determination by a measurement, contains a well-defined internal energy E_n, or equivalently is in a well-defined *stationary* state, easily leads to contradictions. This is true particularly where the older quantum theory talks of 'transition processes' among the various stationary states of the system."

In this chapter a short outline of the main features of lattice vibrations (Sec. 2-2) is followed by a discussion of the classical theory (Sec. 2-3). A primitive picture underlying the quantum mechanical treatment is sketched in Sec. 2-4. Some aspects of the theory usually assumed to be known are presented in Sec. 2-5. Finally, some remarks about the Debye-Waller factor are added.

In all sections, the emphasis is placed on outlining the physical features and providing some elementary discussions which are omitted in the published papers. The complete treatment can be found in the reprints on theory.

2-2 LATTICE VIBRATIONS

Some knowledge of the theory of lattice vibrations is essential for an understanding of the mechanism of recoilless gamma-ray emission. The very simplest aspects are presented here as a reminder. Detailed treatments are contained, for instance, in Refs. 18-21.

One of the puzzles of classical physics was the decrease of the specific heat of solids below a certain critical temperature. Einstein, in 1907, first explained this decrease by assuming that a solid consisted of a large number of independent linear oscillators, each vibrating with a frequency ω_E. The corresponding spectrum of lattice vibrations is shown in Fig. 2-1a.

Einstein's theory explained the decrease of specific heats qualitatively, but the exponential behavior at very low temperatures predicted by his theory differed from the experimentally observed T^3 dependence. Debye, in 1912, derived the T^3 dependence and thus improved the agreement between theory and experiment by introducing a continuum of oscillator frequencies, ranging from zero to a maximum frequency ω_D and obeying a distribution function.

$$c(\omega) = \text{const. } \omega^2 \tag{17}$$

---

[18] M. Blackman in "Encyclopedia of Physics," Springer, Berlin, 1955, Vol. VII, Part 1.

[19] J. DeLauney in F. Seitz and D. Turnbull (eds.), "Solid State Physics," Academic, New York, 1956, Vol. 2, p. 219.

[20] C. Kittel, "Introduction to Solid State Physics," Wiley, New York, 1956, Chaps. 5 and 6.

[21] E. W. Montroll in E. U. Condon and H. Odishaw (eds.), "Handbook of Physics," McGraw-Hill, New York, 1958, Sec. 5-150.

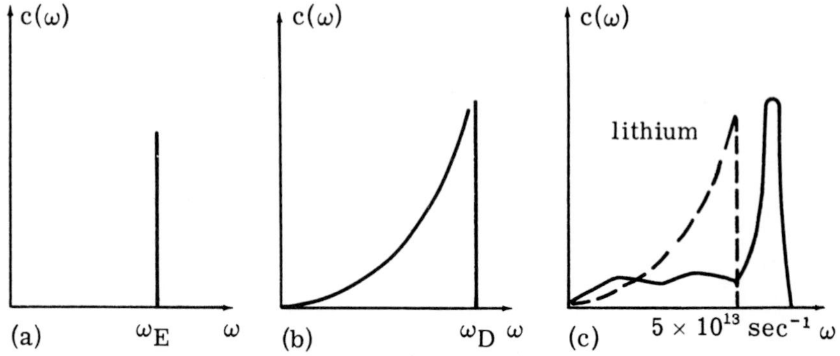

Fig. 2-1 Spectrum of lattice vibrations in a solid: (a) Einstein model, (b) Debye model, (c) Born-von Karman model. [After G. Leibfried and W. Brenig, Z. Physik, **134**, 451 (1953).]

Such a distribution, shown in Fig. 2-1b, can be derived by assuming the solid to be a homogeneous and isotropic medium, the group velocity of waves of all frequencies to be the same, and the total number of (one-dimensional) linear oscillators to be equal to three times the number N of atoms in a solid.

Debye's theory explained the experimental data very well. However it was soon realized that the actual vibrational spectra, while obeying a ω^2 dependence at low frequencies, markedly deviate from it at higher frequencies and calculations to find more detailed spectra were performed. The way to perform these calculations had already been pointed out in 1913 by Born and von Karman. They determined the spectrum by first finding the normal modes of a lattice consisting of mass points connected by springs and by deriving the spring constants from the interatomic force law. A result of a typical calculation is shown in Fig. 2-1c. The deviation from the Debye model is apparent.

One often assumes for simplicity that the Debye model is correct and then defines a characteristic temperature, called *Debye temperature* Θ_D, by the equation

$$E_D = \hbar\omega_D = k\Theta_D \tag{18}$$

Here ω_D is the cut-off frequency shown in Fig. 2-1b, which in the Debye theory is given by the condition that the total number of all oscillators be equal to 3N. Experimentally, one can determine the Debye temperature from specific heat measurements, from X-ray reflection, or from elastic constants. Values range from 88 °K for Pb to 1000 °K for Be. However, one must be careful not to identify, without detailed investigations, the Debye temperature measured in a conventional way with the constant that enters calculations of the Mössbauer effect.

2-3 THE CLASSICAL THEORY

A classical expression for the intensity of the Mössbauer line has been given by Shapiro (Shapiro 1961) and Van Kranendonk (Van Kranendonk 1961, and unpublished lecture notes). Since no relevant reprints are reproduced in this volume, the derivation will be sketched in the present section.

The vector potential of an electromagnetic wave, emitted by a classical oscillator of constant frequency, can be written as

$$\mathbf{A}(t) = \mathbf{A}_0 \exp(i\omega_0 t)$$

where without loss of generality, $\mathbf{A}_0$ is normalized to $|\mathbf{A}_0|^2 = 1$. If the frequency is a function of time, this equation is replaced by

$$\mathbf{A}(t) = \mathbf{A}_0 \exp\left[i \int_0^t \omega(t')\, dt'\right] \tag{19}$$

Assume for simplicity that the emitting oscillator moves in the x direction, with a velocity $v(t)$ which is small compared to the light velocity c. The Doppler effect changes the frequency of the emitted wave

$$\omega(t') = \omega_0 [1 + v(t')/c] \tag{20}$$

Inserting (20) into (19) and integrating yields

$$\mathbf{A} = \mathbf{A}_0 \exp(i\omega_0 t) \exp[i\omega_0 x(t)/c]$$

or

$$\mathbf{A} = \mathbf{A}_0 \exp(i\omega_0 t) \exp[ix(t)/\lambda\!\!\!^-] \tag{21}$$

The essential features can now be discussed by letting the source of the electromagnetic wave execute a simple harmonic motion, with frequency Ω and amplitude x_0,

$$x(t) = x_0 \sin \Omega t \tag{22}$$

The vector potential becomes

$$\mathbf{A} = \mathbf{A}_0 \exp(i\omega_0 t) \exp(ix_0 \sin \Omega t/\lambda\!\!\!^-) \tag{23}$$

Such expressions are well known from the theory of frequency modulation in radio transmission. The spectrum, which originally just contained the carrier frequency ω_0, splits up into lines of frequencies ω_0,

$\omega_0 \pm \Omega$, $\omega_0 \pm 2\Omega$ .... This splitting is derived in the following way. Using the expansion[22]

$$\exp(iy \sin \Theta) = \sum_{n=-\infty}^{\infty} J_n(y) \exp(in\Theta) \tag{24}$$

Eq. (23) becomes

$$\mathbf{A} = \mathbf{A}_0 \sum_{n=-\infty}^{\infty} J_n(x_0/\lambda\!\!\!^{-}) \exp[i(\omega_0 + n\Omega)t] \tag{25}$$

Equation (25) indeed describes an electromagnetic wave which is a superposition of partial waves with frequencies ω_0, $\omega_0 \pm \Omega$, $\omega_0 \pm 2\Omega$.... The amplitude of each wave is given by the Bessel function $J_n(x_0/\lambda\!\!\!^{-})$. The unshifted line can be identified with the Mössbauer line. Its intensity is given by

$$f = |\mathbf{A}(n = 0)|^2 = J_0^2(x_0/\lambda\!\!\!^{-}) \tag{26}$$

Since A_0 is normalized, f directly yields the probability of emission of the unshifted component.

So far, it has been assumed that the emitted wave is modulated by one frequency only. Applied to solids, this assumption corresponds to the Einstein model (Fig. 2-1a). In order to use the previous discussion for real solids, one must generalize (22), (23), and (25) to correspond to the correct frequency spectrum. The frequency Ω and the amplitude x_0 are replaced by a sum over frequencies Ω_m with amplitudes x_m. One finds instead of (26)

$$f = \prod_{m=1}^{3N} J_0^2(x_m/\lambda\!\!\!^{-}) \tag{27}$$

The number 3N of frequencies in a solid is extremely large. Each of the factors J_0^2 in (27) is only very slightly different from unity since the maximum amplitude x_m of each individual frequency component is extremely small. Thus J_0 can be expanded

$$J_0(y) = 1 - (1/4)y^2 + \cdots$$

and (27) can be written

[22] H. Jeffreys and B. S. Jeffreys, "Methods of Mathematical Physics," Cambridge University Press, New York, 1956, Sec. 21.10.

$$\ln f = 2 \sum_m \ln J_0 \simeq 2 \sum_m \ln [1 - (1/4)(x_m^2/\lambda\!\!\!^{-2})]$$

$$\simeq -2 \sum_m (1/4)(x_m^2/\lambda\!\!\!^{-2}) \tag{28}$$

In this expression, $\ln f$ is a function of the maximum excursions x_m. Usually one introduces the mean-square deviation of the vibrating atom from its equilibrium position by the definition

$$\langle x^2 \rangle = (1/2) \sum_m x_m^2 \tag{29}$$

and writes instead of (28)

$$\ln f \simeq -\langle x^2 \rangle / \lambda\!\!\!^{-2}$$

This equation is exact in the limit $N \rightarrow \infty$ (Van Kranendonk 1961), so that the final result can be written

$$f = \exp(-\langle x^2 \rangle / \lambda\!\!\!^{-2}) \tag{30}$$

Equation (30) leads to some interesting remarks:

1. It is not surprising that the classical treatment yields an unshifted line. The exact agreement between the classical expression (30) and the quantum mechanical result, as given in Sec. 2-5, Eq. (56), is unexpected, however.

2. Equation (30) allows a simple physical interpretation. The continuously emitted electromagnetic wave comes from a region of linear dimensions $\langle x^2 \rangle$. If this linear dimension increases beyond the wavelength $\lambda\!\!\!^{-} = \lambda/2\pi$, pieces of the wave train emitted from different points in this region interfere destructively, and the fraction f of photons emitted without energy loss decreases rapidly.

3. The condition for appreciable emission without energy loss, namely, that the amplitude of the emitting atom is small compared to the wavelength of the emitted photon, means that small spatial zero-point vibrations are essential for a large Mössbauer effect. The uncertainty relation then asserts that large zero-point momenta must be present.

4. The wave train described by (23) is infinitely long and the corresponding emission line is infinitely narrow. In decays with a mean life τ, the lines possess a width Γ, Eq. (3), and the spectrum corresponding to (25) then is of the form shown in Fig. 2-2. From this spectrum it is obvious that the Mössbauer line is clearly recognizable only if the line width Γ is smaller than the separation $\hbar\Omega$ from the first satellite, i.e., if the nuclear lifetime τ is larger than the characteristic lattice time $1/\Omega$. This latter time is of the order of 10^{-13} sec.

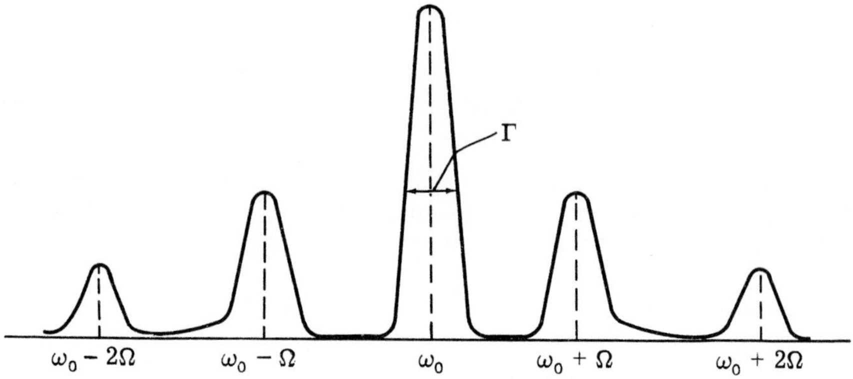

Fig. 2-2 Spectrum of a classical electromagnetic wave of finite length emitted by an Einstein solid.

5. Figure 2-2 gives a somewhat misleading impression since it is based on an Einstein solid without interaction among the various oscillators. In an actual solid, whether described by an Einstein model with interaction (Van Kranendonk 1961) or by a Debye model, only the unshifted line shows the natural width Γ; the satellites overlap each other and give rise to a continuum (Reprints on theory).

6. The treatment outlined in this section can also be applied to experiments where the Mössbauer effect is observed with the source mounted on a crystal that oscillates with a frequency Ω. Such an experiment is described in a reprint (Reprint Ruby and Bolef).

2-4 THE PHYSICAL PICTURE

Before sketching the quantum mechanical theory of the Mössbauer effect, a discussion of the physical picture may elucidate some of the aspects which can be lost easily in the formalism. Much of the discussion is based on the unfailing war horse of physicists, the uncertainty principle. Part of the treatment follows lectures by Weisskopf (Weisskopf 1961).

Three separate questions will be considered; momentum conservation, energy conservation, and the time sequence and duration of events.

2-41 Momentum Conservation

Assume that the nucleus of an atom which is embedded in a solid decays by gamma emission. If free, the nucleus would receive a recoil momentum $\mathbf{p}$ and a recoil energy R, given by (1). How does the binding of the atom in the solid affect recoil momentum and recoil energy? The answer to the first question is straightforward: The momentum is unchanged, but it is taken up by the solid as a whole. In order to justify this statement, consider the two other possibilities, translational motion of the nucleus and phonons (lattice vibrations). The momentum cannot go into translational motion of the nucleus. The energy required to leave a lattice site is at least of the order of 10 ev; the energy available, however, never exceeds a few tenths of an ev. (Even if the recoil were larger, the nucleus would finally come to rest and transfer its momentum to the solid.) Lattice vibrations, on the other hand, cannot take up momentum. They can be represented as standing waves or as the sum of running waves. To each wave with its momentum pointing in one direction will be a corresponding one with its momentum pointing in the opposite direction. The expectation value of the momentum for lattice vibrations vanishes. (Even if the recoiling nucleus initially starts a shock wave that travels through the lattice, the shock wave will finally be damped out, and one is led back to the equilibrium situation discussed here.) The momentum hence must go into translational motion of the entire crystal. If the crystal is glued to a larger body, for instance the earth, this larger body takes up the momentum. The momentum conservation is taken care of and one can now turn his attention to the energy conservation. (Incidentally, the nearly complete separation of the energy transfer from the momentum transfer which occurs in the Mössbauer effect appears also in many classical problems, such as when one shoots a bullet into a very heavy pendulum.)

2-42 Energy Conservation

The discussion of the energy conservation is more complicated, since the transition energy can be shared amont the gamma ray, the individual atom, lattice vibrations, and the solid as a whole. Two of these four parts can be dispenses with quickly. The individual atom does not leave its lattice site (see Sec. 2-41) and hence cannot acquire translational energy. The energy that goes into motion of the entire solid is extremely small and will be neglected. The transition energy, for all practical purposes, is thus shared between the gamma ray and the phonons. A Mössbauer transition occurs if the state of the lattice remains unchanged, and the gamma ray gets the entire transition energy.

The fact that transitions can occur in which the lattice remains in its initial state and the gamma ray receives the full energy follows from the quantum mechanical treatment (Sec. 2-5). A naive picture can be given which makes this result plausible for the Einstein solid, as well as for a solid with a continuously distributed frequency spectrum. For the Einstein solid, the problem is very simple. The smallest amount of energy that can be given to the solid is equal to $E_E = \hbar\omega_E = k\Theta_E$. If the energy R (i.e., the recoil energy of a *free* nucleus) is small compared to this excitation energy, the probability of emission of a phonon will be small, the lattice will not be excited and the gamma ray will escape with the full transition energy. The calculation (Sec. 2-5) shows indeed that the probability f for a transition without energy loss is given by

$$f = \exp(-R/k\Theta_E) \tag{31}$$

For the Debye solid, the situation is more complicated. Assume first that the decay proceeds in such a way that a lattice vibration of the shortest possible wavelength, i.e., the maximum energy $E_D = \hbar\omega_D = k\Theta_D$, is excited. The wavelength of this shortest lattice wave is $\lambda \approx 2d$, where d is the lattice constant. In a continuum theory, such as the Debye theory, the corresponding energy is

$$E_D = \hbar\omega_D = \hbar u/\lambda\!\!\!{}^{-} \approx 2\pi\hbar u/2d \tag{32}$$

where u is the sound velocity in the solid. If this particular lattice wave were the only one that could be excited, one would be in the same case as before and (31) would hold, with Θ_E replaced by Θ_D. However, lattice modes with longer wavelength and hence smaller energy exist, and one would expect that these vibrations can be excited easily, thus making a Mössbauer effect impossible. The fact that these modes with smaller energy cannot be excited as easily as expected can be seen as follows. The highest mode corresponds approximately to a situation where two adjacent atoms move out of phase. Such a wave can be excited most efficiently if the decaying atom is assumed to be free, receives its full share R of the recoil energy, and then bumps into a neighboring atom. A simple mechanical analog is the well-known demonstration experiment in which a number of spheres hang from a frame and tough each other. Lifting the outermost sphere and letting it bump into the row excites a wave which travels through the chain and causes one sphere at the other end to jump off. In order to excite longer waves in this mechanical model, one lifts N spheres at one end, releases them, and N will bounce off at the other end. Similarly, a longer wave can be excited most efficiently in the solid if initially N atoms move together. The wavelength then is approximately 2Nd, and the energy of this wave is, according to (32), about E_D/N. However, in order most efficiently to excite this longer wave, N atoms must move together at the onset, and the recoil energy must be transferred to these N atoms "simultaneously." The decaying system is no longer one atom alone but the N atoms together. The mass of this system is NM, and the recoil energy given to it is R/N. So, even though this wave requires only E_D/N as excitation energy, only R/N is available.

The proper calculation (see Reprints on theory) justifies these considerations and shows that the fraction f of transitions without change in the lattice states is given by an expression similar to (31), but with Θ_E replaced by $(2/3)\Theta_D$:

$$f = \exp(-3R/2k\Theta_D) \tag{33}$$

Equations (31) and (33) are valid only at zero absolute temperature, where all lattice oscillators are in their ground state. At finite temperatures, some of the oscillators are excited and transitions with induced emission of phonons become possible. These transitions contribute an additional term in the exponents of (31) and (33).

The foregoing discussion is obviously oversimplified and, in addition, treata a quantum mechanical problem in a classical way. However the essence is correct. Even though the energies characteristic for the solid are much smaller than the nuclear transition energy, and the nuclear decay occurs in one nucleus only, the entire crystal must be considered as the quantum mechanical system in which the decay occurs. Any statement according to which one can separate the decay into a first step, in which the nucleus decays, and a second step, in which the recoil energy is, or is not, given to the solid, is misleading. The process is indivisible and if, by a *measurement*, one separates the two steps, the Mössbauer effect is destroyed. These statements are justified in the next section.

2-43 Time Considerations

Before discussing the times involved in the Mössbauer effect, a few words about the uncertainty relation between energy and time are in order. It has been pointed out quite early, for instance by Pauli,[23] that this uncertainty relation has two different physical contents. The one of interest here refers to a *measurement*: If a system has two states, E_n and E_m, then any measurement to decide whether the system is in state n or in state m requires *at least* a time T given by

$$T \approx \hbar/(E_n - E_m) \tag{34}$$

This careful definition avoids some of the difficulties that have led to many discussions (for instance, see Ref. 24).

Consider, as a special case, the 14.4-kev transition from the first excited state to the ground state of Fe^{57}. According to (34), the minimum time necessary to decide whether a Fe^{57} nucleus is in its ground state or its first excited state is 4×10^{-20} sec. The question then arises as to whether this time is characteristic for this transition so that one can say that the individual decay always occurs in a time of the order of, or faster than, 4×10^{-20} sec.

[23]W. Pauli, Die allgemeinen Prinzipien der Wellenmechanik, "Handbuck der Physik," Springer, Berlin, 1933, Vol. 24:1, p. 146.

[24]Y. Aharonov and D. Bohm, Phys. Rev., **122**, 1649 (1961).

To answer this question, a gedanken experiment can be performed in which the nucleus is observed at intervals of 4×10^{-20} sec, and thus the moment of decay is determined within this time. Has one then shown that a transition time of 4×10^{-20} sec or less exists, or has the measurement forced the nucleus to decay within this short time? As Pauli's statement in Sec. 2-1 shows, this question had obviously been discussed very thoroughly when quantum mechanics was new, and the second alternative was found to be correct. One of the beautiful aspects of the Mössbauer effect is that it gives a direct experimental confirmation of these quantum mechanical ideas. With Fe^{57} one can indeed perform an experiment similar to the "thought" experiment described above, if only with intervals considerably longer than 10^{-19} sec but still much shorter than 10^{-7} sec, the lifetime of the first excited state of Fe^{57} (see Reprint Lynch 1960 and Sec. 5-6). The spectrum of gamma rays observed in such an experiment no longer displays the natural line width but is considerably broadened. To a good approximation, this broadening is given by (3), with τ now standing for the interval of measurement. This experimental result agrees with the quantum mechanical calculations (Harris 1961) and also with the classical considerations[6]: If the emitted wave train is shortened in time, its energy distribution, which is given by the Fourier transform of the time distribution, must be wider. In the thought experiment above, with time intervals of 4×10^{-20} sec one would find out whether the nucleus has decayed or not, but the gamma ray would show a width of about 15 kev instead of the natural line width of about 10^{-8} ev. Any Mössbauer effect would clearly be impossible. These considerations show that it is meaningless to talk about a "transition time" or about an "instantaneous transition." The times that enter are those characteristic for the *measurement*.

After these preliminary remarks, the discussion of the Mössbauer effect is straightforward. If one wants to ascertain whether or not a transition with energy transfer ΔE to the lattice has occurred, one must measure the energy of the photon or of the solid to within the energy ΔE. The time required for this measurement is given by (34),

$$T \geq \hbar/\Delta E = \lambda\!\!\!^{-}/u \tag{35}$$

where $2\pi\lambda\!\!\!^{-}$ is the wavelength belonging to a phonon with energy ΔE and velocity u. During the time T, the disturbance caused by the decay travels a distance L, given by

$$L = Tu \geq \lambda\!\!\!^{-} \tag{36}$$

Thus, if one wants to determine whether or not an amount of energy ΔE has been transferred to the lattice, one is forced to look at regions of the solid of linear dimensions $\lambda\!\!\!^{-}$ or larger. This argument justifies the statements made in Sec. 2-42.

It is impossible to decide by a measurement whether the original recoil has been imparted to the decaying nucleus only or has been shared among two, three, or more atoms within a region of linear dimensions $\lambda\!\!\!^{-}$.

If no particular time is selected by an external apparatus, the mean life τ of the decaying state will play the role of the measuring interval. During one mean life, the disturbance from the decay will travel for a distance τu. The question then arises whether a measurement can decide that a part of the entire solid, of linear dimensions τu, will begin to move first. It is easy to see, however, that the recoil energy of such a crystallite cannot be measured, because zero-point vibrations will completely mask any recoil effect (Weisskopf 1961).

There remains one last question. How do the parts of the solid far away from the decaying nucleus know how and when to move? Is it possible to decide whether or not the signal travels through the crystal as a shock wave with the velocity of sound u? Again the uncertainty relation prevents such a detailed investigation. The recoil energy given to the entire solid is approximately

$$R_{solid} = R(M_{atom}/M_{solid}) \approx R(d/D)^3 \qquad (37)$$

where R is the recoil energy of the free atom, d is the lattice parameter, and D the linear dimension of the solid. The recoil energy is of the order of the Debye energy, Eq. (32):

$$R \approx \hbar u/d$$

The time required to measure the recoil energy of the entire solid is, according to (34), given by

$$T_S \geq \hbar/R_{solid} \approx \hbar D^3/Rd^3 \approx D^3/ud^2$$

The time t for a signal with the sound velocity u to travel the linear dimension D is $t = D/u$. The ratio of the two times thus becomes approximately

$$T/t \approx (D/d)^2 \qquad (38)$$

The time required for a measurement of the recoil energy of the entire solid is very much larger than the time needed for a signal to travel through the crystal. By the time the measurement of the recoil energy is finished, the crystal moves with uniform velocity (if not glued to some material), and it is impossible to tell how it received its travel orders!

2-5 SKETCH OF THE THEORY

In nearly every theory there exist steps that are omitted in the theoretical papers and not treated in the textbooks. These steps are obviously designed to keep the experimental physicists in their place. The theory of the Mössbauer effect makes no exception; the equation from which all later results are derived [(40) below] is usually written down without detailed derivation. It is the purpose of the present section to supply the steps missing in most papers.

The probability for emission or absorption of a gamma ray from a nucleus embedded in a solid, with the lattice simultaneously undergoing a transition from one state to another, is usually calculated by dispersion theory, as for example described in Heitler.[6] The relevant formula will not be needed in the present section, but it can be found as Eq. (8) in Lamb's paper (Reprint Lamb 1939).† Here the essential fact used is that the transition probability for a given transition is proportional to the square of the matrix element connecting the two states involved in the transition (golden rule). In particular, the probability for a transition in which the nucleus decays from the excited state N_i to the ground state N_f, while simultaneously the lattice goes from its initial state L_i to its final state L_f, is

$$W(N_i \rightarrow N_f,\, L_i \rightarrow L_f) = \text{const.}\, |\langle f\,|H_{int}|\, i\rangle|^2 \tag{39}$$

where $|i\rangle$ and $|f\rangle$ denote the initial and final state of the entire system, including the lattice, and H_{int} is the interaction Hamiltonian responsible for this decay. The energy that can be transferred to the lattice during this transition is very small compared to the gamma-ray energy. The dependence of the density of final states $\rho(E)$ on the energy transfer to the lattice is hence very small, $\rho(E)$ is assumed to be constant, and it is absorbed in the constant in (39).

For calculations, an explicit form of the transition matrix element is needed. Lamb states that, because of the short range of nuclear forces and the corresponding independence of the motion in the crystal of the center of momentum (c.m.) and the internal degrees of freedom of the nucleus, it can be factored into a nuclear and a lattice matrix element:

$$\langle f|H_{int}|i\rangle = \langle L_f|e^{i\mathbf{k}\cdot\mathbf{X}}|L_i\rangle\,\langle N\rangle \tag{40}$$

Here the nuclear matrix element $\langle N\rangle$ depends only on nuclear properties, $\mathbf{k} = \mathbf{p}/\hbar$ is the wavevector of the emitted gamma ray, and $\mathbf{X}$ is the coordinate vector of the c.m. of the decaying nucleus.

---

† A derivation based on time-dependent perturbation theory is given in Appendix A of a paper by Petzold (Petzold 1961).

$\langle L_f|\exp(i\mathbf{k}\cdot\mathbf{X})|L_i\rangle$ is the matrix element for transfer of a momentum $\hbar\mathbf{k}$ to the lattice through the atom of the decaying nucleus with the lattice going from the state L_i to L_f.

Lipkin (Reprint Lipkin 1960) shows that the form Eq. (40) of the matrix element is determined completely by the requirements of translational and Galilean invariance. A more detailed justification of (40) may, however, be desired by many readers since it forms the basis for all the later calculations and arguments. Such a justification, in a very pedestrian way, will be given here.

The Hamiltonian of a charged particle, moving with a momentum $\mathbf{p}$ in an electromagnetic field given by a vector potential $\mathbf{A}$, contains the term $[\mathbf{p} - (e/c)\mathbf{A}]^2$. This term leads to the nonrelativistic interaction Hamiltonian H_{int} = const $(\mathbf{p}\cdot\mathbf{A} - \mathbf{A}\cdot\mathbf{p})$. After expanding $\mathbf{A}$ in plane waves, one finds the well-known expression[6,25]

$$\langle f|H_{int}|i\rangle = \text{const.}\langle f|\exp(i\mathbf{k}\cdot\mathbf{x})p_A|i\rangle \tag{41}$$

where the gradient operator p_A must be applied in the direction of the polarization vector of the electromagnetic wave $\mathbf{k}$, and where $\mathbf{x}$ is the coordinate vector of the decaying nucleon. Equation (41) corresponds to a single-particle description of the nucleus; if the decay occurs through many nucleons in the same nucleus, an appropriate sum over these nucleons must be introduced in (41). For simplicity, this sum is omitted.

The short range and the strength of the nuclear forces now permits the use of the approximation that the nuclear decay is not influenced by the state of the lattice and that the lattice condition does not depend on the nuclear state. The state functions $|i\rangle$ and $\langle f|$ can then be written as products $|N_i\rangle|L_i\rangle$ and $\langle L_f|\langle N_f|$ of nuclear-state functions $|N_i\rangle$ and $\langle N_f|$ and lattice-state functions $|L_i\rangle$ and $\langle L_f|$, with $\langle L_f|L_i\rangle = \delta_{fi}$ and $\langle N_f|N_i\rangle = \delta_{fi}$. In addition, one introduces internal nuclear coordinates $\boldsymbol{\rho}$ by writing

$$\mathbf{x} = \mathbf{X} + \boldsymbol{\rho} \tag{42}$$

where $\mathbf{X}$ is the coordinate vector of the c.m. of the decaying nucleus (Fig. 2-3).

The momentum operator also splits up into a sum

$$p_A = p_X + p_\rho \tag{43}$$

where p_ρ acts on the internal nuclear coordinates and p_X on the c.m. coordinates of the nucleus. After introducing (42) and (43) into (41), the matrix element can be separated into two parts, each consisting of a product of a nuclear and a lattice matrix element:

---

[25] L. I. Schiff, "Quantum Mechanics," McGraw-Hill, New York, 1955, Secs. 23 and 35. R. P. Feynman, "Quantum Electrodynamics," W. A. Benjamin, Inc., New York, 1961, p. 8.

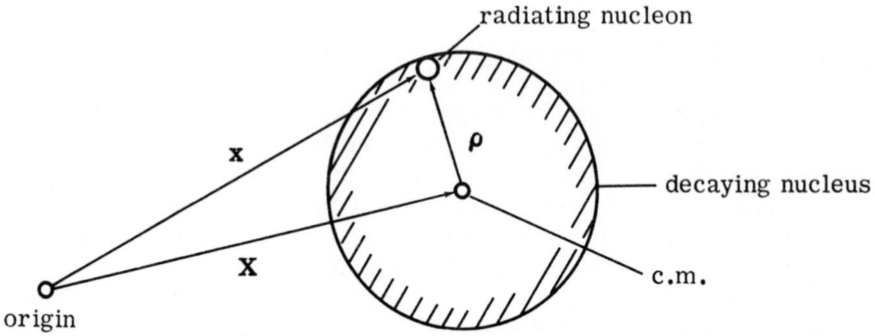

Fig. 2-3 Coordinates used in the evaluation of the transition matrix element. The origin is fixed at the c.m. of the entire crystal.

$$\langle f|H_{int}|i\rangle = \text{const.}\left\{\langle N_f|e^{i\mathbf{k}\cdot\boldsymbol{\rho}}\, p_\rho|N_i\rangle\langle L_f|e^{i\mathbf{k}\cdot\mathbf{X}}|L_i\rangle + \langle N_f|e^{i\mathbf{k}\cdot\boldsymbol{\rho}}|N_i\rangle\langle L_f|e^{i\mathbf{k}\cdot\mathbf{X}}\, p_X|L_i\rangle\right\} \tag{44}$$

To reduce (44) to (40) one must show that the first term in (44) is much larger than the second one. The following arguments are only qualitative, but they yield the right order of magnitude. Using the closure[25,26]

$$\sum_{n'} |n'\rangle\langle n'| = 1 \tag{45}$$

where the summation extends over all intermediate states, the ratio of the lattice matrix elements in the two terms of (44) can be written

$$r_L = \frac{\langle L_f|e^{i\mathbf{k}\cdot\mathbf{X}}\, p_X|L_i\rangle}{\langle L_f|e^{i\mathbf{k}\cdot\mathbf{X}}|L_i\rangle} = \frac{\sum_{L'}\langle L_f|e^{i\mathbf{k}\cdot\mathbf{X}}|L'\rangle\langle L'|p_X|L_i\rangle}{\langle L_f|e^{i\mathbf{k}\cdot\mathbf{X}}|L_i\rangle}$$

The momentum $\hbar\mathbf{k}$ transferred to the lattice during the nuclear decay is much larger than typical momenta components in the lattice. It is therefore to be expected, even without detailed calculation, that the terms $\langle L_f|\exp(i\mathbf{k}\cdot\mathbf{X})|L'\rangle$ for allowed intermediate states L' are of the same order of magnitude as the term $\langle L_f|\exp(i\mathbf{k}\cdot\mathbf{X})|L_i\rangle$. They can then be taken out from under the sum sign, leading to

$$r_L \approx \sum_{L'} \langle L'|p_X|L_i\rangle = \langle p_L\rangle \tag{46}$$

---

[26] P. A. M. Dirac, "The Principles of Quantum Mechanics," Oxford University Press, New York, 1958, 4th ed., p. 63.

where $<p_L>$ denotes an average over lattice momentum components. A similar reasoning is valid for the nuclear matrix elements, where the momentum transfer $\hbar\mathbf{k}$ is much *smaller* than typical nuclear momentum components. The corresponding ratio of the nuclear matrix elements appearing in (44) becomes

$$r_N \approx \sum_{N'} <N'|p_\rho|N_i> = <p_N> \tag{47}$$

The ratio of the first to the second term in (44) thus is

$$r_N/r_L \simeq <p_N>/<p_L> \tag{48}$$

or of the order of 10^5 or larger. A second way of estimating the ratio (48) can be obtained by first calculating r_N, using a multipole expansion, $\exp(i\mathbf{k}\cdot\boldsymbol{\rho}) = 1 + i\mathbf{k}\cdot\boldsymbol{\rho} + \cdots$. One finds for the first nonvanishing terms of the relevant matrix elements: $<N_f|\exp(i\mathbf{k}\cdot\boldsymbol{\rho})|N_i> \simeq ik<N_f|\rho|N_i>$, and $<N_f|\exp(i\mathbf{k}\cdot\boldsymbol{\rho})p_\rho|N_i> \simeq <N_f|p_\rho|N_i>$. The last expression can be evaluated further by assuming a Hamiltonian of the form $H = (p^2/2M) + V(\rho)$. One then easily calculates a commutator $[H,\rho] = (i\hbar/M)p$, or $p = (-iM/\hbar)[H,\rho]$. Hence $<N_f|p|N_i> = (-iM/\hbar)\times <N_f|H\rho - \rho H|N_i> = (+iM/\hbar)(E_i - E_f)<N_f|\rho|N_i> = +iMkc<N_f|\rho|N_i>$. The desired ratio r_N becomes $r_N = -Mc \approx <p_N>$, in agreement with the crude arguments leading to (47). To estimate r_L, one first remarks that the highest momenta occurring in the lattice are of the order of $\hbar/d$ and that the matrix element $<L_f|\exp(i\mathbf{k}\cdot\mathbf{X})p_X|L_i>$ thus cannot be larger than $\hbar/d$. The matrix element $<L_f|\exp(i\mathbf{k}\cdot\mathbf{X})|L_i>$, however, must be larger than a certain minimum value, say 10^{-2}, for the Mössbauer effect to be observable [compare (49) below]. Thus $r_L \approx 10^2\hbar/d$ and $r_N/r_L \simeq Mcd/10^2\hbar \simeq 10^6$. These arguments show that (40) can safely be used.

Using (40), the calculation of the fraction f of gamma rays emitted without energy loss to the lattice $(L_i \to L_i)$ is now straightforward:

$$f = \frac{|<L_i|e^{i\mathbf{k}\cdot\mathbf{X}}|L_i>|^2}{\sum_{L_f} |<L_f|e^{i\mathbf{k}\cdot\mathbf{X}}|L_i>|^2}$$

The denominator is easily shown to be one with the help of (45),

$$\sum_{L_f} |<L_f|e^{i\mathbf{k}\cdot\mathbf{X}}|L_i>|^2 = \sum_{L_f} <L_i|e^{-i\mathbf{k}\cdot\mathbf{X}}|L_f><L_f|e^{i\mathbf{k}\cdot\mathbf{X}}|L_i>$$

$$= <L_i|e^{-i\mathbf{k}\cdot\mathbf{X}}e^{i\mathbf{k}\cdot\mathbf{X}}|L_i> = 1$$

Thus one finds

$$f = |\langle L_i | e^{i\mathbf{k}\cdot\mathbf{X}} | L_i \rangle|^2 \tag{49}$$

Equation (49) has been the starting point for most calculations of the fraction f of gamma rays emitted or absorbed without energy loss. A few examples best illustrate its use.

2-51 The Einstein Solid

The simplest and most pedestrian application is to the Einstein solid. The ground-state wave function for a linear harmonic oscillator of mass M and angular frequency ω is given by

$$\Psi_0(x) = \sqrt[4]{M\omega/\pi\hbar}\ e^{-M\omega X^2/2\hbar} \tag{50}$$

Inserting this wave function into (49) and using the fact that one is dealing with a one-dimensional problem, i.e., that $\mathbf{k}\cdot\mathbf{X} \to kX$, yields after integration

$$f = \exp(-\hbar^2 k^2/2M\hbar\omega) = \exp(-R/\hbar\omega_E) \tag{51}$$

This result agrees with (31), which was quoted earlier without proof.

2-52 The Debye Solid

For the Debye solid, the procedure is somewhat more complicated, because the individual atoms do not all have the same frequency. One introduces normal coordinates and then determines the probability f. This straightforward calculation is performed in a number of papers (Reprints Mössbauer, Lipkin, Visscher). The result can be written

$$f = e^{-2w} \tag{52}$$

where

$$w = 3\frac{R}{k\Theta_D}\left[\frac{1}{4} + \left(\frac{T}{\Theta_D}\right)^2 \int_0^{\Theta/T} \frac{x\,dx}{e^x - 1}\right] \tag{53}$$

This result agrees for $T = 0$ with (33). It must be pointed out that it is only valid if the concept of Debye temperature is applicable. In many instances, even for crystals consisting of only one kind of atom, the Debye theory cannot be used.[18] When estimating f with the help of Eqs. (52) and (53), these restrictions should be kept in mind. For obtaining crude estimates of expected effects, the Debye approximation is, however, very useful. In Sec. 3-6, data helpful for such estimates are collected.

2-53 The Debye-Waller Factor

At this point it is worth remembering that recoilless processes have not been invented by nuclear physicists. The scattering of X rays without loss of energy to the lattice has been used as a standard tool for many years. In studies of Bragg reflection it was found that the temperature had a strong influence on the intensity of the lines. Many authors, particularly Debye and Waller, investigated this effect and found that, for harmonic lattice forces, the intensity as a function of temperature could be expressed as[27-31]

$$I = I_0 \mathbf{F}, \qquad \mathbf{F} = \exp(-2W)$$

$$W = 2\langle u_z^2\rangle \sin^2 \varphi/\lambda\!\!\!^{-}{}^2 \qquad (54)$$

where φ is the Bragg angle, $2\pi\lambda\!\!\!^{-}$ is the X-ray wavelength, and $\langle u_z^2\rangle$ is the mean-square deviation of the component of displacement of the atoms along the direction z which is perpendicular to the reflecting planes. This Debye-Waller factor $\mathbf{F} = \exp(-2W)$ has many similarities with the Lamb-Mössbauer factor f; it is interesting to compare these and also note the differences.

The main difference lies in the times involved. X-ray scattering is "fast," the characteristic time involved is much shorter than the characteristic lattice time. In contrast, the emission and the scattering of gamma rays in the Mössbauer effect is "slow," the relevant time is comparable to, or longer than, the characteristic lattice time. These differences are discussed in papers by Tzara (Reprint Tzara 1961) and Trammell (Trammell 1962), and these and Sec. 6-22 should be consulted for further details.

The essential similarity lies in the appearance of the mean-square deviation of the radiating or scattering atoms from its equilibrium position. For crystals with harmonic lattice forces, it can be shown that the expression (49) can be transformed to

$$f = \exp(-\langle L_i|(\mathbf{k}\cdot\mathbf{X})^2|L_i\rangle) \qquad (55)$$

or

---

[27] P. P. Ewald, "Handbuch der Physik," Springer, Berlin, 1933, Vol. 23:2, p. 307.

[28] F. C. Blake, Revs. Modern Phys., **5**, 169 (1933).

[29] A. H. Compton and S. K. Allison, "X-Rays in Theory and Experiment," Van Nostrand, Princeton, N. J., 1935, p. 437.

[30] M. von Laue, "Röntgenstrahlinterferenzen," Akademische Verlagsgesellschaft, Leipzig, 1948, pp. 204, 242.

[31] R. W. James, "Optical Principles of the Diffraction of X-Rays," Bell, London, 1948.

$$f = \exp\left(-\langle L_i | X_k^2 | L_i \rangle / \lambda\!\!\!^{-2}\right) \tag{56}$$

Here X_k is the component of the coordinate vector **X** in the direction of the emitted photon. Equation (56) is derived in Petzold's paper (Petzold 1961) and the steps leading from (49) to (55) can be found in a paper by Van Hove.[32,33] Incidentally, (56) agrees with the classically derived Eq. (30) and the remarks made there apply also to (56).

2-54 Connection with the Probability Density[34]

If one denotes with $\rho(\mathbf{X})$ the probability of finding the radiating nucleus at a distance **X** from its equilibrium position, one can write

$$f = \left| \int e^{i\mathbf{k}\cdot\mathbf{X}} \rho(\mathbf{X})\, d^3X \right|^2 \tag{57}$$

Equation (56) is obtained from (49) by integrating the latter matrix element over all lattice variables except **X**. It shows that f is the square of the Fourier transform of the density $\rho(\mathbf{X})$.

2-55 Further Calculations

In the back of this volume a number of reprints are collected which further develop the theory of the Mössbauer effect. Mössbauer's paper, in which he adapts Lamb's theory, is reprinted in German and the section on theory is translated. In Visscher's paper, Mössbauer's results are derived in a more modern way and applications to a study of lattice vibrations are indicated. Lipkin's paper deals with simple sum rules which give a deeper physical understanding of recoilless processes. Inglis, in a paper not printed elsewhere, discusses the theory of the Mössbauer effect, first in a very simple one-dimensional case and then generalizes to three dimensions. Singwi and Sjölander use the space-time self-correlation function of Van Hove[33] to arrive at very elegant and general results. This approach is probably the one that is most useful and versatile for applications. Tzara includes the interference with other processes in his paper and also shows the connection with X-ray scattering. For all further details concerning theory, these papers should be consulted.

---

[32] L. van Hove, Phys. Rev., **95**, 249 (1954). Contained in Ref. 33.

[33] L. van Hove, N. M. Hugenholtz, and L. P. Howland, "Problems in the Quantum Theory of Many-Particle Systems," W. A. Benjamin, Inc., New York, 1961.

[34] H. J. Lipkin, unpublished notes, 1961.

3 EXPERIMENTAL APPARATUS AND PROBLEMS

3-1 SURVEY

In contrast with experiments in high-energy physics, investigations involving the Mössbauer effect are quite simple, easy to understand, and inexpensive. Still, difficulties exist, only a few of which have been solved completely. Consider, for instance, the vibration problem in Zn^{67}. This isotope displays a very narrow resonance with a width of about 10^{-10} ev. This width corresponds to a Doppler velocity of about 10^{-5} cm sec^{-1}, or, as the Los Alamos group puts it, a velocity slightly faster than the one with which fingernails grow. If hum exists in a velocity drive used with Zn^{67}, an amplitude of a few times 10^{-8} cm can be sufficient to destroy the resonance!

A basic setup for a Mössbauer experiment and a typical result are sketched in Fig. 3-1. The source is moved with a velocity v with respect to the absorber. (In many experiments, it is more convenient to move the absorber.) The gamma ray then suffers a Doppler shift ΔE,

$$\Delta E = (v/c)E \tag{58}$$

where E is the gamma-ray energy. The velocity v is defined as positive if the source moves toward the absorber. The intensity I_{exp} in the detector is determined as a function of the velocity v. At large velocities, no resonance absorption occurs. The velocity at which resonance absorption becomes vanishingly small depends on the line width and on the line splitting. In each experiment one usually selects a "safe" velocity and denotes it with v_∞. (Visitors to our lab are sometimes startled at seeing signs such as "∞ = 1.3 cm/sec.") One plots $I(v) = I_{exp} - B$, where B is the background.

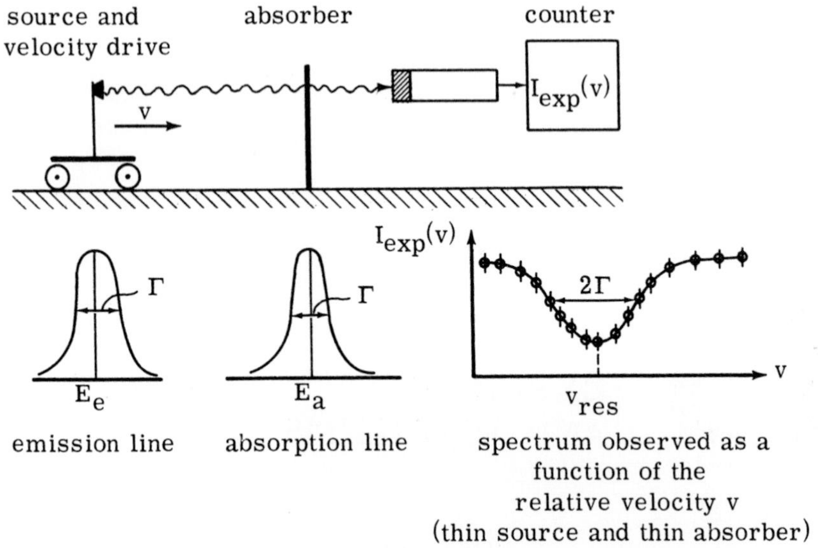

Fig. 3-1 Basic setup, emission and absorption lines, and velocity spectrum in a Mössbauer transmission experiment.

More convenient is the normalized velocity spectrum $I(v)/I(\infty)$, or the deviation from nonresonant absorption,

$$\epsilon(v) = \frac{I(\infty) - I(v)}{I(\infty)} \tag{59}$$

Figure 3-1 displays only the simplest case, single line source and single line absorber, both showing the natural line width. The velocity spectrum can be much more complicated in actual experiments. The emission and the absorption lines can show different widths, Γ_e and Γ_a, and they can be split into components. The magnitude of the splitting and the number of components can be different for source and absorber. There can also be a shift between the centers of emission and absorption lines. From the experimentally determined velocity spectrum for a given source-absorber combination, one tries to determine one or more of the following quantities: Lamb-Mössbauer factor, line shape, line splitting, and line shift. These quantities will be discussed in the Secs. 3-11 to 3-14.

3-11 The Lamb-Mössbauer Factor

The Debye-Waller factor $\exp(-2W)$ for X-ray scattering is expressed by (54). The analogous quantities in the Mössbauer effect, sometimes called the Lamb-Mössbauer factors, are f, the fraction of gamma rays emitted without energy loss, and f′, the corresponding quantity for absorption. The factors f and f′ give information similar to that contained in exp(−2W). Since exp(−2W) is often difficult to determine accurately by conventional X-ray techniques, it is desirable to measure f and f′ as a function of temperature for as many substances as possible.

The usual methods for determining absorption coefficients are not applicable for two reasons: (1) The absorption by a resonant absorber of a gamma-ray beam containing a fraction f of gamma rays emitted without energy loss is not exponential. The deviation is due to the fact that the absorption cross section varies sharply with energy; the energy spectrum of the gamma rays is thus a function of the distance in the absorber. (2) The absorption is not only determined by f′ but also by f. Both f and f′ must be extracted from the experiments.

The determination of f and f′ is simple as long as the self-absorption in the source is small and the emission and absorption lines are unsplit and have Lorentz shapes of identical widths. This case was first treated by the Los Alamos group (Craig et al. 1959) and the relevant equations are given in the paper by Margulies and Ehrman (Reprint Margulies 1961). More information can be found in the review by Cotton (Cotton 1960).

If the emission or the absorption line or both are split, but still display identical line widths, an analysis similar to the one described in the Los Alamos paper can be performed (see Margulies 1962). An analysis along the same lines can also be done if the lines show a Gaussian shape but still have identical widths. In general, however, the experimentally observed shape will be neither Lorentzian nor Gaussian and the data evaluation will hence be more difficult. The evaluation is also considerably more difficult if emission and absorption lines do not have the same widths.

In many cases, the *area method* is useful. Here one considers the area under the absorption curve and derives a value of ff′. Often one may have enough knowledge to separate this product. This method, which was first used by the Argonne group (Hanna et al. 1960), is described in detail in a publication by Shirley, Kaplan, and Axel (Shirley 1961).

3-12 Line Shape

Only in the ideal case do emission and absorption lines display the natural line shape. In actual experiments, the lines are widened by finite source and absorber thickness and usually also by the finite velocity resolution of the apparatus (Secs. 3-4 and 3-5). Furthermore, solid-state effects such as internal fields, imperfections, and impurities broaden the line and change its shape (see Chapter 6).

Experimentally, one wants to find the true shape and width of the emission and the absorption lines, extrapolated to zero source and absorber thickness. If the lifetime of the excited nuclear state is known from independent experiments (electronic delay measurements), one can compare the observed line width with the theoretically expected one.

3-13 Line Splitting

Extranuclear fields can split the emission and the absorption lines into components. These splittings, caused by magnetic and electric hyperfine interactions, are extremely important for the investigation of solid-state properties. Many typical examples are quoted in Chapter 6. One tries experimentally to determine the number of components and their separation from the velocity spectrum. It is clear that this requires a sufficiently high velocity resolution and a knowledge of the absolute velocity scale.

3-14 Shifts

The emission and the absorption lines are only centered at the same energy if the corresponding nuclei are in very similar environments. This is very often not the case, and the two spectra are displaced one with respect to the other. This shift is deduced from the velocity spectrum. Shifts can result from temperature differences between emitter and absorber (Sec. 5-4) and from isomeric effects (Sec. 4-4).

One more remark needs to be added about Fig. 3-1. The classical investigations on optical and conventional nuclear resonance fluorescence were all performed as scattering experiments. In contrast, nearly all the work on the Mössbauer effect is done in transmission. The main reasons for this difference are the relatively large effects (between about 1 and 50 per cent in most cases) and the large intensities and favorable geometry obtainable in transmission. The intensity disadvantage of scattering is increased by the strong conversion of low-energy gamma rays; only a fraction $1/(1 + \alpha)$ of the absorbed gamma rays is reemitted [Eqs. (9), (10), and (13)]. Some scattering experiments have nevertheless been performed, either by observing the gamma rays directly (Reprint Barloutaud 1960), by measuring the X rays that follow the internal conversion process (Frauenfelder 1961), or by detecting the conversion electrons (Kankeleit 1961; Mitrofanov 1961).

3-2 ISOTOPES

Mössbauer discovered the recoilless gamma-ray emission with the 129-kev gamma ray in Ir^{191}. If this isotope were the only one displaying such an effect, experiments would indeed be very difficult, the applications would be limited, and interest would not be very great. Fortunately, however, there exist at least 15 nuclides in which Mössbauer effect has been observed. There is a good chance that more will be found, and the number of possible experiments is extremely large.

In Table 3-1, properties of nuclides that have been used for Mössbauer experiments or which show promise for exhibiting such an effect are collected.[35] Very likely this table is not complete and it is also possible that it contains errors. Before embarking on any experiments based on this table, it is wise to reevaluate all critical data.

The table was originally compiled by D. Nagle (Los Alamos Scientific Laboratory) for the first Mössbauer conference held at the University of Illinois in June 1960. It was modified and checked by G. DePasquali, R. Morrison, and D. Pipkorn (University of Illinois). Similar tables can be found in the review by Cotton and that by Belozerskii and Nemilov.

The entries in the table are mostly self-explanatory, but the following notes may be of some assistance:

Powers of ten are denoted as follows: $1.0 \times 10^{-7} \rightarrow 1.0(-7)$.

a = abundance of stable element, %

Q = ratio of gamma-ray energy E_γ to line width $\Gamma = \hbar \ln 2/T_{1/2}$

α = total internal conversion coefficient (K implies α_K, L implies α_L)

R = recoil energy of free nucleus in units of 10^{-2} ev

σ_0' = Mössbauer absorption cross section in units of 10^{-19} cm^2, calculated with the listed values of the conversion coefficient and assuming natural line width. In the case of an unknown conversion coefficient the cross section has been calculated by assuming $\alpha = 0$. Once α is known, the correct cross section can be found by multiplying the value in the table by $1/(1 + \alpha)$

X = an effect has been observed

Table 3-1

Nuclides of Interest in Mössbauer Experiments

Stable nuclide	a, %	E_γ, kev	$T_{1/2}$, sec	Q	α, e/γ	R, 10^{-2} ev	σ_0', 10^{-19} cm^2	Effect
Fe^{57}	2.17	14.4	1.0(-7)	3.2(12)	9.7	0.19	22.6	X
Ni^{61}	1.25	71	5.2(-9)	8.1(11)	K 0.11	4.4	6.6	X
Zn^{67}	4.11	93	9.4(-6)	1.9(15)	K 0.63	6.9	1.2	X
Ge^{73}	7.67	13.5	4.0(-6)	1.1(14)	3600	0.13	0.022	

(continued)

[35] Most of the information contained in Table 3-1 has been taken

Table 3-1 (continued)

Stable nuclide	a, %	E_γ kev	$T_{1/2}$ sec	Q	α, e/γ	R, 10^{-2} ev	σ'_0, 10^{-19} cm^2	Effect
Kr^{83}	11.55	9.3	1.5(-7)	3.1(12)	10	0.055	21.0	X
Ru^{99}	12.7	89				4.3	1.0	
Ru^{101}	17.0	127	1.4(-9)	3.9(11)	K 0.4	8.5	0.97	
Ag^{107}	51.35	93	44.3	9.0(21)	16	4.3	0.67	X
Sn^{117}	7.57	161			K 0.13	12.0	1.7	
Sn^{119}	8.58	24	1.9(-8)	1.0(12)	7.3	0.26	10.0	X
Sb^{123}	42.75	161	6.0(-10)	2.1(11)		11.0	0.71	X
Te^{123}	0.87	159	1.9(-10)	6.6(10)	K 0.17	11.0	1.7	
Te^{125}	6.99	35	1.6(-9)	1.2(11)	K 12	0.52	3.1	X
I^{127}	100	59			K 2.7	1.5	2.5	
I^{129}	unstable	26.8	1.85(-8)	1.1(12)	5	0.30	25.6	X
Xe^{129}	26.44	40	7.0(-10)	6.2(10)	K 7.5	0.67	30.0	X
Xe^{131}	21.18	80	4.8(-10)	8.4(10)	K 1.73	2.6	0.70	
Cs^{133}	100	81	6.0(-9)	1.1(12)	K 1.5	2.7	1.1	
La^{137}	unstable	10	8.9(-8)	2.0(12)	140	0.039	1.3	
La^{139}	99.9	163	1.5(-9)	5.4(11)	K 0.22	10.0	0.56	
Nd^{145}	8.29	67	3.3(-8)	4.8(12)	K 3.3	1.7	0.63	
		72	< 1(-9)		K 3.3	1.9	0.82	
Sm^{149}	13.8	22	> 2.8(-9)			0.17		X
Sm^{152}	26.63	122	1.4(-9)	3.7(11)	K 0.7	5.3	4.8	
Eu^{151}	47.77	22	9.5(-9)	4.5(11)	L 12	0.17	5.2	X
Eu^{153}	52.23	84				2.5	4.6	
		97	< 1(-9)		K 0.3	3.3	2.0	
		103	3.4(-9)	7.7(11)	K 1.2	3.7	0.70	
Gd^{154}	2.15	123	1.2(-9)	3.2(11)	1.5	5.3	3.2	
Gd^{155}	14.7	60				1.2	10.0	
		87			K 0.4	2.6	2.3	X
		105				3.8	3.3	
Gd^{156}	20.47	89	2 (-9)	3.9(11)	K 1.0	2.7	7.7	
Tb^{159}	100	58	3.5(-11)	4.5(9)	K 6	1.1	1.5	
		137	5.4(-11)	1.6(10)		6.3	2.6	
Dy^{160}	2.294	87	1.8(-9)	3.4(11)	K 1.5	2.6	6.4	X
Dy^{161}	18.88	25.7	2.8(-8)	1.6(12)		0.22	37.0	X
		49				0.8	6.8	
		74.5	3 (-9)	4.9(11)	K 0.46	1.8	2.0	X
Dy^{162}	25.53	81	3.2(-9)	5.7(11)		2.2	19	
Dy^{163}	24.97	75				1.8	5.8	
Dy^{164}	28.18	73	3.5(-9)	5.6(11)	K 2.7	1.7	6.2	
Ho^{165}	100	95	3.3(-11)	6.9(9)	K 1.77	2.9	1.2	
Er^{164}	1.56	91	1.4(-9)	2.8(11)	K 1.9	2.7	5.1	
Er^{166}	33.4	80	1.8(-9)	3.2(11)	K 1.7	2.1	7.1	X
Er^{168}	27.07	79.8	1.84(-9)	3.2(11)	K 2.1	2.0	6.2	
Tm^{169}	100	8.4	4 (-9)	7.4(10)		0.022	700	X
		118	5 (-11)	1.3(10)	K 0.7	4.4	3.1	
Yb^{170}	3.03	84.2	1.57(-9)	2.9(11)	K 1.6	2.2	6.6	X

(continued)

from D. Strominger, J. M. Hollander, and G. T. Seaborg, Revs. Modern Physics, **30**, 585 (1958), and C. L. McGinnis (ed.), "Nuclear Data Sheets," National Academy of Sciences-National Research Council, Washington, D.C., 1958- .

Table 3-1 (continued)

Stable nuclide	a, %	$E\gamma$ kev	$T_{1/2}$, sec	Q	α, e/γ	R, 10^{-2} ev	σ'_0, 10^{-19} cm^2	Effect
Yb^{171}	14.31	66.7	< 5(-7)			1.4	11.0	
Yb^{172}	21.82	78.7				1.9	20.0	
Yb^{173}	16.13	78.7				1.9	5.2	
Yb^{174}	31.84	76.5				1.8	21.0	
Lu^{175}	94.4	113.8	8 (-11)	2.0(10)	K 1.6	4.0	0.90	
Hf^{176}	5.21	88.3	1.35(-9)	2.6(11)	K 1.32	2.4	6.7	
Hf^{177}	18.5	113	4.2(-10)	1.0(11)	K 0.75	3.9	1.4	X
Hf^{178}	27.1	93.1	1 (-9)	2.0(11)		2.6	14.0	
Hf^{180}	35.22	93	1.4(-9)	2.9(11)	KL 4.0	2.6	2.8	
Ta^{181}	100	6.25	6.8(-6)	9.4(13)	44	0.012	17	?
		136.1	5.7(-11)	1.7(10)	K 1.5	5.5	0.66	
W^{180}	0.135	102			5	3.1	2.0	
W^{182}	26.4	100	1.3(-9)	2.9(11)	4.5	2.9	2.2	X
W^{183}	14.4	46.5			9	0.63	2.3	X
		99.1	5.2(-10)	1.1(11)	3.5	2.9	1.7	X
W^{184}	30.6	111	1.3(-9)	3.2(11)	K 0.99	3.6	5.0	
W^{186}	28.4	123	1.0(-9)	2.7(11)	K 0.45	4.4	5.6	
Re^{185}	37.07	125			K 2.4	4.5	0.61	
Re^{187}	62.93	134	2 (-9)	5.9(11)	K 2.1	5.2	0.58	X
Os^{186}	1.59	137	5.1(-10)	1.5(11)	K 0.45	5.4	4.5	
Os^{188}	13.3	155	6.2(-10)	2.1(11)	K 0.40	6.8	3.6	
Os^{189}	16.1	69.5				1.4		
Os^{190}	26.4	187	3.5(-10)	1.4(11)	K 0.2	9.9	2.9	
Os^{192}	41.0	206	2.8(-10)	1.3(11)	K 0.16	12.0	2.5	
Ir^{191}	38.5	82.6	3.9(-9)	7.1(11)		1.9	1.8	
		129	1.4(-10)	4.0(10)	K 2.9	4.7	0.56	X
Ir^{193}	61.5	73	6.0(-9)	9.6(11)		1.5	2.3	X
		139	1.0(-9)	3.1(11)	K 2.2	5.4	0.59	
Pt^{195}	33.8	99	1.4(-10)	3.0(10)	9.0	2.7	0.50	X
		129	5.5(-10)	1.6(11)		4.6	4.4	X
Au^{197}	100	77	1.9(-9)	3.2(11)	2.5	1.6	0.59	X
Hg^{199}	16.84	158	2.4(-9)	8.3(11)	K 0.2	6.7	2.4	
Hg^{201}	13.22	32.1				0.27	24.0	
		167.6	<2.0(-9)		K 1.5	7.5	0.18	

3-3 SOURCES AND ABSORBERS

No time-honored and well-proved recipe exists according to which one can prepare sources and absorbers that yield Mössbauer lines as strong as possible and as sharp as the natural line width. A procedure leading to the best results has to be found for each isotope, mainly by trial and error.[36] In some cases, particularly in nuclides with extremely narrow lines, such as Ta^{181} and Ge^{73}, no resonance has been found as yet. All these difficulties are due to solid-state effects and technical problems, and one must learn more about these

[36] One valuable suggestion was put forward by S. S. Hanna at the second Mössbauer conference: "Find yourself a good chemist."

before he can predict with certainty the outcome of any given experiment. Because of these difficulties, there is little sense in writing down general guidelines; indeed, they would probably mislead experimenters. Indications on source and absorber preparations can be found in nearly all the experimental papers reprinted in the back and listed in the bibliography.[37]

3-4 APPARATUS

Two basically different ways of obtaining the velocity spectrum are in use. In one, the source (or the absorber) moves with a constant velocity for a pre-set time and the counts during this period are recorded. The velocity is then changed to a new value and the procedure is repeated until the entire spectrum is measured. Mössbauer's original work was performed in that way (Reprints Mössbauer 1958, 1959).

In the second method, the source sweeps periodically through a range of velocities and the counts in predetermined ranges of velocity are stored in different channels of a multichannel analyzer. These two methods gather information at the same rate, but each one has advantages for certain types of investigations. With constant velocity drives, small parts of the spectrum can be investigated with high accuracy. With the velocity sweep device, the entire spectrum is obtained simultaneously and a first impression can be obtained quickly. In either case, data from positive and negative velocities of equal magnitude should not be lumped together without ascertaining that the velocity spectrum is symmetric with respect to velocity zero.

One remark is in order about vibration. For isotopes like Au^{197}, where $Q \equiv E_\gamma / \Gamma \approx 5 \times 10^{11}$, vibrations are not very serious and any carefully built equipment will work. For nuclides like Fe^{57}, where $Q \approx 5 \times 10^{12}$, the vibration problem is much more serious. As a rule of thumb, the following "scientific" observation can be useful: If one touches the equipment lightly with the fingertips and notices traces of vibration, the experiment will fail! Bubbling of liquid nitrogen in dewars, for instance, will widen the lines considerably. For nuclides like Zn^{67}, with $Q \approx 10^{15}$, every trace of vibration must be carefully eliminated.

---

[37] The nuclide Fe^{57} is probably the one that is of most interest to groups starting research and to instructors designing experiments for students. A very detailed description of the source preparation is contained in Margulies, 1962. Complete Co^{57} sources and Fe^{57} absorbers can be purchased from Nuclear Science and Engineering Co., Pittsburgh, Pa., and the U.S. Nuclear Corp., Burbank, California.

3-41 Constant-Velocity Drives

During the past three years, a number of constant-velocity drives have been constructed. None of these is so superior to all the others that it has replaced them, and physicists are still waiting for a simple, accurate, easily controllable, and vibration-free drive.

Three typical *mechanical* drives are shown in Fig. 3-2. The *rotating disk* used, for example, by DePasquali et al. 1960, Shirley et al. 1961, and shown in Fig. 3-2a is probably the simplest system. The

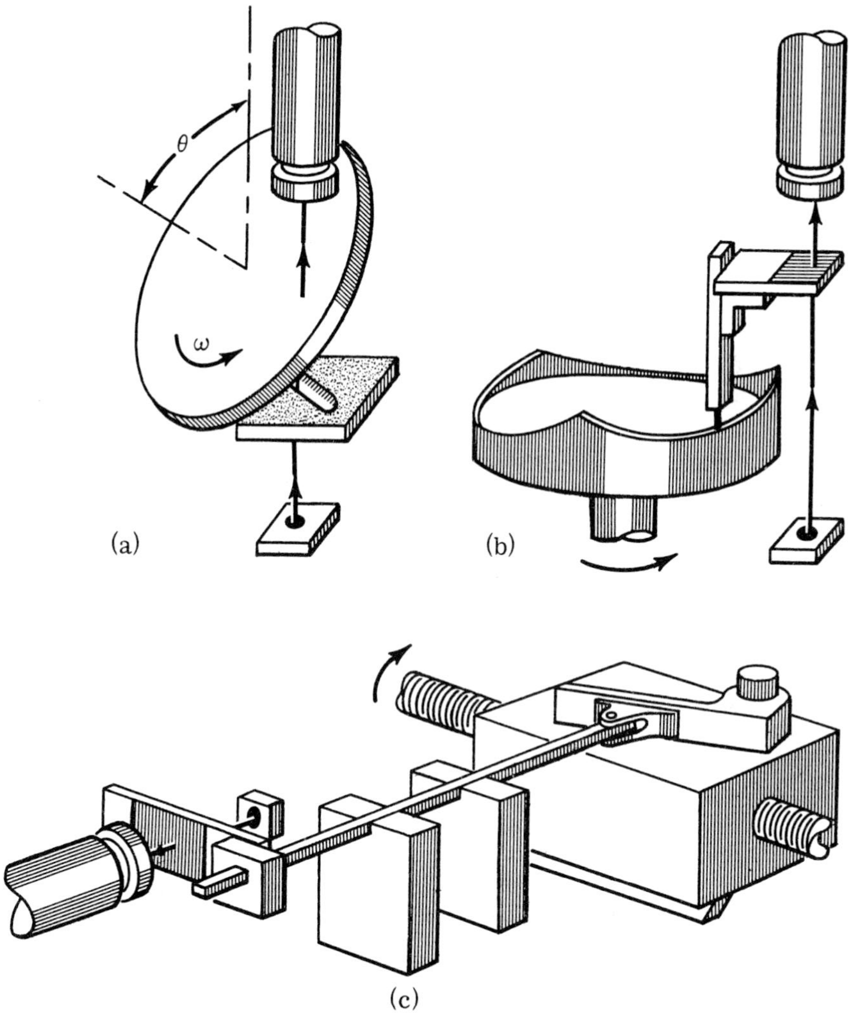

Fig. 3-2 Constant-velocity drives: (a) rotating disk; (b) three-step cam; (c) inclined plane. (From Margulies 1962.)

gamma ray passing through the disk sees in its direction of motion a velocity component $r\omega \sin \theta$, where r is the distance from the axis of rotation to the point where the gamma ray passes through the absorber and θ is the angle between the gamma ray and the axis of rotation. The slit shown in the figure can be designed in such a way that an increase in velocity due to an increase in r is compensated for by a decrease in $\sin \theta$. The velocity is changed by changing the angular velocity ω. The main disadvantage of this system is the large area of absorber needed. (If the *source* is mounted on a wheel, the activity is used very inefficiently.)

A *cam*, as shown in Fig. 3-2b, is quite reliable provided the drive is vibration-free. Usually, one uses photocells to switch the counting system off shortly before the follower on the cam reaches a maximum or minimum and starts it again after passing these points. Counts "up" and "down" are stored in different scalers, and two more scalers count the corresponding times.

The inclined plane (Argonne group), shown in Fig. 3-2c, provides a uniform motion with a very fine speed control. In this device a reversible synchronous motor is employed to drive a carriage by means of an accurately machined lead screw. Mounted rigidly to the moving carriage is a plane whose angle of inclination can be continuously varied between 0 and 45°. A shoe pivoted to the foot of an extension rod slides smoothly along the inclined plane, being held quite firmly to the plane by a thin layer of oil. As the carriage is driven back and forth, the extension rod moves to-and-fro, carrying the absorber with it. In addition to the fine speed control afforded by varying the incline angle, the lead-screw speed can be changed by a system of gears and pulleys not shown.

These three systems are only examples; more possibilities for moving an object with constant velocity exists. An improved version of Fig. 3-2b uses a heart-shaped cam and two followers. The carriage is guided up and down and never coasts freely. *Hydraulic* devices can either be actuated by a hydraulic master connected to a rack-and-pinion drive (Reprint Pound and Rebka 1960) or by a system consisting of an oil pump and valves to control pressure and direction of the oil flow. Surplus servo cylinders from automatic pilot servo units, such as Electric Autolite Mark IV, make excellent and inexpensive hydraulic systems.[38]

Piezoelectric crystals and loudspeakers, when driven so that they execute a saw tooth or a triangular motion, are also versatile velocity drives. Extreme care must be taken, however, to prevent resonances in the system from distorting the wave shape. The best

[38] Such units are available, for instance, from Herbach and Rademan, Inc., Philadelphia, Pa.

method consists in using a feedback mechanism involving a velocity-measuring device.[39]

3-42 Velocity Sweep Devices

Velocity sweep systems, using a multichannel analyzer, permit one to investigate the entire velocity spectrum simultaneously (Reprint Ruby et al. 1960). The basic aspects of such an apparatus are shown in Fig. 3-3.

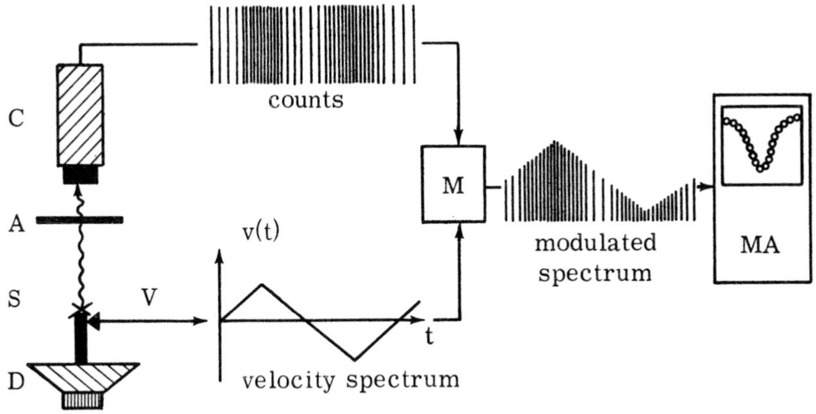

Fig. 3-3 Velocity sweep system. The counts from the counter C are modulated in the modulator M by the velocity spectrum v(t) and are then fed into the multichannel analyzer MA. The source S is mounted on the driver D; V is a velocity pick up and A is the resonant absorber.

The source is moved in such a way that all desired velocities from $-v_{max}$ to $+v_{max}$ are covered during one cycle. Attached to the source is a velocity pickup which measures the instantaneous velocity v(t). This signal is used to route the energy-selected pulses from the counter into different channels of a multichannel analyzer. One way of doing it, not shown in Fig. 3-3, is to feed the signal v(t) directly into the address logic of a multichannel analyzer. In the solution sketched in Fig. 3-3 the amplitude of the pulses from the counter is modulated by the signal v(t). An unmodified multichannel analyzer then sorts the pulses according to their velocity v(t). A third possibility is to use a multichannel

---

[39] The linearity of moving-coil loudspeakers has been investigated and reported on by J. Baumgardner, Argonne National Laboratory Report ANL-6169.

analyzer as a set of scalers and route the counts to the different channels by means of pulses.

The simplest way of moving the source is to feed a sine wave into the driver. The velocity v(t) then varies sinusoidally with time. This choice of v(t) is easy to realize experimentally and one encounters few or no resonances in the driver. However, the source spends unequal times at different velocities and the velocity spectrum must be correspondingly corrected. This problem can be avoided by selecting a linear velocity drive, as shown in Fig. 3-3. The motion x(t) of the source then must be a double parabola. Such motion must be carefully controlled by feedback in order to prevent distortions.

Velocity pickups can be constructed in different ways. The simplest one is to employ a loud speaker with two voice coils, use one for driving the speaker cone and the other to measure v(t). A similar solution consists in coupling two speakers either by a mechanical link or through the air. A pickup coil can also be rigidly attached to the source and placed in a uniform magnetic field. A condenser or a commercially available velocity-measuring device[40] can also be used. All these velocity pickups can be used to route the pulses and to serve as feedback devices in controlling the motion of the driver.

3-43 Special Velocity Drives

In addition to the more conventional systems described in Secs. 3-41 and 3-42, other possibilities exist. One is the *"temperature drive."* If source and absorber have different temperatures, the emission and absorption lines will be shifted with respect to each other (cf. Sec. 5-4). This shift can be used to trace out a resonance line. Another possibility is provided by phase modulation, which is discussed in Sec. 5-5 (see also Reprint Grodzins and Phillips 1961). The *relativistic drive* offers a third possibility. The source is at the center of a rotor and the absorber on the rim. The transverse Doppler effect then provides a small and very accurately controllable shift (cf. Sec. 5-3). These three methods allow the investigation of very small shifts and are hence extremely well suited for the study of very narrow lines.

3-5 CORRECTIONS

Corrections and checks are necessary in order to ensure that the results of a Mössbauer experiment are correct.

3-51 Background

The background B due to other gamma rays and to X rays must be subtracted from the measured counting rates I_{exp} in order to get

[40] E.g., LVsyn Transducers, Sanborn Co., Waltham, Mass.

the true counting rates I(v). Equation (59) then reads

$$\epsilon(v) = \frac{I_{exp}(\infty) - I_{exp}(v)}{I_{exp}(\infty) - B} \tag{60}$$

Mössbauer experiments are usually performed with gamma rays of energies below 100 kev, and X rays hence are often very disturbing. Very careful investigation of the pulse-height spectrum is necessary; additional information about the background can also be gained from absorption experiments.

3-52 Source and Absorber Thickness

The corrections for finite source and absorber thickness can be quite complicated, particularly if the lines do not possess a Lorentzian shape and if they are split. Only a few remarks are given here, in order to outline some of the difficulties.

The broadening of an absorption line in the Mössbauer effect due to finite absorber thickness has first been treated by W. M. Visscher (unpublished notes). He found that if emission and absorption lines have Lorentzian shapes of width Γ, the overlap curve will also be a Lorentzian but will show an apparent width Γ_{app} given by the relations

$$\begin{aligned} \Gamma_{app}/\Gamma &= 2.00 + 0.27T \qquad 0 \leq T \lesssim 5 \\ \Gamma_{app}/\Gamma &= 2.02 + 0.29T - 0.005T^2 \qquad 4 \lesssim T \lesssim 10 \end{aligned} \tag{61}$$

Here T is the effective absorber thickness, given by

$$T = f' na\sigma_0 t \tag{62}$$

where f' is the fraction of gamma rays absorbed without energy loss, n is the number of atoms per cubic centimeter, a the fractional abundance of the resonantly absorbing atoms, σ_0 the absorption cross section at resonance [i.e., Eq. (10) at resonance], and t the absorber thickness. Visscher's relations are useful for quick estimates. Margulies and Ehrman (Reprint) have extended Visscher's calculations and their paper gives graphs for various cases of interest.

If the shape of the emission and the absorption lines is given by a Gaussian distribution, the line broadening is much less pronounced than for Lorentzian shapes. A comparison of the line broadening for the two shapes is given in Fig. 3-4. It is clear from Fig. 3-4 that one must be extremely careful in extrapolations to zero absorber thickness.

So far the discussion has been restricted to unsplit emission and absorption lines. In the case of hyperfine splitting, the analysis of

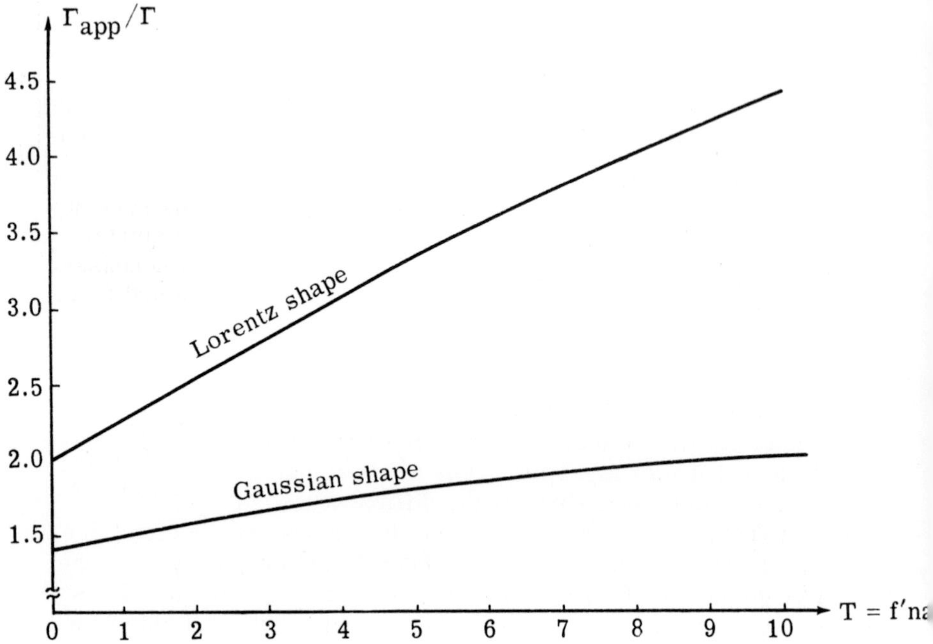

Fig. 3-4 Ratio of apparent full width at half height to the widths of the emission and absorption lines as a functions of the effective absorber thickness T. The source is assumed to be thin (nonresonant). (Margulies 1962.)

the transmission becomes more complicated but it can still be obtained from a straightforward generalization of the results given in the Reprint by Margulies and Ehrman (M-E) (see Margulies 1962). Some of the essential features can be summarized as follows: If only the emission line is split, and if W_i is the relative intensity of the i-th emission line, then equation 16 of M-E is still valid, provided f is replaced by fW_i. If only the absorption line is split, the effective thickness of the resonance absorber corresponding to the j-th absorption line is not T but W_jT, where W_j is the relative intensity of the j-th absorption line. The absorber, for any given line, appears thinner than it really is. This fact must be kept in mind when determining the line broadening from (61) or from Fig. 3-4.

3-53 Velocity Resolution

In any apparatus, the gamma rays will traverse the absorber at various angles, not just normal. This spread in angle introduces a spread in velocity which must be taken into account for accurate line-width determinations.

3-54 Reemission

In most transmission experiments, one assumes that a resonant gamma ray which has been absorbed will not be registered in the counter. In general, this is not true and the amount of reradiation, which depends on the conversion coefficient and the solid angle of the counter, must be calculated and taken into account (Obenshain and Wegener 1961).

3-6 USEFUL INFORMATION

Some data useful in preparing and evaluating Mössbauer experiments are collected in this section.

A nucleus of mass number A decays from an excited state with spin I_B, mean life τ, or half-life $T_{1/2}$, to a stable ground state with spin I_A, and emits a gamma ray of energy E with a total conversion coefficient α. The recoil energy R of the free nucleus, the maximum resonance absorption cross section σ_0' and the natural line width Γ are then given by

$$R(\text{ev}) \simeq 5.37 \times 10^{-4}\, E^2(\text{kev})/A \qquad (63)$$

$$\sigma_0' \text{ (barns)} = \frac{2.45 \times 10^9}{E^2\,(\text{kev})} \frac{2I_B + 1}{2I_A + 1} \frac{1}{1 + \alpha} \qquad (64)$$

$$\Gamma(\text{ev}) = 6.58 \times 10^{-16}/\tau(\text{sec})$$

$$= 4.55 \times 10^{-16}/T_{1/2}\,(\text{sec}) \qquad (65)$$

Assume now that the nucleus is embedded in a solid and that the solid can be described in sufficient approximation by the Debye model, with a Debye temperature Θ. The fraction f of gamma rays emitted without energy loss to the lattice is then given by (52) and (53). These equations have been evaluated by Mössbauer and Wiedemann (1960) and by Cotton (1960). The curves presented in Fig. 3-5 were made by A. H. Muir, Jr.[41]

To determine f from Fig. 3-5 one calculates the ratios Θ/T and R/Θ. T is the temperature of the solid and R is given (in ev) by Eq. (63). The curves in Fig. 3-5 are labeled by R/Θ in units of ev/°K.

The selection of an appropriate Debye temperature is not easy. First, published Debye temperatures (e.g., Refs. 42 to 44) for any given substance vary widely, depending on the method of determination. Second, even if one finds a unique value in the literature, it is not certain that it will fit the results from Mössbauer experiments. In Table

[41] A. H. Muir, Jr., Atomics International Report AI-6699 (1961).

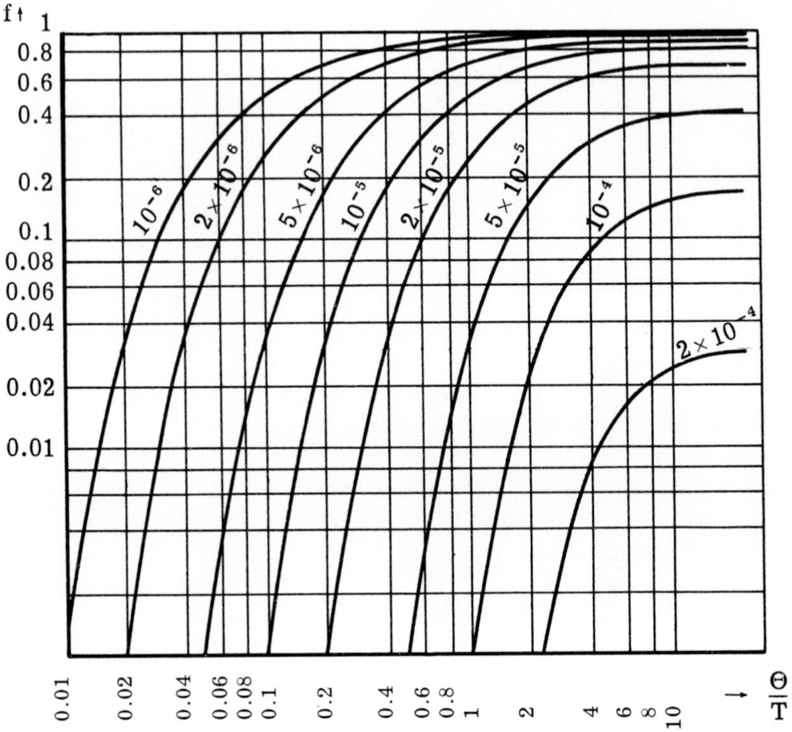

Fig. 3-5 Graph for determining the fraction f as a function of Θ/T for various values of R/Θ. The parameter labeling each curve is R/Θ in units of ev/°K. (From A. H. Muir, Jr., Atomics International Report AI-6699.)

3-2 the Debye temperature of iron, as found in three compilations, is compared with the latest value obtained by the Mössbauer effect. This table shows that one has to be very careful in using published data when designing an experiment.

---

[42] "American Institute of Physics Handbook," McGraw-Hill, New York, 1957, pp. 4-47 to 4-49.

[43] F. Seitz, "The Modern Theory of Solids," McGraw-Hill, New York, 1940, p. 110.

[44] M. W. Holm, "Debye Characteristic Temperatures," Phillips Petroleum Co. Report IDO-16399, Office of Technical Services, U.S. Department of Commerce, Washington 25, D. C.

[45] S. S. Hanna, in "Proceedings of the Second Mössbauer Conference," A. Schoen and D. M. J. Compton (eds.), Wiley, New York, tentative publication Spring 1962.

Table 3-2
Comparison of Debye Temperature of Iron Found by Conventional Methods with That Deduced from the Mössbauer Effect

Method	Θ, °K	Ref.
Conventional	355	42
	420	43
	420 - 460	44
Mössbauer	490	45

4 NUCLEAR PROPERTIES

4-1 INTRODUCTION

In many ways, investigations on the Mössbauer effect follow a path along which nuclear resonance experiments have been going. The discovery of the Mössbauer effect grew out of the study of a nuclear property, namely, the lifetime of the first excited state in Ir^{191}. This goal was attained, but at the same time a powerful tool for solving other problems was created. Indeed, the main applications in the past two years have not been to nuclear physics, but to other fields, such as relativity and solid-state physics. Despite this development in an unexpected direction, applications to nuclear physics remain challenging. A few of these are sketched in Secs. 4-2 to 4-5.

Many of the discussions in this and the following chapters refer to Fe^{57}, probably the most used of the "Mössbauer nuclides." For this reason the decay scheme of Fe^{57} is shown in Fig. 4-1.

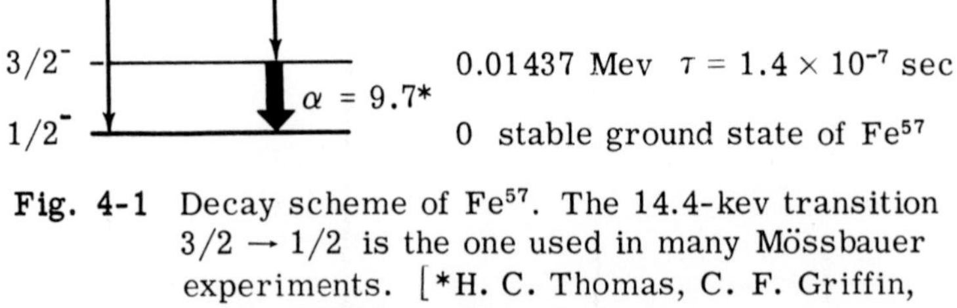

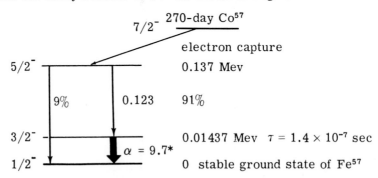

Fig. 4-1 Decay scheme of Fe^{57}. The 14.4-kev transition $3/2 \rightarrow 1/2$ is the one used in many Mössbauer experiments. [*H. C. Thomas, C. F. Griffin, W. E. Phillips, and E. C. Davis, Jr., Bulletin, APS, II, 7, 120 (1962). A. H. Muir, Jr., E. Kankeleit, and F. Boehm, *Phys. Letters*, 5, 161 (1963).]

4-2 LIFETIME AND CONVERSION COEFFICIENT

In conventional nuclear resonance fluorescence experiments[10-12] one can measure the scattering cross section and is able to deduce the gamma-ray width Γ_γ by using (9) modified to take into account the Doppler broadening. This procedure is rather indirect, and the Mössbauer effect permits a more straightforward approach, yielding both Γ and Γ_γ. The total line width Γ is found by tracing out the absorption or the scattering line by using the Doppler effect, as sketched in Fig. 3-1. The ratio of the scattering and the absorption cross section, Eqs. (9) and (10), yields Γ_γ/Γ. From the total line width one immediately gets the total lifetime τ by (3) or (65). From the ratio Γ_γ/Γ, one finds the total conversion coefficient α by (13).

The measurement of the line width to determine the lifetime was first used by Mössbauer (Reprint 1958) in the case of Ir^{191}. In a later investigation, Mössbauer and Wiedemann (1960) were able to find a value of $\tau = (1.5 \pm 0.2) \times 10^{-11}$ sec for the lifetime of the 134-kev excited state in Re^{187}. This lifetime is at present the shortest one that has been determined by the Mössbauer effect.

Despite the simplicity of this method, some difficulties exist. For lifetimes of the order of 10^{-10} sec or longer, extranuclear fields can widen the line, and one may find apparent lifetimes that are shorter than the real ones. The 14.4-kev transition in Fe^{57} (Fig. 4-1) offers an excellent example for these difficulties. The lifetime of the 3/2 state is known from electronic measurements to be $\tau = 1.4 \times 10^{-7}$ sec. According to (65) the corresponding line width is 4.7×10^{-9} ev. All the early experiments, however, yielded line widths considerably larger than that. Only after the source and absorber preparation was carefully investigated did experiments yield values Γ_{exp} within 10 per cent of the expected one. Hence very careful measurements of the line shape and a thorough understanding of the solid-state processes involved in the line widening are prerequisites for valid estimates of lifetimes longer than, say, 10^{-10} sec.

Difficulties may also arise for very short lifetimes. If the nuclear lifetime becomes comparable to, or shorter than, the inverse of the Debye frequency ($\approx 10^{-13}$ sec), it may be impossible to distinguish recoilless transitions from those in which the lattice takes up energy. Furthermore, heat spikes due to previous decays may well destroy the effect. Investigations in this range are very desirable and they will probably yield information not only about nuclear lifetimes, but also about solid-state processes connected with nuclear decays.

4-3 NUCLEAR MOMENTS

The Mössbauer effect permits the determination of nuclear moments, i.e., spin, magnetic dipole moment, and electric quadrupole moment, in a rather direct way, provided certain conditions are met.

Consider as the simplest example a nuclide with spin 0 in the ground state A and spin I_B, magnetic moment μ_B, and g factor g_B in the excited state B. Assume further that emitting and absorbing nuclei are embedded in solids in such a way that the nuclei see no magnetic field or electric field gradient. The emission and absorption lines will be unsplit. If one now applies an external magnetic field H to source or absorber, the corresponding line will split into $2I_B + 1$ equally spaced components, with a separation between components of

$$\Delta = g_B \mu_0 H \tag{66}$$

Here μ_0 is the nuclear magneton, $\mu_0 = 5.05 \times 10^{-24}$ erg/gauss $= 3.15 \times 10^{-12}$ ev/gauss. If the separation is larger than the width 2Γ of the overlap line (Fig. 3-1), i.e., if

$$g_B \mu_0 H \gtrsim 2\Gamma = 2\hbar/\tau \tag{67}$$

the number of components can be counted and one has found the spin I_B. From the splitting Δ, one determines the nuclear g factor g_B if the external field is known. The nuclear g factor and the spin together yield the magnetic moment, $\mu_B = g_B \mu_0 I_B$. As an example for condition (67), take $g_B = 1$, $H = 10^5$ gauss. A separation is then possible for $\tau \gtrsim 6 \times 10^{-9}$ sec.

If condition (67) is not fulfilled, the spin I_B cannot be determined simply by counting the number of components. Nevertheless it is often possible to find an approximate value of the g factor by measuring the increase in line width as a function of the applied field H.

The situation encountered usually is more complicated than outlined above, since the ground-state spin will in general not be zero and very large internal fields are often present. The first problem, nonzero ground-state spin, results in the observation of more than $2I_B + 1$ components. Usually, however, the ground-state spin and moments can be measured with conventional techniques and their knowledge permits one to unravel the complex spectrum. Moreover, polarization experiments can help to reduce the number of components and to make their identification easier (see Sec. 5-9).

The presence of very strong internal magnetic fields in ferromagnetic and paramagnetic substances introduces complications on the one hand, but, on the other, allows the determination of g factors that otherwise would be difficult to find. Indeed, the first observation of the Zeeman effect of a nuclear gamma ray was performed by using the internal magnetic field in Fe^{57} (Pound and Rebka 1959a, DePasquali et al. 1960, Reprint Hanna et al. 1960). Two limiting cases must be distinguished when considering internal fields. One extreme occurs when the field can be considered to be a static external field; the number and splitting of components observed in a given direction is then given by the nuclear moments and the direction and magnitude of the magnetic field. This case is approached, for instance, by Fe^{57} in iron. The other extreme corresponds to free atoms where the hyperfine interaction is governed by the usual spectroscopic rules: If the atomic spin is denoted by J, the multiplicity of components depends on J also. For instance, if $J < I_A$, the ground state splits only into $2J + 1$ magnetic sublevels. Obviously, a free atom cannot exhibit a Mössbauer effect. However, in the rare earth elements situations can arise where transitions without energy loss occur and where at the same time the unfilled inner shells can be treated like free atoms.

To investigate the quadrupole coupling $Q \cdot \nabla E$, where Q is the nuclear quadrupole moment and ∇E the electric field gradient at the nuclear site, one must place source or absorber nuclei in a surrounding with a high electric field gradient ∇E and measure the resulting splitting. If one wants to find the quadrupole moment Q, one must calculate the field gradient.

The first experimental investigation of quadrupole effects was done by Kistner and Sunyar, using Fe^{57}. Fe^{57} is well suited for this purpose, since the ground-state spin 1/2 prevents the ground state from having a quadrupole moment, and only the splitting due to the excited state with spin 3/2 must be taken into account. Kistner and Sunyar showed that the splitting of Fe^{57} embedded in antiferromagnetic Fe_2O_3 can be explained by a superposition of magnetic hyperfine structure and quadrupole interaction (Reprint Kistner and Sunyar 1960). In the meantime, many examples have been found in which only quadrupole splitting exists (see, for instance, Reprint DeBenedetti 1961).

The number of publications reporting investigations of magnetic and quadrupole interactions in various systems with various nuclides is growing steadily, and the reader is referred to the bibliography.

Incidentally, it is interesting to note that the measurements of moments of excited states by the Mössbauer effect have already led to additional theoretical investigations. Attempts to derive the quadrupole moment of the 3/2 state in Fe^{57} have been made,[46,47] and the magnetic moment of the 3/2 state has turned out to be a sensitive measure for the validity of nuclear model calculations.[48] (See also Abragam 1961, Gastebois 1961.)

4-4 ISOMERIC SHIFTS (CHEMICAL SHIFTS)[49]

In atomic spectroscopy, lines from an isotopic mixture show a splitting which is not present in the spectrum of an isotopically pure

[46] R. Bersohn, Phys. Rev. Letters, **4,** 609 (1960).

[47] G. Burns, Phys. Rev., **124,** 524 (1961).

[48] R. D. Lawson and M. H. Macfarlane, Nuclear Phys., **24,** 18 (1961).

[49] Both terms, isomeric and chemical shift, are used in the literature to denote the same effect.

element. In heavy elements, this isotopic splitting is due to the fact that the addition of one or more neutrons changes the nuclear radius. This change, in turn, shifts the atomic energy levels.[50-55] A change in the radius can occur even without a change in nucleon number when the nucleus goes from one state to another, for instance, when it decays from an isomeric state to the ground state. The corresponding shift in energy is called an *isomeric shift* and such a shift of *atomic* energy levels has recently been observed in Hg^{197}.[56]

A change in nuclear radius which shifts the *atomic* energy levels will obviously also affect the *nuclear* levels by the same amount. An isomeric shift has indeed been observed in the Mössbauer effect and this shift may well turn out to yield more information about nuclear and solid-state physics than, for instance, the lifetime measurements described in Sec. 4-2. The first unambiguous observation of an isomeric shift was made by Kistner and Sunyar (Reprint 1960), using Fe^{57}. Subsequently, isomeric shifts were investigated with Fe^{57} (e.g., Solomon 1960; Reprint DeBenedetti 1960, Wertheim 1961); with Sn^{119} (Boyle 1961); and with Au^{197} (Shirley 1961). Systematic discussions of the isomeric shifts have been published by Walker et al. (Reprint 1961) and by Shirley (1961).

In the present section the physical idea underlying the isomer shift will be outlined in simplest terms. As pointed out above, a change in the electrostatic interaction between the nucleus and its electron shell is responsible for the equal energy shifts of the atomic and the nuclear levels. The observation of these two effects is entirely different, however. Consider first the *atomic* isotope and isomer shift. Isotopes and isomers have the same electron shell but different nuclear radii. The same atomic transition hence can have a different energy in two atoms which contain nuclei in different states, provided the two atomic states involved in the transition are affected differently by the change in *nuclear* radius. Otherwise both levels are shifted by equal amounts and no net change in the transition energy results. In the *nuclear* isomer shift, one compares the same nuclear transition in two atomic systems which have different electronic wave functions at the nucleus.

---

[50] H. Kopfermann, "Kernmomente," Akademische Verlagsgesellschaft, Frankfurt, 1956; "Nuclear Moments," Academic Press, New York, 1958.

[51] K. W. Ford and D. L. Hill, Ann. Rev. Nuclear Sci., **5**, 25 (1955).

[52] J. E. Mack and H. Arroe, Ann. Rev. Nuclear Sci., **6**, 117 (1956).

[53] D. L. Hill, Matter and Charge Distribution within Atomic Nuclei, "Encyclopedia of Physics," Springer, Berlin, 1957, Vol. 39, p. 178.

[54] G. Breit, Revs. Modern Phys., **30**, 507 (1958).

[55] L. R. B. Elton, "Nuclear Sizes," Oxford University Press, New York, 1961.

[56] A. C. Melissinos and S. P. Davis, Phys. Rev., **115**, 130 (1959).

A shift can only be seen if the two nuclear states involved have different radii; otherwise both levels involved in the transition change by the same amount, and the gamma-ray energy is not affected. The requirements for the observation of a nuclear isomeric shift hence are:

1. The two nuclear states involved must have different charge distributions.

2. There must be electronic wave functions (usually from s electrons) which overlap appreciably with the nuclear wave functions.

3. These wave functions must be sensitive to external (chemical) changes.

All three requirements are justified by the following simple calculation.

In order to calculate the shift of the nuclear energy levels, consider first a point nucleus, of charge Ze, with two levels A and B, separated by an energy E_0. The electrostatic potential created by this point nucleus is shown as a dotted line in Fig. 4-2. Now consider another nucleus, of equal charge, but with radius R_A in the ground state A and a radius R_B in the excited state B, as shown in Fig. 4-2. Because of the diminished interaction with the electrons, the two levels A and B will lie higher for this nucleus than they did for the point

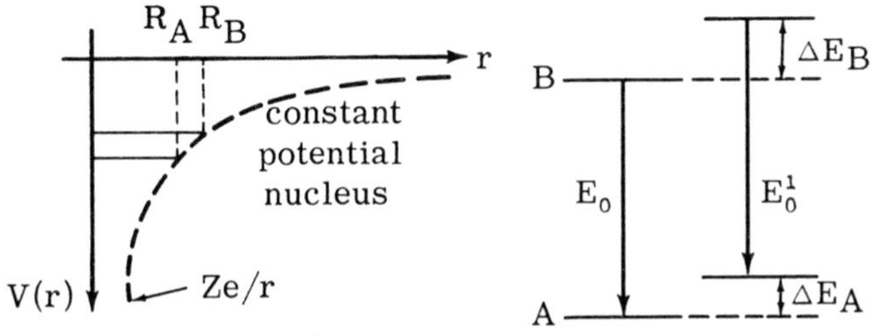

Fig. 4-2 Electrostatic potential for a point nucleus and for a constant potential nucleus. The radius R_A of the ground state is assumed to be smaller than the radius R_B for the excited state. The level shifts from point nucleus to finite-size nucleus are shown on the right.

nucleus (Fig. 4-2). To find for instance the shift ΔE_A one determines the contribution to the total energy of the system which comes from the electrostatic interaction. The potential from R_A to infinity is the same for the finite as for the point nucleus. Hence only the volume from 0 to R_A needs to be taken into account when determining the energy shift. If one assumes that the wave function $\Psi(r)$ of the relevant electrons is essentially constant over the distances involved and can be replaced by $\Psi(0)$, the contribution to the interaction energy from this volume is given by

$$E(R_A) = -\int_0^{R_A} V(r)e\,|\Psi(0)|^2\,4\pi r^2\,dr \tag{68}$$

where V(r) is the electrostatic potential created by the nucleus. For a point nucleus, $V(r) = Ze/r$, and one finds

$$E_p(R_A) = -2\pi Ze^2R_A^2|\Psi(0)|^2 \tag{69}$$

The energy $E(R_A)$ for a finite nucleus depends on the charge distribution. Easiest to calculate is the surface charge model (top-slice model), where the electrostatic potential is constant from the center to the nuclear surface and joins the outside potential at $r = R$. This potential is shown in Fig. 4-2, and its contribution is given by

$$E_s(R_A) = -(4/3)\pi Ze^2R_A^2|\Psi(0)|^2 \tag{70}$$

The difference between the expressions (70) and (69) yields the shift

$$\Delta E_A^s = E_s(R_A) - E_p(R_A) = (2/3)\pi Ze^2R_A^2|\Psi(0)|^2 \tag{71}$$

The assumption of a surface charge is unrealistic, but the calculation can easily be performed with a nuclear charge density $\rho(r)$. The result has exactly the same form as Eq. (71), but the nuclear radius R_A^2 is replaced by the root-mean-square radius

$$\langle r_A^2\rangle = \int \rho(r)r^2\,dv = 4\pi \int \rho(r)r^4\,dr \tag{72}$$

The transition energy between two levels B and A becomes

$$E_0' = E_0 + \Delta E_B - \Delta E_A = E_0 + (2/3)\,\pi Ze^2|\Psi(0)|^2\,[\langle r_B^2\rangle - \langle r_A^2\rangle] \tag{73}$$

Ordinarily, it is impossible to observe such a small energy change. However, if one performs a Mössbauer experiment and uses source and absorber with different chemical environments such that the wave functions at the nuclei in the emitter e and the absorber a are different, one finds for the difference in gamma-ray energy from (73)

$$\delta = E_a - E_e = (2/3)\pi Ze^2\,[\langle r_B^2\rangle - \langle r_A^2\rangle]\{|\Psi(0)_a|^2 - |\Psi(0)_e|^2\} \tag{74}$$

Equation (74) justifies the three requirements listed above, and it gives the correct order of magnitude for the isomeric shift. However, for many applications a more accurate formula is desired. Relevant derivations and equations can be found in refs. 50 to 55 and 57, and in

---

[57] A. R. Bodmer, Nuclear Phys., 21, 347 (1960).

the publication by Shirley (1961). Applications of (74) are contained in the Reprints by DeBenedetti et al. and Walker et al.

Equation (74) also shows that information on two different fields can be obtained from isomeric-shift experiments. On the one hand, differences in the nuclear radius between ground state and excited state can be measured. On the other hand, changes in the wave function of s electrons can be studied in various substances. Both avenues offer exciting possibilities for further investigations.

4-5 PARITY EXPERIMENTS

The observation of the intensity and of the polarization of individual Zeeman components of nuclear gamma rays (Secs. 4-2 and 5-9) permits the investigation of parity conservation in strong and weak interactions. Grodzins and Genovese (1961) have tested the parity conservation in strong interactions in the 14.4-kev transition in Fe^{57} by comparing the transition rates for the $\Delta m = \pm 1$ components in the direction of the nuclear polarization with those opposite to it. They found the relative strength of a parity admixed wave function to be less than 10^{-5}.

Morita (1961) has suggested experiments testing parity conservation and time-reversal invariance in weak interactions.

5 GENERAL PHYSICS

5-1 SURVEY

Those applications of the Mössbauer effect that are not nuclear or solid-state physics are reviewed in this chapter. When going through the various sections, one realizes that such a division is very arbitrary and that it should only be understood as a scheme for arranging things. Actually, one of the beautiful aspects of the Mössbauer effect is that it shows the unity of physics and connects seemingly unrelated fields.

Comparing the applications in Secs. 5-2 to 5-5 with those of Chaps. 4 and 6, one notices that they belong to a different class. Indeed, rather than divide the various topics as is done in this book, one can equally well distinguish two classes: (1) experiments depending on the line width Γ, and (2) experiments depending on $Q = E/\Gamma$, the ratio of the transition energy to the line width.

It is really for class 2 that the Mössbauer effect shows its superiority as a research tool; it is surprising that more experiments have not been done which take advantage of the extremely high Q values available with nuclides such as Fe^{57} and Zn^{67}.

5-2 GRAVITATIONAL RED SHIFT (APPARENT WEIGHT OF PHOTONS)

Einstein's theory of relativity has always held a particular fascination for the scientist and the layman alike, and it has stirred imagination as no other theory has done in the present century. It is therefore not surprising that the use of the Mössbauer effect to study problems connected with relativity has received an enormous amount of attention and publicity. Soon after the discovery of the Mössbauer effect, it was realized by many physicists that this new tool offered possibilities for investigating problems in relativity. A few groups started to explore the feasibility of such experiments. No group has done more admirable work, however, than Pound and his co-workers at Harvard. They have succeeded in unambiguously demonstrating the red shift of photons in the laboratory.

The red shift of spectral lines in a gravitational field was predicted by Einstein[58,59] and a classic description of the relevant facts can be found in Pauli's article[60] (see also Møller 1960). Here a short outline of the essential arguments will be given. Consider a source of radiation at rest in a system K_0, which moves with a velocity $v = \beta c$ with respect to the laboratory system K_{lab}. The radiation source can be used as a clock. If this clock measures in its system K_0 a time t_0 (proper time) between two events, then an observer in K_{lab} will find a longer time t_{lab} between these same events (*time dilation*):

$$t_{lab} = t_0/(1 - \beta^2)^{1/2} \tag{75}$$

If the source in K_0 emits a radiation of frequency ω_0, then the frequency measured in K_{lab} is given by[61]

$$\omega_{lab} = \omega_0 \frac{(1 - \beta^2)^{1/2}}{1 - \beta \cos \alpha_{lab}} = \omega_0 \frac{1 + \beta \cos \alpha_0}{(1 - \beta^2)^{1/2}} \tag{76}$$

In these expressions for the *Doppler shift*, α_0 is the angle between the direction of emission of the photon ω_0 and the velocity $\mathbf{v}$ measured in K_0, and α_{lab} denotes the same angle measured in K_{lab}.

For small velocities, $v \ll c$, (75) and (76) can be approximated by

$$t_{lab} \simeq t_0[1 + (1/2)\beta^2] \tag{77}$$

and

$$\omega_{lab} \simeq \omega_0[1 + \beta \cos \alpha_{lab} + \beta^2(\cos^2 \alpha_{lab} - 1/2)] \tag{78}$$

Now consider a source which is fixed at a radius R to a disk which rotates with an angular frequency Ω. An observer at the center of the disk will receive only photons that have been emitted radi-

---

[58] A. Einstein, Ann. Physik, **35**, 898 (1911); reprinted in "The Principle of Relativity," Dover, New York, 1923.

[59] A. Einstein, "Über die spezielle und allgemeine Relativitätstheorie," Vieweg, Braunschweig, 1956, 17th ed., p. 82; "Relativity, the Special and the General Theory," Methuen, London, 1954.

[60] W. Pauli, "Theory of Relativity," Pergamon, London, 1958, pp. 19, 151-154.

[61] E. L. Hill, Optics and Relativity Theory, in E. U. Condon and H. Odishaw (eds.), "Handbook of Physics," McGraw-Hill, New York, 1958.

ally, i.e., for which $\alpha_{lab} = 90°$. According to Eq. (78), the observer then measures a frequency

$$\omega_{lab} \simeq \omega_0[1 - (1/2)(R\Omega/c)^2] \qquad (79)$$

This relation also follows from the time dilation (77), since an increase in the time interval between two signals entails a corresponding decrease in energy.

The arguments leading to Eq. (79) are based on the Doppler effect; the observer determines the change in frequency due to the transverse motion of the source. Einstein has shown that the frequency shift can be considered from a different point of view—one which leads to an extremely important generalization. Instead of postulating a transverse Doppler effect, the observer can assume that his disk is at rest and that the source instead is in a different gravitational potential. The centrifugal force acting on the source then is interpreted as a gravitational force. The potential at the radius R is equal to the negative of the work required to move a *unit mass* from R to the center:

$$\Phi = -(1/2)R^2\Omega^2 \qquad (80)$$

Equation (79) can now be written as

$$\omega_{lab} \simeq \omega_0(1 + \Phi/c^2) \qquad (81)$$

Einstein postulated Eq. (81) to hold not only for the rotating disk but generally for all situations where observer and clock are situated in different gravitational potentials. Whether the potential is gravitational or due to uniform acceleration does not matter (*principle of equivalence*).

The derivation of Eq. (81) shows that the *gravitational red shift* does not yield information about the equations of general relativity. It only tests the principle of equivalence and shows that photons in a gravitational field behave like particles with mass. Pound correspondingly terms the terrestrial-red-shift experiment "apparent weight of photons." A particle with mass m gains an energy $m\Phi$, if moved from a potential 0 to a potential Φ. According to Eq. (81), a photon of energy $E = \hbar\omega_0$ gains an amount $\hbar\omega_0\Phi/c^2$. The photon thus behaves like a particle with a "mass"

$$m_{photon} = \hbar\omega_0/c^2 = E/c^2 \qquad (82)$$

As expected, the rest mass of photons is zero. One could, of course, start from (82) and arrive at (81).

If a source of resonant gamma rays is situated in the earth's gravitational field at a height H above a resonant absorber, then the potential difference is given by $\Phi = gH$, as long as H is small compared to the radius of the earth. A photon, emitted by this source, will "fall" in the gravitational field toward the absorber and actually undergo a "violet" rather than a red shift. The corresponding relative gain in energy is given in first approximation by (81) as

$$\Delta E/E = (\omega_{lab} - \omega_0)/\omega_0 = gH/c^2 \quad (83)$$

or

$$\Delta E/E = H(cm) \times 1.09 \times 10^{-18} \quad (84)$$

For a difference in height between source and absorber of 10 m, one gets a relative shift of about 1 part in 10^{15}.

One aspect of the red-shift experiment deserves a few more words. The arguments given above assume that the frequency of photons depends on the gravitational potential but that the nuclear levels, measured by an observer at rest with respect to the nucleus and situated in the same gravitational potential, remain unchanged. This assumption is based on the weakness of the gravitational interaction as compared to nuclear and electromagnetic forces. It is, however, possible to select a coordinate frame in which the frequency of the photons moving in a static gravitational field remains constant (Møller 1960, p. 46). Measured in this coordinate frame, the energy of the atomic or nuclear levels depends on the gravitational potential, and it is this dependence that is responsible for the red shift. These two descriptions are equivalent.

The basic idea of a terrestrial-red-shift experiment is very simple. A resonant source is placed at a height H above the resonant absorber, and the relative energy shift is determined by measuring the velocity spectrum. However, the practical difficulties are enormous, particularly because even Fe^{57}, the nuclide used at the present time, has a Q value of "only" 3×10^{12}. For a height H = 10 m, a shift of about one part in 10^3 of the line width must be determined accurately. In addition, many disturbing effects exist and must be eliminated or corrected for with extreme care.

The first completely satisfactory measurement was performed by Pound and Rebka (Reprint 1960), and the reader is referred to their excellent report and to Pound's review (1960, 1961) for an understanding and appreciation of this difficult experiment.

Two additional remarks are in order. During the past few years, physicists have often speculated whether antiparticles will fall or rise in a gravitational field. Winterberg has pointed out recently[62] that the

---

[62] F. Winterberg, Nuovo cimento, **19**, 186 (1961).

positive result of the Pound-Rebka experiment makes it extremely likely that antiparticles and particles have the same sign of the gravitational interaction. Consider the following gedanken experiment. A photon of energy $2mc^2 - \epsilon$ falls in a gravitational field until it has gained an energy ϵ. In the presence of a very heavy nucleus, it then creates a particle-antiparticle pair of total mass $2mc^2$. If the antiparticle is subject to "anti gravity," the pair is weightless and can be brought to the starting point of the photon without energy loss, thus violating energy conservation.

The second remark concerns a suggestion by Cocconi and Salpeter (1960), who proposed to use the Mössbauer effect to set an upper limit on a possible anisotropy of inertia. Corresponding experiments using the Mössbauer effect (Sherwin 1960) and conventional resonance techniques[63,64] failed to observe an effect and hence apparently determined a limit on the anisotropy of inertia. Dicke, however, points out that this null result does not cast doubts on the validity of Mach's principle, but shows that inertial anisotropy effects are universal and the same for all particles.[65]

5-3 ACCELERATED SYSTEMS

The high Q value of isotopes like Fe^{57} allows the observations of effects due to accelerated systems. The simplest such experiment is the measurement of the energy shift of a photon emitted from a system rotating with a frequency Ω. If a resonant emitter is mounted on this system at a radius R_e and a resonant absorber is situated at a radius R_a, one finds for the relative energy shift from Eqs. (79) or (81), in first approximation,

$$(E_a - E_e)/E_0 = (\Omega^2/2c^2)(R_e^2 - R_a^2) \qquad (85)$$

At first one would expect that source and absorber must lie on the same radius or that the absorber must be exactly in the center to avoid a linear Doppler effect. However, a short calculation shows that the first-order terms will cancel. Such a cancellation is to be expected, since the gravitational field equivalent to the acceleration on a rotating system depends only on the distance from the center [Eq. (80)].

The Harwell group (Reprint Hay 1960) first demonstrated experimentally that Eq. (85) is followed within the limits of error. This experiment, together with the Pound-Rebka experiment discussed in

[63] V. W. Hughes, H. G. Robinson, and V. Beltrow-Lopez, Phys. Rev. Letters, **4**, 342 (1960).

[64] R. W. P. Drever, Phil. Mag., **6**, 683 (1961).

[65] R. H. Dicke, Phys. Rev. Letters, **7**, 359 (1961).

Sec. 5-2, shows that the equivalence principle is correct to within about 5 per cent.

Equation (85) indicates that no shift is to be expected if source and absorber move on the same orbit, even if their relative velocity is as high as $2R\Omega$. This absence of a Doppler shift has been verified by Champeney and Moon (Reprint 1961).

Bömmel has performed an experiment in which he tested the frequency shift in a linearly accelerated system[66] by mounting source and absorber on piezoelectric crystals and driving the crystals in phase.

5-4 SECOND-ORDER DOPPLER SHIFT

In the framework of the classical theory of the Mössbauer effect, as sketched in Sec. 2-3, Eq. (78) can be interpreted as follows. The emitting nucleus moves about its equilibrium position with a velocity v(t). As discussed in remark 4 of Sec. 2-3, the characteristic time for the lattice vibrations is much shorter than the lifetime of the nuclear state. The linear term $(v/c)\cos\alpha_{lab}$ in Eq. (76) will hence average out. The quadratic term, $-(1/2)(v/c)^2$, which comes from the expansion of $\sqrt{1-(v/c)^2}$, will remain and it will cause a shift in the energy of the emitted or absorbed gamma ray (second-order Doppler shift). This shift can be calculated, since $(1/2)Mv^2 = E_{kin}$, where M is the mass and E_{kin} the kinetic energy of the decaying atom. Hence one finds

$$\delta E/E = -E_{kin}/Mc^2 \tag{86}$$

In the classical limit, the kinetic energy E_{kin} is equal to $(3/2)kT$, and the relative energy shift becomes

$$\delta E/E = -3kT/2Mc^2 \tag{87}$$

For harmonic lattice forces, where the total energy U is twice the kinetic energy E_{kin}, one finds for the temperature dependence of the relative energy shift from Eq. (86),

$$\frac{\partial}{\partial T}(\delta E/E) = -C_L/2M'c^2 \tag{88}$$

Here $C_L = \partial U/\partial T$ is the specific heat of the lattice and M' is the gram atomic weight of the lattice substance.

The question of whether the temperature motion that causes the shift (86) will also give rise to a broadening of the lines has been

[66] H. Bömmel, in "Proceedings of the Second Mössbauer Conference," Paris, Sept. 13-16, 1961, A. Schoen and D. M. J. Compton (eds.), Wiley, New York, 1962, p. 229.

studied by Snyder and Wick (1960). They find that for a perfect crystalline solid such a broadening does not occur.

If the environment of source and absorber nuclei are the same, the term (86) will be identical for both and hence will not be observable. However, if the source and the absorber are at different temperatures or if source and absorber nuclei are in different surroundings, an observable shift can result. Since such a shift depends on the "chemical state" of source and absorber, it is sometimes difficult to separate it from the isomeric shift discussed in Sec. 4-4.

Actually, the second-order Doppler shift was overlooked until early 1960, when Pound and Rebka (Reprint 1960) realized that such an effect existed. They derived an expression for it and verified this expression [Eq. (88)] experimentally. At the same time and from a different point of view, the effect was predicted by Josephson (Reprint 1960). In an undergraduate examination at Cambridge University, Josephson received the problem to calculate the change in frequency of an oscillator which suddenly changes its mass. He had read about the Mössbauer effect and realized that there was a connection. When the excited state decays by gamma-ray emission, the nucleus loses energy, and its mass is reduced by an amount $\delta M = -E/c^2$. Its thermal momentum p is unchanged, since the solid takes up all the recoil momentum. The reduced mass, however, causes an *increase* in the kinetic energy of the atom:

$$\delta E_{kin} = (\partial E_{kin}/\partial M)\, \delta M = (-p^2/2M^2)(-E/c^2) = (1/2)E(v^2/c^2) \quad (89)$$

which is compensated by a corresponding *decrease* in the energy of the emitted gamma ray. The shift Eq. (89) thus agrees in magnitude and sign with the classical result deduced from Eq. (78). Josephson wrote a short note on his derivation and sent it to Harwell, where it arrived among many crank letters. Marshall realized the importance of Josephson's calculation and tried to reach him by telephone, only to be told that undergraduates were not supposed to receive calls. Despite these difficulties, Josephson's note was published.

The experiments confirming the second-order Doppler shift in Fe^{57} (Reprint Pound and Rebka 1960) and Sn^{119} (Boyle 1960) also constitute a direct proof of the famous "clock paradox" or "twin paradox," as was pointed out by Sherwin (1960). In his original paper on special relativity, Einstein[67] predicted the following effect: At a time $t = 0$, two identical clocks are synchronized at a point A. One clock remains at A and measures the time t. The other clock travels away from A with a velocity v(t). When it eventually returns to A, it will indicate an elapsed time s_0 which is shorter than the time t_0 measured by the stationary clock in the ratio

[67] A. Einstein, Ann. Physik, 17, 891 (1905). Reprinted in "The Principle of Relativity," Dover, New York, 1923, p. 49.

$$s_0/t_0 = (1/t_0) \int_0^{t_0} [1 - (v/c)^2]^{1/2}\, dt \qquad (90)$$

Equation (90) is a generalization of Eq. (75); in one form or another it is an integral part of science fiction literature. The paradox lies in the fact that a straightforward application of "relativity," without a careful definition of its meaning, leads to the conclusion that one should never be able to tell which clock is accelerated and that Eq. (90) should be invalid. This disagreement has been discussed extensively in the literature; Sherwin summarizes the various arguments and then shows that the emitting and absorbing nuclei in a Mössbauer experiment play the roles of the two clocks. Assume the absorber to be at a very low temperature, so that $v \simeq 0$; it then plays the role of the stationary clock. The source at high temperature easily possesses rms velocities $\langle v^2 \rangle^{1/2}$ comparable to that of a jet plane, and it plays the role of the clock moving in a space craft. According to Eq. (86) or (87), the emission line indeed has a lower energy than the absorption line. In other words, the traveling clock goes slower than the stationary clock, Eq. (90) is justified, and the science fiction writers can continue using it.

5-5 FREQUENCY AND PHASE MODULATION

Two methods for slightly shifting the energy of resonant gamma rays will be discussed in this section. These methods are not only useful to shift energies and hence can be employed as velocity drives (Sec. 3-43), but they also serve as tools for other investigations.

The first of these methods can be called "*frequency modulation* of gamma rays." In Sec. 2-3, it was shown that if one moves the source of an electromagnetic wave $[\exp(i\omega_0 t)]$ with a simple harmonic motion, $x(0) \sin \Omega t$, sidebands appear with frequencies $\omega_0 \pm \Omega$, $\omega_0 \pm 2\Omega, \ldots$. Ruby and Bolef (Reprint 1960) have observed these sidebands by fixing a source of Fe^{57} on a quartz transducer and vibrating it with a frequency of 20 Mc/sec. The theory borrowed from Sec. 2-3 is classical; a quantum mechanical treatment has been given by Abragam (1960).

A *phase modulation* of the 14.4-kev gamma ray of Fe^{57} has been observed by Grodzins and Phillips (Reprint 1961). If a medium with a refractive index n and a length L is placed in the path of a resonant gamma ray of frequency ω_0, a phase shift

$$\Phi = (1 - n)\omega_0(L/c) \qquad (91)$$

results. If either the length L or the index of refraction n is a function of time, and if the medium is placed between source and absorber, then the time-dependent part of the wave function of the photon at the absorber is given by

$$f(t) = \exp[-i\omega_0 t + i\Phi(t) - \Gamma t/2\hbar] \tag{92}$$

where Γ is the natural line width. The frequency spectrum of this phase-modulated wave train is given by the absolute square of the Fourier transform $g(\omega)$,

$$g(\omega) = 1/(2\pi)^{1/2} \int_0^\infty dt \ \exp(i\omega t)\, f(t) \tag{93}$$

If one modulates the phase *sinusoidally*, the result is similar to the one found in Sec. 2-3 and in the paragraph above. Sidebands appear and the intensity in the central line of frequency ω_0 is diminished.

The *saw-tooth* modulation of the phase shift is more interesting. Assuming

$$\Phi(t) = \Phi_0 t/t_0 \qquad t_0 \geq t \geq 0 \tag{95}$$

the integral (93) can be evaluated in closed form. All practically obtainable phase shifts Φ_0 and modulation times t_0 are such that the relation

$$\Phi_0 \ll \omega_0 t_0 \tag{96}$$

is easily fulfilled. In the approximation (96), the frequency spectrum is given by

$$I(\omega) = |\, g(\omega)\,|^2 \cong \frac{1/2\pi}{[\omega - \omega_0(1 - \Phi_0/\omega_0 t_0)]^2 + (\Gamma/2\hbar)^2} \tag{97}$$

The width of the original line of energy E is unchanged, but the line is shifted by an amount ΔE given by

$$\Delta E/E = \Phi_0/\omega_0 t_0 \tag{98}$$

If the phase modulation also modulates the intensity I of the photons, for instance, if the photons traverse material with a linear absorption coefficient μ and a thickness varying according to $L = L_0 t/t_0$ so that $I(t) = I_0 \exp(-\mu L_0 t/t_0)$, then the line width Γ in Eq. (97) must be replaced by

$$\Gamma' = \Gamma + \mu\hbar L_0/t_0 \tag{99}$$

5-6 THE UNCERTAINTY RELATION BETWEEN ENERGY AND TIME

A linear harmonic oscillator serves as a simple model for a classical radiation source.[6] If undamped, it will emit an infinitely long wave train of sharp frequency ω_0. If the oscillator is damped, the amplitude f will decrease in time. For the damping force occuring in radiation theory, this decrease will be exponential,[6]

$$f(t) = f(0) \exp[-i\omega_0 t - (1/2)\gamma t] \tag{100}$$

The intensity averaged over one period as a function of time is given by the absolute square of f(t),

$$I(t) = I(0) \exp(-\gamma t) \tag{101}$$

The mean life τ of this exponential decay is equal to $1/\gamma$. The frequency of such a wave train will no longer be sharp, but will be given by the absolute square of the Fourier transform [Eq. (93)] of f(t),

$$I(\omega) = (\gamma/2\pi) \frac{I(0)}{(\omega - \omega_0)^2 + (\gamma/2)^2} \tag{102}$$

Equation (102) represents a Lorentz line with full width at half-height γ centered at ω_0. Decay time τ and line width γ satisfy the relation

$$\tau \cdot \gamma = 1 \tag{103}$$

It is clear from these arguments that the line will invariably broaden if the wave train is shortened. Even if the decay I(t) is not exponential, the relation (103) will yield the right order of magnitude for the line width γ.

In quantum theory, the expression (103) is replaced by the uncertainty relation (34). The arguments which show that a shortening of the time τ results in a broadening of the line width γ are cast in a different language. Rather than speaking about a wave train, one discusses the possibility of measuring a given separation in energy ΔE within a given time T (Sec. 2-43). The emission process and its observation can no longer be separated; both must be incorporated in the quantum mechanical treatment. The relevancy of Eq. (34) to these problems and its detailed interpretation have led to many arguments and discussions. One of the exciting applications of the Mössbauer effect is the demonstration of the correctness of the ideas leading to, and expressed by, Eq. (34).

The corresponding experiments can be performed best with the nuclide Fe^{57} (Fig. 4-1). The 123-kev gamma ray leading from the second to the first excited state is used to signal the time $t = 0$, i.e., the time when the first excited state of Fe^{57} is populated. The 14.4-kev gamma ray then can be observed in delayed coincidence with this "signal" gamma ray. By utilizing a variable delay and a resolving time which is short compared to the mean life of the 14.4-kev photons, one can study the shape of the Mössbauer line as a function of

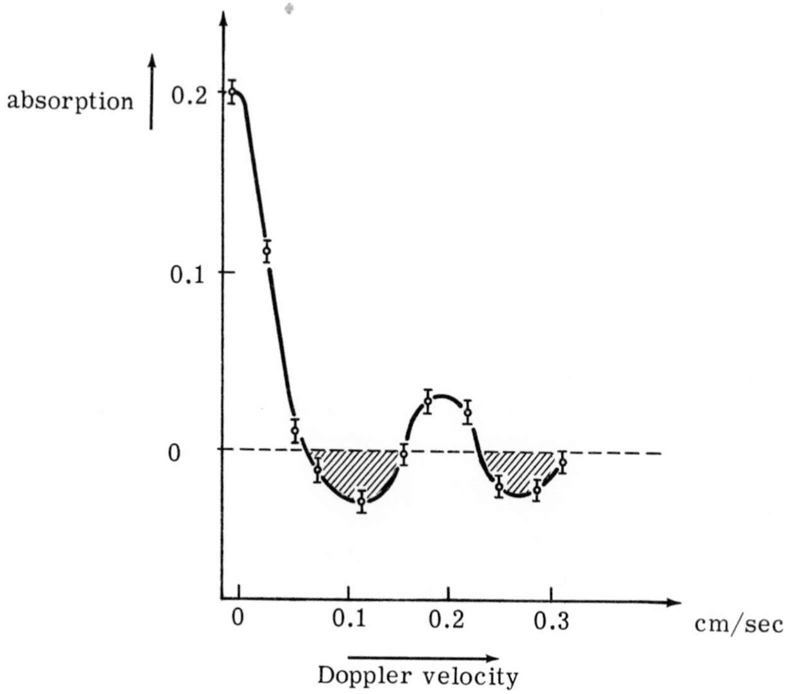

Fig. 5-1 The oscillatory behavior of the Fe^{57} absorption line when observed with delayed coincidences. [Adapted from Wu and co-workers (1960).] Lifetime of the 14.4-kev state in Fe^{57} $\tau \simeq 1.4 \times 10^{-7}$ sec; delay time $\simeq (1/2)\tau$, resolving time $\simeq 0.1\tau$.

the time elapsed between the population of the level and the observation of the photon.

Such experiments were first performed by the Argonne group (Holland 1960, Reprint Lynch 1960), and later repeated by Wu and collaborators (1960). Hamermesh formulated a classical theory of the time-dependent effects (Reprint Lynch 1960). Harris (1961) performed a quantum mechanical calculation and found complete agreement with the classical theory.

Theory and experiment both yield the following results: For delay times short compared to the mean life, the Mössbauer line is broadened in agreement with the expressions (34) and (103). This broadening can be seen clearly in Fig. 10 of the Reprint (Lynch 1960). With increasing delay time, the line narrows and develops a damped oscillatory behavior as shown in Fig. 5-1. For times long compared to the mean life, the oscillations are rapid and the central line becomes narrower than the natural line width. For most delay times, there exist energies close to the resonance energy where the number of gamma rays seen by the detector is greater than if the absorber were not present; the absorber produces a time bunching of photons. This "photon excess" is shaded in Fig. 5-1.

None of these results is new in the sense that it could not have been calculated years ago. However, the experimental observation of these effects has stimulated thinking about elementary radiation theory, and it allows a convincing demonstration of the uncertainty relation between time and energy.

Hack and Hamermesh (Reprint 1961) have treated another application of the Mössbauer effect to line-shape problems. Assume that a constant magnetic field splits the initial state of a gamma transition into components, separated by an energy Δ [Eq. (66)]. If one now applies an external radiofrequency field of frequency ω_{rf}, one expects changes in the radiation pattern of the gamma ray at resonance, $\hbar\omega_{rf} = \Delta$. It may be possible to detect these changes using the Mössbauer effect.

5-7 RECOILLESS RAYLEIGH SCATTERING

Consider a beam of monochromatic X rays of energy E and momentum **k** which is scattered by a crystal. The scattered beam of momentum **k**′ contains a *modified* and an *unmodified* line.[68] The modified line, shifted to lower energies and considerably wider than the incident beam, is due to Compton effect and will not be considered further. The unmodified line is due to Rayleigh scattering: The incident photon of energy E is absorbed by a bound electron that is *virtually* excited to a higher discrete level or to the continuum. A photon of the same energy E is then reemitted while the electron returns to its original state.[29,69,70] The small fraction of the unmodified line due to nuclear Thomson scattering will be neglected.

With the energy resolution available in ordinary X-ray experiments, the unmodified line appears to be essentially identical to the incident line. Actually, however, it consists of a coherent (elastic) and an incoherent (inelastic) part. Both parts transfer the entire recoil momentum $\hbar(\mathbf{k} - \mathbf{k}')$ to the lattice as a whole. The *incoherent* beam also exchanges energy with the lattice by emitting or absorbing phonons. The energies involved in this exchange are of the order of 0.1 ev, or less.

---

[68] R. B. Leighton, "Principles of Modern Physics," McGraw-Hill, New York, 1959, p. 434.

[69] J. M. Jauch and F. Rohrlich, "The Theory of Photons and Electrons," Addison-Wesley, Reading, Mass., 1955, p. 387.

[70] G. W. Grodstein, "X-Ray Attenuation Coefficients from 10 kev to 100 Mev," Natl. Bur. Standards Circ. 583, 1957.

Since the widths of X rays are of the order of 1 ev, these phonon processes simply lead to a line widening and a small line shift, but the incoherent part cannot be separated from the coherent part by conventional X-ray spectrometers. The *coherent* or elastic part, which is now often called the recoilless part, leaves the lattice in its initial state and has exactly the same energy E as the primary beam. It is this coherent part of the unmodified line which is the tool of X-ray diffraction.

The entire unmodified line, coherent and incoherent, is due to Rayleigh scattering; the electronic state of the scatterer is not changed. To calculate the coherent part, one must first find the total Rayleigh scattering. Contributions arise from two sources—from the different electrons in the same atom and from electrons in different atoms. These contributions are partially coherent, and one must combine the amplitudes rather than the intensities due to the various electrons.[71] The scattering from the different electrons of the same atom is described by a form factor; the scattering from different atoms is strong only at certain angles, the Bragg angles, and leads to the Bragg reflection, used for the determination of the structure of crystals.

Once one has calculated the total Rayleigh scattering, the coherent part of the unmodified line is found by taking into account the thermal motion of the atoms. This thermal motion gives rise to the emission and absorption of phonons and thus introduces energy shifts and incoherence. The fraction of scattering events that occurs without energy loss is calculated similarly to the procedure outlined in Sec. 2-5, and it is given by the Debye-Waller factor [Eq. (54)]. (See also Sec. 6-22.)

Before the discovery of the Mössbauer effect, the coherent beam was distinguished from the incoherent one by studying the intensity of Bragg reflections as a function of temperature. Tzara and Barloutaud (Reprint 1960) have shown that the Mössbauer effect permits a direct observation of the recoilless Rayleigh scattering. Resonant gamma rays, for instance, from a Sn^{119} or an Fe^{57} source, are scattered from a crystal that does not contain resonantly absorbing nuclei. The secondary beam $\mathbf{k}'$ contains a fraction of gamma rays that still possess the initial energy E. They can be distinguished from the incoherent background with a resonant absorber in front of the detector. By measuring the velocity spectrum, i.e., by moving the resonant absorber with a velocity v with respect to the stationary source and scatterer, one can trace out the form of the coherent line in a manner similar to the investigation of the transmission line shown in Fig. 3-1.

---

[71] A small problem in semantics arises here. Both the coherent and incoherent part of the unmodified line must be calculated, taking into account the coherence among the various atoms and electrons. The coherence among the atoms is then partly destroyed by temperature motion, and this gives rise to the incoherent part.

The possibility of cleanly separating the coherent from the incoherent line is of course due to the fact that the gamma rays used in these experiments possess a line width of about 10^{-7} ev or less. This width is not changed by the coherent scattering, whereas the incoherent line is shifted and is smeared out over an energy of about 0.1 ev.

5-8 COHERENCE AND INTERFERENCE

The theory of coherence and interference involving Mössbauer scattering has been treated in a number of publications (Reprint Kastler 1960, Reprint Tzara 1961, Podgoretskii 1960, Lipkin 1961, Moon 1961, Raghavan 1961, Trammel 1961, Tassie[72]). Relevant experiments have been performed by Black and Moon (Reprint 1960) and by Major (1961). More recent results have been reported by Black.[73]

The concept of coherence originated in classical optics. Even though it is basically not a difficult concept, its application is often confusing, and errors can arise because the physical situation and the meaning of coherence have not been clearly defined.[74,75] Here, a simple example should suffice. Consider two radiation sources, each emitting waves of frequency ω_0 with amplitudes $a = |a| \exp[i\alpha(t)]$ and $b = |b| \exp[i\beta(t)]$, where α and β are real. The intensity I(t) observed at a given point $\mathbf{r}$ in space and averaged over one period will be the absolute square of the sum of the amplitudes

$$I(\mathbf{r},t) = |a + b|^2 = |a|^2 + |b|^2 + I_{int} \tag{104}$$

where the interference term I_{int} is given by

$$I_{int} = 2\,|a|\,|b| \cos(\alpha - \beta) = 2\,\mathrm{Re}(a^* b) \tag{105}$$

The two waves a and b are said to be incoherent at the point $\mathbf{r}$ if the intensity $I(\mathbf{r},t)$ is the sum of $|a|^2$ and $|b|^2$, i.e., if the interference term vanishes. The waves will be perfectly coherent if the phases of the two bear a definite relationship to each other and slightly coherent if there exists a small correlation between their phases.

In quantum theory the discussion of coherence can be made along the same lines: If the probability of finding photons from two sources at a given point is not equal to the sum of the probabilities, one says that the two waves possess a certain amount of coherence. This definition applies particularly to the scattering of one photon from two

---

72 L. J. Tassie, unpublished report.

73 P. J. Black, in "Proceedings of the Second Mössbauer Conference," Paris, Sept. 13-16, 1961, A. Schoen and D. M. J. Compton (eds.), Wiley, New York, tentative publication Spring 1962.

74 A. T. Forrester, Am. J. Phys., **24**, 192 (1956).

75 E. L. O'Neill and L. C. Bradley, Phys. Today, **14** (6), 28 (1961).

scattering centers (see Ref. 6, pp. 192-194, 202; and Ref. 23, pp. 133-137). The scattered waves can be coherent; i.e., they can interfere with each other provided there is a fixed phase relation between them. The coherence is destroyed, however, if one determines by a measurement, for instance of the recoil of one center, from which center the photon has been scattered. Such an investigation with fixed phase relation is analogous to the famous optical double-slit experiment.

In order to discuss specifically the processes that can interfere with Mössbauer scattering, consider a photon of momentum $\hbar\mathbf{k}$ which strikes a resonant scatterer and excites a nucleus to its first excited state by recoilless absorption. The reemission can result in a photon of momentum $\hbar\mathbf{k}'$ or in a conversion electron. If one detects photons, Rayleigh scattering by the atomic electrons of one atom or by the electrons of many atoms can be coherent with the Mössbauer scattering. If one detects electrons, the photo effect and the internal conversion can interfere.[72] If the resonant nuclei in the absorber are abundant enough, scattering from the different nuclei can be coherent. In all these examples, coherence exists only if one does not determine where the scattering occurs. If, for instance, a hyperfine interaction is present at the resonant nuclei, then its observation shows that resonance scattering has occurred and all coherence with Rayleigh scattering is destroyed.

The equations describing the cross sections in the presence of coherent processes are given by Tzara (Reprint 1961). Here some of the essential facts are summarized. If one observes all processes leading to scattering in the direction $\mathbf{k}'$, without discriminating against those which leave the lattice in an excited state, the cross section is given by (Lipkin 1961)

$$\sigma \propto \left[|R|^2 + |M|^2 f(\mathbf{k}) + 2C \operatorname{Re}(R^*M) f(\mathbf{k})\right] \tag{106}$$

where R is the probability amplitude for Rayleigh scattering plus nuclear Thomson scattering, M is the probability amplitude for the Mössbauer scattering, and $f(\mathbf{k})$ is the Lamb-Mössbauer factor, Eq. (49) or (56). C is a factor describing the degree of coherence between the processes; it is independent of the lattice (Moon 1961).

If one uses a resonant detector to observe only those scattering events which leave the lattice in its initial state, one finds

$$\sigma \propto \left[|R|^2 F'(\mathbf{k} - \mathbf{k}') + |M|^2 f^2(\mathbf{k}) + 2C \operatorname{Re}(R^*M) F^{1/2}(\mathbf{k} - \mathbf{k}') f(\mathbf{k})\right] \tag{107}$$

where $\mathbf{k} - \mathbf{k}'$ is the momentum transferred to the lattice and $F(\mathbf{k} - \mathbf{k}')$ is the corresponding Debye-Waller factor, Eq. (54).

A few remarks about the interpretation and the application of these equations are in order.

1. Equation (106) and Eq. (107) show that one must choose R and M of about equal magnitude in order to make the interference term as large as possible compared with the other terms.

2. The dependence of the interference term on the Debye-Waller factor F (**k** − **k**′) and on the Lamb-Mössbauer factor is clearly exhibited by the two equations, (106) and (107), and needs no further discussion.

3. The interference between Mössbauer scattering and Rayleigh scattering has been observed experimentally by Black and Moon[73] (Reprint 1960). In order to get a large effect, they selected scattering angles such that strong Bragg reflections occurred (compare Sec. 5-7). The interference term changes sign when one changes the energy from slightly above the Mössbauer resonance to slightly below, and vanishes at exact resonance. This effect also is expected (Tzara 1961, Moon 1961).

4. Campbell and Bernstein[76] have observed interference between the Mössbauer scattering and totally reflected gamma rays. This technique permits the study of the chemical and magnetic environment of those nuclei which lie in a very thin layer close to the surface.

5. One possible application of interference effects may well be the observation of a weak Mössbauer line in a strong background, since the interference term depends on M rather than on $|M|^2$ (Moon 1961).

6. Another possible application is to the determination of phases in crystallography (Raghavan).

5-9 POLARIZATION[77]

The optical Zeeman effect has been extremely important for the understanding of atomic structure. In nuclear physics, prior to the discovery of the Mössbauer effect, analogous experiments were impossible. It is true that many polarization experiments have been performed with nuclear gamma rays, but these experiments have been difficult and cumbersome. Moreover, they always had to be performed on components unresolved in energy, and the information gathered about the polarization of individual components was rather indirect.

The discovery of the Mössbauer effect has changed this situation. Particularly with the 14.4-kev gamma ray emitted by Fe^{57}, the nuclear Zeeman effect can be observed easily and in detail (see Sec. 4-3). The individual components of the emitted gamma-ray lines are widely separated compared to the natural line width. The 93-kev gamma ray in Zn^{67} displays a Zeeman splitting of many line widths in fields as small as 100 gauss (Reprint Craig 1960).

---

[76] E. C. Campbell and S. Bernstein, Bull. Am. Phys. Soc., **6**, 443 (1961).

[77] This section follows closely some parts of a Los Alamos publication (Frauenfelder 1962).

Once the Zeeman components are separated clearly, the determination of their state of polarization becomes the next step. Experiments with the plane polarization of the Fe^{57} gamma rays were first performed by the Argonne group in order to complete the understanding of the Mössbauer spectrum of Fe^{57} embedded in iron (Reprint Hanna 1960). The gamma-ray polarization has also been taken into account by Wegener and Obenshain in order to explain the shape of the lines observed in Ni^{61} (Wegener 1961). The elliptical polarization was first used to simplify the investigation of the complicated spectra that appear when Fe^{57} is embedded in CoPd (Reprint Nagle 1960).

Polarization measurements on resolved gamma-ray components can be a very effective tool for unraveling complex spectra, for reducing the number of lines in complicated spectra, and for finding the direction of the internal magnetic field inside magnetic domains in ferromagnets, ferrimagnets, antiferromagnets, and possibly superconducting ferromagnets.

A complete theory of the polarization of gamma rays emitted and absorbed in the Mössbauer effect has been worked out by Visscher (Frauenfelder 1962), and this paper should be consulted for details. In the present section, a few remarks and the description of a simple experiment show the ease with which the *elliptical* polarization can be demonstrated in the Mössbauer effect. A similar very simple experiment showing the *linear* polarization of the Fe^{57} gamma rays has been performed by the Argonne group (Perlow 1960).

The levels of Fe^{57}, embedded in ferromagnetic iron metal and placed in an external magnetic field, are shown in Fig. 2 of the Reprint (Hanna 1960).[78] The radiation pattern emitted by Fe^{57} will generally consist of six lines, as shown in the same figure. However, if one observes the pattern along the axis of the external magnetic field, the transition $\Delta m = 0$ is completely forbidden, and only four components appear. To discuss the polarization of the four components, one notes that a gamma ray is called right circularly polarized if its spin lies in the direction of motion. (This convention is opposite to the one used in optical spectroscopy.) Consider first the highest energy component, namely, the transition $-3/2$ to $-1/2$. The z component of angular momentum must be conserved, and any gamma ray corresponding to this component hence must have a z component of angular momentum of -1. If this gamma ray is emitted along the $+z$ direction, its spin is antiparallel to its momentum, and it is left circularly

[78] The labeling of the magnetic sublevels of Fe^{57} has led to some confusion. The magnetic moment of the excited state is negative; the internal field in iron metal is opposite to the externally applied magnetic field. If one uses the convention that the *external* field is directed along the $+z$ axis, then the $m = -3/2$ state possesses the highest energy, as shown in Fig. 2 of the Reprint (Hanna, 1960).

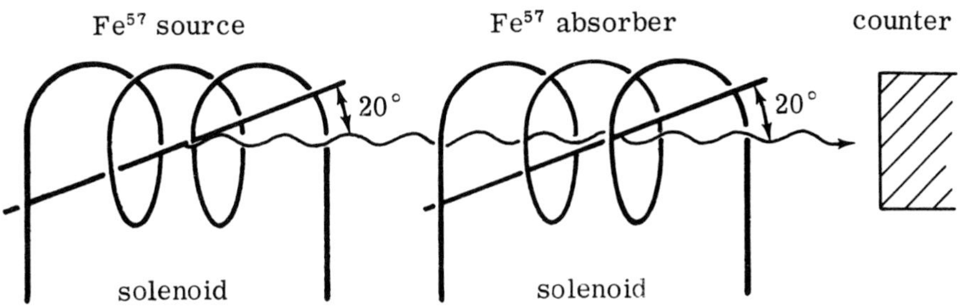

Fig. 5-2 A simple experiment to demonstrate the circular polarization of the 14.4-kev gamma rays from Fe^{57}. The counting rate with parallel fields is much larger than with antiparallel fields at source and absorber.

polarized. If it is emitted in the $-z$ direction, spin and momentum are parallel and the photon is right circularly polarized. Similarly, one can see that the other components are also circularly polarized.

The primitive experimental setup that serves to demonstrate the elliptical polarization of the Fe^{57} gamma rays emitted closely parallel to the field axis is shown in Fig. 5-2. (Emission completely parallel is hard to achieve experimentally.) Source and absorber consist of iron metal and both are placed in solenoids. If the fields in the two solenoids are parallel, the absorption at the central peak, i.e., at zero relative velocity between source and absorber, is very much larger than that for antiparallel fields. The explanation is obvious. At small angles with the field axis, the emitted and the absorbed photons are nearly circularly polarized. In parallel fields, the right circular components of the source have the same energy as the right circular absorption levels, and the left circular emission components have the same energy as the corresponding left circular absorption levels and the absorption is large. Reversing the field, for instance, at the source, changes right into left circular and vice versa. The energies for equal polarization in source and absorber no longer are the same, and the absorption at zero relative velocity is small.

6 SOLID-STATE PHYSICS

6-1 SURVEY

In Chapter 4 it was pointed out that a striking similarity exists between the histories of nuclear magnetic resonance and the Mössbauer effect. Originally both effects belonged to nuclear physics, but the solid-state applications soon dominated both fields. The reason is clear: The number of nuclear properties that can be investigated is limited, but the number of solid-state parameters that can be varied and studied is very large. It seems at the present time as if most of the future investigations involving the Mössbauer effect will be in solid-state physics. In the present chapter a brief sketch of some of the major applications will be given. A more detailed discussion of recent work can be found in the "Proceedings of the Second Mössbauer Conference" (see Sec. 7-3).

The quantities that can be measured in a Mössbauer experiment, namely, the Lamb-Mössbauer factors, the line shape, the line splitting, and the line shift, have been discussed in Chapter 3. The fact that these quantities can be determined under a wide variety of conditions and with a wide range of parameters makes the recoilless gamma-ray emission and absorption such a powerful tool in solid-state physics.

The choice of parameters to be varied determines which solid-state properties will be investigated. One can, first of all, embed the resonant nuclei in the source or in the absorber. The host can be of the same chemical composition as the radioactive material, or it can be different. The resonant nuclei can be interstitial or substitutional impurities; their concentration can be varied over wide ranges. The host lattice can be well annealed or it can be strained. Its temperature can be varied or the external pressure can be changed. External magnetic or electric fields can be applied. The emitted or absorbed radiation and its characteristics can be studied at various angles with respect to internal or external fields or nonisotropic lattice properties. The Mössbauer effect can be measured in transmission or in scattering; one can observe gamma rays, conversion electrons, or X rays following internal conversion. Interference effects can be used. The time dependence of various properties can be studied either by means of a delay technique or by embedding isotopes with different excited-state lifetimes into the same host lattice.

Four typical applications of the Mössbauer effect to solid-state problems will be discussed in the next sections. These four, lattice properties (Sec. 6-2), internal fields (Sec. 6-3), impurities and imperfections (Sec. 6-4), and low-temperature topics (Sec. 6-5), do not exhaust all the possibilities. The Mössbauer effect, for instance, has also been used to get information about atomic wave functions at the nucleus (Reprint Walker 1961) and to determine the index of refraction of lucite (Reprint Grodzins 1961). These are but two examples of investigations that are not contained in Secs. 6-2 to 6-5. Very likely the Mössbauer effect will also be utilized to study surfaces, liquids, and some problems in chemistry and biophysics.

The Mössbauer effect is the youngest of the nuclear guests in solid-state physics. It fits in well indeed with the older ones, complementing them in some areas and allowing checks in others. Table 6-1 lists the major nuclear tools in solid-state physics and indicates the areas of information which they have in common with the Mössbauer effect.

Table 6-1 Nuclear Tools in Solid-State Physics

Tool	Topics in common with the Mössbauer effect	Refs.
X-ray diffraction	Lattice dynamics	18, 27-31, 79
Neutron diffraction	Lattice dynamics Magnetic properties	Reprint Lamb 1939 80-83
Nuclear magnetic resonance	Internal fields Atomic wave functions at the nucleus	84-89
Angular correlation } Oriented nuclei }	Internal fields Aftereffects of radioactive decays	90-93 94, 95

[79] J. Bouman in "Encyclopedia of Physics," Springer, Berlin, 1957, Vol. 32.

[80] C. G. Shull and E. O. Wollan in F. Seitz and D. Turnbull (eds.), "Solid State Physics," Academic, New York, 1956, Vol. 2, p. 138.

[81] G. R. Ringo in "Encyclopedia of Physics," Springer, Berlin, 1957, Vol. 32.

[82] E. Amaldi in "Encyclopedia of Physics," Springer, Berlin, 1959, Vol. 38/2.

6-2 LATTICE PROPERTIES

Boyle recently divided the Mössbauer experiments to determine lattice properties into three classes: difficult and uninteresting, very difficult, impossible.[96] Since even impossible experiments sometimes succeed, a few of the applications of the Mössbauer effect to lattice problems are sketched in the present section.

6-21 The Lamb-Mössbauer Factor f

This factor, Eq. (49), can be determined by measuring the fraction of gamma rays emitted or absorbed without energy loss as a function of the temperature T. From f(T) one finds the mean-square deviation $\langle X^2 \rangle$ by using Eq. (56). Further evaluation depends on the model one selects to describe the solid. Usually one determines a Debye temperature Θ with the help of Eqs. (52) and (54) (see also Ref. 97).

---

[83] L. S. Kothari and K. S. Singwi in F. Seitz and D. Turnbull (eds.), "Solid State Physics," Academic, New York, 1959, Vol. 8, p. 109.

[84] E. R. Andrew, "Nuclear Magnetic Resonance," Cambridge University Press, New York, 1955.

[85] G. E. Pake in F. Seitz and D. Turnbull (eds.), "Solid State Physics," Academic, New York, 1956, Vol. 2, p. 1.

[86] W. D. Knight in F. Seitz and D. Turnbull (eds.), "Solid State Physics," Academic, New York, 1956, Vol. 2, p. 93.

[87] M. H. Cohen and F. Reif in F. Seitz and D. Turnbull (eds.), "Solid State Physics," Academic, New York, 1957, Vol. 5, p. 322.

[88] T. P. Das and E. L. Hahn, "Nuclear Quadrupole Resonance Spectroscopy," Supplement 1 to "Solid State Physics," Academic, New York, 1958.

[89] A. Abragam, "The Principles of Nuclear Magnetism," Oxford University Press, New York, 1961.

[90] H. Frauenfelder in K. Siegbahn (ed.), "Beta- and Gamma-Ray Spectroscopy," North-Holland, Amsterdam, 1955.

[91] R. M. Steffen, Advances in Phys., **4**, 293 (1955).

[92] S. Devons and L. J. B. Goldfarb in "Encyclopedia of Physics," Springer, Berlin, 1957, Vol. 42.

[93] E. Heer and T. B. Novey in F. Seitz and D. Turnbull (eds.), "Solid State Physics," Academic, New York, 1959, Vol. 9, p. 199.

[94] R. J. Blin-Stoyle, M. A. Grace, and H. Halban in K. Siegbahn (ed.), "Beta- and Gamma-Ray Spectroscopy," North-Holland, Amsterdam, 1955.

[95] R. J. Blin-Stoyle and M. A. Grace in "Encyclopedia of Physics," Springer, Berlin, 1957, Vol. 42.

[96] A. J. F. Boyle in "Proceedings of the Second Mössbauer Conference," Paris, Sept. 13-16, 1961, A. Schoen and D. M. J. Compton (eds.), Wiley, New York, tentative publication Spring 1962.

Boyle et al. (Reprint 1961) have shown that one can also get information about anharmonic terms from f(T). The reader is referred to their paper for a discussion of the procedure and of the approximations involved in the evaluation.

Singwi and Sjölander (Reprint 1960) pointed out that in an anisotropic solid, such as graphite, one should expect a dependence of f and of the line width on the direction of emission. Corresponding calculations by Kagan (1961) corroborate this statement, and an anisotropic behavior has actually been found for Fe^{57} embedded in graphite.[98,99]

Two more possible experiments should be mentioned here. It is of interest to determine whether f(T) will follow the Debye behavior at very low temperatures or whether deviations will occur. Investigations in molecular crystals should reveal how additional degrees of freedom affect f(T).

6-22 The Debye-Waller Factor

This factor, $F(\mathbf{k} - \mathbf{k}')$, can be found with the help of the recoilless Rayleigh scattering (Sec. 5-7). A few words about the difference between the Lamb-Mössbauer factor $f(\mathbf{k})$ and the Debye-Waller factor $F(\mathbf{k} - \mathbf{k}')$ are in order here (Reprint Tzara 1961, Lipkin 1961, Trammell 1962). Consider a process in which an incoming beam, neutrons or photons, of momentum $\hbar\mathbf{k}$, is scattered by a solid into a momentum state $\hbar\mathbf{k}'$. If the scattering process is *nonresonant*, then the time delay (collision time, phase shift) between incoming and outgoing wave is of the order of, or less than, v/d, where v is the beam velocity and d the linear dimension of the scatterer.[100] This delay time is much shorter than the characteristic lattice time $\hbar/k\Theta$: An X-ray wave front moves across an atom in a time of the order of 10^{-18} sec, whereas typical lattice vibration times are longer than 10^{-14} sec. In scattering of atomic X rays, the duration of the entire wave train is of the order of 10^{-15} sec or less and hence also short compared to the lattice vibration time. In a crude way of speaking, the entire scatter-

---

[97] W. Marshall in "Proceedings of the Second Mössbauer Conference," Paris, Sept. 13-16, 1961, A. Schoen and D. M. J. Compton (eds.), Wiley, New York, tentative publication Spring 1962.

[98] D. E. Nagle in "Proceedings of the Second Mössbauer Conference," Paris, Sept. 13-16, 1961, A. Schoen and D. M. J. Compton (eds.), Wiley, New York, tentative publication Spring 1962.

[99] H. Pollak, M. DeCoster, and S. Amelincks in "Proceedings of the Second Mössbauer Conference," Paris, Sept. 13-16, 1961, A. Schoen and D. M. J. Compton (eds.), Wiley, New York, tentative publication Spring 1962.

[100] D. Bohm, "Quantum Theory," Prentice-Hall, Englewood Cliffs, N.J., 1951, p. 261.

ing process occurs on atoms that move very little during the scattering process. The entire momentum $\hbar(\mathbf{k} - \mathbf{k}')$ is transferred to the lattice during such a nonresonant collision. The fraction of X rays scattered without energy loss is found by averaging over the various positions of the scattering atom. This calculation leads to the Debye-Waller factor,

$$F(\mathbf{k} - \mathbf{k}') = \exp - < [(\mathbf{k} - \mathbf{k}') \cdot \mathbf{X}]^2 > \tag{108}$$

where $\mathbf{X}$ is the coordinate vector of the c.m. of the decaying nucleus (Fig. 2-3). The fraction $\mathbf{F}$ of recoilless nonresonant scattering depends on the scattering angle 2φ; it increases with decreasing angle φ, i.e., with decreasing momentum transfer $\hbar(\mathbf{k} - \mathbf{k}')$. Since the scattering is elastic, $|\mathbf{k} - \mathbf{k}'| = 2k \sin \varphi$, and Eq. (108) is thus identical with Eq. (54).

The *nonresonant* scattering (Rayleigh scattering) with nuclear gamma rays from a resonant source is also described by Eq. (108). Even though the duration of the wave train is long compared to the lattice vibration time, the time delay is short. At each instant of time the conditions implied in Eq. (108) are fulfilled, and the averaging over the motion of the scattering atoms again leads to Eq. (108). The intensity of the recoilless Rayleigh scattering thus measures the Debye-Waller factor $F(\mathbf{k} - \mathbf{k}')$.

The *resonant* scattering leads to a different expression. Here, the time delay between incident and outgoing wave front is of the order of $\tau = \hbar/\Gamma$, i.e., of the order of the lifetime of the resonant state.[100] In Mössbauer scattering this lifetime is much longer than the lattice vibration times, and there is negligible correlation between the *positions* of absorption and subsequent reemission. The fraction f_S of gamma rays scattered without energy loss is then given by the product of two Lamb-Mössbauer factors,

$$f_S = f(\mathbf{k})\, f(\mathbf{k}') \tag{109}$$

6-23 Phonon Spectra

It has repeatedly been suggested that a detailed measurement of the energy spectrum of the gamma rays in the Mössbauer effect, particularly the observation of the one phonon exchange, will yield valuable information about phonon spectra (Reprint Visscher 1960, Petzold 1961). Unfortunately such experiments are extremely difficult since the energy range to be covered is of the order of 10^{-2} ev and hence much wider than even very wide lines. Neutrons are much better suited for such investigations (Reprint Singwi 1960), except for elements with very large capture cross sections, such as He^3.

6-24 Diffusion

Diffusion should lead to a broadening of the emission and absorption lines close to the melting point (Reprint Singwi 1960). It is very likely that such a broadening can be observed experimentally.

6-25 Lattice Specific Heats

These can be determined by the observation of the second-order Doppler effect, as pointed out in Sec. 5-4, Eq. (88). The main problem is the unambiguous separation of the various temperature-dependent shifts.

6-26 Pressure Effects

Increasing the ambient pressure p on a sample will increase the Lamb-Mössbauer factor f (Hanks 1961) and will shift the resonance line[101] (Pound 1961).

To calculate the pressure dependence f(p) of the Lamb-Mössbauer factor, it is easiest to assume that the Debye model (Secs. 2-2 and 2-52) applies so that $f = f(\Theta)$. Then one has

$$\partial f/\partial p = (\partial f/\partial \Theta)(\partial \Theta/\partial V)(\partial V/\partial p) \tag{110}$$

The dependence of the Debye temperature Θ on the volume V is given by the Grüneisen relation[21]:

$$\partial \ln \Theta/\partial \ln V = -\gamma \tag{111}$$

Neglecting the volume dependence of the Grüneisen constant γ, Eq. (111) can be written

$$\partial \Theta/\partial V = -\gamma\Theta/V \tag{112}$$

The volume V depends on the pressure p through the compressibility κ,

$$\partial V/\partial p = -\kappa V \tag{113}$$

For simplicity assume temperatures low enough so that Eq. (33) holds: $f = \exp(-3R/2k\Theta)$. Then one finds with Eqs. (33) and (110) to (113), after integration,

$$f(p) = f(p = 0) \exp\left[(3R/2k\Theta)\,\kappa\gamma p\right] = \exp[-(3R/2k\Theta)(1-\kappa\gamma p)] \tag{114}$$

---

[101] R. V. Pound in "Proceedings of the Second Mössbauer Conference," Paris, Sept. 13-16, 1961, A. Schoen and D. M. J. Compton (eds.), Wiley, New York, tentative publication Spring 1962.

The Grüneisen constant γ is of the order of 2 (Table 10.3 in Ref. 21), the volume compressibility κ varies from about 3×10^{-7} atm^{-1} for W to about 5×10^{-5} atm^{-1} for Cs. As pointed out by Hanks (1961), it should thus be possible to observe the pressure dependence of f. It should even be feasible to detect a pressure-induced recoilless emission or absorption in substances where f is too small to be seen at normal pressures.

The second manifestation of a change of the ambient pressure, namely, a shift of the Mössbauer line, is mainly due to two contributions. One is caused by a change with pressure of the electronic wave functions at the nucleus; this term can be called the volume dependence of the isomeric shift (Sec. 4-4). The other contribution comes from the volume dependence of the internal energy of the solid; this term is analogous to the second-order Doppler shift (Sec. 5-4). One interesting difference between the second-order Doppler shift and the pressure shift appears: The former does not depend on the zero-point energy and thus goes to zero at low temperatures. The pressure shift, however, does depend on the zero-point energy and thus remains finite even at very low temperatures.

The dependence of the Lamb-Mössbauer factor f on pressure has not yet been observed experimentally. The pressure shift, however, has been investigated by Pound[101] who found a relative shift $(1/E)(\partial E/\partial p) = -2.6 \times 10^{-18}$ atm^{-1} for Fe^{57}, in good agreement with his theoretical estimates (Pound 1961).

6-3 INTERNAL FIELDS

An inspection of the bibliography (Chapter 7) shows that the largest number of publications is devoted to the application of the Mössbauer effect to the study of internal fields. These investigations have already greatly enhanced the knowledge of internal fields and it is very likely that the fast flow of information will continue. Despite the importance of internal field studies, the present section is short. Excellent surveys already exist, for instance in the notes by Abragam (see Sec. 7-1) and in the paper by Wertheim (Reprint 1961). Moreover, the basic ideas underlying the study of internal fields have already been outlined in the discussion of the nuclear moments in Sec. 4-3.

The solid-state physicist's view of Sec. 4-3 is obvious: Instead of measuring nuclear g factors and nuclear quadrupole moments, his interest is directed to the extranuclear fields responsible for the interactions. To determine these extranuclear fields, one requires a knowledge of the magnitude and sign of the nuclear moments. The ground-state moments can usually be determined by conventional techniques. When the ground-state moments are known, the excited-state properties can usually be inferred from the Mössbauer pattern. Once the nuclear moments are known, the dependence of the internal fields on various parameters, such as crystal structure, temperature, pressure, and external fields, can be studied.

In Sec. 6 of the reprints a number of representative papers are collected. These give a fair survey of the problems that have already been examined and the tools used in measuring and interpreting spectra. All these papers use either Fe^{57} or Sn^{119} as the probe. These two nuclides permit a tremendous amount of research, and their use has already led to a deeper understanding of the magnetic properties of solids. The field at the iron nucleus in iron metal constitutes a good example. The first experiments (Reprint Hanna 1960, Sec. 4 of the reprints) yielded a magnitude of the magnetic field $|H| = 3.3 \times 10^5$ oersteds, which was in good agreement with the theoretical predictions. Then the Argonne group went one step farther and determined also the sign of H (Reprint Hanna 1960, Sec. 6 of the reprints). They found the internal field to be opposite to the externally applied field, in direct contradiction to theoretical prediction. Since then theoretical physicists have obtained agreement with experimental facts.[102]

In addition to studies with Fe^{57} and Sn^{119}, a considerable amount of work has been performed with rare earth nuclides, and with nuclides like Au^{197} embedded in ferromagnetic materials (see the bibliography). These areas promise to be as interesting and rewarding as the work discussed above.

Investigations of quadrupole effects have been performed also (Reprint Kistner 1960, Reprint DeBenedetti 1961, see also the bibliography). Quadrupole splittings have been found in many substances and a beginning has been made to correlate these splittings with the chemical and physical state of the solid. The interpretation is difficult when magnetic and quadrupole interactions are simultaneously present. The splitting then depends on the orientation of the magnetic field with respect to the electric field gradient (e.g., Wertheim 1961a), and it is advantageous to work with single crystals.

6-4 IMPURITIES AND IMPERFECTIONS

Every Mössbauer experiment involves nonideal lattices. Sadly, little work has been done so far to systematically investigate the influence of deviations from an ideal lattice on recoilless emission or absorption. A number of publications deal with internal fields at impurity atoms but this aspect will not be discussed.

6-41 Impurities

Impurities actually form a special class of imperfections, but they are singled out here because each radioactive atom that emits a

---

[102] R. E. Watson and A. J. Freeman, Phys. Rev., **123**, 2027 (1961).

gamma ray can be considered an impurity atom. These radioactive atoms can be different from the normal lattice in a number of properties, such as mass, binding, or radius; they can also be in interstitial positions.

The crude models that have been considered so far (Shapiro 1961, Reprint Maleev 1961, Visscher 1962) predict some features which can be checked by experiment. Two of these predictions are particularly simple to describe, namely, the influence of the mass M of the impurity atom and the existence of localized oscillations. Assume that the ideal lattice consists of atoms with a mass m and that the radioactive impurity atom possesses a mass M. The predominant part of the mean-square deviation $\langle X^2 \rangle$ comes from frequencies far below the Debye frequency ω_D because the contribution of each individual mode, $\langle X_i^2 \rangle$, is proportional to $1/\omega_i$. The low-frequency modes have wavelengths long compared to the lattice spacing, and the neighboring atoms move predominantly in the same direction. The displacement of the impurity atom with respect to its neighbors is then small compared to its displacement X from the equilibrium position. The mean-square deviation $\langle X^2 \rangle$ of the impurity atom is in a first approximation the same as that of the normal lattice atoms. In the Debye approximation, the Lamb-Mössbauer factor f is thus given by Eq. (53), with $R = E^2/2mc^2$. If this description is correct, then the fraction f should be determined by the mass m of the atoms in the host lattice, and not by the mass M of the impurity atom. This conclusion has, however, not yet been substantiated by experiments.

An impurity atom in an ideal lattice produces localized oscillations, i.e., oscillations that are large in its immediate vicinity and damp out quickly with increasing distance from it.[103] These localized oscillations should give rise to individual discrete peaks in the recoil spectrum, separated from the unshifted line by energies of the order of 0.01 ev (Reprint Maleev 1961, Visscher 1962).

6-42 Imperfections

A second type of problem occurs when the host lattice is not ideal, which is the situation normally encountered in experiments. Various types of imperfections can then influence the Mössbauer effect. Even though little work has been done on this aspect, there is no doubt that experiments involving imperfections will play an increasingly larger role in future research.

6-5 LOW TEMPERATURES

There exist some problems which are inherently dependent on tem-

---

[103] A. A. Maradudin, P. Mazur, E. W. Montroll, and G. H. Weiss, Revs. Modern Physics, 30, 175 (1958).

peratures close to, or below, the helium boiling point and which can be investigated with the Mössbauer effect. Two of these will be sketched here.

6-51 Nuclear Orientation

In conventional nuclear orientation experiments,[94,95] the degree of orientation must be deduced from angular distributions of nuclear radiations. With the Mössbauer effect, this property can be determined more directly, at least in favorable cases. The ease and accuracy with which such measurements can be performed make it likely that the Mössbauer effect can be used as a thermometer at very low temperatures (Taylor 1962).

As a simple example, consider a single line $Co^{57} \rightarrow Fe^{57}$ source and an Fe^{57} absorber that possesses a strong internal field H. The ground state of the Fe^{57} nuclei in the absorber is split into two magnetic sublevels, separated in energy by $\Delta = g\mu_0 H$ [Eq. (66)]. At a temperature T, the ratio of the equilibrium populations of these two sublevels is

$$N(+1/2)/N(-1/2) = \exp(-\Delta/kT) = \exp(-g\mu_0 H/kT) \qquad (115)$$

The ratio of symmetric absorption components, for instance, $(1/2 \rightarrow 3/2)/(-1/2 \rightarrow -3/2)$, is also given by (115). At very low temperatures, where $\Delta \gg kT$, the component originating from the higher sublevel is absent. In general, both components will be present; their intensity ratio is a direct measure for the Boltzmann factor (115) and hence yields the temperature T if g and H are known.

An Fe^{57} absorber works as a thermometer only at very low temperatures because the magnetic moment of the Fe^{57} ground state is very small. The splitting in iron metal corresponds to a temperature $T^* = \Delta/k = 2.2 \times 10^{-3}$ °K; appreciable effects hence occur only in the millidegree range. The Los Alamos group performed an experiment at higher temperatures by using the much larger magnetic moment of the parent nucleus Co^{57} (Reprint Dash 1961).

6-52 Superconductivity

The application of the Mössbauer effect to superconductivity is tempting at first glance because the energy changes detectable in the Mössbauer effect and the energy change per atom in superconducting transitions are of the same order of magnitude. A more detailed discussion shows, however, that one should not expect sizeable effects, because very few electrons participate in a superconducting transition. Careful experiments by the Los Alamos group (Craig 1960, 1961) have indeed failed to find an influence of a superconducting transition on the Mössbauer effect. Recent experiments (Wiedemann 1961) which indicate a very small change in f, are not conclusive.

7 BIBLIOGRAPHY ON THE MÖSSBAUER EFFECT

Compiled by E. Lüscher, D. Pipkorn, and M. Runkel
Physics Department, University of Illinois

7-1 REVIEW ARTICLES

A. Abragam, L'effet Mössbauer et ses applications à l'étude des champs internes (unpublished lecture notes).

G. N. Belozerskii and Yu. A. Nemilov, The resonance dispersion of γ-rays in crystals, Uspekhi Fiz. Nauk, **72**, 433 (1960) (in Russian); Soviet Physics Uspekhi, **3**, 813 (1961) (in English).

A. J. F. Boyle and H. E. Hall, Mössbauer effect, Repts. Progr. in Phys. (to be published in 1962).

W. E. Burcham, Nuclear resonant scattering without recoil (Mössbauer effect), Sci. Progr., **48**, 630 (1960).

E. Cotton, Emission et absorption de rayonnement gamma sans recul du noyau émetteur emprisonné dans un réseau cristallin (Effet Mössbauer), J. phys. radium, **21**, 265 (1960).

P. P. Craig, Experimental aspects and applications of the Mössbauer effect, in G. M. Graham and A. C. Hollis-Hallett (eds.), "Proceedings of the VIIth International Conference on Low Temperature Physics," University of Toronto Press, Toronto, 1961, pp. 22-35.

S. DeBenedetti, The Mössbauer effect, Sci. American, **202**, 72 (1960).

---

*Entries in this bibliography are arranged (a) alphabetically by author, (b) by added joint authors, (c) alphabetically by title. In cases where two or more papers by the same authors appeared in the same year, the second paper (alphabetically by title) is designated a, the third b, etc.

W. E. Kock, The Mössbauer radiation, Science, **131**, 1588 (1960).

I. Y. Krause and G. Lüders, Kernresonanzabsorption mit eingefrorenem Rückstoss, Naturwissenschaften, **47**, 532 (1960).

H. Lustig, The Mössbauer effect, Am. J. Phys., **29**, 1 (1961).

C. Møller, The Mössbauer effect, pp. 73-79 of Selected Problems in General Relativity, "Brandeis University 1960 Summer Institute in Theoretical Physics Lecture Notes," distributed by W. A. Benjamin, Inc., New York.

P. B. Moon, Developments in gamma-ray optics, Nature, **185**, 427 (1960).

R. L. Mössbauer, Recoilless resonance absorption of gamma quanta in solids, Uspekhi Fiz. Nauk, **72**, 658 (1960) (in Russian); Soviet Physics Uspekhi, **3**, 866 (1961) (in English).

R. V. Pound, On the weight of photons, Uspekhi Fiz. Nauk, **72**, 673 (1960) (in Russian); Soviet Physics Uspekhi, **3**, 875 (1961) (in English).

F. L. Shapiro, "Elementary Theory of the Mössbauer Effect," Press of Phys. Inst., Academy of Sciences, Moscow, 1960 (in Russian).

F. L. Shapiro, The Mössbauer effect, Uspekhi Fiz. Nauk, **72**, 685 (1960) (in Russian); Soviet Physics Uspekhi, **3**, 881 (1961) (in English); Fortschr. Physik, **9**, 329 (1961) (in German).

G. K. Wertheim, The Mössbauer effect: a tool for science, Nucleonics, **19**, No. 1, 52 (1961).

V. Weisskopf, The Mössbauer effect, in W. E. Brittin and B. W. Downs (eds.), "Lectures in Theoretical Physics," vol. 3, Interscience, New York, 1961, pp. 70-80.

7-2 RESEARCH PAPERS

A. Abragam, Effect of ultrasonics on the emission and absorption of γ radiation without recoil, Compt. rend., **250**, 4334 (1960).

A. Abragam and F. Boutron, Moment quadrupolaire du premier état nucléaire excité du fer 57, Compt. rend., **252**, 2404 (1961).

C. Alff and G. K. Wertheim, Hyperfine structure of Fe^{57} in yttrium-iron garnet from the Mössbauer effect, Phys. Rev., **122**, 1414 (1961).

S. I. Aksenov, V. P. Alfimenkov, V. I. Lushchikov, Yu. M. Ostanevich, F. L. Shapiro, and Yen Wu-Kuang, Observation of resonance absorption of gamma rays in Zn^{67}, Zhur. Eksp. i Teoret. Fiz., **40**, 88 (1961) (in Russian); Soviet Physics JETP, **13**, 62 (1961) (in English).

I. Ya. Barit, M. I. Podgoretzkii, and F. L. Shapiro, Several possible applications for the resonant scattering of γ-rays, Zhur. Eksp. i Teoret. Fiz., **38**, 301 (1960) (in Russian); Soviet Physics JETP, **11**, 218 (1960) (in English).

R. Barloutaud, E. Cotton, J. L. Picou, and J. Quidort, Absorption résonnante sans recul dy rayonnement γ de 23.8 de Sn^{119}, Compt. rend., **250**, 319 (1960).

R. Barloutaud, J. L. Picou, and C. Tzara, Diffusion résonnante du rayonnement γ de 23.8 kev de Sn^{119} émis sans recul, Compt. rend., **250**, 2705 (1960a).

R. Bauminger, S. G. Cohen, A. Marinov, and S. Ofer, Hyperfine interactions in the ground state and first excited state of Dy^{161} in dysprosium iron garnet, Phys. Rev. Letters, **6**, 467 (1961).

R. Bauminger, S. G. Cohen, A. Marinov, and S. Ofer, Study of the internal fields acting on iron-nuclei in iron garnet using the recoil free absorption in Fe^{57} of the 14.4 kev gamma radiation from Fe^{57m}, Phys. Rev., **122**, 743 (1961a).

R. Bauminger, S. G. Cohen, A. Marinov, S. Ofer, and E. Segal, Study of the low temperature transitions in magnetite and the internal fields acting on iron nuclei in some spinel ferrites, using Mössbauer absorption, Phys. Rev., **122**, 1447 (1961b).

P. J. Black and P. B. Moon, Resonant scattering of the 14 kev Fe^{57} γ-ray and its interference with Rayleigh scattering, Nature, **188**, 481 (1960).

A. J. F. Boyle, D. St. P. Bunbury, and C. Edwards, The isomer shift in Sn^{119} and the quadrupole moment of the first excited state, Proc. Phys. Soc. (London) (to be published).

A. J. F. Boyle, D. St. P. Bunbury, and C. Edwards, The nuclear Zeeman effect and quadrupole splitting in Sn^{119}, Proc. Phys. Soc. (London), **77**, 1062 (1961b).

A. J. F. Boyle, D. St. P. Bunbury, and C. Edwards, Polarization of the conduction electrons in the ferromagnetic metals, Phys. Rev. Letters, **5**, 553 (1960).

A. J. F. Boyle, D. St. P. Bunbury, C. Edwards, and H. E. Hall, A chemical red shift of the recoilless γ-emission of Sn^{119m}, Proc. Phys. Soc. (London), **76**, 165 (1960a).

A. J. F. Boyle, D. St. P. Bunbury, C. Edwards, and H. E. Hall, The Mössbauer effect in tin from 120°K to the melting point, Proc. Phys. Soc. (London), **77**, 129 (1961a).

V. A. Bryukhanov, N. N. Delyagin, B. Zhvenglinskii, and V. S. Shpinel, The energy shifts of γ-transitions observed in resonance absorption of gamma quanta in crystals, Zhur. Eksp. i Teoret. Fiz., **40**, 713 (1961) (in Russian); Soviet Physics JETP, **13**, 499 (1961) (in English).

A. Bussière de Nercy, M. Langevin, and M. Spighel, Absorption résonnante du rayonnement γ de l'holmium 166 et de l'osmium 193 sans recul de noyau, Compt. rend., **250**, 1031 (1960).

A. Bussière de Nercy, M. Langevin, and M. Spighel, Absorption résonnante du rayonnement γ sans recul du noyau de Ho^{166} et Os^{193}, J. phys. radium, **21**, 288 (1960a).

D. C. Champeney and P. B. Moon, Absence of Doppler shift for γ-ray source and detector on same circular orbit, Proc. Phys. Soc. (London), **77**, 350 (1961).

G. Cocconi and E. E. Salpeter, Upper limit for the anisotropy of inertia from the Mössbauer effect, Phys. Rev. Letters, **4**, 176 (1960).

M. Cordey-Hayes, N. A. Dyson, and P. B. Moon, Width and intensity of the Mössbauer line in Fe^{57}, Proc. Phys. Soc. (London), **75**, 810 (1960).

P. P. Craig, J. G. Dash, A. D. McGuire, D. E. Nagle, and R. R. Reiswig, Nuclear resonance absorption of gamma rays in Ir^{191}, Phys. Rev. Letters, **3**, 221 (1959).

P. P. Craig, D. E. Nagle, and D. R. F. Cochran, Zeeman effect in the recoilless γ-ray resonance of Zn^{67}, Phys. Rev. Letters, **4**, 561 (1960).

P. P. Craig, D. E. Nagle, and R. D. Reiswig, Resonant absorption of gamma radiation in superconductors, Phys. and Chem. Solids, **17**, 168 (1960a).

P. P. Craig, D. Nagle, and R. D. Taylor, Mössbauer effect in superconducting indium, Nuovo cimento, **22**, 402 (1961).

T. E. Cranshaw, J. P. Schiffer, and A. B. Whitehead, Measurement of the gravitational red shift using the Mössbauer effect in Fe^{57}, Phys. Rev. Letters, **4**, 163 (1960).

J. G. Dash, R. D. Taylor, P. P. Craig, D. E. Nagle, D. R. F. Cochran, and W. E. Keller, Mössbauer effect in Fe^{57} at very low temperature, Phys. Rev. Letters, **5**, 152 (1960).

J. G. Dash, R. D. Taylor, D. E. Nagle, P. P. Craig, and W. M. Visscher, Polarization of Co^{57} in Fe metal, Phys. Rev., **122**, 1116 (1961).

S. DeBenedetti, G. Lang, and R. Ingalls, Electric quadrupole splitting and the nuclear volume effect in the ions of Fe^{57}, Phys. Rev. Letters, **6**, 60 (1961).

N. N. Delyagin, V. S. Shpinel, V. A. Bryukhanov, and B. Zhvenglinskii, Hyperfine structure of γ-rays caused by quadrupole interaction in a crystal lattice, Zhru. Eksp. i Teoret. Fiz., **39**, 220 (1960) (in Russian); Soviet Physics JETP, **12**, 159 (1961) (in English).

N. N. Delyagin, V. S. Shpinel, V. A. Bryukhanov, and B. Zhvenglinskii, Nuclear Zeeman-effect in Sn^{119}, Zhur. Eksp. i Teoret. Fiz., **39**, 894 (1960a) (in Russian); Soviet Physics JETP, **12**, 619 (1961) (in English).

G. DePasquali, H. Frauenfelder, S. Margulies, and R. N. Peacock, Nuclear resonance absorption and nuclear Zeeman effect in Fe^{57}, Phys. Rev. Letters, **4**, 71 (1960).

I. P. Dziub and A. F. Lubchenko, On the theory of the Mössbauer effect, Doklady Akad. Nauk SSSR, **136**, 66 (1961) (in Russian); Phys. Express, **3**, No. 9, 34 (1961) (in English); Soviet Physics Doklady, **6**, 33 (1961) (in English).

P. A. Flinn and S. L. Ruby, Local magnetic fields in Fe-Al alloys, Phys. Rev., **124**, 34 (1961).

H. Frauenfelder, D. R. F. Cochran, D. E. Nagle, and R. D. Taylor, Internal conversion from resonance absorption, Nuovo cimento, **19**, 183 (1961).

H. Frauenfelder, D. E. Nagle, R. D. Taylor, D. R. F. Cochran, and W. M. Visscher, Elliptical polarization of Fe^{57} gamma rays (to be published).

J. Gastebois and J. Quidort, Mise en évidence du moment quadrupolaire du noyau de fer 57, Compt. rend, **253**, 1257 (1961).

A. Gelberg, Winkelverteilung und zirkulare Polarisation der γ-Strahlung im Mössbauereffekt, Inst. de Fiz. Atomica Maguerle-Bucuresti Rept. 16.

L. Grodzins and F. Genovese, Experimental investigation of parity conservation in the 14.4 kev gamma transition of Fe^{57}, Phys. Rev., **121**, 228 (1961).

L. Grodzins and A. Phillips, Measurement of the refractive index of lucite by recoilless resonance absorption, Phys. Rev., **124**, 774 (1961a).

M. N. Hack and M. Hamermesh, Effect of radiofrequency resonance on the natural line form, Nuovo cimento, **19**, 546 (1961).

R. V. Hanks, Pressure dependence of the Mössbauer effect, Phys. Rev., **124**, 1319 (1961).

S. S. Hanna, J. Heberle, C. Littlejohn, G. J. Perlow, R. S. Preston, and D. H. Vincent, Observation on the Mössbauer effect in Fe^{57}, Phys. Rev. Letters, **4**, 28 (1960).

S. S. Hanna, J. Heberle, C. Littlejohn, G. J. Perlow, R. S. Preston, and D. H. Vincent, Polarized spectra and hyperfine structure in Fe^{57}, Phys. Rev. Letters, **4**, 177 (1960a).

S. S. Hanna, J. Heberle, G. J. Perlow, R. S. Preston, and D. H. Vincent, Direction of the effective magnetic field at the nucleus in ferromagnetic iron, Phys. Rev. Letters, **4**, 513 (1960b).

S. S. Hanna, L. Meyer-Schützmeister, R. S. Preston, and D. H. Vincent, Nuclear Zeeman effect in Sn^{119}, Phys. Rev., **120**, 2211 (1960c).

S. M. Harris, Quantum mechanical calculation of Mössbauer transmission, Phys. Rev., **124**, 1178 (1961).

H. J. Hay, J. P. Schiffer, T. E. Cranshaw, and P. A. Egelstaff, Measurement of the red shift in an accelerated system using the Mössbauer effect in Fe^{57}, Phys. Rev. Letters, **4**, 165 (1960).

B. Hoffman, Noon-midnight red shift, Phys. Rev., **121**, 337 (1960).

R. E. Holland, F. J. Lynch, G. J. Perlow, and S. S. Hanna, Time spectra of filtered resonance radiation of Fe^{57}, Phys. Rev. Letters, **4**, 181 (1960).

S. Jha, R. K. Gupta, H. G. Devare, G. C. Pramila, and R. Srinivasa Raghavan, Recoilless emission and absorption of 26 kev gamma-ray of Dy^{161}, Nuovo cimento, **19**, 682 (1961).

C. E. Johnson, M. S. Ridout, T. E. Cranshaw, and P. E. Madsen,

Hyperfine field and atomic moment of Fe in ferromagnetic alloys, Phys. Rev. Letters, **6**, 450 (1961).

B. D. Josephson, Temperature dependent shift of γ-rays emitted by a solid, Phys. Rev. Letters, **4**, 341 (1960).

Yu. Kagan, Anisotropy of the Mössbauer effect, Doklady Akad. Nauk SSSR, **140**, 794 (1961). (in Russian); Sov. Phys. Doklady **6**, 881 (1962) (in English).

Yu. Kagan, Determination of the frequency spectrum of phonons in crystals, Zhur. Eksp. i Teoret. Fiz., **40**, 312 (1961) (in Russian); Soviet Physics JETP, **13**, 211 (1961a) (in English).

M. Kalvius, P. Kienle, K. Bockmann, and H. Eicher, Hyperfeinstrukturaufspaltung von rückstossfreien γ-Linien: II. Das 8,42 kev Niveau in Tm^{169}, Z. Physik, **163**, 87 (1961).

E. Kankeleit, Untersuchung von Konversions-Elektronen beim Mössbauereffekt am Wolfram 182 mit einem magnetischen Spektrometer, Z. Physik, **164**, 442 (1961).

A. Kastler, Sur la possibilité de mettre en évidence la cohérence de phase dans la diffusion de résonance des rayons γ par des noyaux atomiques, Compt. rend., **250**, 509 (1960).

M. V. Kazarnovskii, Theory of resonant interaction of γ-ray with crystals, Zhur. Eksp. i Teoret. Fiz., **38**, 1652 (1960) (in Russian); Soviet Physics JETP, **11**, 1191 (1960) (in English).

W. H. Kelly, V. J. Folen, M. Hass, W. N. Schreiner, and G. G. Beard, Magnetic field at the nucleus in spinel-type crystals, Phys. Rev., **124**, 80 (1961).

O. C. Kistner and A. W. Sunyar, Evidence for quadrupole interaction of Fe^{57m} and influence of chemical binding on nuclear gamma-ray energy, Phys. Rev. Letters, **4**, 412 (1960).

O. C. Kistner, A. W. Sunyar, and J. B. Swan, Hyperfine structure of the 24 kev transitions in Sn^{119}, Phys. Rev. **123**, 179 (1961).

I. Y. Krause and G. Lüders, Experimentelle Prüfung der Relativitätstheorie mit Kernresonanzabsorption, Naturwissenschaften, **48**, 34 (1961).

M. A. Krivoglaz, Effect of diffusion on the scattering of neutrons and photons by crystal imperfections, and on the Mössbauer effect, Zhur. Eksp. i Teoret. Fiz., **40**, 1812 (1961) (in Russian); Soviet Physics JETP, **13**, 1273 (1961) (in English).

W. E. Lamb, Jr., Possible use of highly monochromatic gamma rays for microwave spectroscopy, in C. H. Townes (ed.), "Quantum Electronics, a Symposium," Columbia University Press, New York, 1960, p. 588.

L. L. Lee, L. Meyer-Schützmeister, J. P. Schiffer, and D. Vincent, Nuclear resonance absorption of gamma rays at low temperatures, Phys. Rev. Letters, **3**, 223 (1959).

H. J. Lipkin, The Debye-Waller factor in Mössbauer interference experiments, Phys. Rev., **123**, 62 (1961).

H. J. Lipkin, Some simple features of the Mössbauer effect, Ann. Phys., 9, 332 (1960).

H. J. Lipkin, Some simple features of the Mössbauer effect, II, Ann. Phys., **18**, 182 (1962).

W. Low, The effect of relaxation phenomena on Mössbauer experiments, in G. M. Graham and A. C. Hollis-Hallett (eds.), "Proceedings of the VIIth International Conference on Low Temperature Physics," University of Toronto Press, Toronto, 1961, pp. 20-22.

F. J. Lynch, R. E. Holland, and M. Hamermesh, Time dependence of resonantly filtered gamma rays from Fe^{57}, Phys. Rev., **120**, 513 (1960).

V. A. Lyubimov and A. I. Alikhanov, Influence of magnetic fields on resonance absorption of gamma rays, Zhur. Eksp. i Teoret. Fiz., **38**, 1912 (1960) (in Russian); Soviet Physics JETP, **11**, 1375 (1960) (in English); Izvest. Akad. Nauk SSSR, **24**, 1076 (1960) (in Russian); Bull. acad. sci. USRS, **24**, 1084 (in English).

K. J. Major, Recoil-free resonant and nonresonant scattering from Fe^{57}, Nucl. Phys. **33**, 323 (1962).

S. V. Maleev, On the use of the Mössbauer effect for studying localized oscillations of atoms in solids, Zhur. Eksp. i Teoret. Fiz., **39**, 891 (1960) (in Russian); Soviet Physics JETP, **12**, 617 (1961) (in English).

S. Margulies, The Mössbauer effect in iron-57 (unpublished thesis, Univ. Illinois, 1962) [Tech. Rept. 28, on Nonr 1834(05), Physics Dept., Univ. Illinois (October 1961)].

S. Margulies and J. R. Ehrman, Transmission and line broadening of resonance radiation incident on a resonance absorber, Nuclear Instr., **12**, 131 (1961a).

Luise Meyer-Schützmeister, R. S. Preston, and S. S. Hanna, Internal magnetic fields in manganese-tin alloys, Phys. Rev., **122**, 1717 (1961).

K. P. Mitrofanov and V. S. Shpinel, Resonance absorption of the 23.8 kev γ-ray of Sn^{119} observed by means of internally converted electrons, Zhur. Eksp. i Teoret. Fiz., **40**, 983 (1961) (in Russian); Soviet Physics JETP, **13**, 686 (1961) (in English).

P. B. Moon, Interference between Rayleigh and nuclear resonant scattering of gamma rays, Proc. Royal Soc. (London), **A263**, 309 (1961).

M. Morita, Possible parity and time-reversal experiments using the Mössbauer effect, Phys. Rev., **122**, 1525 (1961).

R. L. Mössbauer, Kernresonanzfluoreszenz von Gammastrahlung in Ir^{191}, Z. Physik, **151**, 124 (1958).

R. L. Mössbauer, Kernresonanzabsorption von Gammastrahlung in Ir^{191}, Naturwissenschaften, **45**, 538 (1958a).

R. L. Mössbauer, Kernresonanzabsorption von Gammastrahlung in Ir^{191}, Z. Naturforsch., **14a**, 211 (1959).

R. L. Mössbauer, F. W. Stanek, and W. H. Wiedemann, Hyperfeinstrukturaufspaltung von rückstossfreien γ-Linien: I. Das 80,6 kev-Niveau in Er^{166}, Z. Physik, **161**, 388 (1961).

R. L. Mössbauer and W. H. Wiedemann, Kernresonanzabsorption nicht Dopplerverbreiterter Gammastrahlung in Re^{187}, Z. Physik, **159**, 33 (1960).

D. E. Nagle, P. P. Craig, P. Barrett, D. R. F. Cochran, C. E. Olsen, and R. D. Taylor, Internal fields at low temperatures in CoPd alloys, Phys. Rev., **125**, 490 (1962).

D. Nagle, P. P. Craig, J. G. Dash, and R. R. Reiswig, Nuclear resonance fluorescence in Au^{197}, Phys. Rev. Letters, **4**, 237 (1960).

D. E. Nagle, P. P. Craig, and W. E. Keller, Ultra high resolution γ-ray resonance in Zn^{67}, Nature, **186**, 707 (1960a).

D. E. Nagle, H. Frauenfelder, R. D. Taylor, D. R. F. Cochran, and B. T. Matthias, Temperature dependence of the internal field in ferromagnets, Phys. Rev. Letters, **5**, 364 (1960b).

F. E. Obenshain and H. H. F. Wegener, Mössbauer effect with Ni^{61}, Phys. Rev., **121**, 1344 (1961).

S. Ofer, P. Avivi, R. Bauminger, J. Marinov, and S. G. Cohen, Nuclear resonance absorption in Dy^{161} situated in Dy_2O_3 and dysprosium iron garnet, Phys. Rev., **120**, 406 (1960).

G. J. Perlow, S. S. Hanna, M. Hamermesh, C. Littlejohn, D. H. Vincent, R. S. Preston, and J. Heberle, Polarization of nuclear resonance radiation in ferromagnetic Fe^{57}, Phys. Rev. Letters, **4**, 74 (1960).

J. Petzold, Einige Bermerkungen zur Theorie des Mössbauer-Effektes, Z. Physik, **163**, 71 (1961).

J. Petzold, "Theorie des Mössbauer-Effektes," Sitzber. Heidelberg Akad. der Wissen. (Springer Verlag, Heidelberg, 1961a).

J. L. Picou, J. Quidort, R. Barloutaud, and E. Cotton, Absorption résonante des γ sans recul dans la désintégration du premier état excité de Sn^{119}, Comm. Energie At. (France), Rappt. **1652** (1960); microcarté.

M. I. Podgoretskii and I. I. Roizen, Radiation of a nucleus in the presence of unexcited nuclei of the same type, Zhur. Eksp. i Teoret. Fiz., **39**, 1473 (1960) (in Russian); Soviet Physics JETP 12, 1023 (1960) (in English); Physics Express, **3**, No. 7, 22 (1961) (in English).

M. I. Podgoretskii and A. V. Stepanov, The Doppler width of emission and absorption lines, Zhur. Eksp. i Teoret. Fiz., **40**, 561 (1961) (in Russian); Soviet Physics JETP, **13**, 393 (1961) (in English).

R. V. Pound, G. B. Benedek, and R. Drever, Effect of hydrostatic compression on the energy of the 14.4 kev gamma ray from Fe^{57} in iron, Phys. Rev. Letters, **7**, 405 (1961).

R. V. Pound and G. A. Rebka, Jr., Apparent weight of photons, Phys. Rev. Letters, 4, 337 (1960).

R. V. Pound and G. A. Rebka, Jr., Attempts to detect resonance scat-

tering in Zn^{67}; the effect of zero point vibrations, Phys. Rev. Letters, **4**, 397 (1960a).
R. V. Pound and G. A. Rebka, Jr., Gravitational red-shift in nuclear resonance, Phys. Rev. Letters, **3**, 439 (1959).
R. V. Pound and G. A. Rebka, Jr., Resonant absorption of the 14.4 kev γ-ray from 0.10 μsec Fe^{57}, Phys. Rev. Letters, **3**, 554 (1959a).
R. V. Pound and G. A. Rebka, Jr., Variation with temperature of the energy of recoil-free γ-rays from solids, Phys. Rev. Letters, **4**, 274 (1960).
R. S. Raghavan, On the possibility of a new phase determining method applying the Mössbauer effect, Proc. Indian Acad. Sci. **L111**, 265 (1961).
S. L. Ruby and D. I. Bolef, Acoustically modulated γ-rays from Fe^{57}, Phys. Rev. Letters, **5**, 5 (1960).
S. L. Ruby, L. M. Epstein, and K. H. Sun, Mössbauer effect in ferrocyanide, Rev. Sci. Instr., **31**, 580 (1960).
S. L. Ruby and G. Shirane, Magnetic anomaly in $FeTiO_3-\alpha Fe_2O_3$ system by Mössbauer effect, Phys. Rev., **123**, 1239 (1961).
M. Ruderfer, First order terrestrial ether drift experiment using the Mössbauer radiation, Phys. Rev. Letters, **5**, 191 (1960); correction: Phys. Rev. Letters, **7**, 361 (1961).
J. P. Schiffer and W. Marshall, Recoilless resonance absorption of gamma rays in Fe^{57}, Phys. Rev. Letters, **3**, 556 (1959).
C. W. Sherwin, H. Frauenfelder, E. L. Garwin, E. Lüscher, S. Margulies, and R. N. Peacock, A search for the anisotropy of inertia using the Mössbauer effect in Fe^{57}, Phys. Rev. Letters, **4**, 399 (1960).
C. W. Sherwin, Some recent experimental tests of the "clock paradox," Phys. Rev., **120**, 17 (1960a).
G. Shirane, D. E. Cox, and S. L. Ruby, Mössbauer study of isomer shift, quadrupole interaction, and hyperfine field in several oxides containing Fe^{57}, Phys. Rev., **125**, 1158 (1962).
D. A. Shirley, Interpretation of the isomeric chemical shifts in Au^{197}, Phys. Rev., **124**, 354 (1961).
D. A. Shirley, M. Kaplan, and P. Axel, Recoil-free resonant absorption in Au^{197}, Phys. Rev., **123**, 816 (1961a).
V. H. Shpinel, V. A. Bryukhanov, and N. N. Delyagin, Effect of temperature on the hyperfine structure of gamma radiation, Zhur. Eksp. i Teoret. Fiz., **40**, 1525 (1961) (in Russian); Soviet Phys. JETP (English Transl.), **13**, 1068 (1961).
K. S. Singwi and A. Sjölander, Resonance absorption of nuclear γ-rays and the dynamics of atomic motions, Phys. Rev., **120**, 2211 (1960).
V. V. Sklyarevskii, B. N. Samoilov, and E. P. Stepanov, Temperature dependence of the hyperfine splitting of dysprosium levels in paramagnetic dysprosium oxide, Zhur. Eksp. i Teoret. Fiz., **40**, 1875 (1961) (in Russian); Soviet Phys. JETP (English Transl.), **13**, 1316 (1961).

H. S. Snyder and G. C. Wick, Broadening of the Mössbauer line, Phys. Rev., **120**, 128 (1960).

I. Solomon, Effet Mössbauer dans la pyrite et la marcassite, Compt. rend., **250**, 3828 (1960).

I. Solomon, Mesure par effet Mössbauer de champs locaux dans divers composés du fer, Compt. rend., **251**, 2675 (1960).

R. D. Taylor, A low temperature thermometer utilizing the Mössbauer effect, in C. M. Herzfeld (ed.), "Temperature, Its Measurement and Control in Science and Industry," Reinhold, New York, 1962.

G. T. Trammel, Elastic scattering at resonance from bound nuclei, Phys. Rev., **126**, 1045 (1962).

P.-K. Tseng, N. Shikazono, H. Takehoshi, and T. Shoji, Temperature dependence of nuclear resonance absorption line width in Dy^{161}, J. Phys. Soc. Japan, **16**, 1790 (1961).

C. Tzara, Diffusion des photons sur les atomes et les noyaux dans les cristaux, J. phys. radium, **22**, 303 (1961).

C. Tzara, Sur l'excitation résonnante de niveaux nucléaires metastables de vie très longue, Compt. rend., **250**, 1466 (1960).

C. Tzara and R. Barloutaud, Recoilless Rayleigh scattering in solids, Phys. Rev. Letters, **4**, 405 (1960a).

W. M. Visscher, Neutrino detection by resonance absorption in crystals at low temperature, Phys. Rev., **116**, 1581 (1959).

W. M. Visscher, Resonance absorption of gammas by impurity nuclei in crystals, Phys. Rev., **129**, 28 (1963).

W. M. Visscher, Study of lattice vibrations by resonance absorption of nuclear gamma rays, Ann. Phys., **9**, 194 (1960).

J. van Kranendonk, Theoretical aspects of the Mössbauer effect, in G. M. Graham and A. C. Hollis-Hallett (eds.), "Proceedings of the VIIth International Conference on Low Temperature Physics," University of Toronto Press, Toronto, 1961, pp. 9-20.

F. E. Wagner, F. W. Stanek, P. Kienle, and H. Eicher, Hyperfeinstrukturaufspaltung von rückstossfreien γ-Linien: III. Das 84 kev-Niveau in Yb^{170}, Z. Physik **166**, 1 (1961).

L. R. Walker, G. K. Wertheim, and V. Jaccarino, Interpretation of the Fe^{57} isomer shift, Phys. Rev. Letters, **6**, 98 (1961).

H. H. F. Wegener and F. E. Obenshain, Mössbauer effect for Ni^{61} with applied magnetic fields, Z. Physik, **163**, 17 (1961).

G. K. Wertheim, Hyperfine structure of divalent and trivalent Fe^{57} in cobalt oxide, Phys. Rev., **124**, 764 (1961).

G. K. Wertheim, Hyperfine structure of Fe^{57} in paramagnetic and antiferromagnetic FeF_2 from the Mössbauer effect, Phys. Rev., **121**, 63 (1961a).

G. K. Wertheim, Measurement of local fields at impurity Fe^{57} atoms using the Mössbauer effect, Phys. Rev. Letters, **4**, 403 (1960).

G. K. Wertheim, Mössbauer effect: applications to magnetism, J. Appl. Phys. (Suppl), **32**, 110S (1961b).

G. K. Wertheim and J. H. Wernick, Fe^{57} Mössbauer effect on Cu-Ni alloys, Phys. Rev., **123**, 755 (1961c).

W. H. Wiedemann, P. Kienle, and F. Pobell, Mossbauereffekt im normalleitenden und supraleitenden Zustand von Sn^{119}, Z. Physik, 165, 109 (1961).

C. S. Wu, Y. K. Lee, N. Benczer-Køller, and P. Simms, Frequency distribution of resonance line versus delay time, Phys. Rev. Letters, **5**, 432 (1960).

U. Zahn, P. Kienle, and H. Eicher, Quadrupolaufspaltung und Isomerieverschiebung der 14.4 kev γ-Linie von Fe^{57} in metallorganischen Eisenverbindungen, I. Ferrocen and Ferriciniumkation Z. Physik **166**, 220 (1962).

L. G. Zastavenko and M. I. Podgoretskii, The effect of external fields on the angular correlations and resonance processes during quantum transitions, Zhur. Eksp. i Teoret. Fiz., **39**, 1023 (1960) (in Russian); Soviet Phys. JETP (English Transl.), **12**, 711 (1961); excerpts also translated in Phys. Express, **3**, No. 5, 21 (1961).

7-3 CONFERENCE REPORTS

"Mössbauer Effect; Recoilless Emission and Absorption of Gamma Rays," Hans Frauenfelder and Harry Lustig (eds.) (Discussions of On-Site Conference of the Advisory Committee to the Directorate of Solid State Sciences, Air Force Office of Scientific Research, Univ. Illinois, Allerton House, June 6-7, 1960). Available only as AF-TN 60-698. This unpublished report is known in the field as "The First Mössbauer Conference Report."

D. M. J. Compton and A. H. Schoen (eds.), The Mössbauer Effect (Proceedings of the Second International Conference on the Mössbauer Effect, Saclay, France, September 13-15, 1961), Wiley, New York, 1962.

The Proceedings of the Third International Conference on the Mössbauer Effect (Cornell University, September 4-7, 1963) will be published in *Rev. Mod. Phys.*, **36**, No. 1 (1964).

7-4 NOBEL LECTURE

R. L. Mössbauer, Rückstossfreie Kernresonanzabsorption von Gammastrahlung, *Phys. Blätter*, **18**, 97 (1962).

REPRINTS AND TRANSLATIONS

The Effect of Collisions upon the Doppler Width of Spectral Lines

R. H. Dicke
Palmer Physical Laboratory, Princeton University, Princeton, New Jersey
(Received September 17, 1952)

Quantum mechanically the Doppler effect results from the recoil momentum changing the translational energy of the radiating atom. The assumption that the recoil momentum is given to the radiating atom is shown to be incorrect if collisions are taking place. If the collisions do not cause broadening by affecting the internal state of the radiator, they result in a substantial narrowing of the Doppler broadened line.

QUANTUM mechanically, the Doppler effect results from the recoil momentum given to the radiating system by the emitted photon.[1] This recoil momentum implies a change in the kinetic energy of the radiating atom which is in turn mirrored by a corresponding change in the photon's energy. This change in the photon's energy is proportional to the component of the atom's velocity in the direction of emission of the photon and leads to the normal expression for the Doppler effect. Since for gas pressures commonly encountered the fraction of the time that an atom is in collision is negligibly small, it might seem reasonable to assume that the recoil momentum is absorbed by the single radiating atom or molecule rather than by an atomic aggregate. In this case the Doppler breadth would, within limits, be pressure-independent. Actually, under certain circumstances, this assumption is far from correct. Collisions which do not affect the internal state of the radiating system have a large effect upon the Doppler breadth.

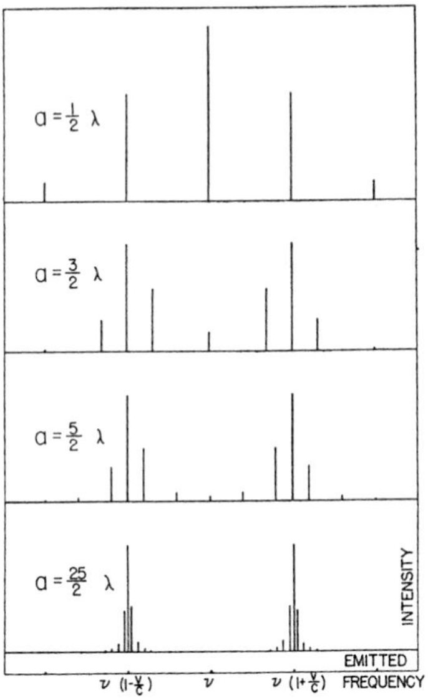

Fig. 1. Spectral distribution of radiation emitted by an atom confined to a one-dimensional box of width a.

The effect of collisions upon the Doppler effect is best illustrated with a simple example treated first classically and then quantum mechanically. Assume that the radiating atom, but not the radiation, is confined to a one-dimensional well of width a, and that it moves back and forth between the two walls with a speed v. The wave emitted by the atom is frequency modulated with the various harmonics of the oscillation frequency of the atom in the square well. For negligible collision and radiation damping, the spectral distribution of the emitted radiation is obtained from a Fourier series. A set of equally spaced sharp lines is obtained. They occur at the non-Doppler shifted frequency plus- or minus-integral multiples of the oscillation frequency of the atom in the square well. The intensity distribution of these lines is shown for several values of a/λ in Fig. 1.

In the quantum-mechanical description of this example, the radiating system possesses two types of energy, internal and external. The external energy is the quantized energy of the atomic center-of-mass moving in the one-dimensional square well. In a transition in which a photon is absorbed or emitted, both the internal and external quantum numbers may change. The frequency of the emitted photon is

$$\nu_{nm}=\nu+(h/8Ma^2)(n^2-m^2).$$

Here ν is the frequency of the non-Doppler shifted line, M is the mass of the radiator, and n, m are integers. A calculation of the transition probabilities gives results for the intensities which are for large n and m essentially the same as the classical results (Fig. 1).

The introduction of a Maxwellian distribution in v in the case of the classical calculation leads to a continuous distribution very similar to a normal Doppler distribution plus a sharp non-Doppler broadened line (see Fig. 2). The fraction of the energy radiated in the sharp line is

$$\frac{\sin^2(\pi a/\lambda)}{(\pi a/\lambda)^2}.$$

[1] E. Fermi, Revs. Modern Phys. 4, 105 (1932).

The sharp line has its origin in the fact that, for a nonintegral value of $\pi a/\lambda$, the normal unshifted frequency is emitted by all atoms independent of their speed. Since for $a \geq \frac{1}{2}\lambda$ the dominant noncentral lines in Fig. 1 are always close to the normal Doppler shifted frequencies, the broad distribution has a line contour nearly identical with the normal Doppler line. For $a < \frac{1}{2}\lambda$, the distribution increases in breadth but becomes much weaker.

For the quantum-mechanical treatment, a Maxwell-Boltzmann distribution among the various energy levels leads to a fine complex of lines having frequencies ν_{nm}. If the zero-point energy of oscillation of the atom in the well is very small compared with kT, the degenerate frequency $\nu = \nu_{nn}$ is usually the most intense single frequency emitted. For a small amount of collision or natural broadening, the complex of lines becomes a continuous distribution (Fig. 2) essentially identical with that given by the classical calculation. Note that although the atom is in contact with the walls of the cavity only an infinitesimal part of the time, the probability of the photon's momentum being given to the walls rather than to the atom is finite, being

$$\frac{\sin^2(\pi a/\lambda)}{(\pi a/\lambda)^2}.$$

For a gas confined to a large volume but with a mean free path small compared with a wavelength, the shape of a Doppler broadened line has been calculated treating the radiation classically and using a statistical procedure. In this treatment the phase of the radiation emitted as a function of the time is given by the position of the radiator as a function of the time. The probability distribution of position given by diffusion theory is used to calculate the mean intensity as a function of frequency. Substantially the same result is obtained also quantum mechanically, using a method similar to Foley's.[2] This quantum-mechanical calculation is valid only if the recoil energy of the radiator is small compared with kT. Assuming that the Doppler effect is the only appreciable source of the line breadth, it is found that the line has a Lorentz rather than Gaussian shape. The line contour is given by

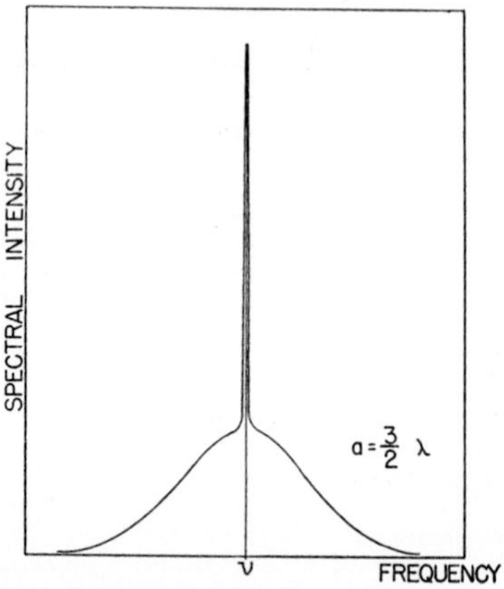

FIG. 2. Doppler broadened line of a gas in a one-dimensional box.

$$I(\alpha) = I_0 \frac{2\pi D/\lambda^2}{(\alpha-\nu)^2 + (2\pi D/\lambda^2)^2}.$$

The width of the line at half-intensity is, in cycles per second, $4\pi D/\lambda^2$. Here D is the self-diffusion constant of the gas. This line width is roughly $2.8L/\lambda$ times that of a normal Doppler broadened line (L is the mean free path). Therefore, under those conditions for which the calculation is valid, the line breadth which is wholly Doppler is greatly reduced.

Because of the requirement that the gas collisions should not influence the internal state of the radiator, the above results are ordinarily valid only for certain magnetic dipole transitions. Nuclear magnetic resonance absorption, paramagnetic resonance absorption, and S-state hyperfine transitions are examples of transitions which are but weakly affected by collisions.

[2] H. M. Foley, Phys. Rev. 69, 616 (1946).

Aus dem Institut für Physik im Max-Planck-Institut für medizinische Forschung, Heidelberg

Kernresonanzfluoreszenz von Gammastrahlung in Ir^{191}

Von

RUDOLF L. MÖSSBAUER*

Mit 8 Figuren im Text

(Eingegangen am 9. Januar 1958)

Die Kernresonanzabsorption der dem Zerfall von Os^{191} folgenden 129 keV-Gammastrahlung in Ir^{191} wird untersucht. Der Wirkungsquerschnitt für die Resonanzabsorption wird als Funktion der Temperaturen von Quelle und Absorber im Temperaturbereich $90°\,K < T < 370°\,K$ gemessen. Die Lebenszeit τ_γ des 129 keV-Niveaus in Ir^{191} ergibt sich zu $(3{,}6^{+1,3}_{-0,8})\,10^{-10}$ sec. Der Absorptionsquerschnitt zeigt bei tiefen Temperaturen einen starken Anstieg als Folge der Kristallbindung der Absorber- und Präparatsubstanzen. Die Theorie von LAMB über die Resonanzabsorption langsamer Neutronen in Kristallen wird auf die Kernresonanzabsorption von Gammastrahlung übertragen. Bei tiefen Temperaturen ergibt sich eine starke Abhängigkeit des Wirkungsquerschnittes für die Kernabsorption von der Frequenzverteilung im Schwingungsspektrum des Festkörpers.

1. Einleitung

Die Kernresonanzfluoreszenz von Gammastrahlung ist das kernphysikalische Analogon zu der bekannten Fluoreszenzerscheinung der Atomhülle: Anregung eines Kernniveaus durch Einstrahlung der eigenen Linie, wobei die Emission und Absorption in Kernen gleicher Art stattfindet. Die Quanten erfahren bei ihrer Emission bzw. Absorption Energieverluste infolge Abgabe von Rückstoßenergie an die emittierenden bzw. absorbierenden Kerne, was zu einer Verschiebung der Emissionslinie gegenüber der Absorptionslinie führt. Bei Kernübergängen ist, umgekehrt wie bei optischen Übergängen, die durch den Rückstoßenergieverlust der Quanten bedingte Linienverschiebung immer groß gegen die natürliche Linienbreite, d.h. die Resonanzbedingung ist verletzt. Da jedoch die tatsächliche Breite der Linien durch die Temperaturbewegung der Kerne in Quelle und Absorber bestimmt wird**, die zu Doppler-Verschiebungen der Quantenenergien führt, wird für einen Teil der Quanten der Rückstoßenergieverlust kompensiert und die durch den Rückstoßeffekt verletzte Resonanzbedingung wiederhergestellt.

---

* Neue Anschrift: Labor für technische Physik, Technische Hochschule München.

** Die natürliche Linienbreite kann in allen hier interessierenden Fällen gegenüber der Doppler-Breite vernachlässigt werden.

Die hohen Rückstoßenergieverluste der Quanten bei Kernübergängen ergeben bei Zimmertemperatur häufig nur eine geringe Überdeckung der Emissions- und Absorptionslinien, d.h. die Resonanzbedingung ist nur für wenige Quanten erfüllt und der Wirkungsquerschnitt für den Resonanzeffekt wird unmeßbar klein. Wie zuerst MALMFORS [*1*] zeigte, läßt sich in günstigen Fällen durch Temperaturerhöhung ein meßbarer Resonanzfluoreszenzeffekt erzielen*. Diese Methode der Temperaturerhöhung, durch thermische Verbreiterung der Linien eine stärkere Überlagerung der Emissions- und Absorptionslinien zu erreichen, wurde seitdem in einer Reihe von Arbeiten erfolgreich angewandt [*3*]. Diese Experimente erfolgten in Form von Streuversuchen, wobei jeweils die an den Kernen resonanzgestreuten Quanten von dem Untergrund der elastisch gestreuten und der durch den Compton-Effekt gestreuten Strahlung abgetrennt werden mußten. Die Messungen mußten im allgemeinen auf Quellen beschränkt werden, die keine härtere Gammastrahlung emittierten als die untersuchte Resonanzstrahlung, um im Nachweiskristall eine Überdeckung des Photomaximums der resonanzgestreuten Quanten durch das Compton-Kontinuum härterer Linien zu verhindern. Die Bestimmung des Kernfluoreszenzeffektes durch Messung der resonanzgestreuten Strahlung bietet bei weicher Gammastrahlung zwei zusätzliche Schwierigkeiten:

1. Mit abnehmender Energie wird es immer schwieriger, die Compton-Streustrahlung von der elastischen Streustrahlung zu unterscheiden, wegen des abnehmenden Energieunterschiedes zwischen primären und Compton-gestreuten Quanten. Erschwerend wirkt sich aus, daß das Auflösungsvermögen der Szintillationsspektrometer mit abnehmender Energie abnimmt. Außerdem steigt der Wirkungsquerschnitt für die Rayleigh-Streuung bei niedrigen Energien stark an [*4*].

2. Der Wirkungsquerschnitt für die Resonanzfluoreszenz ist umgekehrt proportional zur Lebenszeit τ_γ des Resonanzniveaus**. Für Lebenszeitmessungen eignen sich daher gerade die kurzlebigen magnetischen Dipol ($M1$)- und elektrischen Quadrupol ($E2$)-Übergänge ($\tau_\gamma < 10^{-10}$ sec), die mit der Methode der verzögerten Koinzidenzen nicht mehr erfaßt werden können. Die Strahlungsübergänge niedriger Multipolordnung zeigen bei niedrigen Energien eine beträchtliche Konversion. Bei der Resonanzfluoreszenz wird von den resonanzabsorbierten Quanten nur der Bruchteil $(1+\alpha)^{-1}$ (α = Konversionskoeffizient) wieder als Quant reemittiert und nur dieser Bruchteil der resonanzabsorbierten Quanten steht für die Messung zur Verfügung.

---

* Einen Überblick über die verschiedenen Verfahren zur Kompensation der Rückstoßenergieverluste gibt MALMFORS [*2*].

** Diese Beziehung gilt nicht mehr für Festkörper bei tiefen Temperaturen; vgl. Abschnitt 3.

Die genannten Schwierigkeiten lassen sich umgehen, wenn der Kernresonanzeffekt in Absorption gemessen wird. Da jedoch der Effekt, besonders bei weicher Gammastrahlung, sehr klein ist gegenüber den Absorptionseffekten der Atomhülle, werden bei einem Absorptionsexperiment zur Messung der Lebenszeit eines Kernniveaus extreme Anforderungen an die Genauigkeit und Stabilität der Meßapparaturen gestellt. Dafür bietet ein Absorptionsexperiment gegenüber einem Streustrahlungsversuch den Vorteil eines um einen Faktor $1+\alpha$ höheren Wirkungsquerschnittes und ermöglicht eine einfachere Interpretation der Meßergebnisse.

Die Kernresonanzfluoreszenz besitzt besonderes Interesse im Energiegebiet weicher Gammastrahlung, da bei tiefen Temperaturen in diesem Energiegebiet bei Festkörpern Einflüsse der chemischen Bindung zu erwarten sind.

In der vorliegenden Arbeit wurde durch ein Gamma-Absorptionsexperiment die Lebenszeit τ_γ des 129 keV-Niveaus in Ir^{191} bestimmt. Untersuchungen bei der Temperatur des flüssigen O_2 ergaben einen starken Einfluß der chemischen Bindung auf den Wirkungsquerschnitt für die Kernabsorption. Der aufgefundene Bindungseffekt wurde mit Hilfe der Theorie von LAMB, die zu diesem Zweck für den Fall der Emissionslinie erweitert wurde, theoretisch gedeutet. Der Bindungseffekt ist sehr empfindlich vom Schwingungsspektrum des Festkörpers abhängig.

2. Kernresonanzfluoreszenz und chemische Bindung

Die Absorptions- und Emissionslinien sind ihrer Lage und ihrer Form nach vom Bindungszustand abhängig. Insbesondere ist der Rückstoßenergieverlust der emittierten und auch der resonanzabsorbierten Quanten abhängig von den Energieaufnahme- und Energieabgabemöglichkeiten der Systeme, denen die betrachteten Kerne angehören (z.B. Moleküle oder Kristalle).

Ein freier Kern der Masse m übernimmt bei Emission eines Quants der Energie E_0 eine Rückstoßenergie R, die gegeben ist durch

$$R = E_0^2/2m c^2. \qquad (1)$$

Im Falle einer chemischen Bindung des Kernes in einem Kristall muß der Kristall die Rückstoßenergie als innere Energie aufnehmen. Wegen der Quantelung der inneren Energie können jedoch beim Rückstoß nur diskrete Energien aufgenommen werden und die Rückstoßenergie hängt ab von den Wahrscheinlichkeiten für die Anregung der Gitterschwingungen des Kristalles. Bei Temperaturen T, die groß sind gegen die Debyesche Temperatur Θ des Kristalles, ist die statistische Geschwindigkeitsverteilung der Kerne unabhängig von der Bindung und es erfolgt eine ungehinderte Übertragung der vollen Rückstoßenergie nach (1). Mit abnehmender Temperatur gelangt eine zunehmende Anzahl vorzugsweise der hochfrequenten Schwingungsoszillatoren des Kristalles in den Grundzustand. Diese Oszillatoren können keine Energie mehr abgeben und die Linienform wird unsymmetrisch, wenn die Rückstoßenergie nicht groß ist gegen die obere Grenzenergie $\hbar\,\omega_g$ des Schwingungsspektrums des Kristalles. LAMB [5] berechnet die Lage und Form der Absorptionslinie beim Resonanzeinfang langsamer Neutronen in Kristallen und gibt Näherungen für spezielle Bindungsfälle an. Hiernach besitzt die Absorptionslinie im Fall schwacher Bindung und unter der Annahme, daß der Kristall als Debye-Kontinuum aufgefaßt werden kann, dieselbe Form wie in einem idealen Gas, wobei jedoch an die Stelle der tatsächlichen Temperatur T eine Temperatur $T^* > T$ tritt, die der mittleren Energie pro Schwingungsfreiheitsgrad des Kristalles entspricht. Im Falle stärkerer Bindung zeigt die Absorptionslinie bei tiefen Temperaturen eine komplizierte Struktur und eine Verschiebung zu kleineren Energien, verbunden mit dem Auftreten eines Maximums an der Stelle der Resonanzenergie. Die Linienform wird um so unsymmetrischer, je kleiner das Verhältnis $R/k\Theta$ ist.

Die Arbeit von LAMB läßt sich leicht für die Emissionslinie erweitern und kann dann direkt auf die Gammaresonanzprozesse angewandt werden. Bei der Resonanzfluoreszenz des 129 keV Niveaus in Ir^{191} ist $R = 0{,}046$ eV und $k\Theta = 0{,}025$ eV. Der Fall schwacher Bindung in der Definition nach LAMB [5] ist hier bei Temperaturen $T < 200$ °K nicht mehr realisiert.

3. Theorie

Nach LAMB [5] gilt für den Wirkungsquerschnitt für die Resonanzabsorption:

$$\sigma(E) = (\Gamma^2/4)\,\sigma_0\,W_a(E) \tag{2}$$

(Γ = totale Energiebreite des Resonanzniveaus; E = Energie der einfallenden Quanten; σ_0 = Wirkungsquerschnitt für exakte Resonanz). $W_a(E)$ bestimmt Lage und Form der Absorptionslinie:

$$W_a(E)\,(2/\Gamma)\,\mathrm{Real}\int_0^\infty d\mu\,\exp\left[i\,\mu\,(E - E_0 + i\,\Gamma/2) + g_a(\mu)\right]. \tag{3a}$$

Dabei ist

$$\left.\begin{aligned} g_a(\mu) = \sum_s \frac{(\vec{p}\,\vec{e}_s)^2}{2m\,\hbar\,\omega_s\,N} \times \\ \times\left[(\bar{\alpha}_s + 1)\exp(-i\,\mu\,\hbar\,\omega_s) + \bar{\alpha}_s\exp(i\,\mu\,\hbar\,\omega_s) - 1 - 2\bar{\alpha}_s\right]. \end{aligned}\right\} \tag{4a}$$

E_0 ist die Resonanzenergie, ω_s die Frequenz der s-ten Normalschwingung des Kristalles, m die Kernmasse, $\vec{p}$ der Impuls des Gammaquants, $\vec{e}$ der Polarisationseinheitsvektor, $3N$ die Zahl der unabhängigen Freiheitsgrade im Kristall und $\overline{\alpha}_s$ die mittlere Besetzungszahl des s-ten Oszillators:

$$\overline{\alpha}_s = 1/(e^{\hbar\omega_s/kT} - 1). \tag{5}$$

Wie sich leicht zeigen läßt* gilt für die Emissionslinie**:

$$W_e(E) = (2/\Gamma)\,\mathrm{Real}\int_0^\infty d\mu \exp\left[i\mu(E - E_0 + i\Gamma/2) + g_e(\mu)\right] \tag{3b}$$

mit

$$\left.\begin{aligned} g_e(\mu) &= \sum_s \frac{(\vec{p}\,\vec{e}_s)^2}{2m\hbar\omega_s N} \times \\ &\times [(\overline{\alpha}_s + 1)\exp(i\mu\hbar\omega_s) + \overline{\alpha}_s \exp(-i\mu\hbar\omega_s) - 1 - 2\overline{\alpha}_s]. \end{aligned}\right\} \tag{4b}$$

Die Berechnung der Integrale (3) wird in Debyescher Näherung durchgeführt***. Die Debye-Temperaturen der transversalen und der longitudinalen Schwingungskomponenten werden gleichgesetzt.

a) Für $\mu k\Theta \ll 1$ folgt

$$g_a(\mu) \approx -i\mu R - \mu^2 R\varepsilon, \tag{6a}$$

$$g_e(\mu) \approx +i\mu R - \mu^2 R\varepsilon. \tag{6b}$$

R ist die Rückstoßenergie nach (1) und ε die mittlere Energie pro Schwingungsfreiheitsgrad des Kristalles:

$$\varepsilon(T) = kT^* = 3kT(T/\Theta)^3 \int_0^{\Theta/T} \left(\frac{1}{e^t - 1} + \frac{1}{2}\right) t^3\,dt. \tag{7}$$

b) Für $\mu k\Theta \gg 1$ gilt

$$\left.\begin{aligned} g_e(\infty; T) = g_a(\infty; T) = g_\infty(T) &= -2\sum_s \frac{(\vec{p}\,\vec{e}_s)^2}{2m\hbar\omega_s N}\left(\overline{\alpha}_s + \frac{1}{2}\right) \\ &= -2R\int_0^{k\Theta} \frac{1}{N\hbar\omega}\left(\frac{1}{e^{\hbar\omega/kT} - 1} + \frac{1}{2}\right)\frac{3N(\hbar\omega)^2}{(k\Theta)^3}\,d(\hbar\omega) \\ &= -(6R/k\Theta)(T/\Theta)^2 \int_0^{\Theta/T}\left(\frac{1}{e^t - 1} + \frac{1}{2}\right) t\,dt. \end{aligned}\right\} \tag{8}****$$

---

* Der Beweis sei kurz angedeutet: Die Gl. (8) von Lamb [5] ist für die Emissionslinie zu ersetzen durch $W(\{\alpha_s\}; \{n_s\}) = \left|\frac{(\alpha_s|H'|n_s)}{E_0 - E + E(n_s) - E(\alpha_s) + i\Gamma/2}\right|^2$, wo $(\alpha_s|H'|n_s)$ das Matrixelement für einen Übergang $n_s \to \alpha_s$ des Gitters bedeutet, der von der Emission eines Quants mit dem Impuls $\vec{p}$ begleitet ist. In Gl. (17) von [5] erscheint dann n_s an Stelle von α_s. Wenn man dann alle folgenden Summierungen über α_s statt über n_s erstreckt und über n_s statt über α_s mittelt, so erhält man unsere Gln. (3b) und (4b), wenn man im Endergebnis wieder $\overline{\alpha}_s$ statt $\overline{n}_s$ setzt.

** Die Funktionen $W_e(E)$ und $W_a(E)$ und damit auch die Emissions- und Absorptionslinien liegen spiegelsymmetrisch zur Geraden $E = E_0$.

*** Die Summationen in (4) enthalten auch die Summationen über die Polarisationsrichtungen.

**** Unsere Gl. (8) unterscheidet sich um einen Faktor 3 von der bei Lamb [5] angegebenen Gl. (36).

Der experimentell bestimmbare mittlere Wirkungsquerschnitt $\bar{\sigma}_r(T_q; T_a)$ ergibt sich, wenn man $\sigma(E)$ in (2) mit der auf 1 normierten Verteilungsfunktion der emittierten (einfallenden) Quanten multipliziert und über alle Energien summiert (T_q, T_a = Temperatur von Quelle bzw. Absorber). Wegen

$$(\Gamma/2\pi)\int_0^\infty W_e(E)\,dE = 1$$

gilt daher

$$\left.\begin{aligned}\bar{\sigma}_r &= \int_0^\infty \sigma(E)\,(\Gamma/2\pi)\,W_e(E)\,dE\\ \bar{\sigma}_r &= (\Gamma^3/8\pi)\,\sigma_0\int_0^\infty W_a(E)\,W_e(E)\,dE.\end{aligned}\right\}\tag{9}$$

und mit (2)

Wenn der Übergang in den Grundzustand auch durch innere Umwandlung (Konversion) erfolgen kann, dann ist zu unterscheiden zwischen dem Wirkungsquerschnitt $(\sigma_0)_s$ für die Resonanz-Streuung und dem Wirkungsquerschnitt $(\sigma_0)_a$ für die Resonanz-Absorption. Für die Resonanz-Streuung gilt nach JACKSON [6]:

$$(\sigma_0)_s = \frac{(2I_a+1)}{(2I_g+1)}\,\frac{\lambda_0^2}{2\pi}\,H\,\frac{\Gamma_\gamma^2}{\Gamma^2} = \frac{(2I_a+1)}{(2I_g+1)}\cdot\frac{\lambda_0^2}{2\pi}\,H\,\frac{1}{(1+\alpha)^2}.\tag{10}$$

Dabei sind $2I+1$ die statistischen Gewichte des angeregten (a) und des Grundzustandes (g), H die relative Häufigkeit des resonanten Isotops, λ_0 die Resonanzwellenlänge, Γ die totale Energiebreite des Resonanzniveaus, Γ_γ die partielle Energiebreite für Strahlungsemission und α der Konversionskoeffizient.

Bei der Resonanzfluoreszenz geht durch Quantenemission nur der Bruchteil Γ_γ/Γ aller Zwischenzustände in den Grundzustand über, der Bruchteil $(\Gamma-\Gamma_\gamma)/\Gamma$ aber durch Konversion. Bei der Resonanzabsorption tragen alle Zwischenzustände zu dem Wirkungsquerschnitt bei und es gilt daher

$$(\sigma_0)_a = (\Gamma/\Gamma_\gamma)\cdot(\sigma_0)_s = \frac{(2I_a+1)}{(2I_g+1)}\,\frac{\lambda_0^2}{2\pi}\,H(\Gamma_\gamma/\Gamma).\tag{11}$$

Im Falle der Resonanzfluoreszenz an Ir^{191} ($E_0 = 129$ keV) kann die Berechnung der Linienformen bis herab zur Temperatur des flüssigen O_2 näherungsweise in zwei Schritten durchgeführt werden:

1. Im Bereich $|E-E_0| \gg \Gamma$ ergeben nur die Werte $\mu k\Theta < 1$ einen wesentlichen Beitrag zu dem Integral (3), und (6) kann noch als brauchbare Näherung benützt werden:

$$\left.\begin{aligned}W_I(E) &= (2/\Gamma)\int_0^\infty d\mu\,\cos(E-E_0\pm R)\,\mu\,\exp(-\mu\,\Gamma/2-\mu^2 R\,\varepsilon)\\ &= (4/\Gamma^2)\,\psi(\xi;\,x).\end{aligned}\right\}\tag{12}$$

Dabei gilt für die Emissions- (e) und Absorptionslinie (a) bzw.*

$$\psi(\xi_e; x_e) = (1/2)\sqrt{\pi}\,\xi_e \exp(-\xi_e^2 x_e^2/4), \tag{13a}$$

$$\psi(\xi_a; x_a) = (1/2)\sqrt{\pi}\,\xi_a \exp(-\xi_a^2 x_a^2/4), \tag{13b}$$

wobei

$$x_e = (E - E_0 + R)/\tfrac{1}{2}\Gamma; \quad x_a = (E - E_0 - R)/\tfrac{1}{2}\Gamma, \tag{14}$$

$$\varDelta_e = 2\sqrt{R\,k\,T_q^*}\,; \quad \varDelta_a = 2\sqrt{R\,k\,T_a^*}, \tag{15}$$

$$\xi_e = \Gamma/\varDelta_e; \quad \xi_a = \Gamma/\varDelta_a. \tag{16}$$

$\varDelta$ ist die Doppler-Breite des Niveaus und T_a^*, T_q^* bezeichnen die Temperaturen des Absorbers und der Quelle, die nach (7) den mittleren Energien pro Schwingungsfreiheitsgrad des Kristalles entsprechen.

2. Im Bereich um $E = E_0$ erhält man eine gute Näherung für $W(E)$, wenn man den Integrationsbereich in (3) an der Stelle $\mu k\Theta = 1$ aufspaltet und in den beiden Bereichen die Näherungen (6) bzw. (8) benützt:

$$W_{II}(E) = (2/\Gamma)\int_0^{1/k\Theta} d\mu \cos(E - E_0 \pm R)\mu \exp(-\mu\Gamma/2 - \mu^2 R\,\varepsilon) +$$

$$+ (2/\Gamma)\int_{1/k\Theta}^{\infty} d\mu \cos(E - E_0)\mu \exp\big(g_\infty(T) - \mu\Gamma/2\big).$$

Das erste Integral liefert nur einen kleinen Beitrag zu $W_{II}(E)$ und es gilt in guter Näherung ($\Gamma/k\Theta \ll 1$):

$$W_{II}(E) = W_I(E) + \frac{\exp(g_\infty(T))}{(E - E_0)^2 + \Gamma^2/4}. \tag{17}$$

Im Bereich $|E - E_0| \gg \Gamma$ kann der zweite Summand in (17) gegenüber $W_I(E)$ vernachlässigt werden und es folgt durch Zusammenfassen von (12) und (17) für die Emissions- bzw. Absorptionslinie:

$$W_e(E) = (4/\Gamma^2)\,\psi(\xi_e; x_e) + \frac{\exp g_\infty(T_q)}{(E - E_0)^2 + \Gamma^2/4}, \tag{18a}$$

$$W_a(E) = (4/\Gamma^2)\,\psi(\xi_a; x_a) + \frac{\exp g_\infty(T_a)}{(E - E_0)^2 + \Gamma^2/4}. \tag{18b}$$

Die durch die Kristallbindung modifizierten Emissions- und Absorptionslinien des 129 keV-Überganges in Ir^{191} besitzen nach (18)** (mit Ausnahme in der Umgebung der Resonanzstelle E_0) bei der Temperatur T nahezu die gleiche Form und Lage wie in einem idealen Gas bei einer Temperatur T^*, die nach (7) der mittleren Energie pro Schwingungsfreiheitsgrad des Kristalles entspricht. An der Resonanzstelle $E = E_0$

---

* Vgl. LAMB [5], Gl. (32).

** Die Gln. (18) verlieren ihre Gültigkeit bei Temperaturen unterhalb der Temperatur des flüssigen O_2.

erhebt sich darüber bei Temperaturen $T<\Theta$ eine mit abnehmender Temperatur stark ansteigende Linie der Breite Γ (Fig. 1). Die Resonanzbedingung wird also mit abnehmender Temperatur für einen immer größer werdenden Bruchteil der Quanten erfüllt.

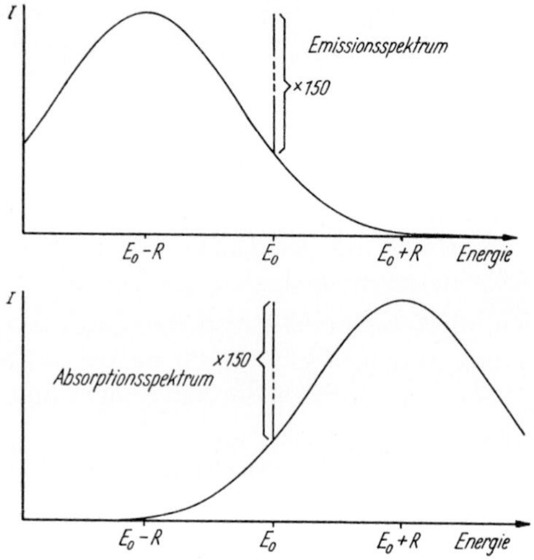

Fig. 1. Lage und Form der Emissions- und Absorptionslinien des 129 keV-Überganges in Ir^{191} bei $T = 88°$ K, für eine Lebenszeit $\tau = 10^{-10}$ sec. Nullpunkt der Energieskala unterdrückt; Einheit der Ordinate willkürlich; Höhe der Linien bei $E = E_0$ (Resonanzenergie) im Verhältnis 1:150 verkürzt dargestellt

Der Wirkungsquerschnitt $\bar{\sigma}_r$ ergibt sich durch Eintragung von (18) in (9). Dabei liefern nur zwei Integrale einen wesentlichen Beitrag:

$$\int_0^\infty (4/\Gamma^2)\,\psi(\xi_e;\,x_e)\,(4/\Gamma^2)\,\psi(\xi_a;\,x_a)\,dE \quad \text{und} \quad \int_0^\infty \frac{\exp\left[g_\infty(T_q)+g_\infty(T_a)\right]}{\left[(E-E_0)^2+\Gamma^2/4\right]^2}\,dE\,.$$

Ausführung der Integrationen ergibt für den mittleren Wirkungsquerschnitt für die Resonanzabsorption:

$$\bar{\sigma}_{r\,a} = \frac{(\sigma_0)_a}{2}\sqrt{\pi}\,\frac{\Gamma}{\sqrt{\Delta_a^2+\Delta_e^2}}\exp\left[\frac{-4R^2}{\Delta_a^2+\Delta_e^2}\right] + \frac{(\sigma_0)_a}{2}\exp\left[g_\infty(T_q)+g_\infty(T_a)\right]. \quad (19)$$

Die Unschärferelation ergibt für die mittlere Lebenszeit τ des Resonanzniveaus und für die mittlere Lebenszeit τ_γ für Zerfall durch Strahlungsemission:

$$\tau = \hbar/\Gamma = \hbar/\Gamma_\gamma(1+\alpha) = \tau_\gamma/(1+\alpha) = T_{\frac{1}{2}}/\ln 2 \quad (20)$$

(α = Konversionskoeffizient, $T_{\frac{1}{2}}$ = Halbwertszeit).

Bei höheren Temperaturen kann der 2. Term in (19) vernachlässigt werden und es folgt nach (11), (19), (20) $\bar{\sigma}_{r\,a} \sim 1/\tau_\gamma$. Bei tiefen Temperaturen dominiert der von der Lebenszeit unabhängige 2. Term in (19).

4. Versuchsanordnung

Fig. 2 zeigt die Versuchsanordnung, Fig. 3 den Aufbau des Absorber-Kryostaten. Die Absorber, zwei je etwa 0,4 mm dicke gewalzte Iridium- bzw. Platinbleche von 35 mm Durchmesser waren so befestigt, daß bei der Abkühlung eine ungehinderte Kontraktion derselben möglich war.

Untersucht wurde die Absorption der beim Beta-Zerfall von Os^{191} ausgesandten 129 keV Gammastrahlung in Iridium. Fig. 4 zeigt das Zerfallschema [7] und das beobachtete Spektrum, das neben der 16d-Aktivität von Os^{191} noch Komponenten der 95d-Aktivität von Os^{185} enthält [8]. Die harten, beim *K*-Einfang von Os^{185} ausgesandten Linien von Re^{185} bei 640 keV und bei 875 keV durchsetzten die Absorber

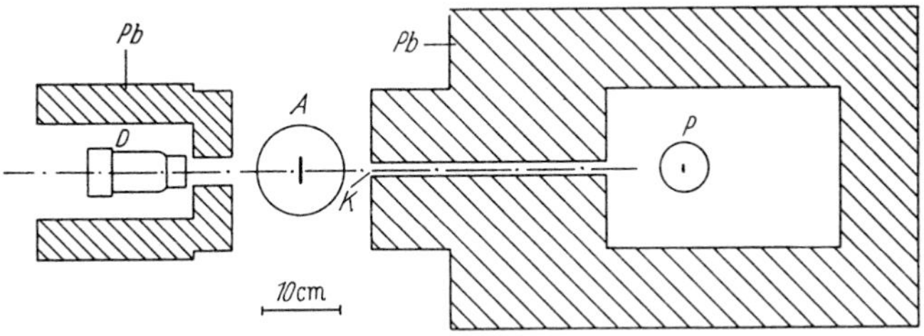

Fig. 2. Versuchsgeometrie. *A* Absorber-Kryostat; *P* Kryostat mit Quelle; *D* Detektor: NaJ(Tl)-Kristall (22 mm hoch, 40 mm Durchmesser) und Photomultiplier; *K* Kollimator (Bohrung 18 mm); *A* und *P* werden von den Armen eines schweren Stativs getragen

nahezu ungeschwächt, während die weiche 129 keV-Strahlung von Ir^{191} durch den Photoeffekt stark absorbiert wurde. Die harten Komponenten von Re^{185} überlagerten daher im Nachweiskristall mit ihrem Compton-Kontinuum erheblich die 129 keV-Resonanzlinie.

Während die Selbstabsorption der Resonanzlinie in der Quelle stark mit der Dicke des Präparates zunimmt, erfahren die harten Strahlungskomponenten von Re^{185} nur eine geringfügige Selbstabsorption. Die von der Quelle emittierte Strahlungsintensität verschiebt sich daher mit zunehmender Schichtdicke des Präparates zugunsten der härteren Strahlungskomponenten. Die Präparatsubstanz wurde deshalb flächenförmig angeordnet (Oberfläche 80 mm^2) und die Menge auf 0,6 g beschränkt. Die Substanz — analysenreiner pulverförmiger Osmiumschwamm — wurde vor der Bestrahlung im Vakuum in eine dünnwandige Quarzküvette eingeschmolzen. Die 65 mCurie starke Quelle wurde an den Boden eines zur Aufnahme von flüssiger Luft dienenden zylinderförmigen Quarzbehälters angeschmolzen, der sich mit dem Präparat in einem Dewargefäß befand. Die beschriebene Montage der Quelle war erforderlich, um Präparatbewegungen infolge einer Kontraktion der Aufhängevorrichtung bei der Abkühlung auf ein Minimum zu beschränken. Derartige Präparatbewegungen könnten zu einer Änderung der von der Quelle „gesehenen" mittleren Schichtdicke des Absorbers führen, sofern dieser nicht vollständig planparallel ist*. Die hauptsächliche experimentelle Schwierigkeit bei der Lebenszeitmessung lag in einer sicheren Ausschaltung eines solchen Einflusses von Änderungen der Geometrie bei der Abkühlung auf die Messung. Das Problem wurde

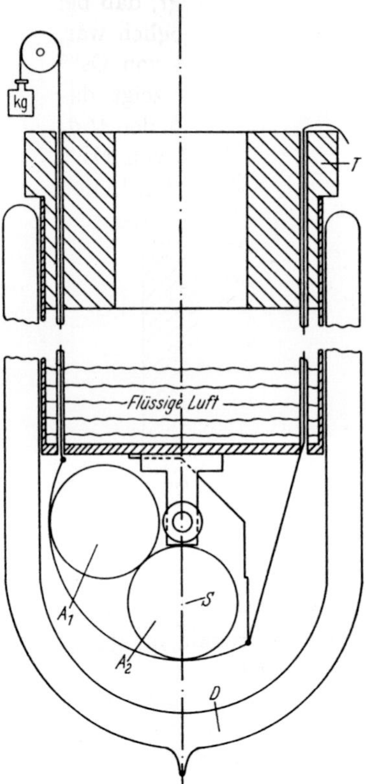

Fig. 3

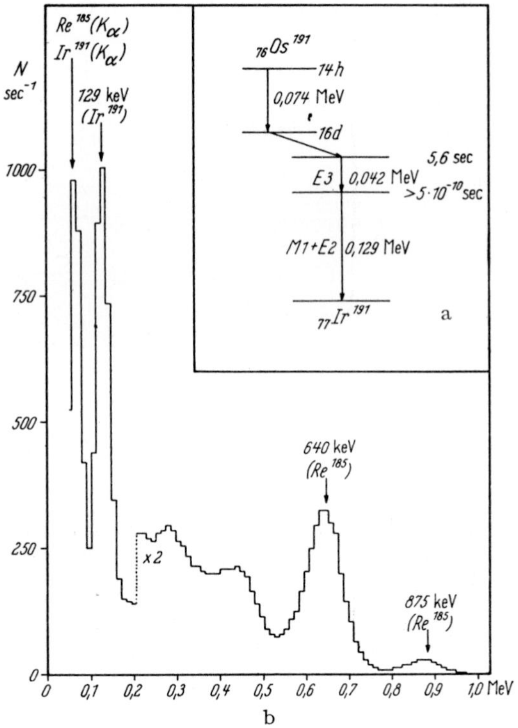

Fig. 4 a u. b

Fig. 3. Absorber-Kryostat (schematisch) mit einer durch zwei Schnurzüge bedienbaren Drehvorrichtung, um abwechselnd zwei verschiedene Absorber A_1 und A_2 in den Strahlengang zu bringen. D Dewargefäß; S Achse des senkrecht zur Zeichenebene verlaufenden Strahlenbündels; T Trolitulisolator. Schnurzug und Thermoelemente werden durch die flüssige Luft in Messingröhrchen geführt, die in den Boden des Luftbehälters eingelötet sind

Fig. 4 a u. b. a Zerfallschema von Os^{191}. b Spektrum des natürlichen Osmiumisotopengemisches, gemessen hinter 0,4 mm Iridium 4 d nach Abschluß der 12 d-Neutronenbestrahlung

befriedigend gelöst durch die beschriebene Art der Aufhängung der Quelle, durch die Verwendung von nahezu planparallelen Absorbern**

* Eine Änderung der Schichtdicke des Absorbers von nur 0,1 μ hätte bereits zu Absorptionseffekten in der Größenordnung der gemessenen Effekte geführt.

** Wir danken der Fa. Heraeus Platinschmelze für die Herstellung und leihweise Überlassung der Edelmetallabsorber.

großer Oberfläche und durch die Wahl eines relativ großen Abstandes der Quelle von den Absorbern (mindestens 50 cm). Die Temperaturen der Quelle und der Absorber wurden mit Eisen-Konstantan-Thermoelementen gemessen. Die ganze Anordnung wurde auf optischem Wege justiert.

Fig. 5 zeigt das Blockschema der elektronischen Nachweisapparatur. Der Aufbau und die Betriebsweise waren darauf abgestellt, Schwankungen in der Zählhäufigkeit auf ein Mindestmaß zu beschränken, z.B.

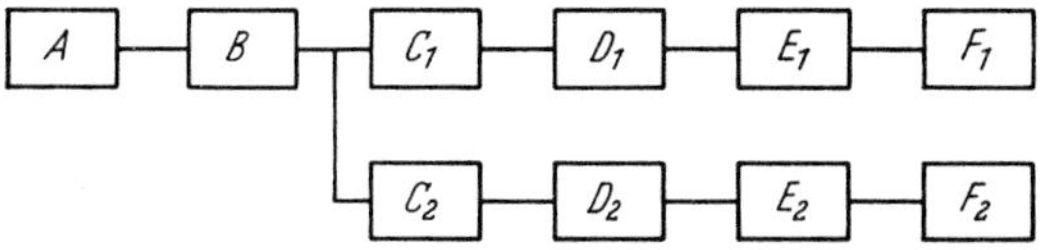

Fig. 5. Blockschaltbild der elektronischen Meßanordnung. (Die Stromversorgung wurde nicht dargestellt.) *A* Photomultiplier RCA 6342 Betriebsspannung 1,3 kV; *B* Vorverstärker [*9*]; *C* Hauptverstärker; *D* Einkanaldiskriminator [*10*]; *E* Dualuntersetzer Untersetzungsfaktor 2^{16}; *F* Registrierstufe mit mechanischem Zählwerk

durch Verwendung von Schaltelementen mit kleinen Temperaturkoeffizienten. Die ganze Anlage wurde von einem auf $\pm 0{,}5\%$ spannungsstabilisierten Netz betrieben. Das Hochspannungsgerät und die Heizung der Verstärker wurden zusätzlich durch einen magnetischen Spannungsgleichhalter stabilisiert.

5. Meßverfahren

Eine direkte Bestimmung des Wirkungsquerschnittes für die Kernresonanzabsorption durch eine Messung des totalen Schwächungskoeffizienten ist im allgemeinen nicht möglich, da die Kernresonanzabsorption gewöhnlich sehr klein ist gegenüber den Absorptionseffekten der Atomhülle. Der Kernresonanzeffekt in Ir^{191} wurde daher durch eine Differenzmessung bestimmt, wobei die Absorption der Resonanzlinie im Resonanzabsorber Iridium bei verschiedenen Temperaturen unter Bedingungen gemessen wurde, bei denen die auftretenden Intensitätsänderungen in direkter Beziehung zu dem Wirkungsquerschnitt für die Resonanzabsorption standen und jegliche Nebeneffekte ausgeschaltet wurden. Der Wirkungsquerschnitt $\bar{\sigma}_{ra}$ ist nach (19) eine Funktion der Temperaturen der Quelle und des Absorbers. Aus Gründen der Temperaturabhängigkeit der totalen Absorption wurden alle Messungen bei konstanter Temperatur des Absorbers durchgeführt, d.h. es wurde jeweils nur die Temperatur der Quelle variiert. Die Temperaturabhängigkeit der totalen Absorption hat ihren anschaulichen Grund darin, daß sich die Zahl der Atome pro cm^2 der Oberfläche einer absorbierenden Substanz mit der Temperatur ändert [*1*]. Dieser Effekt hätte im vorliegenden Fall dem Kernresonanzeffekt entgegengewirkt und ihn dabei vollständig überdeckt, was durch Beschränkung der Temperaturvariationen auf die Quelle verhindert wurde. Natürlich zeigt auch die Selbstabsorption in der Quelle einen (allerdings kleineren) Temperaturgang. Dieser Effekt, der ebenfalls dem Resonanzeffekt entgegenwirkt, konnte jedoch experimentell eliminiert werden durch abwechselnde Intensitätsmessungen mit dem Resonanzabsorber und einem Vergleichsabsorber. Da der Selbstabsorptionseffekt der Quelle die Intensität hinter beiden Absorbern beeinflußt, während der Kernresonanzeffekt nur beim Resonanzabsorber auftritt, fällt ersterer Effekt bei einer Differenzmessung heraus, wenn die Absorber so abgestimmt sind, daß sie ungefähr gleich stark absorbieren.

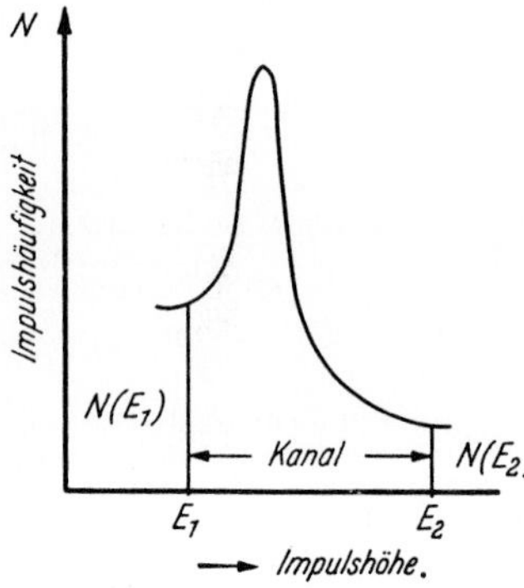

Fig. 6. Einstellung der Begrenzungen des Kanals des Einkanaldiskriminators zur Stabilisierung der Impulshäufigkeit gegenüber Verstärkungsschwankungen

Die Resonanzlinie wurde aus dem Zerfallspektrum des Osmium-Isotopengemisches durch den Einkanaldiskriminator D_1 (Fig. 5) ausgeblendet. Um den Einfluß von Schwankungen des Schwellenwertes des Einkanaldiskriminators auf die Messungen zu vermindern, wurde der Kanal auf 25% des ganzen erfaßbaren Spektralbereiches geöffnet*. Die aus dem Spektrum ausgeblendete Resonanzlinie wurde durch entsprechende Wahl der Verstärkung der maximalen Kanalbreite angepaßt. Die härteren Komponenten des Spektrums führten dabei zu einer Übersteuerung des Hauptverstärkers, die jedoch keinen Einfluß auf den ausgeblendeten Teil des Spektrums hatte.

Um die Schwankungen der Verstärkung (insbesondere des Multipliers) aufzufangen, wurden die Begrenzungen des Kanals so eingestellt, daß kleine Schwankungen der Verstärkung in erster Näherung keine Änderung der Impulshäufigkeit im Kanal verursachten. Das Verfahren wird durch Fig. 6 illustriert: Eine Änderung der Verstärkung führt zu einer Expansion bzw. Kontraktion des Spektrums längs der Abszisse. Wenn der ausblendende Kanal so eingestellt wird, daß $N(E_1)\,E_1 \approx N(E_2)\,E_2$, so wird die Impulshäufigkeit, wie sich leicht zeigen läßt, in erster Näherung nicht durch kleine Verstärkungsschwankungen beeinflußt, weil sich die bei einer Verstärkungsänderung neu in den Kanal eintretenden und die austretenden Anteile des Spektrums kompensieren. Diese Beziehung ist annähernd erfüllt bei der in Fig. 7 gezeigten bei den Messungen benützten Einstellung des Kanals auf die Resonanzlinie. Durch das beschriebene Meßverfahren konnten die

* Hierzu wurde die Gegenkopplung im Fensterverstärker der Schaltung [*10*] erhöht.

relativen Schwankungen nicht-statistischer Natur in der Zählhäufigkeit auf rund 0,1% beschränkt werden.

Als Resonanzabsorber diente Iridium ($Z=77$), als Vergleichsabsorber Platin ($Z=78$). Der Intensitätsunterschied der die beiden Absorber durchsetzenden Strahlung betrug bei Zimmertemperatur etwa 0,1%.

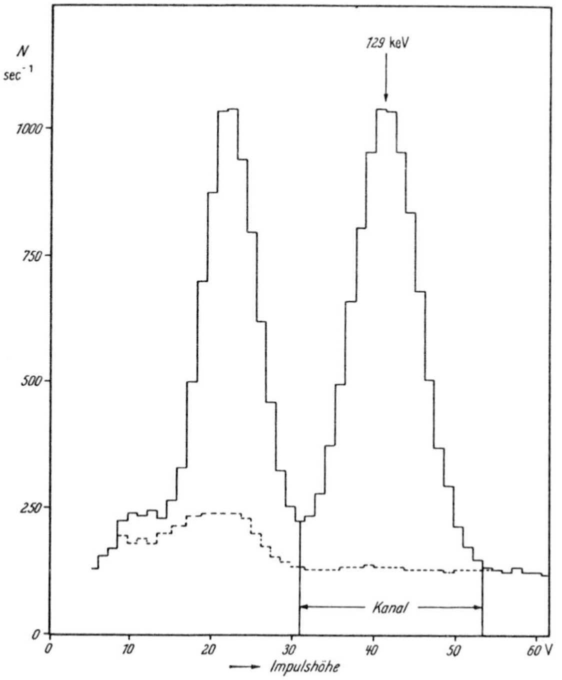

Fig. 7. Einstellung des Kanals des Einkanaldiskriminators auf die 129 keV-Linie in Ir^{191}. ——— Ausschnitt aus dem Zerfallspektrum von $Os^{185}+Os^{191}$ 5d nach der Neutronenbestrahlung. ------ Ausschnitt aus dem Zerfallspektrum einer Osmiumquelle, deren Os^{191}-Aktivität bereits abgeklungen ist. Beide Spektren sind auf gleiche Intensität bei hohen Energien normiert. — Das Verhältnis v der Impulshäufigkeiten der 129 keV-Linie zu allen im Bereich des Kanals liegenden Linien ist $v=0{,}757$

Gemessen wurden die totalen Strahlungsintensitäten I_t^{Ir} und I_t^{Pt} hinter dem Resonanzabsorber (Ir) und dem Vergleichsabsorber (Pt).

Bei den Messungen zur Bestimmung der Lebenszeit des 129 keV-Niveaus in Ir^{191} befanden sich die Absorber stets auf Zimmertemperatur und es wurde nur die Temperatur der Quelle variiert. Bei jeder Meßreihe wurden zunächst wiederholt abwechselnd die Intensitäten $I_t^{\mathrm{Ir}}(T_2)$ und $I_t^{\mathrm{Pt}}(T_2)$ gemessen, wobei sich die Quelle auf der Zimmertemperatur T_2 befand. Nach Abkühlung der Quelle auf die Temperatur T_1 des flüssigen O_2 erfolgten analog wiederholte Messungen von $I_t^{\mathrm{Ir}}(T_1)$ und $I_t^{\mathrm{Pt}}(T_1)$. Jede Messung mit dem Resonanzabsorber wurde eingeschlossen durch zwei Messungen mit dem Vergleichsabsorber, um einen linearen Gang in der elektronischen Apparatur zu eliminieren.

Bei den Messungen zur Untersuchung des Einflusses der chemischen Bindung auf die Kernresonanzabsorption befanden sich die Absorber stets auf der Temperatur des flüssigen O_2. Die Temperatur der Quelle wurde variiert zwischen dem Siedepunkt des O_2 und dem des Wassers.

Mit Hilfe des zweiten Zweiges der elektronischen Nachweisapparatur (vgl. Fig. 5) wurde parallel zum eigentlichen Experiment täglich das gesamte Zerfallspektrum des Osmium-Isotopengemisches aufgenommen. Die hierbei gemessenen Spektren dienten zur Ermittlung des (zeitabhängigen) Beitrags des der Resonanzlinie überlagerten Compton-Kontinuums der harten Komponenten von Re^{185} zu der Zählhäufigkeit im Kanal des Einkanaldiskriminators. In der Versuchsgeometrie der Fig. 2 wurde das Spektrum von Os^{185} (95 d) durch Messungen mit einem Osmiumpräparat bestimmt, dessen 16d-Os^{191}-Aktivität bereits abgeklungen war. Subtraktion des auf den zeitlichen Aktivitätsabfall korrigierten Zerfallspektrums von Os^{185} vom Gesamtspektrum Os^{185} + Os^{191} lieferte dann das Zerfallspektrum von Os^{191}. Aus diesen Daten ergab sich unmittelbar das für die Auswertung der Messungen benötigte zeitabhängige Verhältnis v der Intensität der 129 keV-Resonanzlinie zur gesamten im ausgeblendeten Bereich des Spektrums gemessenen Intensität. Fig. 7 zeigt ein Beispiel.

6. Auswertung der Messungen

Im folgenden bezeichnet der Index 0 die 129 keV-Resonanzstrahlung, der Index $i = 1, 2, \ldots n$ die nicht-resonanten Strahlungskomponenten, die der Resonanzstrahlung im ausblendenden Kanal überlagert sind. σ_i^{Pt} und σ_i^{Ir} sind die Wirkungsquerschnitte (Einheit cm^2) für die Absorption der i-ten Strahlungskomponente in Platin (Pt) bzw. Iridium (Ir). n ist die Zahl der Atome pro cm^2 Absorberoberfläche und T ist die Temperatur der *Quelle*. Für die hinter den Absorbern gemessenen Strahlungsintensitäten gilt

$$I_t^{Ir}(T_1) = \sum_{i=0}^{n} I_i^{Ir}(T_1) = \sum_{i=0}^{n} I_i(T_1) \exp\left[- n^{Ir} \sigma_i^{Ir}(T_1)\right], \tag{21a}$$

$$I_t^{Pt}(T_1) = \sum_{i=0}^{n} I_i^{Pt}(T_1) = \sum_{i=0}^{n} I_i(T_1) \exp\left[- n^{Pt} \sigma_i^{Pt}(T_1)\right], \tag{21b}$$

$$I_t^{Ir}(T_2) = \sum_{i=0}^{n} I_i^{Ir}(T_2) = \sum_{i=0}^{n} I_i(T_2) \exp\left[- n^{Ir} \sigma_i^{Ir}(T_2)\right], \tag{21c}$$

$$I_t^{Pt}(T_2) = \sum_{i=0}^{n} I_i^{Pt}(T_2) = \sum_{i=0}^{n} I_i(T_2) \exp\left[- n^{Pt} \sigma_i^{Pt}(T_2)\right]. \tag{21d}$$

Da nur die Temperatur der Quelle variiert wird, sind n^{Ir} und n^{Pt} konstant und es gelten die Beziehungen

$$\sigma_i^{\mathrm{Pt}}(T_2) = \sigma_i^{\mathrm{Pt}}(T_1) = \sigma_i^{\mathrm{Pt}} \qquad i = 0, 1, 2, \ldots, n, \tag{22a}$$

$$\sigma_i^{\mathrm{Ir}}(T_2) = \sigma_i^{\mathrm{Ir}}(T_1) = \sigma_i^{\mathrm{Ir}} \qquad i = \ 1, 2, \ldots, n, \tag{22b}$$

$$|\sigma_0^{\mathrm{Ir}}(T_2) - \sigma_0^{\mathrm{Ir}}(T_1)| = |\bar{\sigma}_{ra}^{\mathrm{Ir}}(T_2) - \bar{\sigma}_{ra}^{\mathrm{Ir}}(T_1)| \ll 1/n^{\mathrm{Ir}}. \tag{22c}$$

Weiter werden eingeführt die relativen Intensitätsänderungen $\alpha_i > 0$, die sich beim Temperaturübergang $T_1 \to T_2 (T_2 > T_1)$ der Quelle infolge Änderung der Selbstabsorption in der Quelle ergeben:

$$I_i(T_2) = (1 + \alpha_i)\, I_i(T_1) \qquad i = 0, 1, 2, \ldots, n. \tag{23}$$

Die Absorber absorbieren nahezu gleich stark (vgl. Abschnitt 5) und alle Temperatureffekte verursachen nur kleine Intensitätsänderungen, d.h. es gilt

$$|I_i^{\mathrm{Pt}}(T) - I_i^{\mathrm{Ir}}(T)| \ll I_i(T) \qquad i = 0, 1, 2, \ldots, n, \tag{24a}$$

$$\alpha_i \ll 1 \qquad i = 0, 1, 2, \ldots, n. \tag{24b}$$

Führt man als experimentell bestimmbare Größe die Differenz ein:

$$M = \frac{I_t^{\mathrm{Pt}}(T_2) - I_t^{\mathrm{Ir}}(T_2)}{I_t^{\mathrm{Ir}}(T_2)} - \frac{I_t^{\mathrm{Pt}}(T_1) - I_t^{\mathrm{Ir}}(T_1)}{I_t^{\mathrm{Ir}}(T_1)}, \tag{25}$$

so erhält man aus (21) bis (23)

$$M \approx \Big\{ \sum_{i=0}^{n} \alpha_i I_i(T_1) [\exp(-n^{\mathrm{Pt}} \sigma_i^{\mathrm{Pt}}) - \exp(-n^{\mathrm{Ir}} \sigma_i^{\mathrm{Ir}}(T_2))] - \\ - I_0(T_1) [\exp(-n^{\mathrm{Ir}} \sigma_0^{\mathrm{Ir}}(T_2)) - \exp(-n^{\mathrm{Ir}} \sigma_0^{\mathrm{Ir}}(T_1))] \Big\} \Big/ I_t^{\mathrm{Ir}}(T_1).$$

Der erste Term wird nach (24) klein von höherer Ordnung und es folgt

$$\left. \begin{aligned} M &\approx I_0(T_1) \exp(-n^{\mathrm{Ir}} \sigma_0^{\mathrm{Ir}}(T_1)) \times \\ &\times [1 - \exp(n^{\mathrm{Ir}} \sigma_0^{\mathrm{Ir}}(T_1) - n^{\mathrm{Ir}} \sigma_0^{\mathrm{Ir}}(T_2))] / I_t^{\mathrm{Ir}}(T_1). \end{aligned} \right\} \tag{26}$$

Bezeichnet man mit v den zeitabhängigen Bruchteil, der von der gesamten im Bereich des Kanals des Einkanaldiskriminators gemessenen Intensität auf die Intensität der Resonanzlinie entfällt (vgl. Abschnitt 5)

$$v = I_0(T_1) \exp[-n^{\mathrm{Ir}} \sigma_0^{\mathrm{Ir}}(T_1)] / I_t^{\mathrm{Ir}}(T_1), \tag{27}$$

so folgt aus (26) und (22c):

$$M \approx v\, n^{\mathrm{Ir}} [\bar{\sigma}_{ra}(T_2) - \bar{\sigma}_{ra}(T_1)]. \tag{28}$$

Bei den Messungen zur Bestimmung der Lebenszeit wurden die Absorber nicht gekühlt. Dann kann der zweite Term in (19) vernachlässigt werden und der Wirkungsquerschnitt $\bar{\sigma}_{ra}$ für die Resonanzabsorption wird umgekehrt proportional zur Lebenszeit τ_γ des Niveaus. Nach (1), (11), (15), (19), (20) gilt in diesem Fall:

$$\left.\begin{aligned}\bar{\sigma}_{ra} = \frac{2I_a+1}{2I_g+1}\,\frac{\hbar^2 c^3}{4E_0^3}\,H\,\frac{\hbar}{\tau_\gamma}\sqrt{\frac{m}{2k\pi(T_q^*+T_a^*)}}\,\times \\ \times \exp\left[-E_0^2/2mc^2k(T_q^*+T_a^*)\right].\end{aligned}\right\} \quad (29)$$

Bei der Auswertung wurden folgende numerische Daten verwendet:

Spin des Grundzustandes von Ir^{191}:	$I_g = \frac{3}{2}$	[11]
Spin des 129 keV Niveaus von Ir^{191}:	$I_a = \frac{5}{2}$	[7]
Relative Häufigkeit des Isotops Ir^{191}:	$H = 38{,}5\,\%$	
Debye-Temperatur von Iridium:	$\Theta = 285°$ K	[12]

Für die Temperaturen T_a^* und T_q^* von Absorber und Quelle folgt aus (7):

Zimmertemperatur (303° K):	$T^* = 316°$ K
Flüssige Luft (gemessener Mittelwert 88° K):	$T^* = 129°$ K
Zahl der Iridium-Atome pro cm²:	$n^{Ir} = 2{,}78 \cdot 10^{21}\ cm^{-2}$

7. Meßergebnisse

Tabelle 1 enthält die Ergebnisse der Messungen zur Bestimmung der Lebenszeit des 129 keV-Niveaus in Ir^{191}. (Temperaturen der Quelle

Tabelle 1

1	2	3	4	5
Nr.	$(I_t^{Pt}-I_t^{Ir})/I_t^{Ir}$ $T=T_2=303°$ K	$(I_t^{Pt}-I_t^{Ir})/I_t^{Ir}$ $T=T_1=88°$ K	$M \cdot 10^3$	$(M/v) \cdot 10^3$
1	1,346 ± 0,31	1,074 ± 0,24	0,272 ± 0,39	0,341 ± 0,49
2	4,585 ± 0,19	4,359 ± 0,21	0,226 ± 0,28	0,285 ± 0,35
3	0,580 ± 0,25	0,127 ± 0,23	0,453 ± 0,34	0,574 ± 0,43
4	0,653 ± 0,16	0,297 ± 0,28	0,356 ± 0,33	0,453 ± 0,42
5	0,767 ± 0,17	0,579 ± 0,19	0,188 ± 0,26	0,240 ± 0,33
6	0,649 ± 0,23	0,504 ± 0,17	0,145 ± 0,29	0,186 ± 0,37
7	0,249 ± 0,21	0,166 ± 0,16	0,083 ± 0,26	0,108 ± 0,34
8	0,386 ± 0,24	0,001 ± 0,25	0,385 ± 0,35	0,504 ± 0,46
9	0,397 ± 0,24	0,038 ± 0,20	0,359 ± 0,31	0,474 ± 0,41
10	0,404 ± 0,23	0,037 ± 0,25	0,367 ± 0,34	0,488 ± 0,45
11	0,241 ± 0,40	0,052 ± 0,26	0,189 ± 0,48	0,254 ± 0,64
12	0,102 ± 0,14	0,326 ± 0,17	− 0,224 ± 0,22	− 0,303 ± 0,30
13	0,786 ± 0,15	0,266 ± 0,26	0,520 ± 0,30	0,711 ± 0,41
14	0,960 ± 0,29	0,542 ± 0,17	0,418 ± 0,34	0,578 ± 0,47
15	− 1,797 ± 0,25	− 1,775 ± 0,20	− 0,022 ± 0,32	− 0,031 ± 0,45
16	− 2,274 ± 0,19	− 2,379 ± 0,28	0,105 ± 0,34	0,149 ± 0,48
Ausgeglichener Mittelwert $(\overline{M/v}) \cdot 10^3$				0,268 ± 0,07

$T_1 = 88°$ K; $T_2 = 303°$ K.) Spalte 1 der Tabelle gibt die Nummer der Versuchsserie: Jede Serie bestand aus mindestens je 10 Messungen jeder der vier Intensitäten $I_t^{\mathrm{Ir}}(T_1)$, $I_t^{\mathrm{Pt}}(T_1)$, $I_t^{\mathrm{Ir}}(T_2)$, $I_t^{\mathrm{Pt}}(T_2)$. Bei der *einzelnen* Intensitätsmessung betrug der statistische Fehler 0,04 bis 0,05 % und die Meßzeit 12 bis 20 min. Täglich wurde eine Meßreihe aufgenommen. Um systematische Fehler auszuschließen, wurde die Geometrie bei jeder Meßreihe etwas variiert, durch Drehung der Absorber

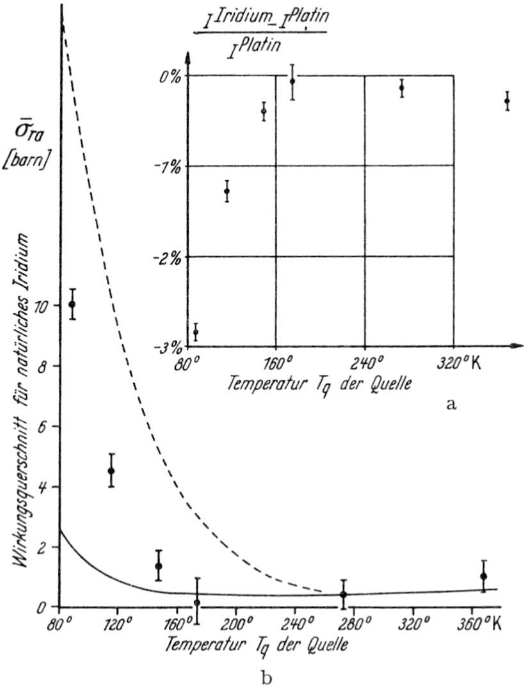

Fig. 8a. Relatives Intensitätsverhältnis $(I^{\mathrm{Ir}} - I^{\mathrm{Pt}})/I^{\mathrm{Pt}}$ der hinter Iridium- bzw. Platinabsorbern gemessenen 129 keV-Gammastrahlung als Funktion der Temperatur der Quelle. Die Temperatur der Absorber betrug konstant 88° K

Fig. 8b. Der Wirkungsquerschnitt $\bar{\sigma}_{ra}$ für die Kernresonanzabsorption in Ir^{191} als Funktion der Temperatur der Quelle, für eine Absorbertemperatur von 88° K. Ī Meßpunkte; ——— theoretischer Verlauf für ein quadratisch mit der Frequenz ν ansteigendes Schwingungsspektrum (Debye-Spektrum); ------ theoretischer Verlauf für eine mit ν^3 proportionale Frequenzverteilung, die bei der gleichen Grenzfrequenz abgeschnitten wurde, d.h. die gleiche Debye-Temperatur besitzt. Die Debye-Temperaturen der transversalen und der longitudinalen Komponenten wurden gleichgesetzt

um ihre Symmetrieachsen, sowie durch kleine Ortsveränderungen von Quelle und Absorbern. Der Einfluß dieser Geometrieänderungen zeigt sich in den Unterschieden der Intensitätsdifferenzen der Spalten 2 bzw. 3 der Tabelle 1. Spalte 4 enthält die Differenz der Meßwerte der Spalten 2 und 3 [vgl. Gl. (25)]. Da die Geometrie bei der einzelnen Meßreihe konstant gehalten wurde, sollten (in guter Näherung) die Werte M der Spalte 4 nicht von der Geometrie abhängen und ein Vergleich etwa der Spalten 2 und 4 läßt auch keinen Einfluß der Geometrie auf M

erkennen. Spalte 5 enthält die auf den Beitrag anderer Linien korrigierten Meßwerte (M/v) [vgl. Gl. (27)]. Die relativen Schwankungen nichtstatistischer Natur der Zählrate betrugen etwa 0,1% über mehrere Stunden. Darüber hinaus zeigte die Zählrate im Verlauf einiger Tage langsame elektronisch bedingte Änderungen von einigen Promille, die natürlich keinen Einfluß auf die Messung hatten. Die angegebenen *mittleren* Fehler wurden aus den Schwankungen der Einzelmessungen ermittelt. Der Fehler jeder Meßreihe setzt sich zusammen aus den Fehlern von vier Intensitätsmessungen [vgl. (25)]. Mit dem Mittelwert $\overline{M/v}$ der Tabelle 1 folgt nach (28):

$$\tau_\gamma = (3{,}6^{+1{,}3}_{-0{,}8}) \cdot 10^{-10}\,\text{sec.}$$

Mit dem Konversionskoeffizienten $\alpha = 2{,}47$ [*13*] ergibt sich die mittlere Lebenszeit τ des Niveaus zu $\tau = \tau_\gamma/(1+\alpha) = (1{,}0^{+0{,}4}_{-0{,}2}) \cdot 10^{-10}$ sec.

Fig. 8 enthält die Ergebnisse der Messungen, bei denen die Absorber gekühlt wurden. In Fig. 8a wurden die Differenzen der hinter dem Resonanzabsorber und dem Vergleichsabsorber gemessenen Intensitäten I aufgetragen, in Fig. 8b der daraus mit Hilfe von (28) berechnete Wirkungsquerschnitt $\bar{\sigma}_{ra}(T_q) = \bar{\sigma}_{ra}(T_1)$. (Bezugstemperatur $T_2 = 0°$ C; Lebenszeit $\tau_\gamma = 3{,}6 \cdot 10^{-10}$ sec; Konversionskoeffizient $\alpha = 2{,}47$ [*13*].) Fig. 8b enthält neben den Meßpunkten den theoretischen Verlauf des Wirkungsquerschnittes nach (19) für zwei verschiedene Frequenzverteilungen des Schwingungsspektrums von Iridium.

8. Diskussion

Die gemessene Lebenszeit ist in Einklang mit der von Sunyar [*14*] angegebenen oberen Schranke von $5 \cdot 10^{-10}$ sec für die Halbwertzeit des Niveaus. Messungen der Konversionskoeffizienten ergaben für die Multipolordnung des 129 keV-Überganges $M1 + E2$ [*15*]. Die Werte für das aus den Konversionskoeffizienten der K- und L-Schalen bestimmte Intensitätsverhältnis $M1/E2$ liegen im Bereich 1,5:1 bis 5:1 [*16*], [*17*], [*18*]. Das hier gefundene τ_γ ergibt mit diesen Daten für die Übergangswahrscheinlichkeit des 129 keV-Überganges einen Verzögerungsfaktor von mindestens 22 gegenüber den theoretischen Vorhersagen des Einteilchenmodelles [*19*] für einen $M1$-Übergang. Der $E2$-Übergang erfolgt dagegen um mindestens einen Faktor 64 schneller als nach dem Einteilchenmodell zu erwarten wäre. Der 129 keV-Zustand ist daher als Mehrteilchenzustand aufzufassen. Das Niveau ist jedoch vermutlich kein reines Rotationsniveau im Sinne des Kollektivmodelles, denn das Verhältnis der Energien des 1. und 2. „Rotationsniveaus" weicht nach [*13*] um rund 10% von dem durch das Kollektivmodell für reine Rotationszustände geforderten Wert ab. Tabelle 2 enthält die durch Messungen der Coulomb-Anregung bestimmten reduzierten Übergangswahrscheinlichkeiten $B(E2)$ für die $E2$-Komponente des 129 keV-Überganges in Ir^{191}, sowie die daraus berechneten Lebenszeiten $\tau_\gamma(E2)$* und Mischungsverhältnisse $M1/E2$.

Die Mischungsverhältnisse der Tabelle 2 deuten auf eine stärkere Bevorzugung der $M1$-Komponente hin, als aus den Verhältnissen der Konversionskoeffizienten folgen würde [*16*], [*17*], [*18*], doch sind die $B(E2)$-Werte für genaue Aussagen noch zu unsicher.

Tabelle 2

Literatur	$B(E2)$ ** $e^2\,cm^4\,10^{+50}$	$\tau_\gamma(E2)$ ($E = 129$ keV)	$M1/E2$ für $\tau_\gamma = 3{,}6 \cdot 10^{-10}$ sec
[*13*]	51	$6{,}1 \cdot 10^{-9}$ sec	16:1
[*20*]	56	$5{,}6 \cdot 10^{-9}$ sec	15:1
[*16*]	97	$3{,}2 \cdot 10^{-9}$ sec	8:1

Die Übereinstimmung der Messungen an der 129 keV-Gammalinie in Ir^{191} bei Temperaturen $T < 200°$ K mit dem in Debyescher Näherung berechneten Verlauf des Absorptionsquerschnittes ist nur qualitativ. Die Debyesche Theorie führt in der hier verwendeten Form, bei der die Debye-Temperaturen der longitudinalen und der transversalen Komponenten gleichgesetzt werden, zu einer Unterdrückung der höheren longitudinalen Komponenten. Eine Berücksichtigung der atomistischen Struktur führt jedoch umgekehrt bei Schwingungen mit Wellenlängen von der Größenordnung der Gitterkonstanten wegen der gegenüber dem Kontinuum größeren Trägheit des Gitters zu einer Verschiebung des Spektrums zu kleineren Frequenzen. Die Messungen deuten auf eine größere Dichte der Frequenzverteilung des Schwingungsspektrums von Iridium bei den höheren Frequenzen hin, als sie die Debyesche Kontinuumstheorie liefert.

Untersuchungen des Verhaltens der spezifischen Wärmen ergaben bei den meisten Metallen bei tieferen Temperaturen einen Anstieg der Debyeschen Temperatur Θ [*21*]. Tatsächlich lassen sich die in Fig. 8 dargestellten Abweichungen der Meßergebnisse von dem nach der Debyeschen Theorie zu erwartenden Verlauf des Wirkungsquerschnittes ebenfalls durch die Annahme eines Anstiegs von Θ mit abnehmender Temperatur erklären. Zur genaueren Untersuchung sollen die Messungen zu tieferen Temperaturen hin ausgedehnt werden.

---

* Es gilt die Relation (vgl. [*13*]): $1/\tau_\gamma(E2) = \left(\frac{4\pi}{75}\right)\frac{1}{\hbar}\left(\frac{E_0}{\hbar c}\right)^5 \frac{2I_i+1}{2I_f+1} \cdot B(E2)$, wobei I_f, I_i = Spin des angeregten und des Grundzustandes, E_0 = Anregungsenergie.

** Die $B(E2)$-Werte sind nach Angabe der Autoren um einen Faktor 2 unsicher.

Die Bestimmung der Lebenszeiten von Kernniveaus mittels Absorptionsmessungen der hier beschriebenen Art sind infolge der außerordentlich kleinen Effekte nur in Ausnahmefällen durchführbar. Dagegen treten bei Untersuchungen der Bindungseigenschaften von Festkörpern bei tiefen Temperaturen um Größenordnungen stärkere Effekte auf. Analoge Bindungseffekte wie bei Ir^{191} sind im ganzen Energiebereich weicher Gammastrahlung zu erwarten. Wegen der starken Abhängigkeit der Absorptionsquerschnitte von den Schwingungsspektren eignet sich die Methode der Resonanzfluoreszenz von Gammastrahlung bei tiefen Temperaturen zu Untersuchungen der Frequenzverteilung der Schwingungsspektren fester Körper. Die Methode kann daneben auch bei der Aufstellung von Zerfallschemas verwendet werden, da die starke Resonanzabsorption bei tiefen Temperaturen nur bei solchen Linien auftritt, die einem Übergang in den Grundzustand entsprechen. Die Untersuchungen werden fortgesetzt.

Es ist mir ein Anliegen, Herrn Professor H. MAIER-LEIBNITZ für die Anregung zu dieser Arbeit, für interessante Diskussionen und freundliche Förderung herzlich zu danken. Herrn Professor J. H. D. JENSEN danke ich für aufschlußreiche Diskussionen. Herrn Professor W. BOTHE (†) und Herrn Professor K. H. LAUTERJUNG danke ich dafür, daß sie die Durchführung dieser Arbeit am Max-Planck-Institut für medizinische Forschung in Heidelberg ermöglicht haben.

Literatur

[1] MALMFORS, K. G.: Ark. Fysik **6**, 49 (1953). — [2] MALMFORS, K. G. in: K. SIEGBAHN, Beta- and Gammaray Spectroscopy. Amsterdam 1955. — [3] METZGER, F. R.: Report at the Glasgow Conference 1954, S. 201. — J. Franklin Inst. **261**, 219 (1956). — Phys. Rev. **101**, 286 (1956); **103**, 983 (1956). — SCHOPPER, H.: Z. Physik **144**, 476 (1956). — SWANN, C. P., and F. R. METZGER: J. Franklin Inst. **261**, 667 (1956). — [4] FRANZ, W.: Z. Physik **98**, 314 (1936). — [5] LAMB jr., W. E.: Phys. Rev. **55**, 190 (1939). Siehe auch STEINWEDEL, H., u. J. H. JENSEN: Z. Naturforsch. **2a**, 125 (1947). — [6] JACKSON, J. D.: Canad. J. Phys. **33**, 575 (1955). — [7] MIHELICH, I. W., M. MCKEOWN and M. GOLDHABER: Phys. Rev. **96**, 1450 (1954). — [8] MARTY, N., et M. VERGNES: J. Phys. Radium **18**, 233 (1957). — [9] FOOTE, R. S., and H. W. KOCH: Rev. Sci. Instrum. **25**, 750 (1954). — [10] JOHNSTONE, C. W.: Nucleonics **11**, No, 1, 36 (Jan. 1953). — [11] MURAKAWA, K., and S. SUWA: Phys. Rev. **87**, 1048 (1952). — [12] SEITZ, F.: The Modern Theory of Solids, S. 110. 1940. — [13] DAVIS, R. H., A. S. DIVATIA, D. A. LIND and R. D. MOFFAT: Phys. Rev. **103**, 1801 (1956). — [14] SUNYAR, A. W.: Phys. Rev. **98**, 653 (1955). — [15] SWAN, I. B., and R. D. HILL: Phys. Rev. **88**, 831 (1952). — [16] BERNSTEIN, E. M., and H. W. LEWIS: Phys. Rev. **105**, 1524 (1957).— [17] MIHELICH, I. W., and A. DE-SHALIT: Phys. Rev. **93**, 135 (1954). — [18] MCGOWAN, F. K.: Phys. Rev. **93**, 163 (1954). — [19] BLATT, I. M., and V. F. WEISSKOPF: Theoretical Nuclear Physics. New York 1952. — [20] HUUS, T., I. H. BJERREGAARD and B. ELBECK: Dan. Mat. Fys. Medd. **30**, Nr. 17 (1956). — [21] LEIBFRIED, G., u. W. BRENIG: Fortschr. Phys. **1**, 187 (1953).

KERNRESONANZFLUORESZENZ VON GAMMASTRAHLUNG IN Ir^{191} †
(Nuclear Resonance Fluorescence of Gamma Radiation in Ir^{191})

3. THEORY

According to Lamb[5]‡ the cross section for resonance absorption is

$$\sigma(E) = (\Gamma^2/4)\,\sigma_0 W_a(E) \tag{2}$$

where Γ = total width of the resonance level, E = energy of the incident photons, and σ_0 = cross section at resonance.

The position and shape of the absorption line is given by $W_a(E)$:

$$W_a(E) = (2/\Gamma)\,\text{Real}\int_0^\infty d\mu\,\exp\left[i\mu(E - E_0 + i\Gamma/2) + g_a(\mu)\right] \tag{3a}$$

where

$$g_a(\mu) = \sum_s \frac{(\mathbf{p}\cdot\mathbf{e}_s)^2}{2m\hbar\omega_s N}$$

$$\times\left[(\bar{\alpha}_s + 1)\exp(-i\mu\hbar\omega_s) + \bar{\alpha}_s\exp(i\mu\hbar\omega_s) - 1 - 2\bar{\alpha}_s\right] \tag{4a}$$

In these equations E_0 is the resonance energy, ω_s the frequency of the s-th normal mode of the crystal, m the nuclear mass, **p** the momentum of the photon, **e** the unit polarization vector, 3N the number of degrees of freedom of the crystal, and $\bar{\alpha}_s$ the average occupation number of the s-th oscillator,

$$\bar{\alpha}_s = 1/[\exp(\hbar\omega_s/kT) - 1] \tag{5}$$

As can easily be shown,§

† Translation of Sec. 3 of the article from Z. Physik, **151**, 124 (1958) which is reproduced in its entirety preceding this translation.

‡ For references see the German original.

§ The proof may be briefly indicated: For the emission line, Eq. (8) of Lamb[5] must be replaced by

$$W(\{\alpha_s\};\{n_s\}) = \left|\frac{(\alpha_s|H'|n_s)}{E_0 - E + E(n_s) - E(\alpha_s) + i\Gamma/2}\right|^2$$

one obtains for the emission line†

$$W_e(E) = (2/\Gamma)\,\mathrm{Real} \int_0^\infty d\mu\, \exp[i\mu(E - E_0 + i\Gamma/2) + g_e(\mu)] \qquad (3b)$$

where

$$g_e(\mu) = \sum_s \frac{(\mathbf{p}\cdot\mathbf{e}_s)^2}{2m\hbar\omega_s N}$$

$$\times [(\bar{\alpha}_s + 1)\exp(i\mu\hbar\omega_s) + \bar{\alpha}_s \exp(-i\mu\hbar\omega_s) - 1 - 2\bar{\alpha}_s] \qquad (4b)$$

The integral in (3) will be evaluated in the Debye approximation with the Debye temperatures of the transverse and longitudinal modes set equal to each other.‡

(a) For $\mu k\Theta \ll 1$ one obtains

$$g_a(\mu) \approx -i\mu R - \mu^2 R\varepsilon$$

$$g_e(\mu) \approx +i\mu R - \mu^2 R\varepsilon \qquad (6a)$$

Here R is the recoil energy as given by (1) (see the German original, p. 126), and ε is the average energy per vibrational degree of freedom of the crystal:

$$\varepsilon(T) = kT^* = 3kT(T/\Theta)^3 \int_0^{\Theta/T} \left(\frac{1}{e^t - 1} + \frac{1}{2}\right) t^3\, dt \qquad (7)$$

(b) For $\mu k\Theta \gg 1$ one has

---

where $(\alpha_s|H'|n_s)$ is the matrix element for a lattice transition $n_s \to \alpha_s$ accompanied by the emission of a photon of momentum **p**. In Eq. (17) of Ref. 5, α_s must be replaced by n_s. Extending all the following sums over α_s instead of n_s and averaging over n_s instead of α_s, one obtains (3b) and (4b), provided $\bar{\alpha}_s$ is substituted for $\bar{n}_s$ in the final relation.

†The emission and absorption lines $W_e(E)$ and $W_a(E)$ are mirror images of each other with respect to $E = E_0$.

‡The summations in (4) also extend over the polarization directions.

$$g_e(\infty; T) = g_a(\infty; T) = g_\infty(T) = -2 \sum_s \frac{(\mathbf{p}\cdot\mathbf{e}_s)^2}{2m\hbar\omega_s N} [\bar{\alpha}_s + (1/2)]$$

$$= -2R \int_0^{k\Theta} \frac{1}{N\hbar\omega} \left(\frac{1}{e^{\hbar\omega/kT} - 1} + \frac{1}{2} \right) \frac{3N(\hbar\omega)^2}{(k\Theta)^3} \, d(\hbar\omega)$$

$$= -(6R/k\Theta)(T/\Theta)^2 \int_0^{\Theta/T} \left(\frac{1}{e^t - 1} + \frac{1}{2} \right) t \, dt \qquad (8)\dagger$$

To get the experimentally determined average cross section $\bar{\sigma}_r(T_q;T_a)$, where T_q and T_a are the source and absorber temperatures, respectively, $\sigma(E)$ in (2) is multiplied by the normalized distribution function $W_e(E)$ of the emitted (incident) photons, and the product integrated over energy. That is,

$$\bar{\sigma}_r = \int_0^\infty \sigma(E)(\Gamma/2\pi) W_e(E) \, dE$$

and, using (2),

$$\bar{\sigma}_r = (\Gamma^3/8\pi)\sigma_0 \int_0^\infty W_a(E) W_e(E) \, dE \qquad (9)$$

where

$$(\Gamma/2\pi) \int_0^\infty W_e(E) \, dE = 1$$

If the transition to the ground state can also take place by internal conversion, one must differentiate between the cross section $(\sigma_0)_s$ for resonance scattering and the cross section $(\sigma_0)_a$ for resonance absorption. For resonance scattering, according to Jackson,[6]

$$(\sigma_0)_s = \frac{2I_a + 1}{2I_g + 1} \frac{\lambda_0^2}{2\pi} H \frac{\Gamma_\gamma^2}{\Gamma^2} = \frac{2I_a + 1}{2I_g + 1} \frac{\lambda_0^2}{2\pi} H \frac{1}{(1 + \alpha)^2} \qquad (10)$$

Here $2I + 1$ are the statistical weights of the excited state a and the ground state g, H the relative abundance of the resonantly absorbing isotope, λ_0 the resonance wavelength, Γ the total energy width of the resonance level, Γ_γ the partial energy width for radiative transition, and α the conversion coefficient.

In the case of resonance fluorescence, only the fraction Γ_γ/Γ of

---

†Our Eq. (8) differs from Eq. (36) of Lamb[5] by a factor of 3.

all intermediate states proceeds to the ground state by photon emission, the fraction $(\Gamma - \Gamma_\gamma)/\Gamma$ proceeding through conversion. In the case of resonance absorption, all intermediate states contribute to the cross section, and we have

$$(\sigma_0)_a = \frac{\Gamma}{\Gamma_\gamma}(\sigma_0)_s = \frac{2I_a + 1}{2I_g + 1}\,\frac{\lambda_0^2}{2\pi}\,H\,\frac{\Gamma_\gamma}{\Gamma} \tag{11}$$

For resonance fluorescence in Ir^{191} ($E_0 = 129$ kev), the line shape down to liquid-oxygen temperature can be calculated using two different approximations.

1. In the region $|E - E_0| \gg \Gamma$, only values of $\mu k\Theta < 1$ yield a substantial contribution to the integral in (3), and (6) is still a useful approximation:

$$W_I(E) = (2/\Gamma)\int_0^\infty d\mu\,\cos(E - E_0 \pm R)\,\mu\,\exp(-\mu\Gamma/2 - \mu^2 R\varepsilon)$$

$$= (4/\Gamma^2)\,\psi(\xi;x) \tag{12}$$

Here, for the emission line

$$\psi(\xi_e;x_e) = (1/2)\sqrt{\pi}\,\xi_e\,\exp(-\xi_e^2 x_e^2/4) \tag{13a}$$

while for the absorption line

$$\psi(\xi_a;x_a) = (1/2)\sqrt{\pi}\,\xi_a\,\exp(-\xi_a^2 x_a^2/4)\dagger \tag{13b}$$

In the above equations

$$x_e = (E - E_0 + R)/(1/2)\Gamma \qquad x_a = (E - E_0 - R)/(1/2)\Gamma \tag{14}$$

$$\Delta_e = 2\sqrt{RkT_q^*} \qquad \Delta_a = 2\sqrt{RkT_a^*} \tag{15}$$

$$\xi_e = \Gamma/\Delta_e \qquad \xi_a = \Gamma/\Delta_a \tag{16}$$

The quantity Δ is the Doppler width of the level; T_a^* and T_q^* denote, respectively, the effective absorber and source temperatures, which, according to (7), correspond to the average energy per vibrational degree of freedom.

2. In the region near $E = E_0$, a good approximation for W(E) is obtained by splitting the integral in (3) at $\mu k\Theta = 1$ and using approximations (6) and (8) in the regions of their validity. Thus

---

†See Lamb,[5] Eq. (32).

$$W_{II}(E) = (2/\Gamma) \int_0^{1/k\Theta} d\mu \cos(E - E_0 \pm R)\, \mu \exp(-\mu\Gamma/2 - \mu^2 R\varepsilon)$$

$$+ (2/\Gamma) \int_{1/k\Theta}^{\infty} d\mu \cos(E - E_0)\, \mu \exp[g_\infty(T) - \mu\Gamma/2]$$

The first integral makes only a small contribution to $W_{II}(E)$, so that for $(\Gamma/k\Theta) \ll 1$ one obtains as a good approximation,

$$W_{II}(E) = W_I(E) + \frac{\exp[g_\infty(T)]}{(E - E_0)^2 + \Gamma^2/4} \tag{17}$$

In the region $|E - E_0| \gg \Gamma$ the second term in (17) is negligible compared to $W_I(E)$. Combining (12) and (17), the energy distributions of the emission and absorption lines become

$$W_e(E) = (4/\Gamma^2)\, \psi(\xi_e; x_e) + \frac{\exp[g_\infty(T_q)]}{(E - E_0)^2 + \Gamma^2/4} \tag{18a}$$

and

$$W_a(E) = (4/\Gamma^2)\, \psi(\xi_a; x_a) + \frac{\exp[g_\infty(T_a)]}{(E - E_0)^2 + \Gamma^2/4} \tag{18b}$$

According to (18),† the crystal binding modifies the emission and absorption lines of the 129-kev transition in Ir^{191} in the following way: Except for the region near resonance, at a temperature T, the lines have almost the same shape and positions as they would have in an ideal gas at a temperature T^*. As shown in (7), T^* corresponds to the average energy per vibrational degree of freedom of the crystal. For temperatures $T < \Theta$ an additional line of width Γ, whose intensity increases greatly with decreasing temperature, appears at the resonance energy $E = E_0$ (Fig. 1; see the German original). Thus, the fraction of photons satisfying the resonance condition increases with decreasing temperature.

The cross section $\bar{\sigma}_r$ is obtained by substituting (18) into (9). Only two of the integrals yield an appreciable contribution:

$$\int_0^\infty (4/\Gamma^2)\psi(\xi_e; x_e)(4/\Gamma^2)\psi(\xi_a; x_a)\, dE \qquad \text{and}$$

$$\int_0^\infty \frac{\exp[g_\infty(T_q) + g_\infty(T_a)]}{[(E - E_0)^2 + \Gamma^2/4]^2}\, dE$$

---

† Equations (18) lose their validity at temperatures below liquid oxygen temperature.

The average cross section for resonance absorption obtained by integration of these expressions is

$$\bar{\sigma}_{ra} = \frac{(\sigma_0)_a}{2}\sqrt{\pi}\,\frac{\Gamma}{\sqrt{\Delta_a^2 + \Delta_e^2}}\,\exp\left[\frac{-4R^2}{\Delta_a^2 + \Delta_e^2}\right] + \frac{(\sigma_0)_a}{2}$$

$$\times\ \exp\left[g_\infty(T_q) + g_\infty(T_a)\right] \tag{19}$$

According to the uncertainty relation,

$$\tau = \hbar/\Gamma = \hbar/\Gamma_\gamma(1 + \alpha) = \tau_\gamma/(1 + \alpha) = T_{1/2}/\ln 2 \tag{20}$$

where τ is the mean life and $T_{1/2}$ is the half-life of the resonance level, τ_γ is the partial life for γ decay, and α is the conversion coefficient.

At higher temperatures one can neglect the second term in (19), and from (11), (19), and (20) it follows that $\bar{\sigma}_{ra} \sim 1/\tau_\gamma$. At low temperatures the second term in (19), which is independent of lifetime, dominates.

NUCLEAR RESONANCE ABSORPTION OF GAMMA RAYS IN Ir^{191}†

Under normal conditions, it is difficult to observe the resonance fluorescence of nuclear gamma rays because of the recoil energy lost by the photons during both emission and absorption. In general, these losses are sufficient to appreciably displace the emission and absorption lines, thereby destroying the resonance condition. It is possible to compensate for the recoil energy losses by, for example, moving the source with respect to the absorber with the aid of an ultracentrifuge,[1] or by increasing the thermal motion of the emitting and absorbing atoms.[2] In performing experiments of the latter type, we found that at low temperatures, contrary to what was expected, a pronounced increase in resonance absorption occurred.[3] With the help of a theory developed by Lamb,[4] this effect was attributed to the fact that in solids the recoil momentum does not always produce a change in the vibrational state of the crystal lattice. Instead, for a fraction of the gamma transitions, the solid as a whole can take up the recoil momentum. Thus, according to this theory, the emission and absorption spectra

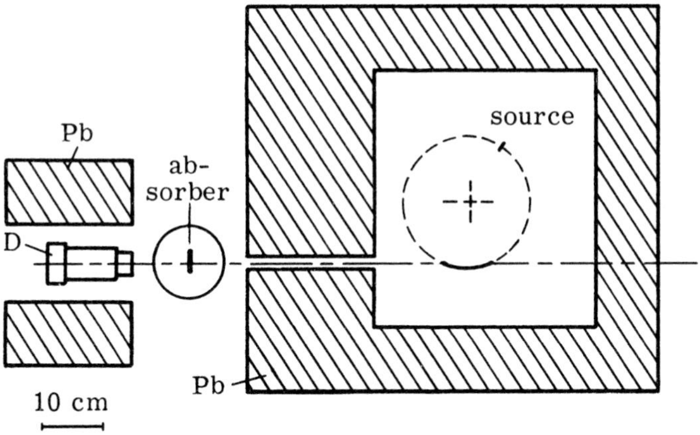

Fig. 1. Experimental arrangement: The detector D accepts only photons emitted by the source while moving on the solid portion of the path shown.

† Translation of article in Naturwissenschaften, **45**, 538 (1958).

contain very strong lines of natural width superimposed upon a broad distribution resulting from the thermal motion of the atoms bound in the crystal lattice. Because of the vanishingly small recoil energy losses, these lines appear undisplaced at the resonance energy position (i.e., at the excitation energy of the nuclear level under investigation).

We have now demonstrated the existence of these unshifted resonance lines by means of a "centrifuge" method, employing velocities of only a few centimeters per second. The experimental arrangement is shown in Fig. 1, while Fig. 2 shows the results obtained for the

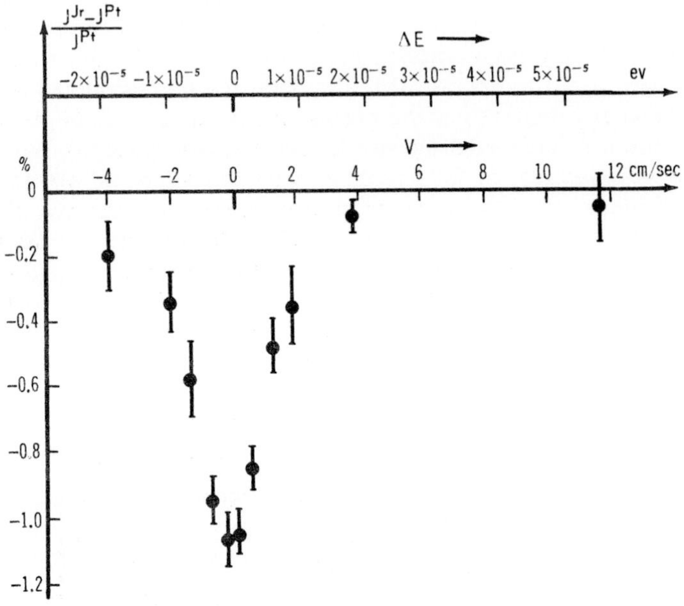

Fig. 2. Difference in intensity of the 129-kev gamma transition in Ir^{191} measured behind a resonance absorber (iridium) and a comparison absorber (platinum). This intensity difference is plotted as a function of v, the relative velocity of the source with respect to the absorber. Both source and absorber are at a temperature of 88°K. $\Delta E = (v/c) E_0$ denotes the energy shift of the 129-kev gamma rays.

129-kev transition in Ir^{191}. Thus, a new method for the direct determination of the level widths of low-lying excited nuclear states has been found. In our case, the line width of the 129-kev level in Ir^{191} agrees, within the limits of error, with the value 6.5×10^{-6} ev determined previously, using a less direct approach.[3] This width corresponds to a lifetime of 1.0×10^{-10} sec.

Laboratorium für Technische Physik der Technischen Hochschule, München, und Max-Planck-Institut für Medizinische Forschung, Heidelberg.

RUDOLF L. MÖSSBAUER

Received August 13, 1958

REFERENCES

1. [a]P. B. Moon, Proc. Phys. Soc. (London), **A64,** 76 (1951). [b]W. G. Davey and P. B. Moon, Proc. Phys. Soc. (London), **A66,** 956 (1953).
2. [a]K. G. Malmfors, Ark. Fysik, **6,** 49 (1952). [b]F. R. Metzger and W. B. Todd, Phys. Rev., **95,** 853 (1954). [c]F. R. Metzger, Phys. Rev., **97,** 1258 (1955); J. Franklin Inst., **261,** 219 (1956). [d]H. Schopper, Z. Physik, **144,** 476 (1956).
3. R. L. Mössbauer, Z. Physik, **151,** 124 (1958).
4. W. E. Lamb, Jr., Phys. Rev., **55,** 190 (1939).

Kernresonanzabsorption von γ-Strahlung in Ir^{191}

Von RUDOLF L. MÖSSBAUER

Aus dem Laboratorium für technische Physik der Technischen Hochschule in München
und dem Institut für Physik im Max-Planck-Institut für medizinische Forschung in Heidelberg

(Z. Naturforschg. **14 a**, 211—216 [1959]; eingegangen am 5. November 1958)

Bei der Emission und Selbstabsorption von weicher γ-Strahlung in Kernen treten bei tiefen Temperaturen in Festkörpern sehr starke Linien mit der natürlichen Linienbreite auf. Diese Linien erscheinen als Folge davon, daß bei tiefen Temperaturen bei einem Teil der Quantenübergänge der γ-Rückstoßimpuls nicht mehr vom einzelnen Kern aufgenommen wird, sondern von dem Kristall als Ganzes. Da die scharfen Emissions- und Absorptionslinien energetisch an der gleichen Stelle liegen, tritt ein sehr starker Resonanzfluoreszenzeffekt auf. Durch eine „Zentrifugen"-Methode, bei der die Emissions- und Absorptionslinien gegeneinander verschoben werden, läßt sich der Fluoreszenzeffekt unterdrücken und so eine unmittelbare Bestimmung der natürlichen Linienbreite von Resonanzlinien vornehmen. Erste Messungen nach dieser Methode ergeben für die Lebenszeit τ des 129 keV-Niveaus in Ir^{191}: $\tau=\left(1{,}4\ {}^{+0{,}2}_{-0{,}1}\right)\cdot 10^{-10}$ sec.

Die Methode, Kernniveaus durch Einstrahlung der eigenen γ-Linie[1] zur Fluoreszenz anzuregen, wird in zunehmender Weise zur Bestimmung der Lebenszeiten τ kurzlebiger Kernzustände ($\tau < 10^{-10}$ sec) verwendet.

Die Kernresonanzfluoreszenz von γ-Strahlung ist unter normalen Bedingungen nur schwer zu beobachten, weil die γ-Quanten bei ihrer Emission und

[1] In besonderen Fällen ist eine Fluoreszenzanregung durch Einstrahlung eines Quantenkontinuums möglich: J. E. DRAPER u. R. L. HICKOK, Phys. Rev. **108**, 1280 [1957]. — E. HAYWARD u. E. G. FULLER, Phys. Rev. **106**, 991 [1957].

Absorption infolge Abgabe von Rückstoßimpuls an die emittierenden und absorbierenden Kerne so hohe Rückstoßenergieverluste erleiden, daß die Emissions- und Absorptionslinien erheblich gegeneinander verschoben werden und daher die Resonanzbedingung verletzt wird. Es gibt im wesentlichen drei Methoden, durch Kompensation der Rückstoßenergieverluste meßbare Werte für den Wirkungsquerschnitt für die Kernresonanzfluoreszenz zu erzielen:

1. Doppler-Verschiebung der Quantenenergien durch mechanische Bewegung der Kerne mit Hilfe von Ultrazentrifugen [2].

2. Doppler-Verbreiterung der Emissions- und Absorptionslinien durch Temperaturerhöhung, um die Überdeckung der beiden Linien zu verbessern [3].

3. Doppler-Verbreiterung oder Doppler-Verschiebung der Quantenenergien durch einen früheren Emissions- oder Absorptionsprozeß, z. B. einen dem γ-Übergang vorangehenden β-Übergang oder einen Teilcheneinfang [4].

In der vorliegenden Arbeit wird über eine Methode berichtet, bei der das Auftreten der Rückstoßenergieverluste verhindert wird und die Resonanzbedingung daher nicht verletzt wird. Das beschriebene Verfahren dient zur unmittelbaren Messung der Lebenszeiten niedriger, angeregter Kernzustände. Erste Messungen an dem 129 keV-Übergang in Ir^{191} werden mitgeteilt.

1. Grundlagen der Meßmethode

In einem früheren Experiment [5] wurde bei tiefen Temperaturen im Gegensatz zur klassischen Erwartung ein starker Anstieg der Kernresonanzabsorption bei dem 129 keV-Niveau in Ir^{191} beobachtet. Dieser Effekt wurde mit Hilfe einer Theorie von Lamb [6] als Folge der Kristallbindung der Absorber- und Präparatsubstanzen gedeutet und ist in Festkörpern allgemein bei tiefen Temperaturen und weicher γ-Strahlung zu erwarten.

Die Emission oder Absorption eines Quants durch einen in einem Kristall gebundenen Kern führt im allgemeinen zu einer Änderung des Schwingungszustandes des Kristallgitters, das den Rückstoßimpuls aufnimmt. Wegen der Quantelung der inneren Energie kann der Kristall die Rückstoßenergie nur in diskreten Beträgen aufnehmen. Mit abnehmender Temperatur nimmt die Wahrscheinlichkeit für die Anregung der inneren Niveaus immer mehr ab, weshalb bei weicher γ-Strahlung [7] bei einem Teil der Quantenübergänge der Kristall als Ganzes den Rückstoßimpuls aufnimmt. Die hierbei emittierten bzw. absorbierten Quanten erleiden wegen der großen Masse des Kristalles praktisch keine Energieverluste und erfüllen ideal die Resonanzbedingung.

Abb. 1 zeigt die theoretischen Emissions- und Absorptionsspektren des 129 keV-Überganges in Ir^{191} bei einer Temperatur von 88 °K.

Die Spektren enthalten je zwei Anteile:

1. Eine breite, die thermische Bewegung der im Kristallgitter gebundenen Atome widerspiegelnde Verteilung. Die in den Bereich dieser „thermischen Linie" fallenden Quantenübergänge sind mit einer Änderung des Schwingungszustandes des Kristallgitters gekoppelt.

2. Eine außerordentlich starke Linie mit der natürlichen Linienbreite, die *die* Quantenübergänge enthält, bei denen kein Rückstoßenergieverlust auftritt, weil der Kristall als Ganzes den Rückstoßimpuls aufnimmt. Diese „rückstoßfreie Linie" er-

[2] P. B. Moon, Proc. Phys. Soc., Lond. A **64**, 76 [1951]. — P. B. Moon u. A. Storruste, Proc. Phys. Soc., Lond. A **66**, 585 [1953]. — W. G. Davey u. P. B. Moon, Proc. Phys. Soc., Lond. A **66**, 956 [1953]. — F. R. Metzger, J. Franklin Inst. **261**, 219 [1956]. — V. Knapp, Proc. Phys. Soc., Lond. A **70**, 142 [1957].

[3] K. G. Malmfors, Ark. Fysik **6**, 49 [1953]. — F. R. Metzger u. W. B. Todd, Phys. Rev. **95**, 853 [1954]. — F. R. Metzger, Phys. Rev. **97**, 1258 [1955]; **98**, 200 [1955]. — F. R. Metzger, J. Franklin Inst. **261**, 219 [1956]. — H. Schopper, Z. Phys. **144**, 476 [1956].

[4] K. Ilakovac, Proc. Phys. Soc., Lond. A **67**, 601 [1954]. — F. R. Metzger, Report at the Glasgow Conference 1954, S. 201; Phys. Rev. **101**, 286 [1956]; **103**, 983 [1956]; **110**, 123 [1958]. — H. Schopper, Z. Phys. **144**, 476 [1956]. — C. P. Swann u. F. R. Metzger, Phys. Rev. **108**, 982 [1957]. — S. S. Hanna u. L. Meyer-Schützmeister, Phys. Rev. **108**, 1644 [1957]. — L. Grodzins, Phys. Rev. **109**, 1014 [1958]. — V. Knapp, Proc. Phys. Soc., Lond. **71**, 194 [1958]. — P. B. Smith u. P. M. Endt, Phys. Rev. **110**, 397, 1442 [1958]. — F. R. Metzger, C. P. Swann u. V. K. Rasmussen, Phys. Rev. **110**, 906 [1958]. — V. K. Rasmussen, F. R. Metzger u. C. P. Swann, Phys. Rev. **110**, 154 [1958]. — B. Duelli u. L. Hoffmann, Z. Naturforschg. **13a**, 204 [1958]. — G. M. Griffiths, Proc. Phys. Soc., Lond. **72**, 337 [1958].

[5] R. L. Mössbauer, Z. Phys. **151**, 124 [1958].

[6] W. E. Lamb jr., Phys. Rev. **55**, 190 [1939].

[7] Bei harter γ-Strahlung ist die Rückstoßenergie groß gegen die obere Grenzenergie des Schwingungsspektrums des Kristalles und es ist eine ungehinderte Aufnahme der Rückstoßenergie in Form von innerer Energie durch den Kristall möglich.

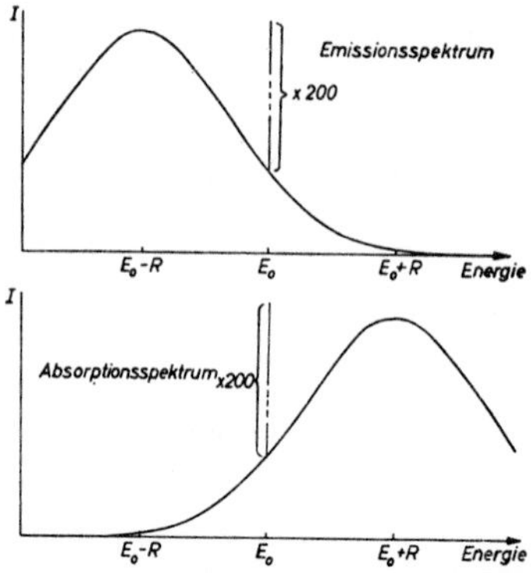

Abb. 1. Lage und Form der Emissions- und Absorptionsspektren des 129 keV-Überganges in Ir^{191} bei $T=88$ °K für eine Lebenszeit $\tau=1{,}4\cdot 10^{-10}$ sec. Nullpunkt der Energieskala unterdrückt; Einheit der Ordinate willkürlich; Höhe der Linien bei $E=E_0$ (Resonanzenergie) im Verhältnis 1 : 200 verkürzt dargestellt.

scheint daher in Emission und Absorption unverschoben an der Stelle der Resonanzenergie E_0.

In der vorliegenden Arbeit wurden am Beispiel von Ir^{191} die „rückstoßfreien" scharfen Emissions- und Absorptionslinien mit Hilfe einer „Zentrifugen"-Methode nachgewiesen. Dabei wurde die Quelle gegen den Absorber bewegt, wobei durch den DOPPLER-Effekt die Emissionslinie nach größeren oder kleineren Energien verschoben wurde. Durch diese Verschiebung der Emissionslinie wurde die bei ruhender Quelle vorhandene vollständige Überdeckung der „rückstoßfreien" Emissions- und Absorptionslinien aufgehoben. Damit wurde die Resonanzbedingung verletzt und der starke Resonanzabsorptionseffekt der „rückstoßfreien" Linien zum Verschwinden gebracht. Eine Analyse der den Resonanzabsorber (Iridium) durchsetzenden 129 keV-γ-Strahlung von Iridium als Funktion der Relativgeschwindigkeit von Quelle und Absorber lieferte dann unmittelbar die Breite der „rückstoßfreien" Linien, d. h. die natürliche Linienbreite und damit auch die Lebenszeit des 129 keV-Niveaus von Ir^{191}.

2. Theorie

Wenn die Quelle mit der Geschwindigkeit v in Richtung auf den Resonanzabsorber bewegt wird, dann gilt [8] für die Intensität I der Resonanzstrahlung hinter dem Resonanzabsorber [9]:

$$I(v) = \text{const} \int_0^\infty W_e\left(E + \frac{v}{c} E_0\right) e^{-\sigma(E)\cdot n}\, dE\,. \quad (1)$$

n ist die Zahl der Atome des resonanten Isotops pro cm^2 Absorberfläche und E_0 ist die Resonanzenergie. $W_e(E)$ ist die Energieverteilung der Quanten einer ruhenden Quelle und $\sigma(E)$ ist der Wirkungsquerschnitt für die Resonanzabsorption:

$$\sigma(E) = (\Gamma^2/4)\ \sigma_0\, W_a(E) \quad (2)$$

mit

$$\sigma_0 = \frac{2\,I_a+1}{2\,I_g+1}\,\frac{\lambda_0^2}{2\,\pi}\,(\Gamma_\gamma/\Gamma)\,. \quad (3)$$

Dabei sind I_a und I_g der Spin des angeregten und des Grundzustandes, λ_0 die Resonanzwellenlänge, Γ die totale Energiebreite des Resonanzniveaus und Γ_γ die partielle Energiebreite des Resonanzniveaus für Strahlungsemission.

Die Absorptionslinie ist nach Lage und Form gegeben durch

$$W_a(E) = (2/\Gamma)\ \text{Real} \int_0^\infty d\mu\, \exp[i\,\mu(E - E_0 + i\,\Gamma/2) + g_a(\mu)]\,. \quad (4\,a)$$

Dabei ist

$$g_a(\mu) = \sum_s \frac{(\vec{p}\,\vec{e}_s)^2}{2\,m\,\hbar\,\omega_s\,N}\,[(\bar{\alpha}_s+1) \cdot \exp(-i\,\mu\,\hbar\,\omega_s) + \bar{\alpha}_s \exp(i\,\mu\,\hbar\,\omega_s) - 1 - 2\,\bar{\alpha}_s]\,. \quad (4\,b)$$

E_0 ist die Resonanzenergie, ω_s die Frequenz der s-ten Normalschwingung des Kristalles, m die Kernmasse, $\vec{p}$ der Impuls des γ-Quants, $\vec{e}$ der Polarisationseinheitsvektor, $3\,N$ die Zahl der unabhängigen Freiheitsgrade im Kristall und $\bar{\alpha}_s$ die mittlere Besetzungszahl des s-ten Oszillators.

Im Fall der Emissionslinie $[W_e(E)]$ ist $g_a(\mu)$ in (4 a) zu ersetzen durch

$$g_e(\mu) = \sum_s \frac{(\vec{p}\,\vec{e}_s)^2}{2\,m\,\hbar\,\omega_s\,N}\,[(\bar{\alpha}_s+1)\exp(i\,\mu\,\hbar\,\omega_s) + \bar{\alpha}_s \exp(-i\,\mu\,\hbar\,\omega_s) - 1 - 2\,\bar{\alpha}_s]\,. \quad (5)$$

Ferner ist

$$\int_0^\infty W_a(E)\, dE = \int_0^\infty W_e(E)\, dE = 2\,\pi/\Gamma\,. \quad (6)$$

Für $\mu\,\hbar\,\omega_g \gg 1$ gilt ($\hbar\,\omega_g$ = obere Grenzenergie des Schwingungsspektrums):

[8] Für Einzelheiten der Ableitung wird auf Anm. [5, 6] verwiesen.

[9] Die Absorption der Hüllenelektronen kann im Bereich der Resonanzlinie als unabhängig von der Energie angenommen werden.

$$g_e(\infty; T) = g_a(\infty; T) \qquad (7)$$
$$= g_\infty(T) = -2 \sum_s \frac{(\vec{p}\,\vec{e}_s)^2}{2\,m\,\hbar\,\omega_s N}\left(\bar{\alpha}_s + \frac{1}{2}\right).$$

Wenn der Wirkungsquerschnitt für die Resonanzabsorption vorzugsweise durch die „rückstoßfreien" Linien bestimmt wird und wenn zwischen der Niveaubreite Γ und der oberen Grenzenergie $\hbar\,\omega_g$ des Schwingungsspektrums die Ungleichung $\Gamma \ll \hbar\,\omega_g$ besteht, dann gilt in der Umgebung der Resonanzstelle E_0 in guter Näherung (T_q, T_a = Temperatur von Quelle bzw. Absorber):

$$W_e(E) = (2/\Gamma) \int_0^\infty d\mu \cos(E - E_0)\,\mu \qquad (8)$$
$$\cdot \exp[g_\infty(T) - \mu\,\Gamma/2] = \frac{\exp g_\infty(T_q)}{(E-E_0)^2 + \Gamma^2/4}$$

und $$\sigma(E) = (\Gamma^2/4)\,\sigma_0 \frac{\exp g_\infty(T_a)}{(E-E_0)^2+\Gamma^2/4}. \qquad (9)$$

Damit folgt für die Strahlungsintensität hinter dem Resonanzabsorber bei einer Verschiebung der Emissionslinie von der Größenordnung der natürlichen Linienbreite aus (1), (8) und (9):

$$I(v) = \text{const} \int_0^\infty \frac{\exp g_\infty(T_q)}{[E + (v/c)\,E_0 - E_0]^2 + \Gamma^2/4} \qquad (10)$$
$$\cdot \exp\left[\frac{-n\,\sigma_0 \exp g_\infty(T_a)}{1 + [(2/\Gamma)(E-E_0)]^2}\right] dE.$$

$I(v)$ ist eine symmetrische Funktion.

Im Fall „schwacher Absorption"[10], d. h. für $n\,\sigma_0 \exp g_\infty(T_a) \ll 1$ folgt aus (10) [mit $(E - E_0)/(\Gamma/2) = x$ und $(v/c)\,E_0/(\Gamma/2) = y$]:

$$I(v) = \frac{\text{const}}{\Gamma/2} \exp g_\infty(T_q) \qquad (11)$$
$$\cdot \left[\int_{-\infty}^{+\infty} \frac{dx}{1+(x+y)^2} - \int_{-\infty}^{+\infty} \frac{n\,\sigma_0 \exp g_\infty(T_a)}{[1+x^2][1+(x+y)^2]}\,dx\right]$$
$$= C_1 - \frac{C_2}{1 + [(v/c)\,E_0/\Gamma]^2}.$$

Die Halbwertsbreite der Intensitätsverteilung $I(v)$ hängt im Fall starker Absorption nach (10) und (7) von der Form des Schwingungsspektrums des Absorbers ab. Im Fall „schwacher Absorption" ist die Halbwertsbreite der Intensitätsverteilung unabhängig von der Form der Schwingungsspektren der Absorber- *und* der Präparatsubstanzen. Dagegen wird die Konstante C_2 in (11), die das Verhältnis der resonanzabsorbierten zu den nicht-resonanten Quanten bestimmt, erheblich durch die Form der Schwingungsspektren beeinflußt.

Mit abnehmender Temperatur wächst die „rückstoßfreie" scharfe Linie auf Kosten der „thermischen" Linie[11]. Beim Übergang zur Temperatur $T = 0$ erreicht die „rückstoßfreie" Linie ihre maximale Höhe, doch existiert daneben immer noch eine breite thermische Verteilung, weil die Quanten bei $T = 0$ zwar keine Phononen mehr absorbieren können, eine Phononenemission aber immer noch möglich ist, wenn auch nur mit einer kleinen Wahrscheinlichkeit.

Für die „rückstoßfreien" Linien gilt bei $T = 0$ für ein Debyesches Schwingungsspektrum:

$$W_e(E) = W_a(E) = \frac{\exp g_\infty(0)}{(E-E_0)^2+\Gamma^2/4} \qquad (12)$$
$$= \frac{\exp[-(3/2)\,(E_0^2/2\,m\,c^2)/k\,\Theta]}{(E-E_0)^2+\Gamma^2/4}.$$

Das in der vorliegenden Arbeit beschriebene Verfahren zur Messung der Lebenszeiten von Kernniveaus ist nur bei energetisch niedrigen Kernzuständen anwendbar, nämlich bei solchen Kernniveaus, bei denen die Rückstoßenergie $E_0^2/2\,m\,c^2$ höchstens etwa das Doppelte der Abschneideenergie $k\,\Theta$ des Debyeschen Schwingungsspektrums beträgt. Nur unter dieser Bedingung tritt nach (12) und (6) wirklich eine starke „rückstoßfreie" Linie aus dem Untergrund der „thermischen" Linie hervor. Der anschauliche Grund hierfür ist, daß bei Rückstoßenergien von der Größenordnung $k\,\Theta$ die Aufnahme der Rückstoßenergie vorzugsweise durch Oszillatoren im energiearmen Bereich des Schwingungsspektrums erfolgen muß. Dieser Bereich besitzt aber nur eine geringe Oszillatordichte[12] und die Wahrscheinlichkeit für die Aufnahme des Rückstoßimpulses ist entsprechend klein, was das Auftreten einer starken „rückstoßfreien" Resonanzlinie zur Folge hat. Wenn dagegen $E_0^2/2\,m\,c^2 \gg k\,\Theta$, so können die im Schwingungsspektrum reichlicher vertretenen hochfrequenten Oszillatoren stärker zur Energieaufnahme herangezogen werden und mit der Zahl der Kombinationsmöglichkeiten steigt die Wahrscheinlichkeit für die ungehinderte Aufnahme des Rückstoßimpulses.

[10] In diesem Fall läßt sich ein „mittlerer" Wirkungsquerschnitt $\bar{\sigma}_r$ definieren:

$$I = I_0 \exp(-n\,\bar{\sigma}_r) \text{ mit } \bar{\sigma}_r = \int_0^\infty (\Gamma/2\,\pi)\,\sigma(E)\,W_e(E)\,dE,$$

vgl. Anm. [5], Gl. (9).

[11] vgl. Gl. (6).

[12] Die Dichteverteilung ist z. B. im Debye-Spektrum proportional dem Quadrat der Oszillatorenenergie $\hbar\,\omega$.

3. Versuchsanordnung und Meßergebnisse

Abb. 2 zeigt die Versuchsanordnung. Der Aufbau der Kryostaten wurde früher [5] beschrieben. Der Resonanzabsorber (Iridium) und ein Vergleichsabsorber (Platin) konnten wechselweise in den Strahlengang gebracht werden. Die Absorber und die Quelle befanden sich auf der Temperatur des flüssigen O_2. Das Szintillationsspektrometer wurde durch eine Photozelle so gesteuert, daß nur solche Quanten registriert wurden, die von der Strahlenquelle während ihres Aufenthaltes längs des markierten Teiles ihres Rotationskreises emittiert wurden.

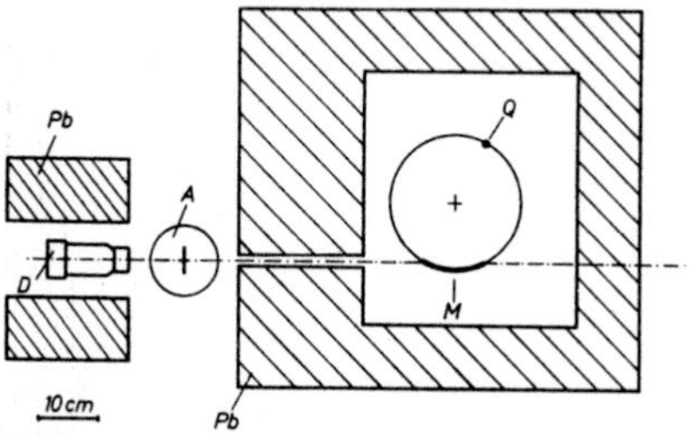

Abb. 2. Versuchsgeometrie. A Absorber-Kryostat; Q rotierender Kryostat mit Quelle; D Szintillationsdetektor. M ist der bei der Messung ausgenützte Teil des Rotationskreises der Quelle.

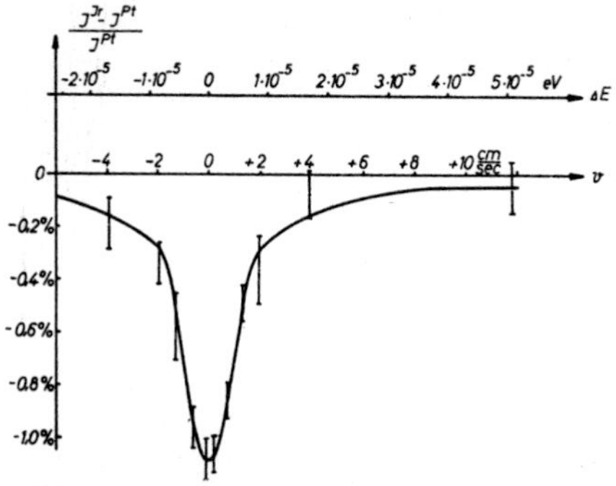

Abb. 3. Relatives Intensitätsverhältnis $(I^{Ir}-I^{Pt})/I^{Pt}$ der hinter Iridium- bzw. Platinabsorbern gemessenen γ-Strahlung als Funktion der Geschwindigkeit der Quelle relativ zu den Absorbern. $E=(v/c)\cdot E_0$ ist die Energieverschiebung der 129 keV-Quanten relativ zu den ruhenden Absorbern. Als Strahlungsquelle diente eine 65 mCurie starke Osmiumquelle, deren Zerfallsspektrum die 129 keV-Linie in Ir^{191} enthält.

Abb. 3 zeigt die Meßergebnisse. Jeder einzelne Meßpunkt wurde aus etwa je 10 Messungen der Strahlungsintensitäten hinter den beiden Absorbern bestimmt. Die gesamte Meßzeit betrug 14 Tage. Die Strahlungsintensität hinter dem Vergleichsabsorber (Platin) war innerhalb der Grenzen der Meßgenauigkeit unabhängig von der Relativgeschwindigkeit v. Die eingetragenen *mittleren* Fehler wurden aus den Schwankungen der Einzelmessungen bestimmt und sind immer größer als die statistischen Fehler. Beim vorliegenden Experiment wurde der Fall „schwacher Absorption" [Gl. (11)] noch nicht verwirklicht. Die eingetragene, den Meßwerten angepaßte Kurve wurde auf numerischem Wege nach (10) berechnet [13] und entspricht einer Niveaubreite $\Gamma=(4{,}6\pm0{,}6)\cdot10^{-6}$ eV für das 129 keV-Niveau in Ir^{191}. Bei der Berechnung des Absorptionsquerschnittes nach (9) wurde das Schwingungsspektrum des Absorbers durch ein DEBYEsches Spektrum mit einer DEBYE-Temperatur $\Theta=285\ °K$ angenähert. Diese Näherung ergibt eine zusätzliche, unter den Bedingungen des vorliegenden Experimentes allerdings unerhebliche Unsicherheit in der Bestimmung von Γ.

4. Diskussion

In der früheren Arbeit [5] wurde für die partielle Lebenszeit τ_γ für Strahlungsemission des 129 keV-Niveaus in Ir^{191} ein Wert von

$$\tau_\gamma=(3{,}6^{+1,3}_{-0,8})\cdot10^{-10}\ \text{sec}$$

gefunden. Mit dem Konversionskoeffizienten $\alpha=2{,}47$ nach DAVIS und Mitarb. [16] folgt daraus für die Lebenszeit $\tau=\tau_\gamma/(1+\alpha)=1{,}0\ ^{+0,4}_{-0,2})\cdot10^{-10}$ sec.
Die Unschärferelation ergibt mit der im vorliegenden Experiment bestimmten Niveaubreite für die Lebenszeit des 129 keV-Niveaus in Ir^{191}:

$$\tau=(1{,}4^{+0,2}_{-0,1})\cdot10^{-10}\ \text{sec}\,.$$

Wir sehen den im vorliegenden Experiment gewonnenen Wert als zuverlässiger an und verzichten auf eine Mittelung der Ergebnisse der beiden nach verschiedenen Methoden vorgenommenen Messungen, wegen der Unsicherheit in dem Wert des Konversionskoeffizienten α und weil sich bei der früheren Messung systematische Fehler wesentlich schwie-

[13] Für die Rechnung wurden verwendet $I_g=3/2$ (s. Anm. [14]); $I_a=5/2$ (s. Anm. [15]); $n=1{,}07\cdot10^{21}\ cm^{-2}$; $T_q=T_a=88\ °K$.
[14] K. MURAKAWA u. S. SUWA, Phys. Rev. **87**, 1048 [1952].
[15] J. W. MIHELICH, M. MCKEOWN u. M. GOLDHABER, Phys. Rev. **96**, 1450 [1954].
[16] R. H. DAVIS, A. S. DIVATIA, D. A. LIND u. R. D. MOFFAT, Phys. Rev. **103**, 1801 [1956].

riger ausschließen lassen als bei der vorliegenden, mehr direkten Messung der Niveaubreite.

Die in der vorliegenden Arbeit beschriebene Methode der Verschiebung „rückstoßfreier" γ-Linien auf mechanischem Wege gestattet eine unmittelbare Bestimmung der Niveaubreiten und damit auch der Lebenszeiten niedriger, angeregter Zustände von Kernen, die in Festkörpern gebunden sind. Die Methode eignet sich u. a. hervorragend zur Messung von Lebenszeiten energetisch niedriger Kernzustände in dem Übergangsgebiet von 10^{-10} bis 10^{-11} sec, das mit der Methode der verzögerten Koinzidenzen schwer erfaßbar ist. Der große Vorteil dieser Methode liegt bei Messungen von Lebenszeiten der Größenordnung 10^{-10} sec darin, daß die erforderlichen Verschiebungen der Quantenenergien nur von der Größenordnung der natürlichen Linienbreite sind und daher nur Relativgeschwindigkeiten der Größenordnung cm/sec benötigt werden, im Gegensatz zu der um Größenordnungen höhere Geschwindigkeiten erfordernden Ultrazentrifugenmethode [2], bei der die thermisch verbreiterten Linien gegeneinander verschoben werden. Das beschriebene Verfahren bietet darüber hinaus im Energiegebiet weicher γ-Strahlung eine einfache Möglichkeit, die Resonanzstreustrahlung von der Streustrahlung der Elektronenhülle, insbesondere von der RAYLEIGH-Streustrahlung gleicher Wellenlänge, zu unterscheiden.

Die Untersuchungen werden fortgesetzt.

Es ist mir ein Anliegen, Herrn Professor H. MAIER-LEIBNITZ für sein reges Interesse und fördernde Diskussionen herzlich zu danken. Herrn Professor K. H. LAUTERJUNG danke ich dafür, daß er die Durchführung der Arbeit am Max-Planck-Institut für medizinische Forschung in Heidelberg ermöglicht hat.

JANUARY 15, 1939 PHYSICAL REVIEW VOLUME 55

Capture of Neutrons by Atoms in a Crystal*

Willis E. Lamb, Jr.
Columbia University, New York, New York
(Received November 21, 1938)

The precise determination of the properties of nuclear resonance levels from the capture of slow neutrons is made difficult by the fact that most of the substances used for absorbers and detectors are in the solid state, so that the calculations of Bethe and Placzek for the influence of the Doppler effect are inapplicable, since these were based on the assumption of a perfect gas. In this paper, their calculations are generalized to include the effect of the lattice binding. Under the assumption that the crystal may be treated as a Debye continuum, it is shown that for sufficiently weak lattice binding, the absorption curve has the same form as it would in a gas, not at the temperature T of the crystal, however, but at a temperature which corresponds to the average energy per vibrational degree of freedom of the lattice (including zero-point energy). In cases of somewhat stronger lattice binding, the line form is found to be more complicated, and may even have a fine structure. Plots are given of the absorption line in several typical cases. An approximate formula for the cross section for self-indication is also derived.

According to the theory of the compound nucleus proposed by Bohr and by Breit and Wigner,[1] the cross section for the capture of a slow neutron with an energy near to a resonance level of a nucleus at rest in free space is given by an equation of the form

$$\sigma=\frac{\Gamma^2}{4}\frac{\sigma_0}{(E-E_0-R)^2+\frac{1}{4}\Gamma^2}, \qquad (1)$$

where σ_0, the cross section at resonance, varies inversely with v, the velocity of the neutron in the rest system, E is the kinetic energy of the neutron, and E_0 is the energy that the neutron

* Publication assisted by the Ernest Kempton Adams Fund for Physical Research of Columbia University.
[1] N. Bohr, Nature **137**, 344 (1936); G. Breit and E. Wigner, Phys. Rev. **49**, 519 (1936).

would have at resonance if the atom were infinitely heavy so that the compound nucleus would take up no recoil energy. For atoms of finite mass, the recoil energy $R=(m/M)E$ must be included in the energy denominator.[2] (We assume that the mass M of the atom is much greater than the mass m of the neutron, and neglect terms of higher order in m/M.) Γ is the total half-value width of the resonance level, and is proportional to the rate of decay of the compound nucleus; in most cases this corresponds to the process of emission of a high energy gamma-ray.

Actually, of course, it never happens that one has to do with a free atom at rest. This somewhat complicates the determination of the properties of the resonance level from slow neutron data. The atoms in a gas may be treated as free, but at finite temperatures, there is a Maxwellian distribution of velocities, and Eq. (1) must be modified, as has been done by Bethe and Placzek[3,4] for this case. It is here necessary to change the resonance energy denominator according to the relative velocity of the neutron and atom, and to average over the Maxwellian distribution of velocities of the gas atoms. The proportionality of the cross section to $1/v$ is thereby unaltered, as this factor arises just from the normalization of the incident neutron wave function to unit flux required by the definition of a cross section. The result of the averaging gives

$$\sigma=\sigma_0\psi(\xi, x), \tag{2}$$

where

$$x=(E-E_0-R)/\tfrac{1}{2}\Gamma, \quad \xi=\Gamma/\Delta \tag{3}$$

and

$$\Delta=2(RT)^{\frac{1}{2}} \tag{4}$$

is the "Doppler" width of the level.[5] The function

$$\psi(\xi, x)=\frac{\xi}{2\pi^{\frac{1}{2}}}\int_{-\infty}^{\infty} dy \frac{e^{-\frac{1}{4}\xi^2(x-y)^2}}{1+y^2} \tag{5}$$

becomes simple in the following limiting cases:

(a) $x\gg 1/\xi^2, \quad \psi\rightarrow 1/(1+x^2),$

i.e., far enough from resonance, the line has its normal form.

(b) $\xi\gg 1, \quad \psi\rightarrow 1/(1+x^2),$

i.e., when the natural breadth is much larger than the Doppler breadth, the line is again normal.

(c) $\xi\ll 1, \quad x\ll 1/\xi^2, \quad \psi\rightarrow \tfrac{1}{2}\pi^{\frac{1}{2}}\xi e^{-\frac{1}{4}\xi^2 x^2},$

i.e., when the natural width is small compared to the Doppler width, the absorption line has an effective width strongly dependent on the temperature.

The total activation induced in a thin detector by a beam of neutrons distributed smoothly in energy is proportional to the area under the absorption curve

$$\int dE\sigma_0\psi(\xi, x)=\tfrac{1}{2}\pi\Gamma\sigma_0, \tag{6}$$

independently of the temperature of the gas. Another quantity of experimental interest is σ_s, the cross section for self-indication[6]

$$\sigma_s=\int\sigma^2 dE\Big/\int\sigma dE=\tfrac{1}{2}\sigma_0\psi(\xi\sqrt{2}, 0)$$
$$=(\tfrac{1}{2}\pi)^{\frac{1}{2}}\xi e^{\frac{1}{2}\xi^2}[1-\Phi(\xi/\sqrt{2})], \tag{7}$$

where Φ is the Gaussian error function.

The above results are valid, however, only for free atoms. Most of the experiments, of course, have been performed with solid absorbers and detectors in which the atoms are bound in a crystal lattice of some sort with a characteristic Debye temperature of the order of room temperature, and if the chemical binding is of importance, as we shall see is the case, it is clearly not permitted to apply the free atom theory of the Doppler broadening, as was done by Bethe,[4] to such cases as silver at ordinary temperatures.

We shall want, therefore, to calculate the shape of the absorption line for an atom which is bound in a crystal lattice. We do not expect that the chemical binding will cause any difference in

[2] As it is usually written, the capture cross section refers to the coordinate system in which the compound nucleus is at rest, so that no energy of recoil appears in the denominator of Eq. (1).

[3] H. Bethe and G. Placzek, Phys. Rev. 51, 462 (1937).

[4] H. Bethe, Rev. Mod. Phys. 9, 140 (1937).

[5] We will measure temperatures in energy units, taking the Boltzmann constant to be unity. The results quoted here were derived on the assumption that the Doppler width of the level is much less than the energy E_0 at resonance of the neutron. This condition is satisfied in all cases of practical interest, and we shall have occasion to assume it in our calculations also.

[6] See reference 4, Eq. (520).

the $1/v$ variation of the capture cross section. This has been shown analytically for the case of capture by bound protons,[7] but the result is much more generally valid, following in every case just from the normalization of the neutron wave function. The calculation will be made without detailed assumptions about the crystal model, but in using the final result, for simplicity, we will treat the crystal as a Debye continuum, and hence the results will not admit of an exact application to experimental cases. Nevertheless, the general features of the dependence of the absorption line on the characteristics of the lattice and on the temperature may be expected to be fairly independent of the detailed model. For just as in the theory of specific heat, there are several limiting cases in which the results may not depend on the model of the lattice assumed, so that any fairly smooth interpolation should approximate the rigorous result fairly closely. For example, let us consider a crystal lattice at the temperature absolute zero. If the lattice binding is sufficiently strong (as defined below), the absorption line will be normal in form, but centered about $E=E_0$, while for very weak binding, as for instance might be the case with a different substance containing the atom in question, the absorption line will again be normal in form, but centered about an energy $E=E_0+R$. Since in practice, this shift R is often of the order of Γ, the half-width of the absorption line, this change in the curve can be experimentally important, even though the recoil energy is numerically quite small. It might thus be possible to detect the effect of the chemical binding, especially at low temperatures, by use of different crystals, containing in common an element with a slow neutron resonance capture level, but in which the remaining elements do not appreciably capture or scatter slow neutrons of the resonance energy.

In the intermediate cases, the shape of the absorption line is in general much more complicated. However, in the case of weak binding, as defined below, it will be possible to treat the bound atoms as if they were in a gas, not however with a temperature T, but at a larger temperature corresponding to the average energy per vibrational degree of freedom (including zero-point energy) of the crystal.

[7] W. E. Lamb, Jr., Phys. Rev. **51**, 187 (1937).

We must now ask for the probability $W(\{\beta_s\};\{\alpha_s\})$ for the capture of a neutron of momentum $\mathbf{p}$ by a definite lattice atom L of nuclear type A to form a nucleus B with emission of a gamma-ray of wave vector $\mathbf{k}$ when the crystal undergoes a transition from a state $\{\alpha_s\}$ to a state $\{\beta_s\}$. Here the set of numbers denoted by $\{\alpha_s\}$ gives the numbers α_s of quanta (phonons) in the various modes s of oscillation in the lattice. We must consider that the final state is reached through an intermediate state in which there is neither neutron nor gamma-ray, but a compound nucleus[8] C with the lattice in a state $\{n_s\}$. The usual dispersion theory gives, apart from a trivial constant factor,

$$W(\{\beta_s\};\{\alpha_s\}) = \left|\sum_{n_s}\frac{(B\beta_s\mathbf{k}|H'|Cn_s)(Cn_s|H'|A\alpha_s\mathbf{p})}{E_0-E+E(n_s)-E(\alpha_s)+(i/2)\Gamma(n_s)}\right|^2, \quad (8)$$

where $\Gamma(n_s)$ is the total half-value width of the intermediate state (C, n_s).[9] Because of the short range of nuclear forces and hence the independence of the motion in the crystal of the center of gravity and the internal degrees of freedom of the nucleus, the matrix elements of the perturbation H' which appear in the numerator of (8) can be factored into

$$\begin{aligned}(Cn_s|H'|A\alpha_s\mathbf{p}) &= (n_s|\exp(i\mathbf{p}\cdot\mathbf{x}_L/\hbar)|\alpha_s)M_{\text{comp}},\\ (B\beta_s|H'|Cn_s) &= (\beta_s|\exp(-i\mathbf{k}\cdot\mathbf{x}_L/\hbar)|n_s)M_{\text{rad}}(\mathbf{k}),\end{aligned} \quad (9)$$

where $M_{\text{rad}}(k)$ and M_{comp} are the matrix elements for radiation and compound nucleus formation, respectively, for a free nucleus, and, for example,

$$(n_s|\exp(i\mathbf{p}\cdot\mathbf{x}_L/\hbar)|\alpha_s)$$

is the matrix element for transfer of a momentum

[8] We will ignore throughout the circumstance that the compound nucleus C is heavier than the atom A. This neglect is certainly valid if $m\ll M$, as is the case in practice, and may be seen to subject our results to a limitation on the effective width of the level analogous to that met by Bethe and Placzek (reference 5) for free atoms. As there, this limitation is of no importance experimentally.

[9] The curly brackets denoting a set of numbers will be dropped when it will not cause confusion.

p to the crystal through the Lth atom with excitation of the lattice from a state $\{\alpha_s\}$ to a state $\{n_s\}$. In practice, the lattice is in thermal equilibrium, therefore not in a definite state $\{\alpha_s\}$, and further, because of the high energy of the gamma-ray, the experiments will give only the total probability of capture, i.e., not

$$W(\{\beta_s\};\ \{\alpha_s\})$$

but $$W(E)=\sum_{\beta_s}\sum_{\alpha_s} g(\{\alpha_s\})W(\{\beta_s\};\{\alpha_s\}), \quad (10)$$

where the sum over the initial states of the lattice is weighted according to the Boltzmann factor $g(\{\alpha_s\})$ for each state when the temperature of the lattice is T. Because of over-all conservation of energy, the magnitude of the wave vector **k** in (8) is a function of the final state of the lattice $\{\beta_s\}$. In all cases of importance, however, one may neglect a variation of **k** of the order of the zero-point energy of oscillation in the lattice, and perform the sum over the final states of the lattice by use of the completeness relations, finding

$$W(E)=|M_{\mathrm{rad}}|^2|M_{\mathrm{comp}}|^2\sum_{\alpha_s} g(\alpha_s)$$
$$\times\sum_{n_s}\frac{|(n_s|\exp(i\mathbf{p}\cdot\mathbf{x}_L/\hbar)|\alpha_s)|^2}{[E-E_0-\sum_s(n_s-\alpha_s)\hbar\omega_s]^2+\frac{1}{4}(\Gamma(n_s))^2}, \quad (11)$$

where the energy of the lattice has been expressed in terms of the frequencies ω_s of the lattice oscillations. Thus one sees that the probability of gamma-ray emission is proportional just to the probability of formation of a compound nucleus C irrespective of the state of the lattice, and this despite the fact that very often a gamma-ray may be emitted in a time short compared to the periods of oscillation of the lattice, giving the atom a recoil energy of the order of a hundred volts. Eq. (11) will be much less complicated if one may neglect the dependence of $\Gamma(n_s)$ on the state $\{n_s\}$ of the lattice. This will be so except in the case, unimportant for our purposes, that the main contribution to Γ comes from the emission of slow neutrons, i.e., in case of a large elastic scattering cross section instead of a large capture cross section. If one were also to neglect the energy given to the lattice, the expression (11), from which we will now drop the factor $|M_{\mathrm{comp}}M_{\mathrm{rad}}|^2$, by use once more of the completeness relation would reduce just to

$$1/[(E-E_0)^2+\tfrac{1}{4}\Gamma^2],$$

since $$\sum_{\alpha_s} g(\{\alpha_s\})=1.$$

We now turn to an evaluation of the matrix elements in Eq. (11). In terms of the wave functions[9]

$$\psi_{n_s}(\mathbf{x}_1,\cdots,\mathbf{x}_N)$$

of the crystal, which is assumed to be periodic in a large volume containing N atoms whose positions are denoted by $\mathbf{x}_1,\cdots,\mathbf{x}_N$, this matrix element is

$$(\{n_s\}|\exp(i\mathbf{p}\cdot\mathbf{x}_L/\hbar)|\{\alpha_s\})$$
$$=\int\cdots\int d\mathbf{x}_1 d\mathbf{x}_2\cdots d\mathbf{x}_N\psi_{n_s}^*(\mathbf{x}_1\mathbf{x}_2\cdots\mathbf{x}_N)$$
$$\times\exp(i\mathbf{p}\cdot\mathbf{x}_L/\hbar)\psi_{\alpha_s}(\mathbf{x}_1\cdots\mathbf{x}_N). \quad (12)$$

We introduce normal coordinates for the crystal in the usual form:[10]

$$\mathbf{x}_G=\mathbf{x}_G^0+\mathbf{u}_G$$
$$\mathbf{u}_G=\frac{1}{N^{\frac{1}{2}}}\sum_{\mathbf{q}}\sum_{j}\mathbf{e}_{\mathbf{q}j}(A_{\mathbf{q}j}\exp(i\mathbf{q}\cdot\mathbf{x}_G^0/\hbar)+\mathrm{conj.}), \quad (13)$$

where $\mathbf{x}_G^0$ is the equilibrium position of the Gth atom, $\mathbf{u}_G$ its displacement from equilibrium, $\mathbf{e}_{\mathbf{q}j}$ is the unit polarization vector for the wave characterized by the propagation vector **q** and polarization j. The spectrum of eigenvibrations is determined by the periodic boundary conditions, and it is cut off at an upper frequency limit such that the number of degrees of freedom agrees with the number $3N$ belonging to the N atoms in the fundamental volume of the lattice. The single index s will often be used to denote the pair of indices $(\mathbf{q}, j)$. In terms of the quantities

$$Q_s=A_s+A_s^*$$
$$P_s=M\dot{Q}_s=iM\omega_s(A_s-A_s^*), \quad (14)$$

where ω_s is the frequency belonging to the sth normal mode, the Hamiltonian of the crystal

[10] See for instance, A. Sommerfeld and H. Bethe, *Handbuch der Physik*, vol. 24/2, second edition (1933), p. 500.

takes the form appropriate for a system of linear harmonic oscillators with coordinates Q_s and momenta P_s

$$H=\sum_s H_s,$$
$$H_s=\tfrac{1}{2}M\omega_s^2Q_s^2+P_s^2/2M. \tag{15}$$

The eigenvalues of this Hamiltonian are

$$E_s=(n_s+\tfrac{1}{2})\hbar\omega_s;\quad n_s=0,1,2,\cdots$$

and the wave functions normalized in terms of

$$\xi_s=Q_s(\hbar/2M\omega_s)^{-\frac{1}{2}}$$

are $\psi_{n_s}(Q_s)=(2\pi)^{-\frac{1}{4}}(n_s!)^{-\frac{1}{2}}e^{-\frac{1}{4}\xi_s^2}h_{n_s}(\xi_s)$,

where $h_{n_s}(\xi_s)$ is the n_sth Hermite polynomial. If, for convenience, we take the rest position of the capturing atom $\mathbf{x}_L{}^0=0$, as may be done without loss of generality, the matrix element (12) with the help of Eq. (13) takes the form

$$\prod_s\int_{-\infty}^{\infty}d\xi_s\psi_{n_s}(\xi_s)\exp\left(i\mathbf{p}\cdot\mathbf{e}\xi_s/(2M\hbar\omega_sN)^{\frac{1}{2}}\right)\psi_{\alpha_s}(\xi_s), \tag{16}$$

where the product is to be extended over all the normal modes. Integrals of the form

$$K(n_s,\alpha_s;q_s)=\int_{-\infty}^{\infty}d\xi\psi_{n_s}e^{iq_s\xi_s}\psi_{\alpha_s}(\xi_s)$$

are readily evaluated[11] by use of the generating formula for the Hermite polynomials. In our case,

$$q_s^2=\frac{(\mathbf{p}\cdot\mathbf{e}_s)^2}{2M\hbar\omega_sN}$$

and is arbitrarily small if we take the fundamental volume of the crystal large enough, so that only terms to the first order in q_s^2 need be kept in $K(n_s,\alpha_s;q_s)$, as will be seen more clearly below. Then there are three possibilities:

$$|K(\alpha_s,\alpha_s;q_s)|^2=(1-2\alpha_sq_s^2)e^{-q_s^2}, \tag{17a}$$
$$|K(\alpha_s+1,\alpha_s;q_s)|^2=(\alpha_s+1)q_s^2e^{-q_s^2}, \tag{17b}$$
$$|K(\alpha_s-1,\alpha_s;q_s)|^2=\alpha_sq_s^2e^{-q_s^2}, \tag{17c}$$

as all the other K's are of higher order. The q_s^2 will enter the final result only linearly in sums like

$$\sum_s q_s^2\backsimeq R/\theta,$$

where θ is the Debye temperature of the substance. Any sums of the form $\sum_s q_s^4$, etc. would vanish as the transition to the continuum is made, which provides a justification for neglect of the higher powers of the q_s^2 in Eqs. (17).

Consider now the expression

$$W(\alpha_s)=\sum_{n_s}\frac{\prod_s|K(n_s,\alpha_s;q_s)|^2}{[E-E_0-\sum_s(n_s-\alpha_s)\hbar\omega_s]^2+\frac{1}{4}\Gamma^2}. \tag{18}$$

This is made difficult to evaluate only by the presence in the denominator of the term $\sum_s(n_s-\alpha_s)\hbar\omega_s$. This suggests that it will be convenient to group together the terms in the expression for which this quantity has the same value. One may accomplish this most easily by the introduction of a delta-function, writing (18) as

$$\int_{-\infty}^{\infty}d\rho\delta(\rho-\sum_s(n_s-\alpha_s)\hbar\omega_s)\times\sum_{n_s}\frac{\prod_s|K(\ )|^2}{(E-E_0-\rho)^2+\frac{1}{4}\Gamma^2}, \tag{19}$$

where for the delta-function, use is made of the usual representation

$$\delta(x)=\frac{1}{2\pi}\int_{-\infty}^{\infty}d\mu e^{i\mu x}. \tag{20}$$

Thus one finds

$$W(\alpha_s)=\frac{1}{2\pi}\int_{-\infty}^{\infty}d\rho\int_{-\infty}^{\infty}d\mu\frac{e^{i\mu\rho}}{(E-E_0-\rho)^2+\frac{1}{4}\Gamma^2}\times\sum_{n_s}\prod_s\{|K(n_s,\alpha_s;q_s)|^2\times\exp\left(-i\mu(n_s-\alpha_s)\hbar\omega_s\right)\}. \tag{21}$$

From Eqs. (17), one finds

$$I_s=\sum_{n_s}|K(n_s,\alpha_s;q_s)|^2\exp -i\mu(n_s-\alpha_s)\hbar\omega_s$$
$$=e^{-q_s^2}\{1+q_s^2[-2\alpha_s+(\alpha_s+1)e^{-i\mu\hbar\omega_s}+\alpha_se^{i\mu\hbar\omega_s}]\}. \tag{22}$$

[11] F. Bloch and A. Nordsieck, Phys. Rev. 52, 54 (1937).

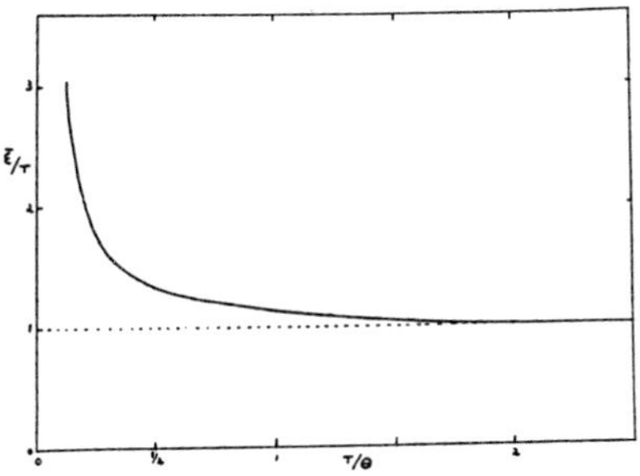

FIG. 1. Plot of the ratio of "effective temperature" and real temperature of a crystal as a function of the real temperature measured in units of the Debye temperature of the substance.

At this point it is most convenient to carry out the average over the values of the initial quantum numbers α_s, since now each α_s appears at most linearly. The result of the averaging is that each α_s above is replaced by its average value $\bar{\alpha}_s$ at thermal equilibrium, where

$$\bar{\alpha}_s = \frac{1}{e^{\hbar\omega_s/kT}-1}. \qquad (23)$$

The product over the various oscillators s is then of the form

$$\prod_s(1+\lambda_s q_s^2) = 1 + \sum_s \lambda_s q_s^2 + \sum\sum_{s<r} \lambda_s \lambda_r q_s^2 q_r^2 + \cdots \qquad (24)$$

and if one remembers the smallness of the q_s^2, the series may be summed to give $\exp(\sum_s \lambda_s q_s^2)$, so that

$$I = \prod_s I_s = \exp \sum_s q_s^2\{(\bar{\alpha}_s+1)e^{-i\mu\hbar\omega_s} + \bar{\alpha}_s e^{i\mu\hbar\omega_s} - 2\bar{\alpha}_s\}. \qquad (25)$$

Thus one has

$$W(E) = \frac{1}{2\pi}\int_{-\infty}^{\infty} d\rho \int_{-\infty}^{\infty} d\mu \frac{e^{i\mu\rho+g(\mu)}}{(E-E_0-\rho)^2+\frac{1}{4}\Gamma^2}. \qquad (26)$$

where the function $g(\mu)$ is given by

$$g(\mu) = \sum_s q_s^2\{(\bar{\alpha}_s+1)e^{-i\mu\hbar\omega_s} + \bar{\alpha}_s e^{i\mu\hbar\omega_s} - 1 - 2\bar{\alpha}_s\}. \qquad (27)$$

The integral over ρ in (26) may be done at once by residue formation, and one has the generally valid final result

$$W(E) = 2/\Gamma \text{ Real} \int_0^\infty d\mu \times \exp[i\mu(E-E_0+i\Gamma/2)+g(\mu)]. \qquad (28)$$

Naturally, it would be most difficult to evaluate $W(E)$ exactly. One may however easily obtain simple expressions which are valid in the various limiting cases. The function $g(\mu)$ is the cause of the complication, and it is possible to evaluate the integral (28) analytically only in cases where the values of μ given by $\mu\theta \sim 1$ do not play a dominant role. For $\mu\theta \ll 1$, one may expand in powers of μ and obtain

$$g(\mu) = -i\mu\sum_s q_s^2 \hbar\omega_s - \mu^2 \sum_s q_s^2(\bar{\alpha}_s+\tfrac{1}{2})(\hbar\omega_s)^2 + \cdots. \qquad (29)$$

The sums may be evaluated under the assumption of an isotropic crystal, i.e., the velocity of a wave is assumed to be independent of its direction of propagation, although not necessarily of its polarization; and one finds

$$g(\mu) = -i\mu R - \mu^2 R\bar{\epsilon}, \qquad (30)$$

where R is again the recoil energy and $\bar{\epsilon}$ the average energy per vibrational degree of freedom of the crystal (including zero point energy). If the condition

$$\tfrac{1}{2}\Gamma + (R\bar{\epsilon})^{\frac{1}{2}} \gg \theta \qquad (31)$$
("weak binding")

is met, only small values of μ in $g(\mu)$ in the integral (28) need be considered, and one finds

$$W(E) = \frac{2}{\Gamma}\int_0^\infty d\mu \cos\mu(E-E_0-R) \times \exp(-\tfrac{1}{2}\Gamma\mu - \mu^2 R\bar{\epsilon}) = \frac{4}{\Gamma^2}\int_0^\infty dy \cos yx \exp(-y-y^2/\xi^2) \equiv (4/\Gamma^2)\psi(\xi, x), \qquad (32)$$

where $\psi(\xi, x)$,[12] x, and ξ are as defined by Eqs.

[12] Equation (32) gives Reiche's form of the ψ-function. See Born, *Optik* (1933), p. 482.

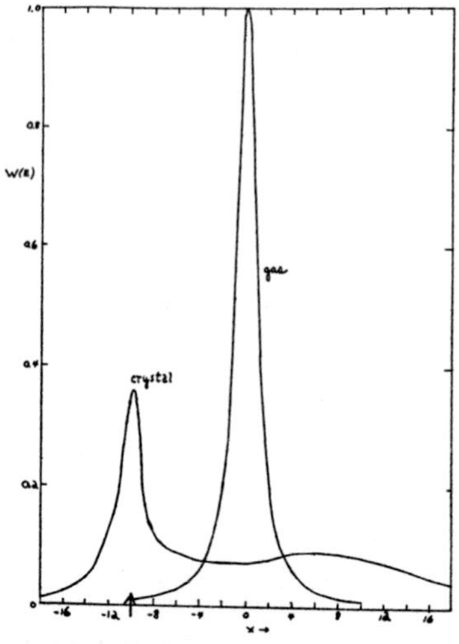

FIG. 2. Plot of the neutron resonance absorption curve in cold solid silver for an assumed value of Γ equal to $\theta/4$. The curve one would obtain with free atoms is shown for comparison. The abscissa measures the distance from resonance in units of $\frac{1}{2}\Gamma$. If the lattice binding were very strong, the curve for the crystal would have the same form for the gas, except that it would be centered about the point shown by the arrow.

(5) and (3), but now with an effective Doppler width

$$\Delta=2(R\bar{\epsilon})^{\frac{1}{2}}, \tag{33}$$

which involves $\bar{\epsilon}$ instead of T. Thus we see that provided only the condition $\Delta+\Gamma\gg 2\theta$ is met, the atoms in a crystal at a temperature T give the same absorption line as they would in a gas at a temperature $\bar{\epsilon}$ equal to the average energy per vibrational degree of freedom of the crystal. This quantity is well known from the theory of specific heats

$$\bar{\epsilon}=\tfrac{1}{3}(\bar{\epsilon}_l+2\bar{\epsilon}_t), \tag{34}$$

where

$$\bar{\epsilon}_j(T)=3\left(\frac{T}{\theta}\right)^3 T\int_0^{\theta_j/T} dt\, t^3\left(\frac{1}{e^t-1}+\tfrac{1}{2}\right), \tag{34j}$$

where the indices l and t refer to the longitudinal and transverse waves. One has the limiting values

$$\bar{\epsilon}=T+\theta\cdot O(\theta/T) \qquad T\gg\theta \tag{34a}$$

$$\bar{\epsilon}=\tfrac{3}{8}(\theta_l+2\theta_t)+T\cdot O(T^3/\theta^3). \tag{34b}$$

In Fig. 1, a plot is given of $\bar{\epsilon}(T)/T$ as a function of T/θ for the case that the various characteristic temperatures are equal.

The other limiting case is $\mu\theta\gg 1$. Here one finds

$$g(\infty)=-2\sum_s q_s^2(\bar{\alpha}_s+\tfrac{1}{2})= -\tfrac{1}{3}[G(T/\theta_l)+2G(T/\theta_t)], \tag{35}$$

where

$$G(x)=\frac{2R}{T}x^3\int_0^{1/x} dt\, t\left(\frac{1}{e^t-1}+\tfrac{1}{2}\right) \tag{36}$$

with

$$G(x)=xR/T \quad x\ll 1, \tag{36a}$$

$$G(x)=\frac{2R}{T}x^2 \quad x\gg 1. \tag{36b}$$

For special ranges of values of $E-E_0$, one may obtain a good approximation to $W(E)$ by splitting the range of integration in Eq. (28) at $\mu\theta=1$, and in each range, using the appropriate expansion for $g(\mu)$. One finds in this way that for very strong binding of the atoms in the crystal ($\theta\rightarrow\infty$),

$$W(E)=\frac{1}{(E-E_0)^2+\frac{1}{4}\Gamma^2}, \tag{37}$$

i.e., the normal absorption line centered about $E=E_0$.

In general, however, a certain amount of numerical integration is required to find the shape of the line. To illustrate the possibility of using the general Eqs. (28) and (27) except in the two limiting cases of Eqs. (31) and (37), we give plots of a $2\frac{1}{2}$-volt resonance energy absorption line in a substance at a temperature much lower than the Debye temperature of $\theta=210°$K (Case of cold silver if one abstracts from the difference between θ_l and θ_t), for several assumed values of Γ. In each case, the curve for free atoms at the same temperature is also shown. One sees that for these cases of intermediate binding, there is a rudimentary fine structure in the probability of capture which is suggestive of the neutron absorption *lines* that one would obtain from an atom harmonically bound, say in a molecule with energy levels separated by θ. (See Figs. 2 and 3.)

The area under the general absorption curve (28) may be evaluated immediately, again under the assumption of footnote (4), and one finds

$$\int_0^{\infty} dEW(E) = \frac{2}{\Gamma} \qquad (38)$$

which, of course, agrees with the result for free atoms. The expression for the cross section for self-indication, which involves the integral of the square of $W(E)$ is more complicated, but may be reduced to

$$\sigma_s = \Gamma \int_0^{\infty} d\mu \exp\left[-\Gamma\mu + g(\mu) + g(-\mu)\right]. \qquad (39)$$

In the case $\Gamma + \Delta \gg \theta$, this integral may again be evaluated by expanding $g(\mu)$ for small μ, and the cross section for self-indication has the value corresponding to that for a gas at an effective temperature $\bar{\epsilon}$ instead of T. In the general case of arbitrary Γ, Δ and θ, however, one may derive an approximate formula by splitting the range of integration at $\mu\theta = 1$,

$$\sigma_s = (\tfrac{1}{2}\pi)^{\frac{1}{2}} \xi e^{\frac{1}{2}\xi^2} \left[\Phi\left(\frac{\xi}{\sqrt{2}} + \frac{\Delta}{\sqrt{2}\theta}\right) - \Phi\left(\frac{\xi}{\sqrt{2}}\right)\right] + \exp\left[2g(\infty) - \Gamma/\theta\right], \qquad (40)$$

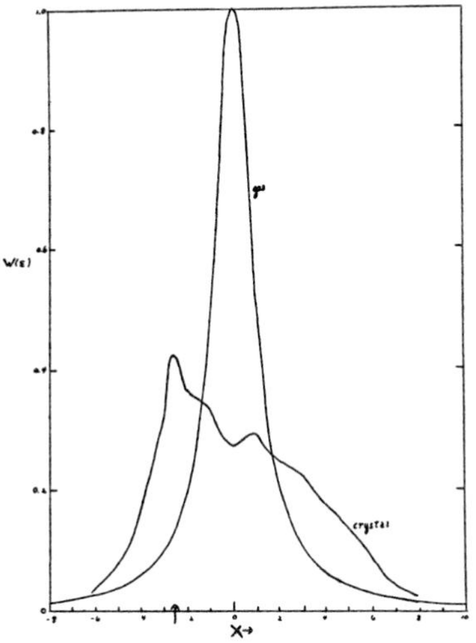

FIG. 3. Same as Fig. 2 except that the assumed value of Γ is now equal to θ. For values of $\Gamma \gtrsim 4\theta$, one is already in the domain of applicability of Eq. (32). The precise value of Γ for silver is not well known experimentally.

which may be used provided the result does not depend too much on the precise value of θ.

This research was largely carried out during the summer session at Stanford University, and I wish to thank Professor F. Bloch for his generous advice and hospitality. I am also greatly indebted to Professor G. Placzek and to Dr. A. Nordsieck for many valuable discussions and suggestions.

ANNALS OF PHYSICS: **9**, 194–210 (1960)

Study of Lattice Vibrations by Resonance Absorption of Nuclear Gamma Rays*

WILLIAM M. VISSCHER

University of California, Los Alamos Scientific Laboratory, Los Alamos, New Mexico

It has recently been demonstrated by Mössbauer that in a large proportion of emissions or absorptions of gamma rays by nuclei bound in crystals at low temperature the recoil energy is taken up by the crystal as a whole (no phonons are emitted). This makes it possible to observe resonance absorption of nuclear gamma-rays without high-speed rotors or elevated temperatures, as had been done in the past. In the present paper we show that an extension of Mössbauer's technique can be utilized to directly observe the frequency distribution of lattice vibrations in the crystal. Specifically, if the emitter and absorber have the same favorable crystal structure, then the self-absorption cross section observed in a rotor experiment at low temperature will be proportional to $N(S)/S$, where $N(S)\ dS$ is the number of phonon states in an energy interval dS, and S is the doppler shift in the gamma-ray energy induced by the rotor motion. Criteria are given for determining favorable cases.

I. INTRODUCTION

The observation of resonantly scattered or absorbed nuclear γ-rays has been made difficult in the past by the fact that the natural width of nuclear isomeric states is almost always small compared to the energy of the recoiling nucleus.[1] Thus if E_0 is the energy of the nuclear excited state, the spectrum of gammas emitted by a free nucleus at rest will be centered at energy $E_0 - R$, where $R = E_0^2/2Mc^2$ is the recoil energy of the nucleus whose mass is M. A gamma can be absorbed, however, by a free nucleus at rest only if the gamma energy is within the natural width Γ of $E_0 + R$. The devices which had been used to observe resonance scattering before 1958 all supplied, in one way or another, the $2R$ difference between the energy of the emitted γ and the energy which it needs to be absorbed. One way to supply the difference is to spin the source on a high-speed rotor, to Doppler shift the emitted gammas. A Doppler shift of $2R$ requires a linear velocity of E_0/Mc, which amounts to 2×10^4 cm/sec for a typical case ($E_0 = 100$ kev, $A = 150$). Another method involves varying the tem-

* This work performed under the auspices of the U. S. Atomic Energy Commission.

[1] For a review of this field, see Malmfors (*1*).

peratures of the source and absorber (or scatterer) over rather wide ranges, to Doppler broaden the gamma spectra. Temperature ranges comparable to the recoil energy must be used in order to observe the change in overlap of the emission and absorption spectra. A third method utilizes as a source a nucleus which is recoiling from a previous decay. The decay product is required by coincidence techniques to be travelling in a certain direction with respect to the direction of the subsequently emitted gamma, thus fixing the component of velocity of the nucleus along that direction and the Doppler shift in the gamma energy.

A remarkable new method was devised last year by Mössbauer (*2*), and was used to measure the width of the 129-kev level in Ir^{191}. His method is different in principle from those preceding it, in that the emitting (or absorbing) nucleus is not allowed to recoil, thus obviating the need to have the emitting and absorbing nuclei in rapid motion relative to one another. This is accomplished simply by having the nuclei bound in crystals at low temperature. Mössbauer showed that when the 129-kev gamma is emitted or absorbed by such a nucleus, the recoil momentum is taken up a large part of the time by the whole crystal, with no energy transferred to internal excitations of the lattice. The kinetic energy associated with the crystal recoiling as a whole is negligible compared to Γ, even for crystals as small as a fraction of a cubic micron in volume. Thus, the recoil shift discussed above is essentially zero, and many of the gammas emitted by a nucleus in a crystal at rest can be resonantly absorbed or scattered by another nucleus in another crystal at rest, in marked contrast to the situation when gaseous or room-temperature crystalline sources and absorbers are used.

The emissions which take place without energy transfer to the lattice give rise to a pip of width Γ in the energy spectrum of gammas emitted by the crystal. The height of this "no-recoil pip" is a strongly decreasing function of temperature. The absorption cross section, too, contains a no-recoil pip with similar properties. In both cases the pip is centered at $E = E_0$, the nuclear excitation energy.

We will now give a brief resume of some of Mössbauer's experimental results and of the theory due to Lamb (*3*) which explains them.

II. MÖSSBAUER'S EXPERIMENTS

In the interest of brevity, we will only outline the essential features of two of Mössbauer's observations.

Mössbauer measured the transmission of Ir^{191} 129-kev gamma rays through a crystalline natural iridium (38.5% Ir^{191}) absorber. His source was Os^{191}, which β-decays with a 16-day half-life to a long-lived (5.6-sec) state of Ir^{191} at 171 kev. A 42-kev γ is emitted, and the iridium nucleus is left in its first excited state (129 kev) which has a lifetime of 1.4×10^{-10} sec.

The most startling result which Mössbauer obtained was the "turntable

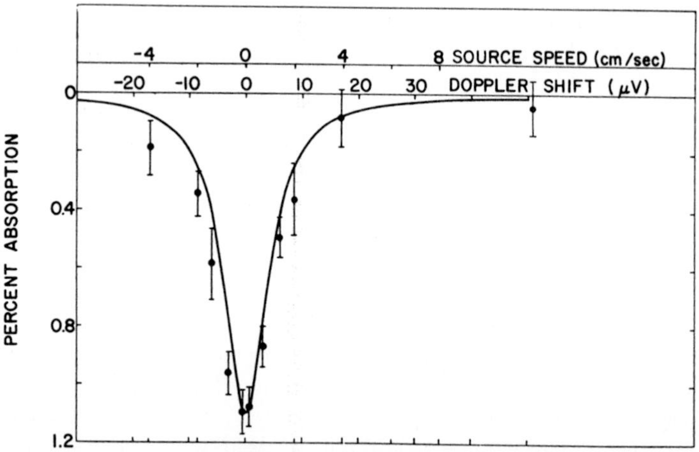

FIG. 1. The relative intensity of 129-kev gamma rays transmitted by the iridium absorber as measured by Mössbauer with both source and absorber at 88°K, as a function of source speed. The ordinate is dependent upon the source thickness. The width of the dip in the transmission for a thin absorber is dependent only on the natural width of the 129-kev nuclear level. The curve here is theoretical and will be discussed in Part IV; the experimental points are taken from the third of Mössbauer's papers (*2*), Fig. 3.

effect." Here he kept both source and absorber at 88° K, but had the source mounted on a turntable, so that the relative velocity of the source and absorber during the time the source was seen by the absorber could be controlled. Figure 1 shows the variation of transmission he observed as a function of turntable speed. The absorption peak is centered at zero relative speed of the source with respect to the absorber; it has a half-width of about 1 cm/sec.

When the abscissa is converted to energy units corresponding to the Doppler shift in the gamma energy $\Delta E = (v/c)E_0$, the points can be fitted within statistical error by a Breit–Wigner curve of width $(9.2 \pm 1.2) \times 10^{-6}$ ev. This is interpreted to be twice the natural width of the 129-kev level, the factor of 2 arising because the observed absorption is the result of folding an emission spectrum together with an absorption cross section, each of which have a "no-recoil pip" of width Γ. In the thin-absorber approximation, the absorption is proportional to the product of the emission spectrum with the absorption cross section, integrated over all energies. At zero relative velocity the pips overlap perfectly; at velocities large compared to $\Gamma c/E_0$ the overlap is destroyed, and the absorption disappears.

The other measurement of Mössbauer's which we wish to discuss here is his observation of the "temperature effect." Here he had both source and absorber at rest, with the absorber at a fixed temperature of 88° K, and the source temperature variable from 88° to above room temperature. He measured the trans-

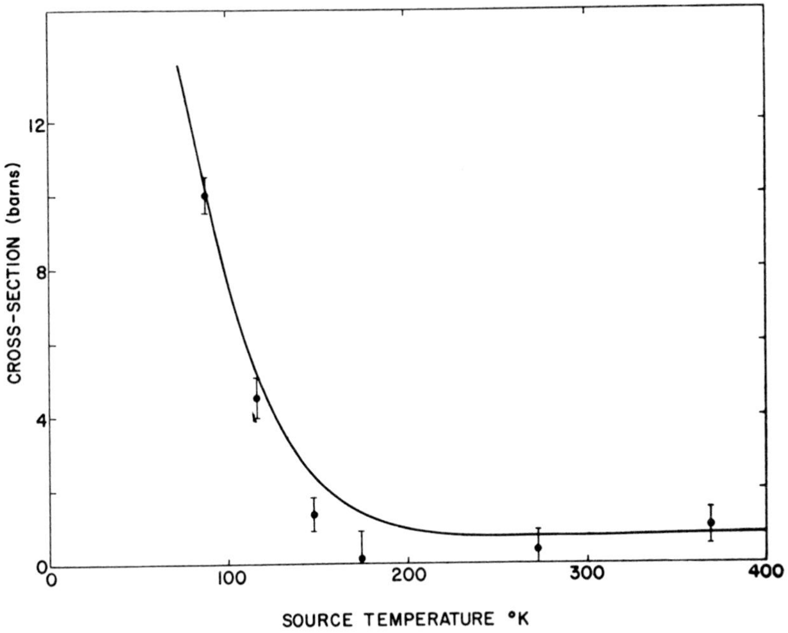

FIG. 2. The effective absorption cross section per Ir^{191} nucleus, for the absorber crystal at 88°K and the source temperature given by the abscissa. The curve is a theoretical one to be discussed in Part IV; the experimental points are taken from Mössbauer's first paper (*2*), Fig. 8b.

mission of the 129-kev gammas through the absorber as a function of source temperature. His results, which were expressed in terms of effective absorption cross sections, are shown in Fig. 2. The rise in the cross section with decreasing temperature (quite contrary to its behavior with gaseous sources and absorbers) is interpreted as being caused by the increase in the probability of no-recoil emission by the nuclei in the source as the temperature is lowered. The absorber temperature was not varied in this measurement because any temperature dependence of the non-nuclear absorption cross section of the atoms in the crystal (mostly K-photoeffect) would obscure the temperature dependence of the nuclear absorption which Mössbauer sought to measure.

An explanation of these results was achieved by Mössbauer by modifying a theory due to Lamb (*3*), describing the resonance absorption of neutrons by nuclei bound in crystals, to apply to the gamma-absorption process.

III. THEORY

We will now explain Lamb's notation and outline his theory.

The crystal is described by a wave function which depends on the center-of-mass coordinate of each of the N constituent nuclei. $\mathbf{x}_G = \mathbf{x}_G^0 + \mathbf{u}_G$ is the coordinate of the Gth nucleus, where $\mathbf{x}_G^0$ is its equilibrium position and $\mathbf{u}_G$ is its displacement from equilibrium. If the interactions between the nuclei in the crystal can be approximated by harmonic forces, the crystal Hamiltonian can be written as the sum of $3N$ independent harmonic oscillator Hamiltonians. This transformation to normal coordinates is carried out as follows. Let

$$\mathbf{u}_G = \sum_{s=1}^{3N} \sqrt{\frac{\hbar}{2M\omega_s N}}\, \mathbf{e}_s[a_s \exp(i\mathbf{q}_s \cdot \mathbf{x}_G^0) + a_s^* \exp(-i\mathbf{q}_s \cdot \mathbf{x}_G^0)] \qquad (1)$$

be a Fourier expansion of $\mathbf{u}_G$ in terms of the $3N$ normal modes characterized by polarization vectors $\mathbf{e}_s$, frequencies ω_s, and propagation vectors $\mathbf{q}_s$.

If a_s and a_s^* satisfy

$$[a_{s'}, a_s^*] = \delta_{s's}, \qquad (2)$$

then the commutation relations between the components of $\mathbf{u}_G$ and their conjugate momenta are satisfied, and if we define normal coordinates and momenta

$$\begin{aligned} Q_s &= \sqrt{\frac{\hbar}{2M\omega_s}}\,(a_s + a_s^*), \\ P_s &= -i\sqrt{\frac{\hbar M\omega_s}{2}}\,(a_s - a_s^*), \end{aligned} \qquad (3)$$

they satisfy $[P_{s'}, Q_s] = -i\hbar\delta_{s's}$.

The Hamiltonian becomes separable into

$$\begin{aligned} H &= \sum_{s=1}^{3N} H_s\,; \\ H_s &= P_s^2/2M + \tfrac{1}{2}M\omega_s^2 Q_s^2 \\ &= \hbar\omega_s(a_s^* a_s + \tfrac{1}{2}) = \hbar\omega_s(N_s + \tfrac{1}{2}); \end{aligned} \qquad (4)$$

where $N_s = a_s^* a_s$ can, with the help of Eq. (2), be seen to have eigenvalues 0, 1, 2, $\cdots$. The state of the crystal can therefore be specified by a set of numbers $\{\alpha_s\}$ which are the eigenvalues of the phonon number operator N_s for each normal mode s. To describe the entire system for a gamma-ray resonance absorption or emission problem we must also specify the state of internal excitation of each of the nuclei, and the momentum $\mathbf{p}$ of the gamma if any is present. Thus, for example, the ket $| A\{\alpha_s\}\mathbf{p})$ means that a gamma ray of momentum $\mathbf{p}$ is present, the crystal is in state $\{\alpha_s\}$, and a specific nucleus is in state A. All the effects due to excitation of different nuclei are incoherent with one another, so it is legitimate to consider each nucleus separately.

If we assume that each nucleus has two states, the ground state A and an excited state C which has energy E_0 and decays like $e^{-\Gamma t/2}$, then application of perturbation theory yields the following results.

The probability that a gamma of momentum **p** incident on the crystal in state $\{\alpha_s\}$ will be resonantly scattered by a particular nucleus into momentum **k**, leaving the crystal in state $\{\beta_s\}$ is proportional to

$$W(\{\beta_s\}\mathbf{k}, \{\alpha_s\}\mathbf{p}) = \left| \sum_{\{n_s\}} \frac{(A\{\beta_s\}\mathbf{k} \mid H' \mid C\{n_s\})(C\{n_s\} \mid H' \mid A\{\alpha_s\}\mathbf{p})}{E_0 - pc + E(n_s) - E(\alpha_s) + i\Gamma/2} \right|^2, \quad (5)$$

where pc is the energy of the incident gamma, $E(\alpha_s) = \sum_s \hbar\omega_s(\alpha_s + \frac{1}{2})$ is the crystal energy in the initial state, and H' is the energy operator describing the interaction between the gamma ray and the nucleus in question. The sum is over all intermediate crystal states $\{n_s\}$ in which the nucleus is in its excited state C and no gamma is present. Energy conservation is implicit in Eq. (5); final states $\{\beta_s\}$ are possible only if

$$E(\beta_s) + ck = E(\alpha_s) + cp. \quad (6)$$

In the derivation of Eq. (5) it is also assumed that the state of the crystal $\{n_s\}$ remains unchanged during the time the nucleus is excited. It is therefore valid only when the relaxation time of the crystal is long compared to the lifetime $\hbar/\Gamma$ of the nuclear excited state.

On the other hand, if we ask only for the absorption probability, it is not necessary to assume that the crystal relaxation time is long. In this case one is led to the expression

$$W(\{\alpha_s\}, \mathbf{p}) = \sum_{\{n_s\}} \frac{|(C\{n_s\} \mid H' \mid A\{\alpha_s\}\mathbf{p})|^2}{(E_0 - pc + E(n_s) - E(\alpha_s))^2 + \Gamma'/4^2} \quad (7)$$

for the absorption probability, where Γ' is equal to the nuclear level width plus the widths of the crystal states $\{n_s\}$ and $\{\alpha_s\}$. The calculations will be greatly simplified if we assume the relaxation time to be independent of the crystal state; we will, in fact, assume it to be infinite, or $\Gamma' = \Gamma$.

The probability for the emission process is also proportional to (7), with $\{\alpha_s\}$ and $\{n_s\}$ interchanged in the summand.

The matrix elements of H' which occur in Eqs. (5) and (7) can each be expressed as a product of two factors. One factor depends only on the change in internal state of the radiating nucleus, and only weakly on the gamma energy. It will be hereafter omitted, since it is common to all subsequent formulas. The other factor describes the absorption of the gamma's momentum by the lattice. Thus we make the following replacements:

$$\begin{aligned} (C\{n_s\} \mid H' \mid A\{\alpha_s\}\mathbf{p}) &\rightarrow [\{n_s\} \mid \exp(i\mathbf{p}\cdot\mathbf{x}_L/\hbar) \mid \{\alpha_s\}], \\ (A\{\beta_s\}\mathbf{k} \mid H' \mid C\{n_s\}) &\rightarrow [\{\beta_s\} \mid \exp(-i\mathbf{k}\cdot\mathbf{x}_L/\hbar) \mid \{n_s\}] \end{aligned} \quad (8)$$

for the absorption and emission matrix elements, respectively. We have singled out nucleus L at $\mathbf{x}_L = \mathbf{x}_L^0 + \mathbf{u}_L$; without loss of generality we can, following Lamb, choose $\mathbf{x}_L^0 = 0$, the origin of our coordinate system. After substituting $\mathbf{u}_L$ (Eq. 1) into the matrix elements (8) they may be factored into $3N$ matrix elements, one for each phonon state.

$$[\{n_s\} | \exp(i\mathbf{p}\cdot\mathbf{u}_L/\hbar) | \{\alpha_s\}] = \prod_{s=1}^{3N} \left[n_s \middle| \exp\left(i \frac{\mathbf{p}\cdot\mathbf{e}_s(a_s + a_s^*)}{\sqrt{2M\hbar\omega_s N}} \right) \middle| \alpha_s \right]. \quad (9)$$

Because of the factor $1/\sqrt{N}$ in the exponent, no term of order higher than $(\mathbf{p}\cdot\mathbf{e}_s)^2 = p_s^2$ in the expansion of the exponential on the right can give a non-vanishing contribution to $W(\{\alpha_s\}, \mathbf{p})$ after the sum over $\{n_s\}$ is performed and the limit $N \to \infty$ is taken. The terms which do contribute are

$$\exp\left[i \frac{p_s(a_s + a_s^*)}{\sqrt{2M\hbar\omega_s N}} \right] \approx 1 - \frac{p_s^2}{2MN\hbar\omega_s}(2N_s + 1) + i \frac{p_s(a_s + a_s^*)}{\sqrt{2MN\hbar\omega_s}}. \quad (10)$$

Since a_s and a_s^* are phonon absorption and creation operators, respectively, we see that any phonon state can change its occupation number by at most one. Also, Eq. (10) exhibits explicitly the reason for the existence of the "no-recoil pip." It is that the phonon creation or absorption matrix element is of order $1/\sqrt{N}$ smaller than the no-phonon ($\{\alpha_s\} = \{n_s\}$) matrix element. After summing over phonon states, the two can give contributions to W of the same order of magnitude.

Of physical interest is the quantity

$$W(E) = \sum_{\{\alpha_s\}} g(\{\alpha_s\}) W(\{\alpha_s\}, \mathbf{p}), \quad (11)$$

where $g(\{\alpha_s\})$ is the probability that the crystal will initially be in a state $\{\alpha_s\}$, and where we have assumed, for simplicity, that the crystal is isotropic, so that (11) is dependent only on $E = pc$, and not on the crystal orientation relative to $\mathbf{p}$. $W(E)$ can be evaluated by methods standard to field theory. The only information about $g(\{\alpha_s\})$ which is needed is the average value of the occupation number $\bar{\alpha}_s$ of each phonon state s. For thermal equilibrium,[2]

$$\bar{\alpha}_s = [\exp(\omega_s/T) - 1]^{-1},$$

since the phonons obey Bose statistics. The result of performing the sum in Eq. (11) is that

$$W(E) = 2/\Gamma \operatorname{Re} \int_0^\infty d\mu \exp[i\mu(E - E_0 + i\Gamma/2) + g(\mu)], \quad (12)$$

where

[2] From now on, we will express frequencies and temperatures in energy units.

$$g(\mu) = \sum_s \frac{p_s^2}{2NM\omega_s} [\bar{\alpha}_s e^{i\mu\omega_s} + (\bar{\alpha}_s + 1)e^{-i\mu\omega_s} - 2\bar{\alpha}_s - 1]. \tag{13}$$

$W(E)$ is proportional to the resonance absorption cross section of a nucleus in a crystal for a monochromatic γ-ray of energy E.

$$\sigma(E) = \frac{\Gamma^2}{4} \sigma_0 W(E), \tag{14}$$

$$\sigma_0 = 2 \frac{(2I_C + 1)}{(2I_A + 1)} \pi\lambda^2 \frac{\Gamma_\gamma}{\Gamma}. \tag{15}$$

σ_0 is the cross section at resonance for nuclear absorption of a gamma ray by a free atom. Γ is the total width of the nuclear excited state, while Γ_γ is the partial width for γ-emission; $\Gamma_\gamma = (1 + \alpha_T)^{-1}\Gamma$, where α_T is the total internal conversion coefficient. If we were considering resonance scattering, the factor Γ_γ/Γ in σ_0 would be squared.

$W(E)$ for emission differs from (12) only in that $g(\mu)$ is replaced by $g(-\mu)$. Thus the self-absorption cross section is, for a thin absorber,

$$\sigma' = \frac{\int \sigma(E) W_E(E)\, dE}{\int W_E(E)\, dE} = \frac{\Gamma^3}{8\pi} \sigma_0 \int W_A(E) W_E(E)\, dE, \tag{16}$$

where W_E and W_A are the Lamb integrals (12) for emission and absorption, respectively.

If we suppose now that our emitter is moving relative to the absorber, then the argument of W_E in (16) should be $E + v/cE_0 = E + S$, where v is the relative velocity. It is easy to show that

$$\int W_A(E) W_E(E + S)\, dE = \frac{4\pi}{\Gamma} W'(S), \tag{17}$$

where $W'(S)$ is given by Eq. (12), with $E - E_0$ replaced by S, Γ by 2Γ, and $g(\mu)$ by $g_A(\mu) + g_E(-\mu)$. g_A is (13) with parameters appropriate to the absorbing crystal; g_E with the parameters of the emitting crystal. Then σ' becomes

$$\sigma'(S) = \Gamma^2 \sigma_0 W'(S)/2. \tag{18}$$

IV. NUMERICAL CALCULATIONS

If the assumption is made that the crystal is isotropic, p_s^2 in Eq. (13) can be replaced by $\frac{1}{3}p^2$.[3] Then, on replacing the sum by an integral, $g(\mu)$ becomes

[3] This can best be seen in Eq. (19) of Lamb's paper, where each of the p_s^2's occurs at most linearly.

$$g(\mu) = \frac{R}{3N}\int_0^{\omega_{\max}} \frac{N(\omega)}{\omega}\, d\omega\, [\bar{\alpha}e^{i\mu\omega} + (\bar{\alpha}+1)e^{-i\mu\omega} - 2\bar{\alpha} - 1], \qquad (19)$$

where $N(\omega)\, d\omega$ is the number of phonon states in $d\omega$ at ω, and $\omega_{\max}$ is the maximum phonon energy. The total number of states is equal to the number of degrees of freedom in the crystal;

$$\int_0^{\omega_{\max}} N(\omega)\, d\omega = 3N. \qquad (20)$$

According to the Debye model, $N(\omega) = 9N\omega^2/\theta^3$ and $\omega_{\max} = \theta$. With $N(\omega)$ thus specified, $g(\mu)$ can be evaluated quite accurately by making polynomial approximations to the hyperbolic function which occurs in the integrand, and $W(E)$ can then be integrated on a digital computer. We have calculated $\sigma(E)$ and $\sigma'(S)$ for the Ir^{191} 129-kev γ-ray with parameters taken to be $E_0 = 129$ kev, $R = 46$ millivolts, $\Gamma = 4.6$ microvolts, $\alpha_K = 2.47$, $I_C = 5/2$, $I_A = 3/2$, and abundance = 38.5 percent. For simplicity we assumed that the crystal structure of the emitter is the same as that of the absorber, and found that to fit the self-absorption cross section as measured by Mössbauer with both emitter and absorber at 88°K one must use a Debye temperature $\theta = 316$°K. The calculated cross section is sensitive to the shape of the spectrum for moderate and high phonon energies where the Debye spectrum is known to be a poor approximation; therefore little significance should be attached to the difference between this Debye temperature and that determined from specific heat, namely 285°K.

The curves on Figs. 1 and 2, which respectively show Mössbauer's experimental points for the turntable effect and temperature effect, are some of the results of this calculation. Our adjustment of θ guarantees that the turntable effect curve coincide with the experimental point at zero velocity, and that the temperature effect curve agree with experiment at 88°K. These two experimental points really represent the same measurement.

The curve of Fig. 1, which is fitted to the bottom of the transmission dip, agrees satisfactorily with the rest of the points even though the calculations are for a thin absorber. A correction for the moderately thick (10^{21} atoms/cm^2) absorber which Mössbauer used would be in a direction such as to improve the fit for large velocities.

The curve of Fig. 2 deviates noticeably from the experimental points at 148 and 175°K. This deviation could probably be corrected by using a phonon spectrum which is more realistic than the Debye spectrum.

Figure 3 shows the results of the calculation for $\sigma(E)$, Eq. (14), for several temperatures. The emission spectrum $W_E(E)$ has the same shape as $\sigma(E)$ when it is reflected through the pip at $E = E_0$. The pip in both $\sigma(E)$ and $W_E(E)$ has width $\Gamma = 4.6\ \mu$v. It is interesting to notice that the pip has virtually disappeared at $T = 300$°K, and that the rest of the curve has very nearly acquired the shape

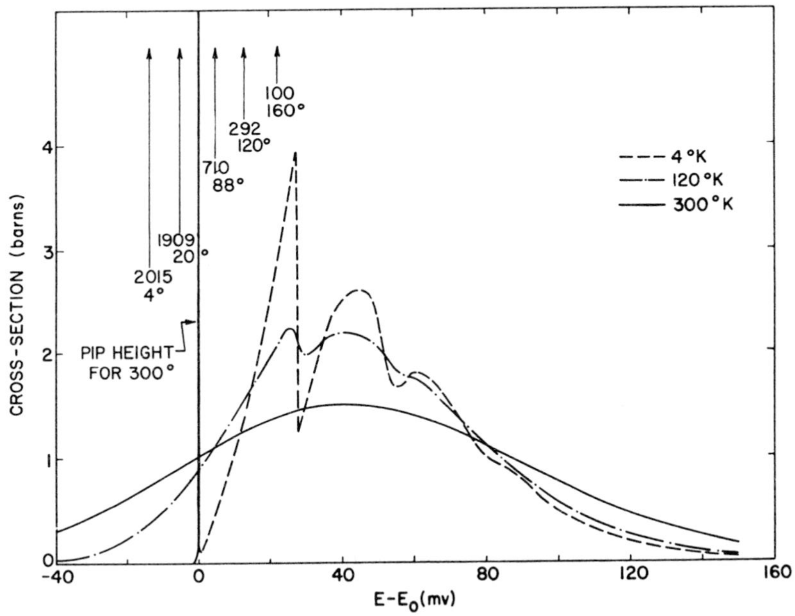

FIG. 3. The absorption cross section per nucleus in a crystal of natural iridium, for a monochromatic γ-ray beam and a Debye spectrum for the phonons. The lowest temperature plotted is 4°K. 20°K would be indistinguishable from it except within 3 mv of $E - E^0 = 0$, where the 20° curve is up to 1/10 barn higher, and at the Debye energy $\theta = 27.2$ mv, where the corners are slightly rounded.

which one would expect for a gaseous absorber; namely, a Gaussian centered at $E - E_0 = R = 46$ mv with width $2\sqrt{RT} = 69$ mv.

Some results of the calculation of $\sigma'(S)$, the self-absorption cross section in the thin-absorber approximation, are given in Fig. 4 as a function of Doppler shift S. The width of the pip in this curve is $2\Gamma = 9.2$ μv.

The variation of the self-absorption cross section $\sigma'(0)$ is shown in Fig. 5 as a function of the Debye temperature θ, for both source and absorber at 88°K. The curve levels off below $\theta = 200$°K because here the no-recoil pip has essentially entirely disappeared.

Figure 6 shows $\sigma'(0)$ as a function of source and absorber temperature. Mössbauer measured $\sigma'(0) = 10.0 \pm 0.5$ barns at $T = 88$°K; this point has, as we stated above, been fit by taking $\theta = 316$°K. The calculation predicts that at liquid helium temperature the self-absorption cross section will rise to 80 barns and that it will decrease by only about 10% when the temperature is raised to 20°K.

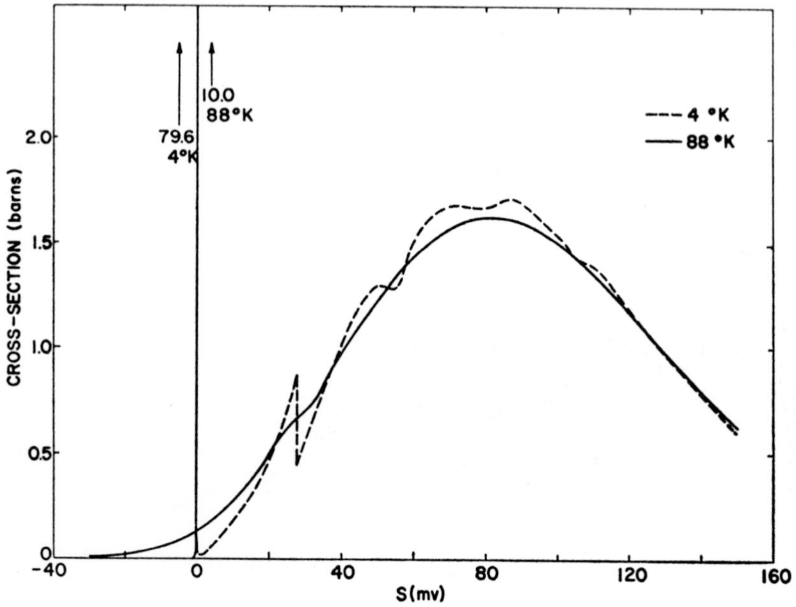

FIG. 4. Same as Fig. 3 except in this case the γ-ray beam is that coming from an activated iridium crystal at the same temperature as the absorber. The abscissa is here the Doppler shift in the emitted gammas induced by mechanical motion of the source relative to the absorber. A speed of 2330 cm/sec is required for $S = 10$ mv.

V. APPLICATION TO THE STUDY OF LATTICE VIBRATIONS

The behavior of the calculated absorption cross section $\sigma(E)$ (Fig. 3) at liquid helium temperature, with a fairly linear rise from the pip at $E = E_0$ until $E - E_0 = \theta$, then a vertical drop, strongly suggests that the cross section for $\Gamma < E - E_0 < \theta$ is due mostly to absorption accompanied by emission of a single phonon. The bumps at higher values of $E - E_0$ might be identified with 2, 3, 4, $\cdots$ phonon processes.

This conjecture can be easily expressed in analytical terms, in the limit of zero temperature. $g(\mu)$ for $T = 0(\bar{\alpha} = 0)$ becomes

$$g(\mu)\,|_{T=0} = g_0 + g_1(\mu), \tag{21}$$

where

$$g_0 = -\frac{R}{3N}\int_0^{\omega_{\max}} \frac{N(\omega)}{\omega}\, d\omega$$

and

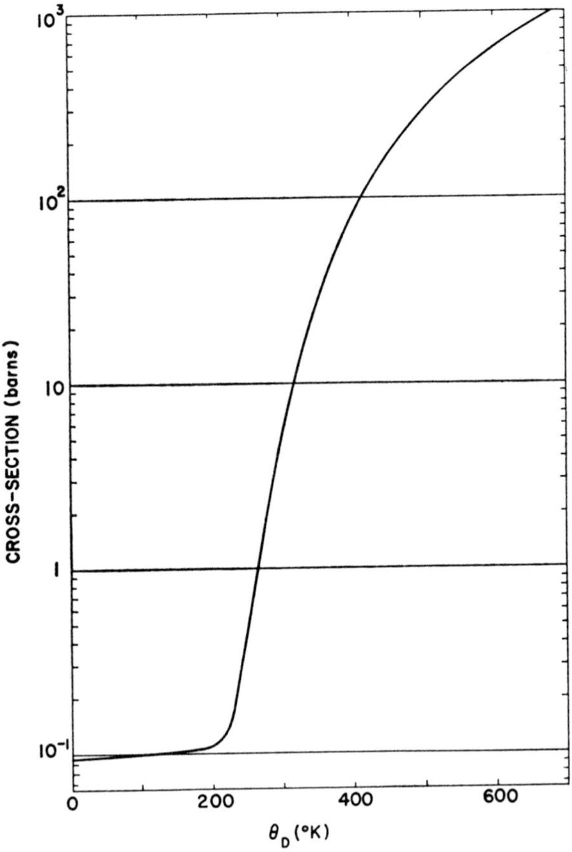

FIG. 5. The variation of the self-absorption cross section as a function of Debye temperature θ, for both source and absorber at 88°K, and no mechanical motion. Below about θ = 200°K the no-recoil pip disappears entirely for this temperature.

$$g_1(\mu) = \frac{R}{3N} \int_0^{\omega_{\max}} \frac{N(\omega)}{\omega} e^{-i\mu\omega} \, d\omega.$$

$g_1(\mu)$ is just the square of the single-phonon emission matrix element, integrated over the phonon spectrum, and e^{g_0} is the probability that no phonons will be created in the γ-emission process. The term containing $\exp(+i\mu\omega)$ in Eq. (19) is the phonon absorption matrix element; since $T = 0$ and there are no phonons in the initial state, it does not occur in Eq. (21). We now expand

$$e^{g(\mu)} = e^{g_0} \left\{ 1 + g_1(\mu) + \frac{[g_1(\mu)]^2}{2!} + \cdots \right\},$$

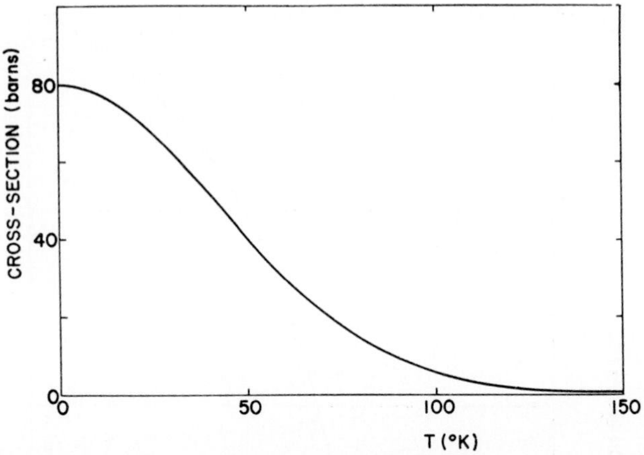

FIG. 6. The self-absorption cross section as a function of temperature of source and absorber. This curve has been fitted to Mössbauer's measurement of $\sigma' = 10$ barns at $T = 88°$ by taking $\theta = 316°$K.

and substitute into Eq. (12), which then becomes

$$W(E) = W_0(E) + W_1(E) + W_2(E) + \cdots , \tag{22}$$

where

$$W_n(E) = \frac{2e^{g_0}}{n!\Gamma} \operatorname{Re} \int_0^\infty [g_1(\mu)]^n e^{i\mu(E-E_0+i\Gamma/2)}\, d\mu. \tag{23}$$

It is clear that $W_n(E)$ is the contribution to $W(E)$ from n-phonon emission.

$W(E)$ is not directly observable but $W'(S)$ is, because it is proportional to the absorption cross section $\sigma'(S)$ in a thin absorber in a Mössbauer-type experiment. If, for simplicity, we again assume that the structures of the absorber and emitter crystals are the same, then $W'(S)$ can be written, in the limit of zero temperature,

$$W'(S) = W_0'(S) + W_1'(S) + \cdots , \tag{24}$$

where

$$W_0'(S) = \frac{e^{2g_0}}{S^2 + \Gamma^2} \tag{25}$$

is the no-recoil pip, and

$$W_1'(S) = \frac{2\pi R}{3N\Gamma}\, e^{2g_0}\, \frac{N(S)}{S} \tag{26}$$

is the single-phonon contribution. In general

$$W_n'(S) = \frac{e^{2g_0}}{n!}\frac{\pi}{\Gamma}\left(\frac{2R}{3N}\right)^n \int_0^{\omega_{\max}} \frac{N(\omega_1)}{\omega_1}\, d\omega_1 \cdots \int_0^{\omega_{\max}} \frac{N(\omega_n)}{\omega_n} \cdot d\omega_n\, \delta(S - \omega_1 - \cdots - \omega_n). \tag{27}$$

If one could find a crystal which contains an isomer with parameters such that $W_n'(S)$ for $n \geqq 2$ could be neglected compared to W_1' for $S \leqq \omega_{\max}$, then a measurement of the self-absorption cross section $\sigma'(S)$ for $\Gamma < S \leqq \omega_{\max}$ would yield a result proportional to $N(S)/S$. This experiment would require a moderately high-speed rotor (capable of speeds up to 10^4 cm/sec), and ideally would be done with source and absorber both at absolute zero. At a finite temperature which still is very small compared to the Debye temperature, the measured $\sigma'(S)$ would be proportional to $N(S)/S$ smeared out over a range in S of the order of the temperature; thus any structure of $N(S)$ with wavelength $\Delta S \lesssim T$ would be lost.

In order to find criteria which indicate whether or not a given nucleus and a given crystal could form a system with which the above experiment could profitably be performed, we will once again use the Debye model.

For a Debye crystal $g_0 = -3R/2\theta$, and

$$W_0'(S) = \frac{e^{-3R/\theta}}{S^2 + \Gamma^2},$$

$$W_1'(S) = \begin{cases} \dfrac{6\pi RS}{\Gamma\theta^3}\, e^{-3R/\theta} & 0 \leqq S \leqq \theta, \\ 0 & \text{otherwise}, \end{cases}$$

$$W_2'(S) = \frac{\pi}{2\Gamma}\left(\frac{6R}{\theta^3}\right)^2 e^{-3R/\theta} \times \begin{cases} \dfrac{S^3}{6} & \theta \leqq S \leqq \theta, \\ S\theta^2 - \dfrac{S^3 + 4\theta^3}{6} & \theta < S \leqq 2\theta, \\ 0 & \text{otherwise}, \end{cases} \tag{28}$$

$$\vdots$$

$$W_n'(S) = \begin{cases} \dfrac{e^{-3R/\theta}}{n!}\left(\dfrac{6R}{\theta^3}\right)^n \dfrac{\pi}{\Gamma}\dfrac{S^{2n-1}}{(2n-1)!} & 0 \leqq S \leqq \theta, \\ 0 & S < 0 \\ & S > n\theta. \end{cases}$$

$\sum_{n=0}^{\infty} W_n'(S)$ always converges rapidly for $0 \leqq S \leqq \theta$, since in this range, for $n > 0$,

$$\frac{W'_{n+1}(S)}{W_n'(S)} = \frac{6R}{\theta^3} \frac{S^2}{2n(2n+1)(n+1)}. \tag{29}$$

Equation (29) attains its maximum value at $S = \theta$, so W_2'/W_1' is at most $R/2\theta$, W_3'/W_2' at most $R/10\theta$, etc. Therefore an ideal crystal would be one which has a relatively high Debye temperature, while containing nuclei having an isomeric state such that $E_0^2/2Mc^2 = R$ is fairly small.

In choosing examples of nuclei which might be usable, the mechanisms by which the isomeric state can be excited must be considered. The first possibility which suggests itself is that used by Mössbauer, who used a source of Os^{191} which β-decays to an isomeric state of Ir^{191}. This scheme, however, involves different crystals in the source and absorber; thus W_1' would be a superposition of phonon spectra for the two. If the source crystal were mostly constructed of the same nuclei as the absorber, with only a small doping of the parent nucleus, then this difficulty would be avoided, at the expense of intensity.

Another possibility is excitation by bremsstrahlung. One might think in this case that one of the basic premises on which the theory rests, namely that the initial state in the emission process is one of thermal equilibrium, is violated. It can be shown, however, by using Eq. (5) rather than Eq. (7) as a starting point, that as long as the incoming bremsstrahlung beam contains a range of frequencies large compared to $\omega_{\max}$, that the same result obtains for $W(E)$, provided that the relaxation time of the crystal is long compared to the isomer lifetime. Excitation by particle bombardment generally will leave the nucleus with enough recoil energy to remove it from its lattice site.

For a system for which $R/2\theta \ll 1$, the absorption cross section per atom in the absorber is given, in the Debye approximation, by

$$\sigma_A(S) = \sigma_{\mathrm{NN}} + \frac{1}{2}\sigma_0 e^{-3R/\theta}\left[\frac{\Gamma^2}{S^2+\Gamma^2} + \frac{6\pi R\Gamma S}{\theta^3}\right], \tag{30}$$

for $0 \leqq S \leqq \theta$. σ_{NN} is the non-nuclear absorption cross section per atom; predominantly due to K-photoeffect for gammas near 100 kev, it varies from only a few barns to many thousand barns, depending on Z and gamma energy.[4] The one-phonon term in Eq. (30) can be rewritten as

$$\sigma_1'(S) = \frac{121}{A}\left(\frac{300}{\theta}\right)^2 \frac{2I_C+1}{2I_A+1} \frac{e^{-3R/\theta}}{\tau_\gamma} \frac{S}{\theta} \times 10^3 \text{ barns}, \tag{31}$$

where $R = 6.19E_0^2/A$ °K, if E_0 is expressed in kilovolts, θ and S in °K, and $\tau_\gamma = \hbar/\Gamma_\gamma$ in units of 10^{-10} sec.

[4] Tables of γ-absorption cross sections are given by Davisson (4).

σ_1' will be large for a short-lived isomer of low excitation energy, two conditions which are hard to satisfy simultaneously.[5] As an example, if an isomer were found with $\tau_\gamma = 10^{-10}$ sec, $E_0 = 80$ kev, $A = 200$, $\theta = 300$ °K, then $R/2\theta = 0.33$, and $\sigma_1'(\theta) = 2000$ barns, much larger than σ_{NN} if 80 kev is just below the K-absorption edge. The listed isomers seem not to have properties this favorable; Te^{125} for example has $\sigma'(\theta) \approx 5$ barns, but at an energy (35 kev) where the non-nuclear absorption is several thousand barns. Since the background is nearly all absorption by bound electrons, however, a resonance scattering measurement would be better from the point of view of statistics and might be preferable to an absorption experiment. The scattering cross section is just $\Gamma_\alpha/\Gamma = (1 + \alpha_T)^{-1}$ times the self-absorption cross section $\sigma'(S)$.

VI. SUMMARY

The technique of resonance absorption of gamma rays by nuclei bound in crystals at low temperature has been shown by Mössbauer to be a valuable tool in the measurement of natural level widths of nuclear isomers. In the present paper we have shown that it can also be used to determine the frequency distribution of crystal lattice vibrations, in a different and perhaps easier manner than the methods used previously.[6]

The assumption has been made throughout the calculations that we are dealing with simple, isotropic crystals, and the numerical estimates have all been based on the Debye model. The theory describing more complicated situations will of course be more involved, but its results should be proportionately richer in interpretation. If, for example, one had anisotropic crystals as source and absorber, a Mössbauer type experiment could separate the frequency distributions of the normal modes with different polarizations. If the nuclei were aligned, still more information would be obtainable, about the spins of the nuclear states and possibly about the crystal structure, too.

Numerous and fruitful discussions of these problems with many colleagues at Los Alamos are hereby appreciatively acknowledged. Nuclear gamma-ray resonance absorption experiments are currently in progress at this Laboratory.

Note added in proof: Some experiments have been completed both at this laboratory (Craig, *et al.*, *Phys. Rev. Letters* **3,** 221 (1959)), and at Argonne (Lee, *et al.*, *Phys. Rev. Letters* **3,** 223 (1959)). The results agree with and extend those of Mössbauer to lower temperatures.

Received: May 7, 1959

[5] A table of short-lived isomeric states is given by Alburger (*5*). The half-life of Au^{197}, given there as 1.90×10^{-10}, should be 1.90×10^{-9} sec.

[6] These methods involve scattering of slow neutrons or x-rays. The field of neutron interactions with solids has recently been reviewed by Kothari and Singwi (*6*).

ANNALS OF PHYSICS: **9**, 332–339 (1960)

Some Simple Features of the Mössbauer Effect*

HARRY J. LIPKIN†

Department of Physics, University of Illinois, Urbana, Illinois, and Argonne National Laboratory, Lemont, Illinois

A simple description is given of the change in the state of a crystal lattice upon emission or absorption of a nuclear gamma ray. A sum rule is derived for the average energy transfer to the lattice. The probability of zero energy transfer is calculated. The results are general and do not assume a particular model for the crystal. Conclusions are presented as simple principles which may be useful as a guide to experimentalists.

INTRODUCTION

Recent experiments by Mössbauer (*1*) and others (*2*) have shown that it is possible for nuclei bound in crystal lattices to emit or absorb gamma radiation having an energy equal to that of the nuclear transition. The recoil momentum is taken by the crystal as a whole, with negligible energy transfer, and there is an appreciable probability, although small, that there is no energy transfer to or from the lattice vibrations.

The theory of this Mössbauer effect is similar to that of other phenomena involving transitions in atoms or nuclei bound in lattices (3, *4*) such as excitons or neutron capture. Calculations based on the treatments of these other cases have been made (*5*). These are rather complicated, involving the evaluation of difficult integrals to obtain detailed information in specific cases. Results can only be obtained when certain simplifying assumptions are made regarding the nature of the crystal.

Because the experimental effect is small, it is of interest to look for simple qualitative conclusions having a general validity (i.e., independent of the details of a particular model of a crystal) which can serve as a guide to experimenters in choosing experimental parameters. These can be obtained rather simply, avoiding the complications of the other treatments, if we only consider the property of greatest interest; namely, the change in the lattice state when a gamma ray is emitted or absorbed. For this calculation, the line shape of the nuclear transition is irrelevant, and the Breit–Wigner formula does not appear. All nuclear proper-

* This research was supported in part by the joint program of the U. S. Atomic Energy Commission and the Office of Naval Research.

† On leave from the Weizmann Institute of Science, Rehovoth, Israel.

ties drop out in the calculation except the momentum transfer in the transition and the nuclear mass.

THE TRANSITION MATRIX ELEMENT

Let us first consider the emission or absorption of a gamma ray by a free nucleus which is not bound in a lattice. This transition can be described in terms of a matrix element M of some operator A between the initial state $i)$ and the final state $f)$ of the nucleus:

$$M = (f \mid A(x_i, p_i, \sigma_i) \mid i). \tag{1}$$

The operator A depends upon the coordinates, momenta and spins of the particles in the nucleus. Let us now express the operator A in terms of the center-of-mass coordinate of the nucleus, $\mathbf{X}$, and a set of relative coordinates q which include spins. The dependence of A upon the center-of-mass coordinate $\mathbf{X}$ is determined completely by the requirements of translational and Galilean invariance; i.e., by the requirements that momentum should be conserved and that the transition probability for a moving observer (nonrelativistic) should not depend upon the velocity of the observer. For the emission of a gamma ray of momentum $\hbar K$, the above requirements are satisfied only if the operator A has the form

$$A = \exp(i\mathbf{K}\cdot\mathbf{X})a(q), \tag{2}$$

where the operator $a(q)$ depends only upon the relative variables and spins of the particles and has an explicit form depending upon the nature of the transition (electric, magnetic, dipole, quadrupole, etc.). The explicit form of $a(q)$ is of no interest for our present purposes.

Let us now consider the emission or absorption of a gamma ray by a nucleus bound in a crystal. The operator describing the transition is the same operator A, but we must now take the matrix element between initial and final states of the whole lattice, rather than of the free nucleus. Because the crystal forces are very weak compared to the internal nuclear forces, we can assume that the binding forces act only upon the center-of-mass motion of the nucleus and do not perturb the internal degrees of freedom. We can now write down an expression for the matrix element describing the transition in which a gamma-ray of momentum $\hbar K$ is emitted by a nucleus whose center-of-mass coordinate is X_L, while the lattice goes from a state specified by quantum numbers n_i to a state specified by quantum numbers n_f, and the internal state of the emitting nucleus changes from $i)$ to $f)$. This is

$$M_L = (n_f \mid \exp(i\mathbf{K}\cdot\mathbf{X}_L) \mid n_i)\cdot(f \mid a(q) \mid i). \tag{3}$$

The matrix element thus separates into the product of a factor depending only upon the lattice and a factor depending only upon the internal structure of the nucleus. The transition probability is proportional to the square of the matrix element (3).[1] We are not interested in the absolute transition rate, but in the relative probability of different energy transfers to the lattice. That is, we are interested in the probability $P(n_f, n_i)$ that the lattice will be in a particular state n_f after the transition if it is initially in the state n_i. The probability $P(n_f, n_i)$ is proportional to the square of the matrix element (3), with the constant of proportionality chosen to make the total probability of a transition from the state n_i to any other state to be unity,

$$\sum_{n_f} P(n_f, n_i) = 1. \tag{4}$$

The dependence of the matrix element M_L upon the nuclear structure matrix element $(f \mid a(q) \mid i)$ occurs as a common factor for all lattice states and can be dropped in calculating the relative probability. We therefore have

$$P(n_f, n_i) = \mid (n_f \mid \exp(i\mathbf{K}\cdot\mathbf{X}_L) \mid n_i) \mid^2. \tag{5}$$

The proportionality constant turns out to be unity, as can be verified by substituting (5) into (4) and evaluating the sum by closure.

A SUM RULE

We can now derive a sum rule by making the following assumption; that the interatomic forces in the crystal depend only upon the positions of the atoms and not upon their velocities. The only term in the Hamiltonian H for the lattice which does not commute with $\mathbf{X}_L$ is the kinetic energy of that nucleus, $\mathbf{P}_L^2/2M$, where M is the mass of the nucleus and $\mathbf{P}_L$ is the momentum. We therefore have

$$[H, \mathbf{X}_L] = -i\hbar\mathbf{P}_L/M \tag{6a}$$

$$\{[H, \exp(i\mathbf{K}\cdot\mathbf{X}_L)], \exp(-i\mathbf{K}\cdot\mathbf{X}_L)\} = -(\hbar K)^2/M \tag{6b}$$

Writing Eq. (6b) as a matrix equation and taking the diagonal element for the state n_i we obtain the sum rule

$$\sum_{n_f} \{E(n_f) - E(n_i)\} \mid (n_f \mid \exp(i\mathbf{K}\cdot\mathbf{X}_L) \mid n_i) \mid^2 = \sum_{n_f} \{E(n_f) - E(n_i)\} P(n_f, n_i) = \frac{(\hbar K)^2}{2M}, \tag{7}$$

where $E(n_f)$ and $E(n_i)$ are the energies of the states n_f and n_i.

[1] We neglect the dependence of the density of final states of the emitted γ-ray upon the energy transfer to the lattice. This is justified since the γ-ray energy is greater than lattice energies by a factor of at least 10^5. This approximation is not valid for neutron capture.

The sum rule (7) says that the average energy transferred to the lattice is *just the energy which the individual nucleus would have if it recoiled freely.*[2]

Note that the Mössbauer transitions in which no energy is transferred to the lattice $[E(n_f) = E(n_i)]$ do not contribute to the sum rule. Thus if we want an appreciable probability that there be *no energy transfer to the lattice* the sum rule requires an appreciable probability for an energy transfer which is *greater* than that which a freely recoiling nucleus would receive. We will tend to get an increased Mössbauer effect when the nucleus can transfer energy to high frequency lattice modes; i.e., in a crystal with a high Debye temperature. If the nucleus under consideration is an impurity in a lattice, it should be strongly bound in a localized position.

An ideal situation would occur if the nucleus were bound in a localized well and could oscillate in this well without appreciably perturbing the other lattice modes. If the excitation energy of this mode were larger than the free recoil energy $(\hbar K)^2/2M$), the sum rule (7) would be exhausted by a probability less than unity for exciting this mode. The remaining probability would all go into the Mössbauer effect.

A MORE DETAILED CALCULATION

Let us now attempt to calculate explicitly the probability $P(n_i, n_i)$ that the lattice remains in its initial state after the emission of the gamma ray, which therefore carries the full energy of the nuclear transition. We now need a more detailed model of the lattice. Let us assume that the interatomic forces are harmonic, so that a simple transformation to normal modes is possible. These modes will be described by normal coordinates ξ_s. The state of the lattice can be specified by the set of quantum numbers $\{n_s\}$ describing the state of excitation of each normal mode.

Let us express the coordinate X_L in terms of the normal coordinates and introduce this into Eq. (5). We have

$$\boldsymbol{\varepsilon}_{\mathbf{K}} \cdot \mathbf{X}_L = \sum_s a_{Ls}\xi_s , \tag{8}$$

where $\boldsymbol{\varepsilon}_{\mathbf{K}}$ is a unit vector in the direction of the vector **K**. We can choose the normalization of the normal coordinates such that

$$\sum_s (a_{Ls})^2 = 1. \tag{9}$$

[2] This result has been derived for the emission process. The author is indebted to W. M. Visscher for pointing out that it applies as well to absorption only if the incident γ-radiation has a flat spectrum over the resonance region.

We then have

$$P(\{n_s\},\{n_s\}) = |(\{n_s\} \mid \exp(iK \sum_s a_{Ls}\xi_s) \mid \{n_s\})|^2$$
$$= \prod_s |(n_s \mid \exp(iKa_{Ls}\xi_s) \mid n_s)|^2. \tag{10}$$

Elegant methods have been developed for the evaluation of expressions having the form (10) including averaging over all states $\{n_s\}$ with the appropriate statistical factor corresponding to thermal equilibrium at a given temperature (*6*). We shall use a simple approximate method. We note that if we expand the exponentials in (10), only the even powers of ξ_s have nonvanishing matrix elements. We can therefore write

$$P(\{n_s\},\{n_s\}) = [\prod_s (1 - h_s)]^2, \tag{11}$$

where

$$h_s = (n_s \mid (Ka_{Ls}\xi_s)^2 \mid n_s)/2 + \text{terms of order } K^4a_{Ls}^4(n_s \mid \xi^4 \mid n_s).$$

Let us expand

$$\prod_s (1 - h_s) = 1 - \sum_s h_s + \sum_{s \neq t} h_s h_t/2 + \cdots . \tag{12}$$

We note that the expansion (12) is the same as that for $\exp(-\sum_s h_s)$, except for the exclusion of repeated indices. If each h_s is small compared to unity, even though $\sum_s h_s$ may not be small, we can write

$$\prod_s (1 - h_s) = \exp(-\sum_s h_s) + \text{terms of order } \sum_s h_s^2. \tag{13}$$

We therefore have

$$P(\{n_s\},\{n_s\}) = \exp \sum_s \{-K^2a_{Ls}^2(n_s \mid \xi_s^2 \mid n_s)\}$$
$$+ \text{terms of order } K^4 \sum_s a_{Ls}^4\langle\xi_s^4\rangle. \tag{14}$$

The expectation value of ξ_s^2 in the state n_s is easily evaluated by noting that the potential energy for a harmonic oscillator $\frac{1}{2} M\omega_s^2\xi_s^2$, has an expectation value of $(n_s + \frac{1}{2})\hbar\omega_s/2$, where ω_s is the oscillator frequency for the s-mode.[3] We therefore obtain

$$P(\{n_s\},\{n_s\}) \approx \exp \sum_s \{-(2n_s + 1)[(\hbar K)^2/2M\hbar\omega_s]a_{Ls}^2\} \tag{15}$$

neglecting the higher order terms.

[3] The mass M is the mass of the nucleus emitting the γ-ray. This relation is valid even if the crystal consists of different types of atoms having different atomic masses.

The factor $(\hbar K)^2/2M\hbar\omega_s$ is just the ratio of the free recoil energy to the energy of the sth lattice vibration normal mode. If the lattice is in its lowest state (at 0°K), every n_s is zero and the exponent in (15) is just the ratio of the free recoil energy to some average lattice vibration energy $\hbar\omega_{\mathrm{Av}}$ defined by

$$(\hbar\omega_{\mathrm{Av}})^{-1} = \sum_s a_{Ls}^2/\hbar\omega_s . \tag{16}$$

This is a harmonic mean, in which each mode is given a statistical weight corresponding to the contribution of that mode in the expansion of $\mathbf{X}_L$ in normal modes (Eqs. 8, 9). We see that the probability of an effect (15) decreases very rapidly if the free recoil energy increases above this average lattice energy.

The neglect of the higher order terms in (15) is justified in the region of interest, where the argument of the exponential is of the order of unity. If the number of relevant normal modes is large, then each individual term is small. The sum of the squares of these terms is therefore very small and can be neglected.

At finite temperatures the effect is reduced because of the presence of the factor $2n_s + 1$ in the exponent of Eq. (16). This reduction becomes serious at temperatures corresponding roughly to the mean lattice energy (16) where the factor $2n_s + 1$ is different from unity in a region which contributes appreciably to the sum (16).

The results (15) and (16) are general in that they apply to any crystal in which the forces are harmonic. The particular case of the Debye model has been considered by Visscher (*5*). We can get his result by setting a_{Ls} = constant and taking a density of lattice modes which is proportional to ω_s^2. For this case

$$(\hbar\omega_{\mathrm{Av}})_{\substack{\mathrm{Debye}\\ T=0^\circ}} = \tfrac{2}{3}(\hbar\omega_{\max}) = \tfrac{2}{3}\,k\Theta. \tag{17a}$$

Thus

$$P(\{n_s\},\{n_s\})_{\substack{\mathrm{Debye}\\ T=0^\circ}} = \exp\{-\tfrac{3}{2}(\hbar K)^2/2Mk\Theta\}. \tag{17b}$$

CONCLUSIONS

The expressions (15) and (17) lead to the same conclusions as the sum rule (7); that probability of gamma-ray emission without energy transfer to or from the lattice increases with the average energy of the lattice modes which are coupled to the recoiling nucleus and the effect becomes appreciable when this average energy is of the same order of magnitude as the free recoil energy. From the explicit form of the relations (15) and (17) with their exponential dependence upon the parameters of interest, we see that the effect is very sensitive to the experimental conditions. The experimental results (*1, 2*) indicate that

$$P(\{n_s\},\{n_s\})$$

is of the order of a few per cent. In this region, a change in the exponent in (15) or (17) by a factor of two can change the effect by an order of magnitude.

The influence of the ambient temperature upon the effect [the factor $(2n_s + 1)$ in Eq. (15)] is easily understood as "stimulated emission and absorption" of phonons: the probability of energy exchange between the lattice and the recoiling nucleus increases with the degree of excitation of the lattice.

The results might be summarized crudely by the following simple statement which could have been made in advance without any calculation: The Mössbauer experiment is described in terms of three characteristic temperatures or energies; (1) the energy of the free recoil, (2) a characteristic temperature for the lattice (e.g., the Debye temperature), and (3) the ambient temperature. To obtain an effect, the lattice temperature should be of the same order as the free recoil energy, and the ambient temperature should be low compared to these. The explicit results add two further important features which are of considerable interest to the experimentalist trying to increase the effect by varying parameters. First, there is the exponential dependence in Egs. (15) and (17), indicating that a small change in these parameters can have a large effect on the experiment. Second, there is the definition of the average lattice vibration energy (16), which is clearly a different kind of an average from those used by solid state physicists to compute properties such as specific heats. There is therefore no simple relation between the characteristic lattice temperature for Mössbauer scattering and the Debye temperature, except for very simple models which are generally not exactly valid. These two temperatures will be of the same order of magnitude, but the effect of the difference is very much accentuated by the exponential dependence of (15).

It is therefore of interest for the experimentalist to look for transitions having a *low free recoil energy*, and for crystals having a high "effective Mössbauer temperature," Eq. (16). More complicated crystals (compounds, alloys, or impurities) should be chosen for strong binding of the source or absorber atoms, rather than for high Debye temperatures. The latter may be due to irrelevant normal modes. This is particularly true in light elements where low mass, rather than strong binding gives high Debye temperature (7).

The author would like to express his appreciation to F. Seitz, T. D. Schultz, G. Rickayzen, and R. Knox for illuminating discussions on the solid-state aspects of the problem; to D. R. Inglis for many stimulating discussions; to J. P. Schiffer and L. Meyer-Schützmeister for discussions of experimental results; and to R. M. Thaler and W. M. Visscher for information about the Los Alamos calculations.

RECEIVED: September 25, 1959

REFERENCES

1. R. L. MÖSSBAUER, *Z. Physik* **151**, 124 (1958); *Naturwiss.* **45**, 538 (1958); *Z. Naturforsch.* **14a**, 211 (1959).

2. L. L. Lee, Jr., L. Meyer-Schützmeister, J. P. Schiffer, and D. Vincent, *Phys. Rev. Letters* **3**, 223 (1959); P. P. Craig, J. G. Dash, A. D. McGuire, D. Nagle, and R. R. Reiswig, *Phys. Rev. Letters* **3**, 221 (1959).
3. W. E. Lamb, *Phys. Rev.* **55**, 190 (1939).
4. R. E. Peierls, *Ann. Physik* **13**, 905 (1932).
5. W. M. Visscher, *Annals of Physics* **9**, 194 (1960).
6. L. S. Kothari and K. S. Singwi, *Solid State Phys.* **9**, 109 (1959).
7. J. P. Schiffer and W. Marshall (private communication).

RESONANCE RADIATION OF NUCLEI BOUND IN A LATTICE

DAVID R. INGLIS
Argonne National Laboratory
Lemont, Illinois

The understanding of the processes involved in resonance radiation emitted and absorbed by nuclei bound in crystal lattices has acquired a new interest as a result of the recent revealing experiments of Mössbauer[1] and others. In the literature the interpretation of these experiments has been based on analogy with a similar problem involving resonance absorption of neutrons by bound nuclei, a problem treated by Lamb,[2] who took results from the earlier neutron resonance work of Breit and Wigner, and of Bethe and Placzek, who, in turn, had based the treatment of neutron resonances on analogy with radiation. For the sake of a concise, qualitative understanding of the problem it seems desirable to have a simple treatment of the electromagnetic radiation problem itself, eliminating the detour via neutrons.

Some of the features of the problem may be presented most simply in terms of the analogous one-dimensional problem, and this is the approach we shall use. We consider a nucleus as one bead of a string of beads, connected by springs and vibrating longitudinally. The lattice points are at $l_r = ra$, where $r = 1,2, \ldots N$, and each has a longitudinal displacement x_r, which may be Fourier-analyzed into normal coordinates q_s:

$$x_r = (2/N)^{\nu/2} \Sigma_s q_s \sin (rs\pi/N) \qquad (1)$$

Here ν is the number of dimensions; for the string of beads $\nu = 1$. The exponent $\nu/2$ is introduced for the sake of a later discussion of a crystal in which these longitudinal modes are a subset of a much larger number of modes, and where the coefficients for these modes accordingly become smaller (varying inversely as the square root of the number of atoms, which in a square or cube is N^{ν}).

The Lagrangian of the mechanical lattice is

---

† Work performed under the auspices of the U.S. Atomic Energy Commission.

[1] R. L. Mössbauer, Z. Physik, **151**, 124 (1958); Naturwiss., **45**, 538 (1958).

[2] W. E. Lamb, Jr., Phys. Rev., **55**, 190 (1939).

$$\mathcal{L}_0 = (M/2)\,\Sigma\,\dot{x}_r^2 - (K/2a)\,\Sigma\,(x_{r+1} - x_r)^2$$

$$= (M/2)\,\Sigma\,\dot{q}_s^2 - (K/a)\,\Sigma\,q_s^2[1 - \cos(\pi s/N)] \qquad (2)$$

We consider N large, without detailed concern for the end conditions, as we make the following approximation in this substitution:

$$\Sigma_r \sin^2(rs\pi/N) = N/2 \qquad \Sigma_r \sin(rs\pi/N)\cos(rs\pi/N) = 0 \qquad (3)$$

The integer s here refers to a mode of vibration of the string, indicating the number of nodes in what becomes a sine wave along the string as the string becomes continuous with large N; $(2/N)^{1/2}\,q_s$ is the amplitude of such a wave, normalized to become small with large N so that a mass factor M is retained in the last line of (2), even though a total mass NM is involved in the vibration.

We first assume a monochromatic incident electromagnetic wave described by the vector potential (or by its x component)

$$A(x,t) = \mathcal{A}\,e^{i(kx - \omega t)} \qquad (4)$$

and consider the absorption by one nucleus in the string endowed with an electric dipole $x'e$. In the real lattice, of course, each nucleus has a charge Ze, and the elastic force constant K results from the interaction of this charge with the charges of the electrons, as it appears in the quantum-mechanical treatment of the whole electrostatic energy of the system unperturbed by (4). Thus, the absorbing nucleus (which we call R) is endowed with a charge Ze, which is in effect at the nuclear center of mass when averaged over the time of lattice vibration, plus an electric dipole that shows how this nucleus differs from the others in interacting with the electromagnetic field (4). The dipole consists of a positive charge e on a proton of mass m and the rest of the nucleus which we call a core (though it need not be a closed shell), of mass (M − m). In order not to deviate from the total charge Ze assumed in K, the core is given an equivalent charge −e.

It is then fairly obvious that the coupling with the radiation comes essentially through the acceleration of the proton, in the approximation $M \gg m$, but let us nevertheless formulate this point and see how the correct position coordinate enters in the vector-potential term. The vector potential enters† the Lagrangian of a many-particle system thus:

†The simple proof of this consists in showing that the Lagrange equations in cartesian coordinates then include, among other terms, the deflecting force of the magnetic field, $F_{mag} = (e/c)\mathbf{v} \times \mathbf{H}$ with $H = \nabla \times \mathbf{A}$, as is shown for example in Van Vleck's book, "Electric and

$$\mathcal{L} = (1/2)\,\Sigma_n\, mv_n^2 - V + \Sigma_n (e/c)\mathbf{v}_n \cdot \mathbf{A} \tag{5}$$

If we neglect the interaction of A with the nuclear charges Ze and with the electrons, which would be of importance in problems of crystal optics, we have for our system

$$\begin{aligned}\mathcal{L} = {} & (1/2)M\,\Sigma^{(N-1)}\,\dot{x}_r^2 + (1/2)(M - m)\dot{x}_c^2 + (1/2)m\dot{x}_p^2 \\ & - (K/2a)\Sigma(x_{r+1} - x_r)^2 - V(x_p - x_c) + (e/c) \\ & \times [\dot{x}_p A(x_p) - \dot{x}_c A(x_c)]\end{aligned} \tag{6}$$

The sum (N − 1) includes all N values of r except r = R. Here x_p and x_c are the positions of the proton and core, and we of course reduce them to the center-of-mass and difference coordinates for the R-th nucleus,

$$x_R = [(M - m)x_c + mx_p]/M \qquad x' = x_p - x_c \tag{7}$$

and have

$$\begin{aligned}\mathcal{L} = {} & \mathcal{L}_0 + (1/2)\mu\dot{x}'^2 - V(x') + (e/c)[(\dot{x}_R + (\mu/m)\dot{x}')A(x_R + (\mu/m)x') \\ & - (\dot{x}_R - (m/M)\dot{x}')A(x_R - (m/M)x')]\end{aligned} \tag{8}$$

Here we have the usual reduced mass, $\mu = m(M - m)/M$, and the first term in $\mathcal{L}_0$ is a sum over N terms, not just $\Sigma^{(N-1)}$ over (N − 1) terms excluding $\dot{x}_R^2$ as in Eq. (6). The two cartesian momenta are

$$\begin{aligned} & P_R = \partial\mathcal{L}/\partial\dot{x}_R = M\dot{x}_R + f \qquad f = (e/c)[A(x_R + (\mu/m)x') \\ & \qquad - A(x_R - (m/M)x')] \\ & p = \partial\mathcal{L}/\partial\dot{x}' = \mu\dot{x}' + g \qquad g = (e/c)[(\mu/m)A(x_p) - (m/M)A(x_c)]\end{aligned} \tag{9}$$

If, neglecting the mass of the proton compared to the mass of the core, we put $m/M \approx 0$, $\mu/m \approx 1$, we have

$$f \approx (e/c)[\partial A/\partial x]_{x_R}\, x' + \cdots \qquad g \approx (e/c)A(x_p) \tag{9$'$}$$

Magnetic Susceptibilities,'' Oxford University Press, New York, 1932, p. 19. The fact that the acceleration in the transverse direction is involved in the longitudinal radiation process means that the problem is not truly one-dimensional, although the essential lattice part of the formulation is.

The Hamiltonian contains for these two coordinates the terms

$$(P_R - f)^2/2M + (p - g)^2/2\mu \tag{10}$$

and we may here first use the approximation (9′) and further neglect f altogether, both because it appears as f/M, which is small compared to g/μ from the mass disparity, and because the gamma-ray wavelength of interest is rather large compared to nuclear dimensions. With these approximations, and with neglect of g^2, the Hamiltonian $\mathcal{H} = \Sigma p\dot{q} - \mathcal{L}$ is

$$\mathcal{H} = (1/2M)[\Sigma^{(N-1)} P_r^2 + (P_N - f)^2] + (K/2a)\Sigma(x_{r+1} - x_r)^2$$

$$+ (p - g)^2/2\mu + V(x')$$

$$\approx (1/2M)\,\Sigma P_r^2 + (K/2a)\Sigma(x_{r+1} - x_r)^2 + p^2/2\mu + V(x')$$

$$- (e/mc)\,p \cdot A(x_p) \tag{11}$$

as some readers would have considered obvious without all this talk. One purpose of this detailed discussion has been to show why it is x_p that appears as the argument of A.

In the approximation f = 0, the lattice-point momenta are simply $P_r = M\dot{x}_r$, and the transformation to the normal coordinates and momenta p_s and q_s proceeds as in (2), $\mathcal{H} = \Sigma_s \mathcal{H}_s + \mathcal{H}_N + \mathcal{H}'$

$$\mathcal{H}_s = p_s^2/2M + (M\omega_s^2/2)q_s^2 \qquad \omega_s^2 = (2K/Ma)(1 - \cos \pi s/N)$$

$$p_s = \partial\mathcal{L}/\partial\dot{q}_s = M\dot{q}_s \rightarrow (\hbar/i)\partial/\partial q_s$$

$$\mathcal{H}_N = p^2/2\mu + V(x')$$

$$\mathcal{H}' = -(e/mc)\,p \cdot A(x_p) \tag{12}$$

The lattice part of the Hamiltonian, $\Sigma\mathcal{H}_s$, is the sum of terms s referring to the normal modes separately, and so is separable into oscillator equations each of which involves one factor in the composite wave function. The time-independent oscillator wave equation,

$$[-(\hbar^2/2M)\,\partial^2/\partial q_s^2 + (M\omega_s^2/2)q_s^2 - E_s]\,U_s(q_s) = 0 \tag{13}$$

is expressed, as shown in Eq. (13′), in the usual convenient oscillator coordinates $\xi_s = (\omega_s M/\hbar)^{1/2} q_s$:

$$(-\partial^2/\partial\xi_s^2 + \xi_s^2 - \lambda_s)\,U_s(\xi_s) = 0 \qquad \lambda_s = 2E_s/\hbar\omega_s = 2n_s + 1 \quad (13')$$

The well-known solutions $U_s(\xi_s)$ have between them the following matrix elements of ξ^2, which we shall need shortly:

$$
\begin{aligned}
\langle n|\xi^2|n+2\rangle &= (1/2)(n+1)^{1/2}(n+2)^{1/2} \\
\langle n|\xi^2|n\rangle &= (n+1/2) \\
\langle n|\xi^2|n-2\rangle &= (1/2)n^{1/2}(n-1)^{1/2} \\
\langle n|\xi\ |n+1\rangle &= [(n+1)/2]^{1/2} \\
\langle n|\xi\ |n-1\rangle &= (n/2)^{1/2}
\end{aligned} \tag{14}
$$

The nuclear part of the wave equation

$$(H_n - e_n)u_n(x) = 0 \tag{15}$$

need not be specified in any detail, as all we shall demand of the nuclear wave functions $u_n(x)$ is that there be an electric dipole transition between two of them, u_i and u_f, characterized by an energy difference $e_i - e_f = h\omega_0$.

The interaction with the electromagnetic field (4) is of course treated as the perturbation, and we shall be particularly interested in the relative contributions made by various Fourier components that enter here, without concern for the absolute strength factor C.

$$
\begin{aligned}
\mathcal{H}' &= (i\hbar e/mc)(\partial/\partial x')A[x_R + (\mu/m)x'] \\
&\approx Ce^{i[k(x_R + x') - \omega t]} \\
&= Ce^{-i\omega t}e^{ikx'}\prod_s e^{ib_s\xi_s} \\
&= Ce^{i\omega t}(1 + ikx' + \cdots)\prod_{s=1}^{n-1} e^{ib_s\xi_s}\left[1 + i\sum_{s=n}^{N} b_s\xi_s \right. \\
&\qquad \left. - \frac{1}{2}\left(\sum_{s=n}^{N} b_s\xi_s\right)^2 + \cdots\right]
\end{aligned}
$$

$$C = i\alpha e\hbar/mc \qquad b_s = C_1\omega_s^{-1/2}\sin(Rs\pi/N)$$

$$C_1 = (2/N)^{\nu/2}(\hbar/M)^{1/2}k \tag{16}$$

We see that the lattice Fourier components of the motion of the nucleus R, on which the dipole rides, enter the coefficients b_s, which contain a factor $N^{-\nu/2}$ and thus in general become small as N becomes large, but we shall see that they make a finite contribution because one obtains a sum of about N^ν terms in b_s^2.

In the fourth line of Eq. (16) the terms in the product have been separated into two classes and only those exponentials with $s \geqslant n$ have been expanded in a power series. The others have been retained as exponentials to avoid the "infrared catastrophe."† For the long-wave lattice vibrations, $s \ll N$, we have from Eq. (12)

$$\omega_s^2 = (2K/Ma)(1 - \cos \pi s/N) \approx \pi^2 K s^2/N^2 Ma \qquad = (\pi/2)^2(s\omega_N/N)^2$$

$$b_s \lesssim b_s/\sin(Rs\pi/N) = (2/N)^{\nu/2} (\hbar/M\omega_s)^{1/2} k$$

$$= 2^{3/4} (2/N)^{1/2(\nu-1)} (h/\pi Ms)^{1/2} (Ma/K)^{1/4} \omega/c \qquad (16')$$

$$\rightarrow (1/4) 2^{3/4} (2/N)^{1/2(\nu-1)} (m_e/\pi Ms)^{1/2} (m_e c^2/\hbar)^{1/2} (a/v)^{1/2}$$

$$\approx 2(2/N)^{1/2(\nu-1)} s^{-1/2}$$

Here we have introduced the velocity of sound, $v = (Ka/M)^{1/2}$, and in the sample evaluation following the arrow we have used the typical value $v/a = 3 \times 10^{13}$ sec^{-1} (the frequency corresponding to the time for sound to travel a lattice distance, or approximately the Debye frequency) and we have used $\hbar\omega = m_e c^2/4$, since the gamma ray of Ir^{191} used in Mössbauer's first demonstration of the effect has the energy 129 Kev. We have taken $M = Am = 200 \times 1840\ m_e$.

Thus, the dividing line, which we have called n in Eq. (16), between b_s greater than and less than unity, is in the neighborhood of $s \approx 4$ for one dimension and there exists no such distinction for more dimensions (given the crystal constants and gamma energy of our example).‡ For considerably larger s one may expand the individual exponentials, but there are so many terms in the sum of factors in the product that the validity of the expansion must be further examined.§

Formulation of the Transition Probabilities

In the usual time-dependent wave equation

$$[\mathcal{H} - (\hbar/i)(\partial/\partial t)]\psi = 0 \qquad (17)$$

one considers the approximate solution of interest to be a superposition of the initial state i and a growing admixture of the final state f,

---

†The infrared catastrophe does not occur for three dimensions, as we shall see. For that case, $\nu = 3$, one may set $n = 1$ and eliminate a part of the following discussion, which applies explicitly to the one-dimensional model and is presented in order to facilitate an understanding of the importance of the three dimensions of actual crystals in determining the shape of the absorption spectrum.

‡The dividing integer n becomes greater as the crystal binding becomes weaker and the limit of weak binding will be of interest.

§See page 187.

$$\psi = a_i(t)\,\psi_i + a_f(t)\,\psi_f \qquad 18)$$

where

$$\psi_i = u_i(x')\,\Pi_s\, U_{n_s}(\xi_s)\, e^{i(E_i/\hbar)t}$$

$$\psi_f = u_f(x')\,\Pi_s\, U_{n_s'}(\xi_s)\, e^{i(E_f/\hbar)t}$$

are solutions of Eq. (17) without $\mathcal{H}'$. The coefficient a_i is initially unity and the initial rate of growth of a_f is

$$a_f = (1/i\hbar)\int \psi_f\,\mathcal{H}'\psi_i\, d\xi_1 \cdots d\xi_N\, dx' = De^{i(\Sigma_s(n_s' - n_s)\omega_s + \omega_0 - \omega)t}$$

$$\equiv De^{i\Delta\omega t}$$

$$D = (Ck/\hbar) < f\,|\,x'|\,i > D_1 D_2$$

$$ik < f\,|x'|\,i > \approx \int u_f^* e^{ikx'} u_i\, dx' = \int u_f^*(1 + ikx' + \cdots)u_i\, dx'$$

$$D_1 = <n_1{}' \cdots n_{n-1}{}' \left| \prod_{s=1}^{n-1} e^{ib_s\xi_s} \right| n_1 \cdots n_{n-1}>$$

$$D_2 = < n_{n'} \cdots n_{N'} \left| 1 + i\sum_{s=n}^{N} b_s\xi_s - (1/2)\left(\sum_{s=n}^{N} b_s\xi_s\right)^2 \right| n_n \cdots n_N > \qquad (19)$$

Here $\omega_0 = (e_f - e_i)/\hbar$ is the resonant frequency of the nucleus at rest without recoil, $E_f = e_f + \Sigma_s n_s'\omega_s$ is the final energy of the system and, similarly, $E_i = e_i + \Sigma_s n_s\omega_s$, and $\Delta\omega$ is the amount by which the incoming wave is out of exact resonance with the energy change from the initial to the final condition of the system as a whole, nucleus plus lattice. In Eq. (19) we have selected the electric dipole term of the nuclear transition as the usual case, but this is not essential. The early values of a_f, for small t, are

$$a_f = \int_0^t De^{i\Delta\omega t}\, dt = (D/i\Delta\omega)(e^{i\Delta\omega t} - 1)$$

and thus the probability per unit time that the transition has been made to the final state, for t small enough that a_i remains not far from unity, is

$$(1/t)|a_f|^2 = (D/\Delta\omega)^2 \left|e^{i\Delta\omega t/2}\right|^2 \left|e^{i\Delta\omega t/2} - e^{-i\Delta\omega t/2}\right|^2$$

$$= (1/2)D^2 t \left[\frac{\sin(\Delta\omega t/2)}{\Delta\omega t/2}\right]^2 \quad (20)$$

The last factor, the square of the square bracket, is clearly a function which approaches unity for very small $\Delta\omega t$ and becomes zero for $\Delta\omega = 2\pi/t$. Thus it describes a resonant peak of half-width about π/t, becoming narrower as the time becomes longer, in keeping with the uncertainty principle, and the factor t in Eq. (20) makes the peak higher as the time becomes longer. For larger values of $\Delta\omega t$, the function goes through a series of small maxima of rapidly decreasing amplitude† which have no great importance compared to the central sharp peak.

In the resonant absorption of gamma rays, the time t during which the radiation causing the transition takes place is taken to be essentially the half-life of the emitting state (the same as the half-life of the final state of the absorbing nucleus, the two nuclei being identical).

The shape of the resonant peak given by Eq. (20) is similar to, but not the same as, the shape factor of the dispersion formula,‡ $|(\Delta\omega) - i\Gamma/2|^{-2}$. The latter is derived by treatment of the steady state resulting from the equilibrium between the absorption here treated and the corresponding emission that is responsible for the half-life of the final state f; the nonresonant "tail" obtained does not display the "beats" found in Eq. (20) for large $\Delta\omega$. To obtain a qualitative understanding, it does not matter which resonant line shape is used.

As the half-life in a case of interest is known from experiment, we consider t given. The structure of the theory is then as follows: In exploring the shape of the absorption spectrum, we consider at first a given ω. There is then a range of energies of ω within about $\Delta\omega = 2\pi/t$, in which some final states f, $n_{s'}$ may be found for which the matrix elements in D of Eq. (19) do not vanish. One could think of searching out these states, and then computing their contributions by means of Eq. (20), and adding the values obtained to get the absorption intensity at ω.

Alternatively and more conveniently, we may first consider all the final states to which matrix elements exist, and calculate for each state, by means of (20), the contribution it can make to the absorption

---

†The shape of this function, as well as the formulation of this simple (Dirac) approach to the radiation problem, is to be found conveniently in L. I. Schiff, "Quantum Mechanics," McGraw-Hill, New York, 1949, pp. 189-193.

‡G. Breit and E. Wigner, Phys. Rev., **49**, 519 (1936).

at various ω's within the range $\Delta\omega$ of its resonant frequency $\omega_0 + \Sigma(n_{s'} - n_s)\omega_s$, as its influence is spread out by the line shape. The various contributions at each ω must then be added to obtain the absorption spectrum.

To do this we must examine the lattice matrix elements. When the constant and nuclear elements which are the same for all terms are left out, the lattice factor for the low frequencies, D_1 of Eq. (19) is a product of $(n-1)$ factors of the type

$$\langle n_{s'} \left| e^{ib_s \xi_s} \right| n_s \rangle = \int U^*_{n_{s'}}(\xi) U_{n_s}(\xi)\, e^{ib_s \xi}\, d\xi \qquad (20')$$

where $U_n(\xi) = H_n(\xi)\, e^{-\xi^2/2}$. The hermite polynomial H_n is a sum of about $n/2$ powers of ξ in terms of alternating sign, giving about $n/2$ nodes on each side of zero, and about $n/2$ maxima of H_n^2 with amplitudes that increase until the wave function is cut off by the exponential factor. The appearance of U_{10}^2 is shown in Fig. 1, along with dotted lines giving the classical probability distribution for a harmonic oscillator. The faithfulness to the correspondence principle is clear, and in the central region, where the parabolic potential curve is relatively flat, $U_n(\xi)$ is given approximately by the standing-wave wave function of a free particle in a box, $U_n \approx e^{i\lambda^{1/2}\xi} - e^{-i\lambda^{1/2}\xi}$ with $\lambda = 2n_s + 1$,

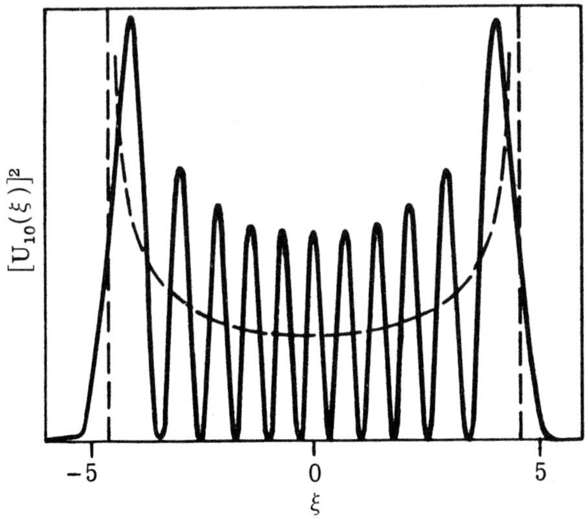

Fig. 1. Square of the oscillator wave function for $n_s = 10$. The broken lines show the probability distribution for a classical oscillator which slows down and stops at the end of its swing.

satisfying Eq. (13′) with $\xi = 0$. In the matrix elements (20′), with $b_s \gg 1$, the exponential factor $e^{ib_s\xi}$ varies rapidly in phase and makes the integral very nearly vanish if the product of the two wave functions varies much more slowly, as it does if $n_{s'} \approx n_s$. For the integral (20′) to have a value nearly unity, it is necessary for the product of the wave functions in the important central region to have the same periodicity as $e^{ib_s\xi}$. If $n_s = 0$, as it would be at a very low temperature, U_i varies slowly and has no periodicity; the periodicity, therefore, comes from U_f and we have $\lambda^{1/2} = (2n_{s'} + 1)^{1/2} = \pm b_s$ if $e^{i(b_s \pm \lambda^{1/2})\xi}$ is to keep the same phase through the important range of integration and if the matrix element is thus to be large. With $\nu = 1$ and with b_s taken as an average over several adjacent modes s (because the radiating nucleus R is in a position to have good "leverage" in interacting with some of the normal modes of vibration and not with others), we may use $(\sin^2)_{av} = 1/2$ in Eq. (16) and then have

$$(2n'_s - 1)\omega_s = \hbar k^2/NM$$

The contribution to $\Delta\omega$ of Eq. (19) by all terms of this type is

$$\sum_{s=1}^{n-1} n'_s\omega_s \approx n\hbar k^2/2NM$$

This is the recoil Doppler shift produced by the motion of the radiating atom in phase with other atoms in the same region in these long-wave vibrations. A large block consisting of about N/n atoms can move together without exciting too much photon energy and can recoil as a unit. In the limit of very weak binding, all the b_s values become large, the sum extends to N, and we obtain the usual recoil Doppler shift for a free atom initially at rest, $\delta\omega = \hbar k^2/2M$.

If n_s and n'_s are both large, we may use the free-particle standing-wave approximation for both and have $(2n'_s + 1) - (2n_s + 1) = \pm b_s$. The contribution to $\Delta\omega$ of a given normal-mode excitation n'_s is

$$(n'_s - n_s)\omega_s = (n'^{1/2}_s + n^{1/2}_s)(n'^{1/2}_s - n^{1/2}_s)\omega_s \approx (2n^{1/2}_s \pm b_s/2^{1/2})(\pm b_s/2^{1/2})$$

Addition of these contributions from the various modes s would involve a combinatorial problem, such as taking account of the fact that there are relatively many states with very small total contribution because the ± sign is about equally divided between plus and minus. This would amount to a treatment, by means of fourier analysis, of the ordinary Doppler shift that results from the thermal motion of that large block of atoms whose common motion may be described by these long-wave modes. One sees that the same large block is again involved by noting that the statistical problem may give a factor $n^{1/2}$ from summing over n terms with random sign, and one thus has a factor (n/NM) where a factor $(1/M)$ would appear in the Doppler shift of a free atom.

In favorable cases, n is less than N by several orders of magnitude, a fact which both keeps the spike sharp and which means that the great majority of normal modes fall in the category of s greater than n.

Now let us consider the high-frequency end of the phonon spectrum. We do so with the idealized approximation that the b_s values are sufficiently small for us to use the expansion in D_2 of Eq. (19). There we have made the expansion with the summation in the exponent, and require the sum to be small. We could take instead a product of exponentials for the individual modes s, expand each, and require only that the individual term $b_s \xi_s$ be small, a seemingly less stringent requirement. Even in this case the expansion would be questionable as s approaches the borderline n. We must thus leave some region untreated, and consider the lower limit n somewhat larger than that borderline n. After expanding the individual exponentials, one has a product of $(N - n)$ sums and, in any order above the first, one has an enormous number of products which are not obviously negligible and which yet do not appear when one expands as in (16). It will be shown below that the two forms are equivalent, and thus the less stringent requirement is sufficient.

With this limitation on the range s under consideration, the shortwave factor obtained by taking the square of D_2 in Eq. (19) is

$$|D_2|^2 \sim |\langle n'_n \cdots n'_N | 1 + i\Sigma_s b_s \xi_s - (1/2)\Sigma_s b_s^2 \xi_s^2 | n_n \cdots n_N \rangle|^2$$

$$= \begin{cases} [1 - (1/2)\Sigma_s b_s^2 \langle n_s | \xi_s^2 | n_s \rangle]^2 & \text{if all } n'_j = n_j \\ b_s^2 \, |\langle n_s \pm 1 | \xi_s | n_s \rangle|^2 & \text{if all } n'_j = n_j \text{ except } n'_s = n_s \pm 1 \\ (1/4) b_s^4 \, |\langle n_s \pm 2 \, | \xi_s^2 | n_s \rangle|^2 & \text{if all } n'_j = n_j \text{ except } n'_s = n_s \pm 2 \end{cases} \tag{21}$$

For a given initial state $n_1 \cdots n_N$ there is just one final state of the first type, and its lattice factor may be written more explicitly,

$$|D_2|^2 \sim \{1 - \Sigma_s [n_s + (1/2)] b_s^2 + \cdots\} \qquad \text{if all } n'_j = n_j \tag{21'}$$

There are about N states with lattice factors of the following type, one for each of the lattice modes s that may be excited:

$$|D_2|^2 \sim (1/2)(n_s + 1) b_s^2 \qquad \text{if all } n'_j = n_j \text{ except } n'_s + 1 \tag{21''}$$

As long as most of the n_j are not zero there are about N states with factors of the type

$$|D_2|^2 \sim (1/2)n_s b_s^2 \qquad \text{if all } n_j' = n_j \text{ except } n_s' = n_s - 1 \qquad (21''')$$

If we confine our attention to powers of b_s no higher than b_s^2, these are all the transitions we need to consider. Transitions to the single state of the type (21′) give an absorption line having the natural width at the undisplaced resonant frequency ω_0, except as slightly broadened and displaced by the long-wave modes in D_1. The second type (21″) gives the possibility that any one of the lattice modes may absorb one quantum of excitation, contributing to the spectrum in the immediate neighborhood of $(\omega_0 + \omega_s)$. Since there are many lattice modes and thus many ω_s, these modes, through this term, can contribute a broad part of the spectrum. The last type (21‴) corresponds to the nuclear excitation receiving most of its energy from the gamma ray, but part of it from the crystal mode s, and the factor n_s assures that this cannot happen unless mode s is excited. This process, of course, contributes to the spectrum of the low-energy side of ω_0. In the single term of type (21′) there is subtracted a sum of n terms in b_s^2. This compensates in the total intensity the absorption by the N states of type (21″) and of type (21‴), in this order, leaving the total intensity unaffected by the influence of the lattice.

It is clear that the shape of the absorption spectrum depends on the prevailing magnitude of the n_s, that is, on the degree of excitation of the crystal modes, and this, of course, depends on the temperature. At absolute zero, with all values of $n_s = 0$, the "central spike," or almost undisplaced line, at ω_0 is considerably weakened by a wing covering the range of crystal-mode energies on the high-energy side. At moderately low temperatures, n_s will be fairly large for the low-frequency modes with small s, and n_s will be small for large s, as s approaches N. The low-frequency modes will make their very small contribution to the Doppler broadening of the spike, and the high-frequency modes (as well as the untreated intermediate modes), will start to develop a wing on the low-frequency (phonon de-excitation) side, which further detracts from the intensity of the spike. As the temperature becomes higher, the central spike disappears and the strong outer part of the wings is also much enhanced. The fact that according to Eq. (22) the spike is even negative (and not only in the limit of large n_s) shows that the simple approximation used is not valid, particularly in its neglect of terms of order b_s^4. An improved approximation is discussed below.

As a simple extreme case, let us consider further the shape of the spectrum in the limit of very low temperatures where few phonons are present. Consider in particular the shape of the high-energy wing given by (21″) with all $n_s = 0$. The energies of the lattice modes are

$\hbar\omega_s$ with $\omega_s^2 = (1/2)\omega_N^2(1 - \cos \pi s/N)$ and $\omega_N^2 = 4K/Ma$, according to Eq. (12). This type of frequency spectrum as a function of ω_s^2 is illustrated vertically in Fig. 2, for the case $N = 20$. As a function of ω_s, or oscillator energy, it is plotted horizontally, the transfer being

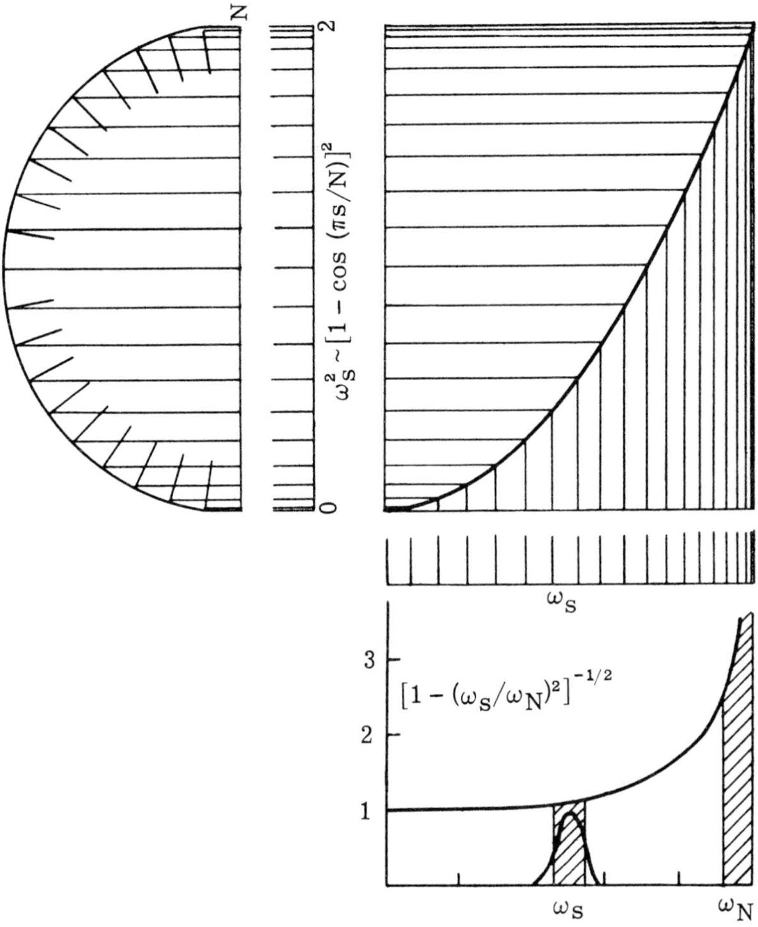

Fig. 2. Distribution of frequencies of the normal modes of a string of twenty beads ($N = 20$), showing graphically how they bunch at the high-frequency end, in terms of the first line of Eq. (12). The lower graph gives the corresponding density of states for a larger value of N.

made by means of the parabola shown. For the large values of N that are of interest, the lines crowd together in the extreme $\omega_s \to \omega_N$, too closely to permit drawing them. For a very large N, the spectrum is almost a continuum of varying density and the number of modes per unit ω is

$$N(\omega_S) = (\partial\omega_S/\partial s)^{-1} = (2^{3/2}N/\pi\omega_N)(1 - \cos \pi s/N)^{1/2}/\sin(\pi s/N)$$
$$= (2N/\pi\omega_N)/[1 - (\omega_S/\omega_N)^2]^{1/2} \quad (22)$$

Here we have used the relation $\sin \pi s/N = 2(\omega_S/\omega_N)[1 - (\omega_S/\omega_N)^2]^{1/2}$ in transforming from a function of s to a function of ω_S. This is plotted to show the comparison with the horizontal spectrum in the lower part of Fig. 2.

In practice the natural line width w of the gamma line will be greater than the spacing of the levels, particularly at the crowded upper end of the spectrum, because N is very large, and the intensity of absorption is given by the integral of (21″) multiplied by (22), or of $b_S^2 N(\omega_S) \sim \omega_S^{-1}/[1 - (\omega_S/\omega_N)^2]^{1/2}$, multiplied further by the line shape and integrated over the entire width of the line. For qualitative purposes it suffices to square off the line shape and let it have a constant height over the width w (on the scale of ω_S). The number of states involved, or the integral of (22) is then indicated by the shaded areas given as examples in the lower part of Fig. 2, and these are to be multiplied by the median ω_S^{-1} to obtain the relative intensity of absorption (since, again with an average $\sin^2 = 1/2$, we have $b_S^2 = (1/2)C_1^2/\omega_S$, and C_1^2 is a common factor).

The line width thus blunts the singular peak of the function $N(\omega_S)$ at the upper limit of the spectrum, ω_N. The area of the shaded region under this peak is

$$\int_{\omega_N - w}^{\omega_N} d\omega/[1 - (\omega/\omega_N)^2]^{1/2} \approx \omega_N \int_0^{w/\omega_N} d\varepsilon/(2\varepsilon)^{1/2} = (2\omega_N w)^{1/2} \quad (23)$$

The intensity at the peak is thus approximately given by $(2w)^{1/2}\omega_N^{-1/2}$. The corresponding intensity, that is, the intensity with the common factor $(NC_1^2/\pi\omega_N)$ again omitted from $\int_w b_S^2 N(\omega_S N(\omega_S)\, d\omega_S$, in the non-singular part of the spectrum is $w/\omega_S[1 - (\omega_S/\omega_N)^2]^{1/2}$ and the ratio of this to the intensity at the peak is

$$I(\omega_S)/I(\omega_N) = (w/2\omega_N)^{1/2}(\omega_N/\omega_S)/[1 - (\omega_S/\omega_N)^2]^{1/2} \quad (24)$$

Here we have considered $w \ll \omega_N$, and have called the peak intensity $I(\omega_N)$, although in this treatment the peak is reached more exactly at $\omega_N - (1/2)w$ and the intensity falls to zero again at $\omega_N + (1/2)w$. These points are used in the sketch of the ratio (24) shown in Fig. 3 for the case in which $w = (1/10)\omega_N$ is rather large. For a smaller w the peak is obviously narrower and higher, relative to the rest of the spectrum. The peculiar shape of the peak is artificial, arising from

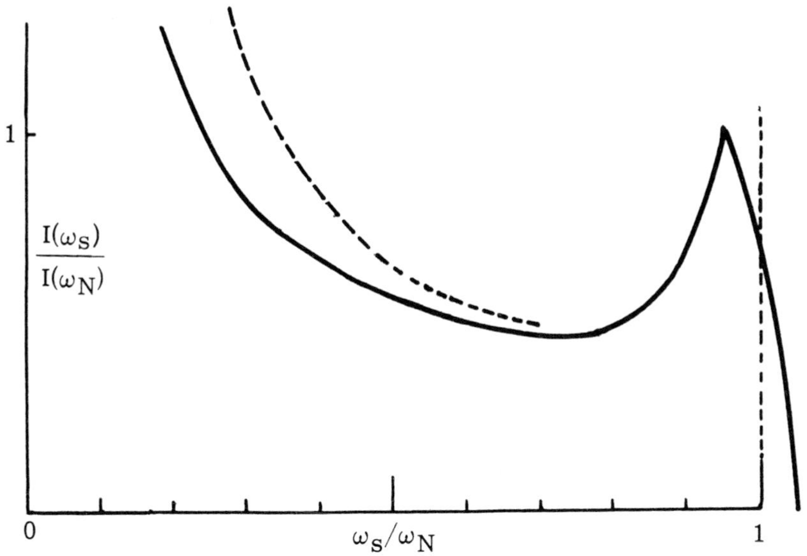

Fig. 3. Rough sketch of absorption spectrum of a gamma ray with assumed square intrinsic line shape having a width $w = \omega_N/10$) of a nucleus in a one-dimensional lattice. The broken curve indicates that the rise toward a cusp at the undisplaced line is steeper at finite temperatures than at $T = 0$.

our use of a rectangular line shape. With the realistic line shape given by Eq. (20) it would of course be rounded off nicely.

For small ω_S, much less than ω_N, the spectrum is linear in ω_N/ω_S. This may still apply in the low end of the high-frequency region $n < s \ll N$. When we introduce a small but finite temperature, T, with $kT < \hbar\omega_N$, there is a region of small ω_S with $\hbar\omega_S < kT$ wherein there is a Boltzmann distribution of excitation of the phonon quantum numbers n_S, and, for our qualitative discussion, we may insert the average excitation $n_S = kT/\hbar\omega_S$. Equation (21″) with $n_S = 0$ was used as a factor in obtaining (24), and in the region of (24) where $\omega_S \ll \omega_N$, reintroduction of n_S has the effect of multiplying by $n_S + 1 \approx n_S$. For small ω_S Eq. (24) then becomes

$$I(\omega_S)/I(\omega_N) \approx (kT/\hbar\omega_S^2)(w\omega_N/2)^{1/2}$$

This gives a steep approach to a singularity at $\omega_S = 0$ and for $w = (1/10)\omega_N$, and $kT/\hbar\omega_N = 1/2$ suggests a curve about like that shown by the dotted line in Fig. 2a, the peak at $s = N$ being practically unaffected. In the region $s \approx n$ we expect (21″) and thus also this dotted curve to be an upper limit. For a higher temperature, $kT > \hbar\omega_N$,

(23) is also to be multiplied by a factor $n_N \sim kT/\hbar\omega_N$ and thus (24) is multiplied by ω_N/ω_s, giving

$$I_T(\omega_s)/I_T(\omega_N) = (w/2\omega_N)^{1/2}(\omega_N/\omega_s)^2/[1-(\omega_s/\omega_N)^2]^{1/2} \tag{25}$$

for $\omega_s < (\omega_N - w)$. This curve is similar to the previous one indicated by the dotted line but with the low frequencies further enhanced.

This gives us an idea of the shape of the absorption spectrum for the one-dimensional problem on the high-energy side, gamma-ray energy having been absorbed by the lattice vibrations as well as by the nucleus. In the last step we have considered the temperature high enough for us to consider $n + 1 \approx n_s$. In this approximation the emission strength (21‴) is the same as the absorption strength (21″), and we have on the low-energy side a distribution of approximately the same shape, part of the energy for the nuclear transition being supplied by the lattice vibrations. Thus, we expect the spectrum to consist of two wings, each with something like a peak near its outer extremity, and both flanking a central "spike." The peak at the high-frequency end of each wing is probably not to be expected to be so sharp in nature, because it comes at the frequency where one cuts off the idealized "Debye" spectrum of the crystal, and the actual cutoff at high frequencies is doubtless somewhat different, depending on details of the crystal structure.

As ω_s decreases below about $(1/2)\omega_N$, the intensity rises seemingly toward a cusp at the center, but the approximation becomes unreliable as the cusp is approached. If we take $w/\omega_N < 0.07$, let us say $w/\omega_N = 1/20$ rather than $1/10$ as above, then the line width would pick out individual lines in Fig. 2 for small values of ω_s, and for each of them would contribute a peak to the absorption spectrum, with a small energy shift corresponding to a one-phonon jump at that frequency ω_s. If w spans the undisplaced position $\omega_s = 0$ on the scale of Fig. 2, it gives rise to the undisplaced peak in the spectrum corresponding to no phonon jump for any s. For this no-phonon transition, the intensity at zero temperature is given by the term unity from Eq. (21′) for all s, rather than to have $(1/2)b_s^2$ from Eq. (21″) for one of the s values. Thus, the intensity of the peak of the wing relative to that of the central peak [according to both Eq. (23) and the remark following it] is

$$[(1/2)(2w/\omega_N)^{1/2}(NC_1^2/\pi\omega_N)] = (2w/\omega_N)^{1/2}\hbar k^2/\pi\omega_N M$$

With $k = E_\gamma/\hbar c$, this becomes

$$[(2w/\omega_N)^{1/2}/\pi](E_\gamma/\hbar\omega_N)(E_\gamma/Mc^2) \approx (1/2)(w/\omega_N)^{1/2} \times 10^4 \times 10^{-4}$$

$$\approx (1/2)(w/\omega_N)^{1/2}$$

if we use, for example, $E_\gamma \approx 10^5$ ev and $\hbar\omega_N \approx 10$ ev. Thus the central peak becomes relatively rather high as the line becomes narrow. The suppression of this peak at higher temperatures is discussed in the next section. The line is undisplaced by recoil. This is possible (despite the physical expectation that the crystal should recoil as a whole) because in the Fourier analysis (1) it is assumed that the ends of the string are fixed.

This simple remark about the height of the central peak only applies, however, if the springs are stiff enough so the zero-phonon transition may be evaluated by Eq. (21′) for all s values down to $s = 1$, that is, that the dividing line between D_1 and D_2 becomes $n = 1$ and that none of the factors fall into D_1. This requires that b_1^2 be considerably less than unity. For a string of beads $N\omega_s = s\omega_N$, and b_s^2 may accordingly be written in two ways, $b_s^2 = \hbar k^2/sM\omega_N$ or $b_s^2 = \hbar k^2/NM\omega_s$. The requirement $b_1^2 = \hbar k^2/M\omega_N < 1$ is very nearly satisfied by the sample numbers ($10^4 \times 10^{-4}$) given above. If it is not satisfied for $s = 1$ but the corresponding requirement is satisfied for $s = 2$, that is, if $b_1 \approx 1$, or only slightly less, and b_2 is well below unity, then D_1 contains a factor for $s = 1$ and D_2 contains no-phonon-transition factors about equal to unity for all values of s.

This provides a simple illustration with small quantum numbers, similar to the more general discussion above of Eq. (20′) for large quantum numbers. Even here in this simple case we have the complication that D_1 can have a value not only for the one-phonon jump but also for the several-phonon jumps of n_1, from 0 to several values of n_1'. We may simply evaluate the first few transition probabilities D_1^2 by explicit use of the normalized Hermite polynomials.

$$H_0 = \pi^{-1/4} \qquad H_2(\xi) = 2^{1/2}\pi^{-1/4}(\xi^2 - 1/2)$$

$$H_1(\xi) = 2^{1/2}\pi^{-1/4}\,\xi \qquad H_3(\xi) = 3^{-1/2}\pi^{-1/4}(2\xi^2 - 3\xi)$$

From Eq. (20′) we have

$$|D_1^2| = e^{-(1/2)b_1^2}\,|\int H_0 H_{n_1'}[\eta - (1/2)_i b_1]\, e^{-\eta^2}\, d\eta|^2$$

and find that the successive transition probabilities for the zero-, one-, two-, and three-phonon jumps are $e^{-(1/2)b_1^2}$ multiplied by 1, $(1/2)b_1^2$, $(1/2)(b_1^2/2)^2$, and $(1/3)(b_1^2/2)^3$, respectively. This is again a question of obtaining an approximate match between the periodicity of $e^{-ib_s\xi}$ and of $H_{n_s'}(\xi)$ so as to destroy as effectively as possible the orthogonality between the latter and H_0. For $b_1 = 1$, we see that the strongest peak of the spectrum is still at the undisplaced position; then, half as strong as that, there is the one-phonon peak at the $s = 1$ position in the sequence of Fig. 2, and then, one-eighth as strong, there is the two-phonon peak, which happens to be near the $s = 2$ line in Fig. 2 because the lines are almost equally spaced. With $b_1^2 = 2$, the zero-phonon peak is reduced to equality with the one-phonon peak and, as b_1 increases, the highest intensity moves further out through several phonons. As the spring grows weaker and b_1 increases further, the other modes $s = 2, 3$, etc., start to contribute to the intensity of the "wings" in a similar fashion and their factors $e^{-(1/2)b_s^2}$ for the no-s-phonon jump further detract from the intensity of the zero-phonon peak.

Thus, in this very simple system we see with especial clarity that we first start to get phonon excitation to detract from the intensity of the central peak when the originally very stiff springs become weak enough to satisfy the condition $b_1^2 \approx 1$. The momentum carried away by the γ-ray is $\hbar k$, and this condition (see previous page) may be written either as

$$(\hbar k)^2/2NM = (1/2)\hbar\omega_1$$

or in the form

$$(\hbar k)^2/2M = (1/2)\hbar\omega_N$$

The first form suggests that we have the proper "impedance match" when the kinetic energy of the recoil (provided the recoil momentum is divided among all the N atoms which move in phase with each other in the first vibrational mode) is about equal to the kinetic energy involved in the one-quantum excitation of this mode. (The specification of kinetic energy is here not essential, for there are still factors 2 floating around depending on such details as whether or not nucleus R is at the middle of the string, $R = (1/2)N$, to give it maximum "leverage" for this and other odd modes.) This is perhaps the most graphic physical explanation of the sharp central peak: when the γ-ray momentum is less than enough to supply this collective motion of the atoms in the middle relative to the ends of the string, there is apt to be no phonon excitation.

In our simple model, with the ends of the string fixed, the central peak is undisplaced by recoil. In a more realistic model, we could merely constrain the end atoms (by a light frame) to remain a fixed distance apart and to conserve total momentum. The central peak would then be slightly displaced by recoil of the whole system and the $s = 1$ line would be further displaced by this additional recoil [if $R \approx (1/2)N$] arising from excitation of the first one-phonon jump.

The second form of the condition shows that the recoil momentum of the free nucleus, not shared with any others, corresponds to an energy about great enough to excite even the highest-frequency mode of vibration. The interesting fact is that high-frequency modes are nevertheless not excited. One might say that there is an impedance mismatch, or that there is no way for a gradual transfer of momentum to the vibratory system via nucleus R to excite the various nuclei in their high-frequency motions with contrary phases. If nucleus R should shoot off a bullet with this much momentum at a given time, classically, for any finite stiffness of spring, the nucleus and bullet act as an isolated system with no time for transfer of momentum to them during the instant of ejection. The full free recoil of the nucleus would be detracted from the energy of the bullet, and the energy of recoil would first excite a localized traveling wave packet which could then be expanded in terms of various fairly high frequency vibrational modes with specified phases. If the γ ray we have discussed were emitted at a given instant, this energy would be sufficient to excite a localized wave of much higher amplitude than the one-quantum amplitude of ω_N. Corresponding to the expansion of the localized wave, there should be perhaps a one- or several-quantum excitation of a few of the moderately high frequency waves. Such excitation does not occur with γ-ray emission because the emission does not take place at a given time. Instead, it takes place at an unknown time with a probability which builds up very gradually in a coherent manner as we have seen in Eqs. (19) and (20), and, in the case discussed, it may either excite a low-frequency phonon or none at all.

Discussion of the Approximation in Expanding the Exponentials

The insufficiency of the approximation in expanding exponentials is apparent in the possibility that the diagonal element, Eq. (21′), may go negative even with all the $n_s = 0$, and a fortiori at a higher temperature. In one dimension, if we use the approximation and constants of Eq. (16′), we have

$$(1/2)\sum_{s} b_s^2 \approx (3/4) \int_0^N (ds/s) = (3/4) \ln N > 1 \tag{26}$$

Here we have used a factor 1/2 from a mean value of $\sin^2(Rs/N)$ of Eq. (16). In three dimensions the corresponding sum is

$$(1/2) \sum_{stu} b_{stu}^2 \approx (3/4N^2)(\pi/2) \int_0^N (\rho^2\, d\rho/\rho) = 3\pi/16$$

$$\rho^2 = s^2 + t^2 + u^2 \tag{26′}$$

which is still of order unity, although the importance of the long waves has been suppressed. We should therefore examine the expansion of the exponentials more carefully.

In place of the square bracket representing the high-frequency modes toward the end of Eq. (16), we may write a product of exponentials and for its matrix element in place of Eq. (21) we may write

$$|D_2|^2 \sim |\langle n'_n \cdots n'_N|\, e^{ib_s\xi_s}\, |n_n \cdots n_N\rangle|^2 = |\prod_{s=n}^{N} \langle n'_s|\, e^{ib_s\xi_s}\, |n_s\rangle|^2$$

$$\approx |\Pi \langle n'_s|1 + ib_s\xi_s - (1/2)b_s^2\xi_s^2 \cdots |n_s\rangle|^2$$

$$= |\Pi\,[1 + ib_s\langle n'_s|\xi_s|n_s\rangle - (1/2)b_s^2\langle n'_s|\xi^2|n_s\rangle \cdots]|^2 \quad (27)$$

Considering now only the diagonal element, $n'_s = n_s$, we have matrix elements of only the even powers of ξ, as follows:

$$|\Pi_s[1 - (1/2)b_s^2\langle n_s|\xi_s^2|n_s\rangle + (1/4!)\langle n_s|\xi_s^4|n_s\rangle + \cdots]|^2 \quad (28)$$

This product is of the form

$$\Pi_s(1 + \varepsilon_s) = 1 + \sum \varepsilon_s + \sum_{s \neq t} \varepsilon_s\varepsilon_t/2! + \sum_{r \neq s \neq t} \varepsilon_r\varepsilon_s\varepsilon_t/3! \cdots$$

which differs from the exponential

$$e^{\sum \varepsilon_s} = 1 + \sum \varepsilon_s + (\sum \varepsilon_s)^2/2! + (\sum \varepsilon_s)^3/3! \cdots$$

only by about N of the N^2 terms in ε_s^2 and by about N^2 of the terms in ε_s^3, etc., leaving us one order better off than one might otherwise expect. We can now in this approximation put

$$|D_2^2| = e^{-\sum b_s^2\langle n_s|\xi_s^2|n_s\rangle + (2/4!)\sum b_s^4\langle n_s|\xi_s^4|n_s\rangle + \cdots}$$

$$\approx e^{-\sum b_s^2\langle n_s|\xi_s^2|n_s\rangle} = e^{-\sum (n_s + 1/2)b_s^2} \quad (29)$$

This replaces Eq. (21′) and is clearly more satisfactory in that it indicates a gradual reduction of the intensity of the central peak to zero as the sum increases.

Shape of the Wings in One and Three Dimensions

The derivation is slightly modified for two or three dimensions. We are of course interested in three, but shall write the equations in two dimensions for the sake of economy of symbols. Each component of the vector displacement of atom qr can be described in normal coordinates, but we shall write only the x component of such a displacement. (The Lagrangian also contains the other components independently.) The force constant between adjacent atoms, owing to a relative displacement in the x direction, is a longitudinal force constant, K, if they are neighbors in the x direction, a transverse one, $K_{transv.}$

= fK, if they are neighbors in the y direction. The Lagrangian is

$$\mathcal{L} = (M/2)\sum \dot{x}_{qr}^2 - (K/2a)\sum[(x_{q+1,r} - x_{q,r})^2 + f(x_{q,r+1} - x_{q,r})^2$$
$$= (M/2)\sum \dot{q}_{st}^2 - (K/a)\sum q_{st}^2\{[1 - \cos(\pi s/N)] + f[1 - \cos(\pi t/N)]\} \tag{2'}$$

where

$$x_{qr} = (2/N)^{\nu/2} \sum_{st} q_{st} \sin(qs\pi/N)\sin(rt\pi/N) \qquad \nu = 2$$

Taken for all lattice points qr, this is a wave of x displacement having q nodes in the x dimension and r nodes in the y dimension. The frequency of a normal mode is given by

$$\omega_{st}^2 = (2K/Ma)\{[1 - \cos(\pi s/N)] + f[1 - \cos(\pi t/N)]\}$$
$$\approx (K/Ma)(\pi/N)^2(s^2 + ft^2)$$

The perturbation term $\mathcal{H}'$ contains a factor [see Eq. (16)]

$$e^{ikx_{QR}} = \Pi_{st}\, e^{ib_{st}\xi_{st}}$$
$$b_{st} = (2/N)^{\nu/2}(\hbar/M\omega_{st})^{1/2} k \sin(qs\pi/N)\sin(rt\pi/N) \tag{16''}$$

or, averaged over the factors $\overline{\sin^2} \approx (1/2)$, in the neighborhood of a given st,

$$\overline{b_{st}^2} = N^{-\nu}(\hbar/M\omega_{st})k^2 \approx (3/2N^{\nu-1})/(s^2 + ft^2)^{1/2}$$

or, in three dimensions,

$$b_{stu}^2 = (3/2N^2)/[s^2 + f(t^2 + u^2)]^{1/2} \tag{16'''}$$

In three dimensions, the number of modes with ω_{st} between ω and $\omega + d\omega$ is $N(\omega)\,d\omega$, with

$$N(\omega) = (N^3/2\pi^2)(Ma/K)^{3/2}\omega^2 \tag{30}$$

for the simple extreme case f = 1. For the other extreme, f = 0 (no shear strength), we have instead

$$N(\omega) = (N/\pi)(Ma/K)^{1/2} \tag{22'}$$

independent of ω, just as in the one-dimensional case. For f = 1, the shape of the wings (in the lower-frequency part of the spectrum) is given by

$$[n_s + (1/2)]b_s^2 N(\omega_s) \sim \begin{cases} \omega_s & n_s = 0 \\ \text{const.}, & n_s + 1/2 \approx n_s = kT/\hbar\omega_s \end{cases} \quad (24')$$

as indicated by the broken line and the solid line, respectively, in Fig. 4.

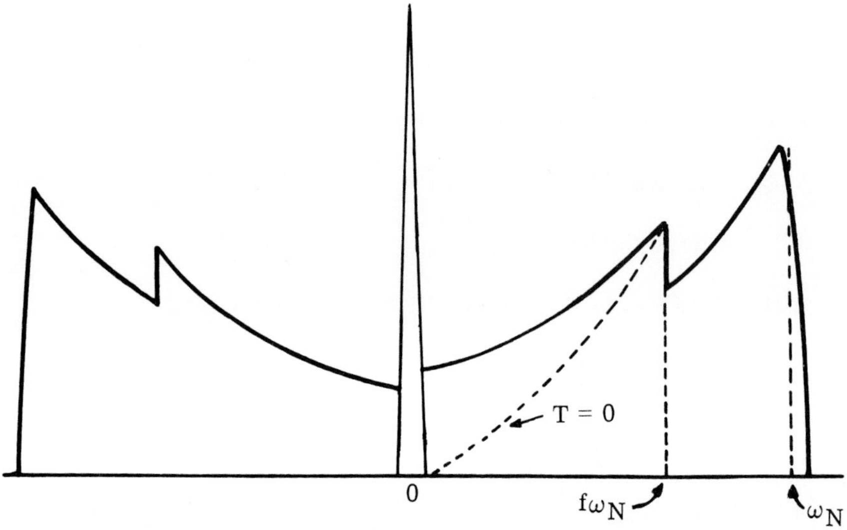

Fig. 4. Spectrum for a three-dimensional lattice. The outer peak corresponds to the upper limit of the (oversimplified Debye) spectrum for compression waves, the peak at $f\omega_N$ similarly corresponds to the upper limit for shear waves.

Here we see the real source of the difference between the behavior in one and in three dimensions. In one dimension, there is a low-frequency divergence in the shape of the absorption wing. The same is true in three dimensions without a consideration of shear strength. In the latter case one has justification for the intuitive feeling that the problem is mainly one-dimensional in its essence, because the photon excites vibratory motion along its direction of incidence. However, in three dimensions with shear strength taken into account, the frequency of this longitudinal vibration of the absorbing atom is affected by the transverse variation of the wave amplitude. There are so many possible wave numbers in the two transverse dimensions that there are many more high-frequency than low-frequency modes. Thus, the low frequencies are effectively suppressed, and the shape of the wing, rather than going up as ω_S^{-1} as the central spike is approached, is linear in ω_S at zero temperature. For finite temperature, it is constant over the low-frequency part of the spectrum for three dimensions with shear strength, as compared with the ω_S^{-2} dependence for one dimension.

Meaning of the Sharp Peak

Perhaps the greatest surprise that one encounters when thinking intuitively about the dynamics of the crystal motion is that there can exist such a very sharply defined component of the absorption as the central spike, so nearly exactly at its undisplaced position, in spite of the complexity of the motion of the absorbing nucleus and in spite of the normal process of recoil, which for a free atom gives a very appreciable Doppler shift. Between free nuclei the recoil Doppler shift is quite enough to throw them out of resonance, unless they have an initial velocity toward each other to compensate, whereas between the nuclei in solids of Mössbauer's experiments the resonance is quite exact when the solid bodies are at rest, and is destroyed by a relative velocity of a few centimeters per second in either direction.

In this analysis we see how it is possible, in principle, for the central line to be quite sharp and almost undisplaced, even in the presence of a considerable amount of excitation of the lattice vibrations. The sharpness is a typical quantum effect, like the sharpness of atomic spectral lines that was not expected classically. It arises from the fact that the crystal vibrations are quantized and that they may not receive an arbitrarily small amount of excitation energy except in arbitrarily large wavelength. There is indeed a small broadening and shift due to the long waves. If the process of gamma absorption or emission were to be thought of as a completely sudden process, giving the nucleus a sudden kick in a time much shorter than a lattice vibration, one would expect this impulsive initial motion to show up as a recoil Doppler shift, as it does in a free atom, and subsequently to have its energy divided between the various lattice modes in a manner equivalent to a Fourier analysis of the impulsive velocity. Actually, as we see in the theory, the possibility of transition is not determined merely by the energy and instantaneous momentum balance, but rather the probability of transition is built up by integration over the mean life of the nuclear state involved. This is time enough for ample transfer of momentum between the nucleus and the lattice by way of the forces involved in the lattice vibrations. In some cases, the recoil momentum is divided equally between all the atoms of the crystal, with no phonon excitation, and the corresponding contribution to the sharp line is practically undisplaced by recoil. With phonons initially excited and the radiating nucleus thus in a vibrational motion, the transition involving no additional phonon excitation continues to occur. For this transition, the to-and-fro motion of the radiating nucleus does not make any Doppler contribution to the character of the radiation, even though it would classically.† This is exactly analogous to the fact that the to-and-fro motion on the charge on an electron in a Bohr orbit does not contribute to the radiation without a quantum jump, even though it would contribute classically. For high phonon quantum numbers, the one-phonon transition between states of the vibrational motion should correspond to a classical result, just as the $\Delta n = 1$ quantum jump does in the more familiar correspondence-principle discussion of the radiation from large Bohr orbits. As the temperature is raised well above zero, the wings we have described thus have a close correspondence to the classical "side bands" from a moving source. As in the classical case, the wings merely detract

---

† The classical Doppler contribution due to a sinusoidal motion $x = a \sin \omega_m t$ of a radiating source is in the form of weak "side bands." These one obtains analytically from the Doppler-shifted frequency $\omega(t) = \omega_0[1 + (a\omega_m/c) \cos \omega_m t]$ in the expression $\exp(i \int \omega\, dt)$ by simply treating $a\omega_m/c$ as small in expanding the exponential and by expressing $\sin \omega_m t$ in terms of exponentials. In physical terms, the appearance of a strong central line ω_0 flanked by weak lines at $\omega_0 \pm \omega_m$ may be understood by thinking of the effect of this slightly varying $\omega(t)$ on a tuned detector. At the end of a swing, $\omega(t)$ becomes instantaneously stationary at $\omega_0 \pm \omega_m$ and comes back in phase at this frequency at the end of the following swing, so that a detector will respond to these frequencies. Now consider a detector tuned to ω_0. If it is in phase with the signal just when $\omega(t) = \omega_0$ and if $\omega(t) > \omega_0$ for the next half-cycle, then the signal will gradually get ahead of the detector in phase during this half-cycle. If the cycle is short enough so that the phase lead remains less than $\pi/4$, there will be no destructive interference (and, if less than $\pi/2$, there will still be a preponderance of constructive interference). The unique feature of ω_0 is that for it alone this advance in phase will be exactly compensated for by the retardation in the following half-cycle, so that the response will continue to build up, being fed by most of each later cycle and giving a strong line. The condition that the phase lead remain less than $\pi/4$ is $a < \pi c/4\omega_0 = \lambda/2$. The γ-ray wavelength $\lambda = (h/mc^2)(mc^2/137E_\gamma)$ is much smaller than the atomic unit of distance h/mc^2, and the intensity of the central line dies away as the vibrations of the atoms in the crystal attain an amplitude larger than λ. The corresponding condition for zigzag motion over a distance a is $a < \lambda/4$. This may be understood from the picture used in the usual graphic explanation of the Doppler shift, showing an original wave train and one compressed into a shorter space by the motion of the source. The detector tuned to receive the uncompressed wave receives the compressed wave instead.

from the intensity of the central line and do not widen it except, eventually, by making it disappear in the wider background as the probabilities of phonon transitions increase with the pre-excitation of many modes.

Acknowledgments

I am indebted to Dr. Maria G. Mayer and Dr. H. J. Lipkin, particularly for discussion of the situation with three dimensions and of the improved expansion of the exponentials, also to Dr. John Schiffer for informing me of the experimental phenomenon.

Resonance Absorption of Nuclear Gamma Rays and the Dynamics of Atomic Motions*

K. S. Singwi and A. Sjölander
Argonne National Laboratory, Argonne, Illinois
(Received June 13, 1960)

The theory of resonance absorption of nuclear γ rays is generalized for an arbitrary system of interacting particles by expressing the relevant transition probability in terms of a space-time self-correlation function; and thus relating the resonance line shape to the incoherent differential scattering cross section for slow neutrons. Two limiting cases: (i) a gas and (ii) a solid have been considered. Discussion regarding the justification of the use of a classical self-diffusion function for a liquid is given and expressions for the broadening of the resonance line due to diffusive motions of the atoms of the interacting system are derived. It is suggested how Mössbauer-type experiment could be used to give information regarding the diffusive motions of atoms in a solid and also, under more favorable circumstances, in a liquid.

INTRODUCTION

THE observation by Mössbauer[1] that nuclear γ rays can be resonantly absorbed or scattered by nuclei bound in a crystal lattice has recently led to some very interesting applications[2] and holds promise for more applications particularly in the field of solid-state physics. Mössbauer's observation rests on the fact that in the case of a nucleus bound in a crystal, a γ ray can be emitted or absorbed without any energy transfer to and from the lattice. The probability of such a recoilless transition is, in most cases, small and is governed by the usual Debye-Waller factor, familiar in the theory of x ray and neutron scattering. Mössbauer explained his experimental results on the basis of a theory due to Lamb[3] for the Doppler broadening of neutron absorption resonance. Both in the theory of neutron and γ-ray resonance absorption the relevant matrix element corresponding to a transition of the crystal lattice from one state to the other is the same.

The purpose of this paper is two-fold: one is to generalize the theory for an arbitrary system of interacting particles by expressing the transition probability in terms of a space-time self-correlation function, which as is well known, determines the incoherent scattering for slow neutrons; and the second is to show how Mössbauer technique can be used to gain information concerning the nature of diffusive motions of atoms in a solid and also, under more favorable circumstances, in a liquid. The cross section for γ-ray resonance absorption in the case of a gas (Bethe Placzek formula in the case of neutrons) and in the case of a solid, in the limit of both weak and strong binding (two limiting cases of Lamb's theory in the case of neutrons), follows very simply from one general formula. Furthermore, the generalized formula can be of great help in more complicated systems as for instance liquids, where it is difficult to treat the dynamics of atomic motions in detail.

MATHEMATICAL FORMULATION

We are interested in calculating the probability of absorption or emission of a γ ray of momentum $\mathbf{p}$ by a single nucleus of an interacting system (say solid or liquid) such that the nucleus makes a transition from a state A to a state B and at the same time the interacting system makes a transition from a state, say $|n0\rangle$ to a state $|n\rangle$. Since the interaction within a nucleus is much stronger than that between two nuclei, the total wave function can be written as a product of wave functions one of which depends only on the coordinates of the centers of masses of different nuclei and the other depends on the coordinates of the nucleons relative to the centers of masses of their respective nuclei. The transition matrix element, corresponding to the absorption of a photon, can be written as $\langle Bn|H'|n0Ap\rangle$, where H' represents the interaction between the radiation field and the nucleus and has the following form:

$$H'=\sum_i ca_{\mathbf{p}} \exp(i\mathbf{p}\cdot\mathbf{r}_i/\hbar)$$
$$=\exp(i\mathbf{p}\cdot\mathbf{R}_a/\hbar)\sum_i ca_{\mathbf{p}} \exp[i\mathbf{p}\cdot(\mathbf{r}_i-\mathbf{R}_a)/\hbar].$$

c is a constant depending on $\mathbf{p}$, $a_{\mathbf{p}}$ is the annihilation operator for a photon with momentum $\mathbf{p}$, $\mathbf{r}_i$ is the coordinate of a nucleon of the nucleus a, and $\mathbf{R}_a$ is the coordinate of the center of mass of the nucleus. The interaction operator H' is thus a product of two terms, one of which depends only on the coordinates of the nucleons relative to their center of mass and the other depends only on the coordinates of the center of mass. Thus the matrix element of the transition is a product of two matrix elements, one of which corresponds to the change in the internal state of the nucleus and the other is $\langle n|\exp(i\mathbf{p}\cdot\mathbf{R}_a/\hbar)|n0\rangle$, corresponding to a change in the state of the collective motions of the centers of masses. The first matrix element is just a constant for our purpose, and it is the second one with which we shall be mainly concerned here. It then follows

* Based on work performed under the auspices of the U. S. Atomic Energy Commission.

[1] R. L. Mössbauer, Z. Physik **151**, 124 (1958); Naturwissenschaften **45**, 538 (1958); Z. Naturforsch **14a**, 211 (1959).

[2] During the last year and this year a number of communications concerning the Mössbauer effect and its various applications have appeared in the Physical Review Letters to which the reader is referred.

[3] W. E. Lamb, Phys. Rev. **55**, 190 (1939).

from the usual dispersion theory[4] that the absorption cross section per nucleus for a γ ray of energy E is given by

$$\sigma_a(E)=\frac{\sigma_0\Gamma^2}{4}\sum_{n,n0} g_{n0}\frac{|\langle n|\exp(i\mathbf{p}\cdot\mathbf{R}/\hbar)|n0\rangle|^2}{(E_0-E+\epsilon_n-\epsilon_{n0})^2+\Gamma^2/4}, \quad (1)$$

where E_0 is the energy difference between the final and the initial nuclear states of the absorbing nucleus, ϵ_n and ϵ_{n0} are, respectively, the energies of the states $|n\rangle$ and $|n0\rangle$ of the interacting system, Γ is the natural width of the excited state of the nucleus and g_{n0} is the statistical weight factor for the state $|n0\rangle$. In Eq. (1) the nuclear width Γ has been assumed to be independent of the state $|n\rangle$. Also the suffix a in $\mathbf{R}$ has been omitted. The constant before the summation sign has been so chosen that $\sigma_a(E)$ goes over to the familiar Breit-Wigner formula for a fixed nucleus, σ_0 being the resonance absorption cross section.

Now Eq. (1) can be written as follows:

$$\sigma_a(E)=\frac{\sigma_0\Gamma^2}{4}\sum_{n,n0} g_{n0}|\langle n|\exp(i\mathbf{p}\cdot\mathbf{R}/\hbar)|n0\rangle|^2\int_{-\infty}^{\infty}\frac{\delta[\rho-(\epsilon_n-\epsilon_{n0})/\hbar]}{(E-E_0-\hbar\rho)^2+\Gamma^2/4}d\rho$$

$$=\frac{\sigma_0\Gamma^2}{4}\frac{1}{2\pi}\int_{-\infty}^{\infty}dt\{\sum_{n,n0} g_{n0}|\langle n|\exp(i\mathbf{p}\cdot\mathbf{R}/\hbar)|n0\rangle|^2\exp[it(\epsilon_n-\epsilon_{n0})/\hbar]\}$$

$$\times\int_{-\infty}^{\infty}\frac{\exp(-it\rho)}{(E-E_0-\hbar\rho)^2+\Gamma^2/4}d\rho$$

$$=\frac{\sigma_0\Gamma}{4\hbar}\int_{-\infty}^{\infty}\exp[-it(E-E_0)/\hbar-(\Gamma/2\hbar)|t|]dt$$

$$\times[\sum_{n,n0} g_{n0}\langle n0|\exp(-i\mathbf{p}\cdot\mathbf{R}/\hbar+itH/\hbar)|n\rangle\langle n|\exp(i\mathbf{p}\cdot\mathbf{R}/\hbar-itH/\hbar)|n0\rangle]$$

$$=\frac{\sigma_0\Gamma}{4\hbar}\int_{-\infty}^{\infty}\exp[-it(E-E_0)/\hbar-\Gamma/2\hbar|t|]\langle\exp[-i\mathbf{p}\cdot\mathbf{R}(0)/\hbar]\exp[i\mathbf{p}\cdot\mathbf{R}(t)/\hbar]\rangle_T dt, \quad (2)$$

where $\mathbf{R}(t)$ is the Heisenberg operator defined by

$$\mathbf{R}(t)=\exp(itH/\hbar)\mathbf{R}\exp(-itH/\hbar).$$

H being the Hamiltonian of the interacting system, and $\langle\cdots\rangle_T$ means both the quantum mechanical and the statistical average at temperature T. We shall here restrict ourselves to a system for which Boltzmann statistics is applicable. In the above derivation the Fourier representation of the δ function and the identity $\sum_n|n\rangle\langle n|=1$ have been used. We now define a function $G_s(\mathbf{r},t)$ through the following equation

$$\langle\exp[-i\mathbf{p}\cdot\mathbf{R}(0)/\hbar]\exp[i\mathbf{p}\cdot\mathbf{R}(t)/\hbar]\rangle_T=\int\exp(i\mathbf{p}\cdot\mathbf{r}/\hbar)G_s(\mathbf{r},t)d\mathbf{r}. \quad (3)$$

The inversion then gives

$$G_s(\mathbf{r},t)=(2\pi)^{-3}\int\exp(-i\mathbf{p}\cdot\mathbf{r}/\hbar)\times\langle\exp[-i\mathbf{p}\cdot\mathbf{R}(0)/\hbar]\exp[i\mathbf{p}\cdot\mathbf{R}(t)/\hbar]\rangle_T d(\mathbf{p}/\hbar)$$

$$=\left\langle\int d\mathbf{r}'\delta[\mathbf{r}+\mathbf{R}(0)-\mathbf{r}']\delta[\mathbf{r}'-\mathbf{R}(t)]\right\rangle_T. \quad (4)$$

For $t=0$, $G_s(\mathbf{r},0)=\delta(\mathbf{r})$. $G_s(\mathbf{r},t)$ describes the correlation between the position of one and the same particle at different times. It gives, in the classical case, the probability of finding a particle at time t at position $\mathbf{r}$, if the same particle was at the origin at time $t=0$. The interpretation of this function is not quite clear in a quantum mechanical treatment and is discussed in the Appendix. Van Hove[5] has discussed the $G_s(\mathbf{r},t)$ function in detail and we shall refer to his original paper.

From (2) and (3) we have

$$\sigma_a(E)=\frac{\sigma_0\Gamma}{4\hbar}\int\exp[i(\boldsymbol{\kappa}\cdot\mathbf{r}-\omega t)-(\Gamma/2\hbar)|t|]\times G_s(\mathbf{r},t)d\mathbf{r}dt, \quad (5)$$

where $\hbar\omega=E-E_0$, $\hbar\boldsymbol{\kappa}=\mathbf{p}$.

As shown by Van Hove,[5] the incoherent differential scattering cross section for slow neutrons is proportional to the integral in (5) with $\Gamma=0$. In Lamb's theory,[3] the probability of resonance absorption of neutrons of energy E is also given by Eq. (1) besides a constant factor and is, therefore, proportional to the integral in (5). Thus the relevant term in the cross section for all the three processes—resonance absorption of neutron and γ rays by nuclei and neutron scattering (with $\Gamma=0$) is given by an expression of the type (5). We shall see in the sequel that the cross section for the

[4] W. Heitler, *The Quantum Theory of Radiation* (Oxford University Press, New York, 1944), 2nd ed., p. 110.

[5] L. Van Hove, Phys. Rev. 95, 249 (1954). See also R. J. Glauber, Phys. Rev. 98, 1092 (1955).

resonance absorption of γ rays by nuclei whether in a gas or bound in a solid or a liquid will follow from (5) depending on the explicit form of $G_s(\mathbf{r},t)$. It is possible to calculate the function $G_s(\mathbf{r},t)$ rigorously in the case of a Maxwellian gas and in the case of a solid in the harmonic approximation but it is not possible to do so in the case of a liquid. Nevertheless, in the latter case one could use in an approximate way the classical form of $G_s(\mathbf{r},t)$; e.g., the solution of the usual diffusion equation or better the solution of Langevin's equation for Brownian motion. The behavior of $G_s(\mathbf{r},t)$ for very small and very large times is known and for intermediate values of the time one could try different forms of $G_s(\mathbf{r},t)$ so as to fit the experimental data. Thus, a general formulation of the absorption probability (the same holds for emission) in terms of the self-correlation function $G_s(\mathbf{r},t)$ as expressed by Eq. (5), has a definite advantage.

It has been shown by Van Hove[5] that the self-correlation function in the case of a gas or a solid (cubic symmetric crystals) has the general form

$$G_s(\mathbf{r},t)=[2\pi\gamma(t)]^{-\frac{3}{2}}\exp[-r^2/2\gamma(t)]. \tag{6}$$

There is no obvious reason to believe that in the case of a liquid $G_s(\mathbf{r},t)$ has also the above general form. It seems, however, reasonable to assume that (6) is a good approximation for a liquid too. We know that it is correct for small as well as large times.

The probability $w_e(E)$ for the emission of a γ ray is also given by Eq. (1) except that the signs of ϵ_n and ϵ_{n0} are interchanged and the constant is different.[4] Proceeding as before, it is easy to show that $w_e(E)$ is given by

$$w_e(E)=\frac{1}{2\pi\hbar}\int \exp[i(\boldsymbol{\kappa}\cdot\mathbf{r}-\omega t)-(\Gamma/2\hbar)|t|]\times G_s(\mathbf{r},-t)d\mathbf{r}dt. \tag{7}$$

It is normalized such that $\int_0^\infty w_e(E)dE=1$.

The quantity of experimental interest is the self-absorption cross section σ which for a thin absorber is defined by

$$\sigma=\int_0^\infty \sigma_a(E)w_e(E)dE\Big/\int_0^\infty w_e(E)dE=\int_0^\infty \sigma_a(E)w_e(E)dE. \tag{8}$$

In a γ-ray resonance absorption experiment if the emitter is made to move with velocity v relative to the absorber, the emitted γ ray gets an energy Doppler shift $s=(v/c)E_0$, c being the velocity of light, and in that case the argument of $\sigma_a(E)$ should be replaced by $s+E$. If we do this and make use of (5), (6), and (7) in (8), it follows that the self-absorption cross section is given by, noticing that the integration over E can be extended to $-\infty$ without any appreciable error,

$$\sigma(s)=\frac{\sigma_0\Gamma}{4\hbar}\int \exp\left(-\frac{its}{\hbar}-\frac{\Gamma}{\hbar}|t|\right)\times\exp\left\{-\frac{\kappa^2}{2}[\gamma_e(t)+\gamma_a(t)]\right\}dt. \tag{9}$$

And if the emitter and the absorber are identical (9) becomes

$$\sigma(s)=\tfrac{1}{2}\sigma_a(s), \tag{10}$$

where $\sigma_a(s)$ is given by (5) with Γ replaced by 2Γ and $\gamma(t)$ replaced by $2\gamma(t)$. Before we proceed to calculate $\sigma(s)$ for a nucleus bound in a solid, we shall evaluate the absorption cross section $\sigma_a(E)$ for a nucleus in a perfect gas.

ABSORPTION OF A γ RAY BY AN ATOM IN A PERFECT GAS

It has been shown by Van Hove[5] that for a perfect gas the quantum mechanical form of $G_s(\mathbf{r},t)$ is the one given by (6) with

$$\gamma(t)=-i\frac{\hbar t}{M}+\frac{k_BTt^2}{M}, \tag{11}$$

where M is the mass of the atom and k_B is the Boltzmann's constant, and T is the temperature of the gas. The term linear in t is purely of quantum mechanical origin and the term quadratic in t survives in the classical limit. Vineyard[6] has shown that for very small times for an arbitrary interacting system described by a time-independent Hamiltonian $\gamma(t)$ is given by

$$\gamma(t)=-i\frac{\hbar t}{M}+\frac{1}{3M^2}\langle\mathbf{p}^2\rangle_T t^2, \tag{12}$$

where $\mathbf{p}$ is the momentum operator of an atom. This result easily follows from (3) if we expand the operator $\mathbf{R}(t)$ in powers of t and define $\gamma(t)$ by the relation

$$\gamma(t)=\frac{1}{3}\int r^2G_s(\mathbf{r},t)d\mathbf{r},$$

and assume that the system is isotropic.

Substituting (11) in (6) and using the resulting $G_s(\mathbf{r},t)$ in (5) and after performing integration over $\mathbf{r}$ we have

$$\sigma_a(E)=\frac{\sigma_0\Gamma}{4\hbar}\int_{-\infty}^{\infty}\exp\left[-\frac{it}{\hbar}(E-E_0-R)-\frac{\Gamma}{2\hbar}|t|-\frac{\Delta^2t^2}{4\hbar^2}\right]dt, \tag{13}$$

where we have put

$$R\text{ (the recoil energy)}=\hbar^2\kappa^2/2M=E_0^2/2Mc^2,\quad \Delta=2(Rk_BT)^{\frac{1}{2}}. \tag{14}$$

[6] G. H. Vineyard, Phys. Rev. 110, 999 (1958).

Putting $y=t\Gamma/2\hbar$ and making use of the convolution formula for the Fourier transform of a product, we have

$$\sigma_a(E)=\frac{\sigma_0}{2}\int_{-\infty}^{\infty}dz$$

$$\times\left\{\frac{1}{(2\pi)^{\frac{1}{2}}}\int_{-\infty}^{\infty}\exp\left[-iyz-iy\frac{(E-E_0-R)}{\Gamma/2}-y^2\frac{\Delta^2}{\Gamma^2}\right]dy\right\}$$

$$\times\left\{\frac{1}{(2\pi)^{\frac{1}{2}}}\int_{-\infty}^{\infty}\exp(iy'z-|y'|)dy'\right\},$$

which gives

$$\sigma_a(E)=\sigma_0\frac{\xi}{2\sqrt{\pi}}\int_{-\infty}^{\infty}\frac{dz}{1+z^2}\exp[-\tfrac{1}{4}\xi^2(z+x)^2],\quad(15)$$

where

$$x=\frac{E-E_0-R}{\Gamma/2};\quad \xi=\frac{\Gamma}{\Delta}.\quad(16)$$

Formula (15) is the same as given by Bethe and Placzek[7] in the case of resonance capture of neutrons by atoms forming a Maxwellian gas.

RESONANCE ABSORPTION OF γ RAYS BY ATOMS IN A CRYSTAL

We shall here restrict ourselves to cubic Bravais lattices. Again Van Hove[5] has shown that for a monoatomic cubic crystal $\gamma(t)$ is given by

$$\gamma(t)=\frac{\hbar^2}{M}\int_0^{\infty}\left[\coth\left(\frac{z}{2k_BT}\right)\left(1-\cos\frac{zt}{\hbar}\right)-i\sin\frac{zt}{\hbar}\right]\frac{f(z)}{z}dz,\quad(17)$$

where $f(z)$ is the distribution of energy levels of the phonons and such that

$$\int_0^{\infty}f(z)dz=1.$$

$f(z)$ is zero beyond $z=z_{\max}$.

Equation (5) with the help of (6) can be written after integration over $\mathbf{r}$ as

$$\sigma_a(E)$$

$$=\frac{\sigma_0\Gamma}{4\hbar}\left\{\exp[-\tfrac{1}{2}\kappa^2\gamma(\infty)]\int_{-\infty}^{\infty}\exp\left(-i\omega t-\frac{\Gamma}{2\hbar}|t|\right)dt\right.$$

$$+\exp[-\tfrac{1}{2}\kappa^2\gamma(\infty)]\int_{-\infty}^{\infty}\exp\left(-i\omega t-\frac{\Gamma}{2\hbar}|t|\right)$$

$$\left.\times\{\exp[\tfrac{1}{2}\kappa^2(\gamma(\infty)-\gamma(t))]-1\}dt\right\},$$

where $\gamma(\infty)$ is the value of $\gamma(t)$ at $t=\infty$. The exponential within the square brackets can now be expanded in a power series, and we have

$$\sigma_a(E)=2\pi\frac{\sigma_0\Gamma}{4\hbar}\exp(-2W)\left\{\frac{\hbar\Gamma}{2\pi}\frac{1}{(E-E_0)^2+\Gamma^2/4}+\sum_{n=1}^{\infty}\frac{(\kappa^2/2)^n}{n!}\frac{1}{2\pi}\int_{-\infty}^{\infty}\exp\left(-i\omega t-\frac{\Gamma}{2\hbar}|t|\right)[\gamma(\infty)-\gamma(t)]^n dt\right\}$$

$$=\frac{\pi\sigma_0\Gamma}{2}\left[\frac{\Gamma}{2\pi}\frac{1}{(E-E_0)^2+\Gamma^2/4}+\sum_{n=1}^{\infty}\frac{(2W)^n}{n!}g_n(E-E_0,T)\right]\exp(-2W),\quad(18)$$

since Γ can be neglected in the integrand in Eq. (18), and where

$$g_1(E,T)=\frac{f(|E|)}{2EF(T)}\left[\coth\left(\frac{E}{2k_BT}\right)-1\right],\quad(19)$$

$$g_n(E,T)=\int_{-\infty}^{\infty}g_1(E-E',T)g_{n-1}(E',T)dE',\quad(20)$$

$$F(T)=\int_0^{\infty}\frac{f(z)}{z}\coth\left(\frac{z}{2k_BT}\right)dz,\quad(21)$$

and

$$2W=\tfrac{1}{2}\kappa^2\gamma(\infty)=\frac{\hbar^2\kappa^2}{2M}F(T).\quad(22)$$

$2W$ is the usual Debye-Waller factor. The above formulation is the same as that used by Sjölander[8] in connection with neutron scattering by solids. It is instructive to compare formula (18) with that for the incoherent differential scattering cross section for neutrons in solids. The first term inside the curly brackets gives a sharp absorption peak of width Γ and represents the recoilless absorption of γ rays, and corresponds to elastic scattering in the neutron case (where it is a delta function). The other terms give a broad peak extending at least over an energy $z_{\max}$ and corresponds to phonon exchange.

In the Debye approximation,

$$\begin{aligned} f(z)&=3z^2/(k_B\Theta)^3 &&\text{for } z\leq k_B\Theta\\ &=0 &&\text{for } z>k_B\Theta,\end{aligned}\quad(23)$$

Θ being the Debye temperature of the solid. Using (23) in (21) it is easy to show that

$$F(T)=\frac{6}{k_B\Theta}\left[\frac{1}{4}+\frac{T}{\Theta}\phi\left(\frac{\Theta}{T}\right)\right],\quad(24a)$$

[7] H. Bethe and G. Placzek, Phys. Rev. **51**, 462 (1937).
[8] A. Sjölander, Arkiv Fysik **14**, 315 (1958).

where

$$\phi(z)=\frac{1}{z}\int_0^z \frac{ydy}{e^y-1}.$$

The function $\phi(z)$ has been tabulated by Zener.[9] Now

$$F(T)=3/(2k_B\Theta) \quad \text{for} \quad T\ll\Theta$$
$$=6T/(k_B\Theta^2) \quad \text{for} \quad T\gg\Theta. \tag{24b}$$

We also notice that

$$\int_{-\infty}^{\infty} g_n(E)dE=1.$$

Experimentally we are interested in the self-absorption cross section; i.e., in $\sigma(s)$ given by (9). Here the emitter and the absorber are assumed to be of the same material but at different temperatures, say T_e and T_a, respectively. Let v be the relative velocity of the emitter and absorber. $s=(v/c)E_0$ is positive f the two move towards each other and negative if they move away from each other. Proceeding as before, it follows from (9) that

$$\sigma_a(s)=\frac{\pi\sigma_0\Gamma}{2}e^{-(2W_e+2W_a)} \times\left[\frac{\Gamma}{\pi}\frac{1}{s^2+\Gamma^2}+\sum_{n=1}^{\infty}\frac{(2W_e+2W_a)^n}{n!}\bar{g}_n(s)\right], \tag{25}$$

where

$$2W_e=(\hbar^2\kappa^2/2M)F(T_e),$$

$$2W_a=(\hbar^2\kappa^2/2M)F(T_a),$$

$$\bar{g}_1(s)=\frac{1}{F(T_e)+F(T_a)} \times[F(T_e)g_1(s,T_e)+F(T_a)g_1(s,T_a)], \tag{26}$$

$$\bar{g}_n(s)=\int_{-\infty}^{\infty}\bar{g}_1(s-s')\bar{g}_{n-1}(s')ds'.$$

It should be borne in mind that the energy distribution of the phonons changes with temperature and hence the Debye temperature also changes. There will be a very slight shift of the resonance absorption peak due to the fact that when a γ ray is emitted or absorbed the mass of the emitting or the absorbing nucleus changes. This second order Doppler effect[10] has not been considered here.

If the emitter and the absorber are both identical and are at the same temperature, Eq. (25) simplifies to

$$\sigma(s)=\frac{\pi\sigma_0\Gamma}{2}e^{-4W}\left[\frac{\Gamma}{\pi}\frac{1}{s^2+\Gamma^2}+\sum_{n=1}^{\infty}\frac{(4W)^n}{n!}g_n(s,T)\right]. \tag{27}$$

The first term in (27) gives a sharp resonance peak having a full width 2Γ. For $s=0$, the first term is

$$\sigma'(0)=\tfrac{1}{2}\sigma_0e^{-4W}. \tag{28}$$

The resonance self-absorption cross section is thus diminished by a factor e^{-4W}, where $2W$, in the Debye approximation, is given by Eqs. (22) and (24). From the expression for $2W$, it is clear that to have a large Mössbauer effect the recoil energy R of the nucleus must be small; i.e., the γ ray should have a low energy and the Debye temperature Θ of the solid should be large and the temperature as low as possible. Recently Lipkin[11] has derived the expression for $2W$ in a simple manner and has also come to the same conclusions. In the original Mössbauer experiment in which Ir^{191} 129-kev gamma rays were used ($R=0.046$ ev, $k_B\Theta=0.025$ ev, $T=88°$K), $2W$ was nearly equal to 3; and hence the resonance effect was very small. For a large resonance effect $\sigma'(0)$ has to be greater than the non-nuclear cross section such as the cross section for the photoelectric effect. Unfortunately for isotopes so far investigated, the Mössbauer effect is very small except in the case of Fe^{57}, where because of the low γ-ray energy ($E_0=14.4$ kev), $2W$ is nearly 0.1 at $T=0°$K, and this is the reason why it is possible to observe the Mössbauer effect even at very high temperatures. Because of this comparatively large effect and the extreme sharpness of the resonance line ($\Gamma\sim5\times10^{-9}$ ev), the Mössbauer effect in Fe^{57} nucleus has found recently so many interesting applications.

The second term in (27), corresponding to phonon exchange, gives the shape of the wings of the sharp resonance absorption line; the wings extending at least up to an energy of the order $k_B\Theta$. If $2W\ll1$, all terms except the first in the sum are negligible. In that case the shape of the wings is related in a very simple way through Eq. (19) to the energy spectrum $f(E)$ of the crystal vibrations. It is thus at least in principle possible to measure the energy distribution function of the phonons as has been pointed out earlier by Visscher.[12] In this connection it is important to realize that if the nucleus emitting the γ rays constitutes a foreign atom in a host lattice, what one measures is not the vibrational spectrum of the host lattice but a spectrum which is characteristic of the local surroundings of the emitting nucleus. In addition to this, the one-phonon cross section is very small and this limits the possibility of using the Mössbauer effect to investigate the vibrational spectra of solids. A better way to study the real vibrational spectra is through the use of slow neutron scattering.

If $2W\gg1$, then we have what is called the weak-binding case. For example in the original Mössbauer experiment $2W\simeq3$ and it falls under this category.

[9] C. Zener, Phys. Rev. 49, 122 (1936).
[10] B. D. Josephson, Phys. Rev. Letters 4, 341 (1960).
[11] H. Lipkin, Ann. Phys. 9, 332 (1960).
[12] W. M. Visscher, Ann. Phys. 9, 194 (1960).

From (17) it follows that

$$\tfrac{1}{2}\kappa^2[\gamma_e(t)+\gamma_a(t)]$$

$$=-i2R\frac{t}{\hbar}+2\Delta^2\frac{t^2}{4\hbar^2}+\cdots \quad \text{for } t\ll\frac{\hbar}{k_B\Theta} \tag{29a}$$

$$=R[F(T_e)+F(T_a)] \quad \text{for } t\gg\frac{\hbar}{k_B\Theta}, \tag{29b}$$

where

$$\Delta^2=(8/3)R(E_{\text{kin}}{}^e+E_{\text{kin}}{}^a). \tag{30}$$

E_{kin} is the mean kinetic energy per atom and is given by

$$E_{\text{kin}}=\frac{3}{4}\int_0^\infty z\coth\left(\frac{z}{2k_BT}\right)f(z)dz.$$

For $T>\Theta$, $E_{\text{kin}}\approx\frac{3}{2}k_BT$.

Now Eq. (9) can be written as

$$\sigma(s)=\frac{\sigma_0\Gamma}{4\hbar}\left\{\int_{-\tau}^{\tau}+\int_{-\infty}^{-\tau}+\int_{\tau}^{\infty}\right\}dt$$

$$\times\exp\left\{-i\frac{ts}{\hbar}-\frac{\Gamma}{\hbar}|t|-\frac{\kappa^2}{2}[\gamma_e(t)+\gamma_a(t)]\right\}, \tag{31}$$

where $\tau\sim\hbar/k_B\Theta$.

In (31) the exponent $\frac{1}{2}\kappa^2[\gamma_e(t)+\gamma_a(t)]$ in the first integral can be replaced by (29a), and in the second and third integrals by (29b), without introducing appreciable error. It is then easy to show that

$$\sigma(s)=\frac{\sigma_0\Gamma}{4\hbar}\left\{\int_{-\infty}^{\infty}\exp\left[-\frac{it}{\hbar}(s-2R)-\frac{\Gamma}{\hbar}|t|-\frac{2\Delta^2}{4\hbar^2}t^2\right]dt\right.$$

$$\left.+\frac{2\hbar\Gamma}{s^2+\Gamma^2}\exp(-2W_e-2W_a)\right\}. \tag{32}$$

The integral in (32) is the same as the one which occurs in (13) and can be evaluated as before. Hence

$$\sigma(s)=\frac{\sigma_0\Gamma^2}{2}\frac{\exp-(2W_e+2W_a)}{s^2+\Gamma^2}$$

$$+\sigma_0\frac{\xi}{4\sqrt{\pi}}\int_{-\infty}^{\infty}\frac{dz}{1+z^2}\exp[-\tfrac{1}{4}\xi^2(x+z)^2], \tag{33}$$

where we have defined

$$\xi=2\Gamma/\Delta,\quad \Delta^2=(8/3)R(E_{\text{kin}}{}^e+E_{\text{kin}}{}^a)=\Delta_e^2+\Delta_a^2,$$
$$x=(s-2R)/\Gamma,\quad R=E_0^2/2Mc^2. \tag{34}$$

If $\xi\ll1$; i.e., the linewidth Γ is much smaller than the Doppler width Δ Eq. (33) for $s=0$ simplifies to

$$\sigma(0)=\frac{\sigma_0}{2}\exp(-2W_e-2W_a)$$

$$+\frac{\sigma_0\sqrt{\pi}}{2}\frac{\Gamma}{(\Delta_e^2+\Delta_a^2)^{\frac{1}{2}}}\exp\left[-\frac{4R^2}{\Delta_e^2+\Delta_a^2}\right]. \tag{35}$$

Equation (35) is the same as the formula (19) of Mössbauer.[13]

DIFFUSION BROADENING OF THE RESONANCE LINE

In this section we shall show how Mössbauer technique could be used to investigate the nature of diffusive motions in solids and probably under more favorable circumstances in a liquid too. In a solid the slow jumping movement of an atom from one lattice site to another gives rise to a broadening of the resonance line. At ordinary temperatures the broadening due to such a diffusive motion is small compared to the natural linewidth but at elevated temperatures the former can become of the same order of magnitude as the latter and even greater. In liquids the diffusive broadening is, however, many orders of magnitude greater than the linewidth but, unfortunately, the resonance absorption cross section is in most cases small compared to non-nuclear absorption cross section. This makes it difficult to distinguish the resonance line from the background.

The self-correlation function $G_s(\mathbf{r},t)$ as defined by Eq. (3) is a complex quantity and cannot, therefore, easily be interpreted as a self-diffusion function except in the case that its imaginary part is negligible. The imaginary part, as we know, is quantum mechanical in origin. It is, however, possible as Schofield[14] has done to define a real function which in the classical case goes over to the classical self-diffusion function and which is related to the absorption cross section in a similar way as is Van Hove's $G_s(\mathbf{r},t)$ function. The transformation suggested by Schofield and the question of using the real part of the Van Hove's $G_s(\mathbf{r},t)$ function are discussed in detail in the Appendix of this paper. Such a discussion besides being relevant to the context of this paper is of importance in connection with neutron scattering by liquids.

Following the suggestion of Schofield, if we replace t by $t+(i\hbar/2k_BT)$, $G_s(\mathbf{r},t)$ goes over to $F_s(\mathbf{r},t)$, which is given by (8A) of the Appendix and $\gamma(t)$ goes over to $\rho(t)$, where $\rho(t)$ is given by Eqs. (9A) and (10A) of the Appendix in the case of a gas and a solid, respectively. In the Appendix we have derived the expression for the resonance absorption cross section $\sigma_a(E)$ and for the emission probability $w_e(E)$, which are, respectively, given by Eqs. (11A) and (12A). We shall rewrite them

[13] R. L. Mössbauer, Z. Physik **151**, 124 (1958).
[14] P. Schofield, Phys. Rev. Letters **4**, 239 (1960).

here

$$\sigma_a(E)=\frac{\sigma_0\Gamma}{4\hbar}\exp\left[\frac{\hbar\omega}{2k_BT}-\frac{\hbar^2\kappa^2}{8Mk_BT}\right]\times\int_{-\infty}^{\infty}\exp\left[i(\boldsymbol{\kappa}\cdot\mathbf{r}-\omega t)-\frac{\Gamma}{2\hbar}|t|\right]\times F_s^c(\mathbf{r},t)d\mathbf{r}dt, \quad (36)$$

$$w_e(E)=\frac{1}{2\pi\hbar}\exp\left[-\frac{\hbar\omega}{2k_BT}-\frac{\hbar^2\kappa^2}{8Mk_BT}\right]\times\int_{-\infty}^{\infty}\exp\left[i(\boldsymbol{\kappa}\cdot\mathbf{r}-\omega t)-\frac{\Gamma}{2\hbar}|t|\right]\times F_s^c(\mathbf{r},t)d\mathbf{r}dt, \quad (37)$$

where $F_s^c(\mathbf{r},t)$ is the classical self-diffusion function and $\hbar\omega=E-E_0$.

We shall consider two simple cases: (i) in which the diffusive motion of an atom in the absorber is governed by the simple diffusion equation, and (ii) in which the atom jumps from one lattice site to another. Diffusion in normal liquids probably comes under case (i) whereas in solids it comes under case (ii). These two cases are considered here more as illustrations rather than to give a precise relationship between the resonance line shape and diffusive motions.

Case (i)

In this case $F_s^c(\mathbf{r},t)$ is given by

$$F_s^c(\mathbf{r},t)=(4\pi D|t|)^{-\frac{3}{2}}\exp(-r^2/4D|t|), \quad (38)$$

where D is the diffusion coefficient. This function has the right limiting form for large t but not for $t\rightarrow 0$. One should rather use for $F_s^c(\mathbf{r},t)$ the solution of Langevin's equation for the Brownian motion with $\rho(t)$ as given by (13A). $\rho(t)$ varies as t^2 for $t\rightarrow 0$. We shall not use the latter form of $\rho(t)$ since the change in the linewidth as a result of this refinement is negligible (see Singwi and Sjölander[15] in connection with neutron scattering).

Let us suppose that the absorber is in the liquid state. The cross section for the absorption of a γ ray of energy E is obtained by substituting (38) in (36) and after performing the integrations we have

$$\sigma_a(E)=(\sigma_0\Gamma/4)\exp(-2W_a)(\Gamma+2\hbar\kappa^2D)/[(E-E_0)^2+\tfrac{1}{4}(\Gamma+2\hbar\kappa^2D)^2], \quad (39)$$

where in deducing (39) we have replaced

$$\exp[-(E-E_0)/2k_BT]$$

by unity, since $E-E_0\ll 2k_BT$ in the resonance peak and where we have put $\hbar^2\kappa^2/8Mk_BT=2W_a$. $2W_a$ is analogous to the Debye-Waller factor in the case of a solid.

From (39) it is evident that the broadening $\Delta\epsilon$ of the resonance line due to diffusion is given by

$$\Delta\epsilon=2\hbar\kappa^2D=2E_0^2D/\hbar c^2, \quad (40)$$

where E_0 is the energy of the γ ray and c is the velocity of light. As an example let us take iron for which $D\sim 10^{-5}$ cm^2/sec in the molten state, and $E_0=14$ kev (for Fe^{57}). Equation (40) gives $\Delta\epsilon\simeq 6\times 10^{-3}$ ev which is several orders of magnitude greater than the natural width Γ.

Experimentally what one measures is the self-absorption cross section

$$\sigma(s)=\int_0^\infty w_e(E)\sigma_a(E+s)dE.$$

Here $w_e(E)$ is the emission probability in the case of a solid, since the emitter is in the form of a solid. If we neglect the phonon part, the expression for $w_e(E)$ is

$$w_e(E)=\frac{\Gamma}{2\pi}e^{-2W_e}\frac{1}{(E-E_0)^2+\Gamma^2/4}. \quad (41)$$

Using (39) and (41) in the expression for $\sigma(s)$, we get

$$\sigma(s)=\frac{\sigma_0\Gamma}{2}\exp(-2W_e-2W_a)\frac{\Gamma+\hbar\kappa^2D}{s^2+(\Gamma+\hbar\kappa^2D)^2}. \quad (42)$$

Recently a cold-neutron scattering method has been used to measure the diffusive broadening of the "quasi-elastic" scattering in liquids.[16-18] This method, unfortunately, suffers from the disadvantage of having a poor energy resolution. But if we were to study the diffusive broadening by Mössbauer technique, such a disadvantage does not exist since the natural width of the line is negligible compared to the diffusive broadening. However, this method seems at present to be hardly practicable because of the smallness of $\sigma(s)$ compared to the other non-nuclear cross section such as the photoelectric effect. But under very favorable circumstances such that $\Gamma/\Delta\epsilon$ is not too small this method could be used to investigate the shape of the resonance line and determine the diffusion coefficient from the measurement of line broadening.

Case (ii)

Let τ_0 be the mean time for which an atom stays on a given lattice site before jumping to a new lattice position. If we now assume that there is no correlation in motion between one jump and the next, it is possible

[15] K. S. Singwi and A. Sjölander, Phys. Rev. **119**, 863 (1960).

[16] B. N. Brockhouse, Phys. Rev. Letters **2**, 287 (1959).

[17] D. J. Hughes, H. Palevsky, W. Kley, and E. Tunkelo, Phys. Rev. Letters **3**, 91 (1959).

[18] I. Pelah, W. L. Whittemore, and A. W. McReynolds, Phys. Rev. **113**, 767 (1959).

to calculate $F_s^c(\mathbf{r},t)$ or rather its Fourier transform as has been done earlier by Singwi and Sjölander[15] in connection with diffusive motions in water and cold-neutron scattering. The problem under consideration is in fact a special case of the more general formula of Singwi and Sjölander. The present case consists in taking $\tau_1 \rightarrow 0$, where τ_1 is the mean time for which the particle diffuses between its two oscillatory states and in taking the function $h(r,t)$ to be independent of time. It is then easy to show by the use of formula (36) that

$$\sigma_a(E)=\frac{\sigma_0\Gamma}{4}\exp(-2W_a) \times\frac{\Gamma+(2\hbar/\tau_0)(1-\alpha)}{(E-E_0)^2+[\Gamma+(2\hbar/\tau_0)(1-\alpha)]^2/4}, \quad (43)$$

where

$$\alpha=\int \exp(i\boldsymbol{\kappa}\cdot\mathbf{r})h(\mathbf{r})d\mathbf{r}, \quad (44)$$

$h(\mathbf{r})$ gives the probability of finding the particle at the position $\mathbf{r}$ after a single jump, if the particle was at the origin before the jump. Using (43) and (41) we have for the self-absorption cross section

$$\sigma(s)=\frac{\sigma_0\Gamma}{2}\exp(-2W_e-2W_a) \times\frac{\Gamma+(\hbar/\tau_0)(1-\alpha)}{s^2+[\Gamma+(\hbar/\tau_0)(1-\alpha)]^2}. \quad (45)$$

The diffusion coefficient D is defined by

$$D=\frac{1}{6\tau_0}\int r^2h(\mathbf{r})d\mathbf{r}. \quad (46)$$

From formula (43) it is clear that the broadening $\Delta\epsilon$ of the resonance peak due to diffusive motions is

$$\Delta\epsilon=2\hbar/\tau_0\left[1-\int \exp(i\boldsymbol{\kappa}\cdot\mathbf{r})\, h(\mathbf{r})d\mathbf{r}\right]. \quad (47)$$

We thus see that the maximum value of the broadening is $2\hbar/\tau_0$ and the broadening depends on the angle between the direction of motion of the diffusing atom and the direction of the γ-ray quantum. Consider a Fe^{57} nucleus sandwiched between two layers of a graphite lattice (it is possible to introduce iron atoms between the layer planes of a graphite single crystal). The Fe^{57} nucleus finds it hard to move in the direction of the c-axis but can diffuse with ease in the basal plane. If the γ ray from the emitter falls on the absorber parallel to the c axis and the counter is also pointing along the c axis, the diffusive broadening $\Delta\epsilon$ in this case will be negligible and the resonance line will have its natural width. If we now rotate the absorber relative to the direction of the incident γ ray, the diffusive broadening should increase. At the same time the magnitude of the resonance absorption would decrease due to the anisotropy of the Debye-Waller factor (our formulas can easily be extended for an anisotropic solid).

Let us consider self-diffusion in iron. The emitter is at low temperature and the resonance absorption is studied as a function of the velocity of the emitter for various temperatures of the absorber. At ordinary temperatures, the self-diffusion in iron is so small that the line broadening due to diffusive motion is negligible compared to the natural width Γ. For example even at 760°C, the diffusion coefficient is only 1.5×10^{-12} cm^2/sec, which would give a value of 6×10^{-5} sec for τ_0; since $\tau_0 \simeq l^2/6D$, l being the interatomic spacing. This would correspond to a broadening $(\Delta_b)_{\max}\simeq 2\times10^{-11}$ ev, whereas $\Gamma=4.6\times10^{-9}$ ev. However, at higher temperatures, say 1000°C and above, it should be possible to detect the diffusive broadening by a Mössbauer-type experiment. At such high temperatures the Debye-Waller factor e^{-2W_a} (since $2W_e \ll 2W_a$) would no doubt decrease but it is still not too small ($\sim e^{-3}$) as to preclude the possibility of observing the resonance effect.

It has been reported[19] that the rate of self-diffusion in iron at 757°C, under plastic deformation, increases by as much as a factor of thousand.[20] And if it is true, the line broadening due to diffusion would now be nearly 2×10^{-8} ev which is greater than the natural line-width and it might, therefore, be possible to detect it by a Mössbauer-type experiment. It would be valuable to perform such an experiment in view of the fact that there exists a controversy between different experimental workers regarding the enhancement of the self diffusion and the range of temperature for which it is significant. Besides a Mössbauer-type experiment is different from the usual diffusion experiments using tracers and should, therefore, provide an independent check. One could also study the impurity diffusion of iron in other metals like copper and silver. Such an experiment would give a direct measure of the mean time τ_0 and its temperature variation.

APPENDIX

The function $G_s(\mathbf{r},t)$ as defined by Eq. (3) could only in the classical limit be interpreted as the self-diffusion function. For small times when the particle under consideration has moved only a distance of the order of the de Broglie wavelength, quantum effects are important and $G_s(\mathbf{r},t)$ is complex. In fact, according to Van Hove[5] it is only the real part of $G_s(\mathbf{r},t)$ which has the above physical interpretation. It is, however, possible to express the emission or the absorption probability in terms of the real part of $G_s(\mathbf{r},t)$.

---

[19] N. Ujiive, B. Averbach, M. Cohen, and V. Griffiths, Acta Met. 6, 68 (1958).

[20] For a general discussion see the review article by D. Lazarus, *Solid State Physics*, edited by F. Seitz and D. Turnbull (Academic Press, Inc., New York, 1960), Vol. 8, p. 71.

Now

$$\frac{1}{2\pi}\int_{-\infty}^{\infty}\exp(-i\omega t)\langle\exp[-i\boldsymbol{\kappa}\cdot\mathbf{R}(0)]\exp[i\boldsymbol{\kappa}\cdot\mathbf{R}(t)]\rangle_T dt$$
$$=\sum_{n,n0}g_{n0}|\langle n|\exp(i\boldsymbol{\kappa}\cdot\mathbf{R})|n_0\rangle|^2$$
$$\times\delta[\omega-(\epsilon_n-\epsilon_{n0})/\hbar],\quad (1\text{A})$$

which follows from the definition of $\langle\cdots\rangle_T$ and $g_{nn0}=\exp(-E_{n0}/k_BT)/\sum_n\exp(-E_n/k_BT)$. Further

$$\frac{1}{2\pi}\int_{-\infty}^{\infty}\exp(-i\omega t)\langle\exp[-i\boldsymbol{\kappa}\cdot\mathbf{R}(t)]\exp[i\boldsymbol{\kappa}\cdot\mathbf{R}(0)]\rangle_T dt$$
$$=\sum_{n,n0}g_{n0,}|\langle n|\exp(i\boldsymbol{\kappa}\cdot\mathbf{R})|n0\rangle|^2\delta[\omega+(\epsilon_n-\epsilon_{n0})/\hbar]$$
$$=\sum_{n,n0}g_{n0}|\langle n0|\exp(i\boldsymbol{\kappa}\cdot\mathbf{R})|n\rangle|^2\delta[\omega-(\epsilon_n-\epsilon_{n0})/\hbar]$$
$$=e^{-\beta\hbar\omega}\sum_{n,n0}g_{n0}|\langle n|\exp(i\boldsymbol{\kappa}\cdot\mathbf{R})|n0\rangle|^2$$
$$\times\delta[\omega-(\epsilon_n-\epsilon_{n0})/\hbar]$$
$$=e^{-\beta\hbar\omega}\frac{1}{2\pi}\int_{-\infty}^{\infty}\exp(-i\omega t)$$
$$\times\langle\exp[-i\boldsymbol{\kappa}\cdot\mathbf{R}(0)]\exp[i\boldsymbol{\kappa}\cdot\mathbf{R}(t)]\rangle_T dt.\quad (2\text{A})$$

The last step in (2A) follows from (1A). The relation $g_n=\exp[-\beta(\epsilon_n-\epsilon_{n0})]g_{n0}$ has been used in the second step in (2A); $\beta=1/k_BT$.

Introducing the real part of $G_s(\mathbf{r},t)$, which is defined by

$$\text{Re}[G_s(\mathbf{r},t)]=(2\pi)^{-3}\int\exp(-i\boldsymbol{\kappa}\cdot\mathbf{r})$$
$$\times\tfrac{1}{2}\{\langle\exp[-i\boldsymbol{\kappa}\cdot\mathbf{R}(0)]\exp[i\boldsymbol{\kappa}\cdot\mathbf{R}(t)]$$
$$+\exp[-i\boldsymbol{\kappa}\cdot\mathbf{R}(t)]\exp[i\boldsymbol{\kappa}\cdot\mathbf{R}(0)]\rangle_T\}d\boldsymbol{\kappa},\quad (3\text{A})$$

and using (1A) and (2A) in Eq. (5) of the text we get the following expression for the absorption cross section:

$$\sigma_a(E)=\frac{\sigma_0\Gamma}{4\hbar}\frac{\exp(\beta\hbar\omega/2)}{\cosh(\beta\hbar\omega/2)}$$
$$\times\int\exp[i(\boldsymbol{\kappa}\cdot\mathbf{r}-\omega t)-(\Gamma/2\hbar)|t|]$$
$$\times\text{Re}[G_s(\mathbf{r},t)]d\mathbf{r}dt,\quad (4\text{A})$$

considering that $\Gamma\ll k_BT$.

Recently Schofield[14] has also suggested in connection with neutron scattering that $G_s(\mathbf{r},t+i\hbar/2k_BT)$ rather than $G_s(\mathbf{r},t)$ should be considered as a self-diffusion function. He points out that if, for instance, $G_s(\mathbf{r},t)$ is replaced by its classical equivalent obtained from the simple diffusion equation, as suggested by Vineyard,[6] the scattering cross section will not satisfy the condition of detailed balance. If, however, $G_s(\mathbf{r},t+i\hbar/2k_BT)$ is replaced by the classical self-diffusion function the principle of detailed balance will be satisfied. The same is also true if we replace $\text{Re}[G_s(\mathbf{r},t)]$ in (4A) by its classical equivalent.

Schofield's result is easily obtained by noting that

$$\frac{1}{2\pi}\int_{-\infty}^{\infty}\exp(-i\omega t)\langle\exp[-i\boldsymbol{\kappa}\cdot\mathbf{R}(0)]\exp[i\boldsymbol{\kappa}\cdot\mathbf{R}(t)]\rangle_T dt$$
$$=\sum_{n,n0}g_{n0}|\langle n|\exp(i\boldsymbol{\kappa}\cdot\mathbf{R})|n0\rangle|^2\delta[\omega-(\epsilon_n-\epsilon_{n0})/\hbar]$$
$$=\exp(\beta\hbar\omega/2)\sum_{n,n0}(g_ng_{n0})^{\frac{1}{2}}|\langle n|\exp(i\boldsymbol{\kappa}\cdot\mathbf{R})|n0\rangle|^2$$
$$\times\delta[\omega-(\epsilon_n-\epsilon_{n0})/\hbar],\quad (5\text{A})$$

and introducing a function

$$F_s(\mathbf{r},t)=(2\pi)^{-3}\int\exp(-i\boldsymbol{\kappa}\cdot\mathbf{r})$$
$$\times\{\sum_{n,n0}(g_ng_{n0})^{\frac{1}{2}}\langle n0|\exp[-i\boldsymbol{\kappa}\cdot\mathbf{R}(0)]|n\rangle$$
$$\times\langle n|\exp[i\boldsymbol{\kappa}\cdot\mathbf{R}(t)]|n0\rangle\}d\boldsymbol{\kappa}.\quad (6\text{A})$$

We then have for the absorption cross section

$$\sigma_a(E)=\frac{\sigma_0\Gamma}{4\hbar}\exp(\beta\hbar\omega/2)\int\exp[i(\boldsymbol{\kappa}\cdot\mathbf{r}-\omega t)-(\Gamma/2\hbar)|t|]$$
$$\times F_s(\mathbf{r},t)d\mathbf{r}dt.\quad (7\text{A})$$

$F_s(\mathbf{r},t)$ is real and is an even function of t and thus the integral in (7A) is an even function of ω. It is easily shown by using the definition (3) of $G_s(\mathbf{r},t)$ that $F_s(\mathbf{r},t)=G_s(\mathbf{r},t+i\hbar/2k_BT)$. If one uses the classical self-diffusion function instead of $F_s(\mathbf{r},t)$ in (7A) or for $\text{Re}[G_s(\mathbf{r},t)]$ in (4A), the two expressions are identical to the first order in $\hbar\omega/k_BT$.

If we make the transformation as suggested by Schofield, we have

$$F_s(\mathbf{r},t)=[2\pi\rho(t)]^{-\frac{3}{2}}\exp[-r^2/2\rho(t)],\quad (8\text{A})$$

where

$$\rho(t)=\hbar^2/4Mk_BT+(k_BT/M)t^2,\quad (9\text{A})$$

for a free gas, and

$$\rho(t)=(\hbar^2/M)\int_0^{\infty}\frac{f(z)}{z}\tanh(z/4k_BT)dz$$
$$+(\hbar^2/M)\int_0^{\infty}\frac{f(z)}{z}\frac{1-\cos(zt/\hbar)}{\sinh(z/2k_BT)}dz,\quad (10\text{A})$$

for a solid. Equations (9A) and (10A) follow from Eqs. (11) and (17) of the text, respectively.

We notice from (9A) that even at $t=0$, the particle is distributed over a finite region. The finite extension is given by the first term in (9A) and is consistent with Heisenberg's uncertainty principle for a particle with mean velocity $(k_BT/M)^{\frac{1}{2}}$. The real part of $G_s(\mathbf{r},t)$ on the other hand, goes over to a δ function around the origin at $t=0$. It, therefore, appears that $F_s(\mathbf{r},t)$ as given by (8A) is more directly connected with self-diffusion.

Schofield's suggestion, in the case of a liquid, is to replace $F_s(\mathbf{r},t)$ in the first approximation by a classical self-diffusion function obtained, for instance, from Langevin's equation. In that case $\rho(t)$ will go to zero as t^2 for small times and will approach $2D|t|$ for large times. If we, however, add a constant to $\rho(t)$ corresponding to a finite extension of the probability cloud at $t=0$, the resulting formula for the cross section will be valid to some extent also for large momentum transfers.

For a liquid it seems reasonable to take the same constant as that for a gas, since we know that for large momentum transfers corresponding to small times the scattering cross section approximately goes over to a free gas formula. Adding of this constant to $\rho(t)$ will simply amount to multiplying the right-hand side of (7A) by $\exp(-\hbar^2\kappa^2/8Mk_BT)$. In the case of neutron scattering by liquids this factor is often nearly equal to unity except for large incident neutron energy, whereas in the case of γ-ray resonance absorption it could be quite small depending on the recoil energy of the nucleus.

As a result of the foregoing discussion it seems plausible to write (7A) in the form

$$\sigma_a(E)=\frac{\sigma_0\Gamma}{4\hbar}\exp(\hbar\omega/2k_BT-\hbar^2\kappa^2/8Mk_BT)\times\int\exp[i(\boldsymbol{\kappa}\cdot\mathbf{r}-\omega t)-(\Gamma/2\hbar)|t|]\times F_s{}^c(\mathbf{r},t)d\mathbf{r}dt, \quad (11A)$$

and similarly,

$$w_e(E)=\frac{1}{2\pi\hbar}\exp(-\hbar\omega/2k_BT-\hbar^2\kappa^2/8Mk_BT)\times\int\exp[i(\boldsymbol{\kappa}\cdot\mathbf{r}-\omega t)-(\Gamma/2\hbar)|t|]\times F_s{}^c(\mathbf{r},t)d\mathbf{r}dt, \quad (12A)$$

where for $F_s{}^c(\mathbf{r},t)$ we take the expression (8A) with $\rho(t)$ as given from Langevin's equation, and is[21]

$$\rho(t)=(2D/\beta')[\beta't-1+\exp(-\beta't)]. \quad (13A)$$

The characteristic time $1/\beta'$ is given by

$$\beta'=k_BT/DM, \quad (14A)$$

D being the diffusion coefficient. Of course, this is possible only if the diffusion can really be described by Langevin's equation.

Note added in proof. Recent measurements of the specific heat of indium by Bryant and Keesom [Phys. Rev. Letters **4**, 460 (1959)] and of niobium by Broose *et al.* [Phys. Rev. Letters **5**, 246 (1960)] both in the superconducting and normal phases seem to show that the lattice part of the specific heat is different in the two phases, thus indicating that *perhaps* the phonon spectrum in the two phases is not the same. Broose *et al.*, in an attempt to explain their measurements on niobium have suggested in the superconducting phase an altered value of the Debye temperature as 243°K, which value in the normal state they arrive at is 231°K. Thus, there is a change of five percent in the value of θ_D.

Here we wish to suggest an alternative and perhaps more direct experiment to decide whether there is any appreciable change in the value of θ_D in going from the normal to the superconducting phase. The experiment consists in studying the intensity of the Mössbauer line both in the normal and superconducting phases. The choice for such an experiment is very severely limited to only a few isotopes. The intensity of the Mössbauer line is determined by the Debye-Waller factor e^{-4w}, and in the limit $T\ll\theta_D$, $4w$ is equal to $3R/k_B\theta_D$, where R is the recoil energy. In order to have an appreciable change in the intensity of resonance absorption for a very small change in the value of θ_D, one would demand a large value of $4w$; i.e., a large recoil energy and a small θ_D. Re^{187} is such an example. It becomes superconducting and the values of R and θ_D are, respectively, 0.051 ev and 417°K. An almost trivial calculation will show that a ten percent increase in the value of θ_D will give a 35% increase in the intensity of the resonance absorption, which should be easy to observe. Other isotopes which one could study are Ta^{181} and Hf^{177}.

The authors have been informed privately by Meyer-Schuetzmeister and Hanna that their very preliminary experiment on the Mössbauer effect in Sn, both in the normal and superconducting phases, indicates that there is an increase of a few percent in the intensity of resonance absorption in the latter phase. A five percent increase in the value of θ_D would, in this case, give nearly three percent increase in the intensity.

[21] See for instance S. Chandrasekhar, Revs. Modern Phys. **15**, 1 (1943).

LE JOURNAL DE PHYSIQUE ET LE RADIUM TOME 22, MAI 1961, PAGE 303.

DIFFUSION DES PHOTONS SUR LES ATOMES ET LES NOYAUX DANS LES CRISTAUX

Par C. TZARA,
Section de Physique Nucléaire à Moyenne Énergie, C. E. N., Saclay.

Résumé. — On étudie la diffusion des photons par les atomes et les noyaux liés dans un solide avec ou sans cession de phonons. Selon la largeur de l'état excité (atomique ou nucléaire), relativement au spectre de vibration du cristal, la proportion de diffusion « sans recul » varie entre deux limites, l'une étant le facteur de Debye-Waller, l'autre le carré du facteur de Mössbauer-Lamb. L'interférence entre les processus atomique et nucléaire est examinée. Enfin l'émission sans recul d'un photon nucléaire à la suite d'une cascade de transitions est calcnlée sans faire appel à un phénomène de réarrangement des états cristallins.

Abstract. — Photon scattering by atoms and nuclei in solids is investigated. Depending on the excited (nuclear or atomic) state width compared to the crystal vibration spectrum, the proportion of recoilless scattering varies between two limits : the Debye-Waller factor on one side, the square of the Mössbauer-Lamb on the other. Interference between the two processes is examined. Finally the recoilless emission of a nuclear photon following a sequence of transitions is calculated without requiring a rearrangement phenomenon in the solid.

L'interaction des photons avec les atomes ou les noyaux liés dans un solide peut se produire sans cession de phonons au cristal. La diffraction des rayons X est un exemple de ce phénomène. Récemment Mössbauer a découvert l'émission et l'absorption sans recul de photons par les noyaux dans un solide [1]. Dans le présent travail, nous examinons entre autres les diffusions atomique et nucléaire dans les solides et leur interférence éventuelle en utilisant la théorie de Lamb [2].

Le cristal est composé d'atomes de masse M, à Z électrons. Les états et énergies propres du système électronique sont ψ_i et E_i, ceux du noyaux sont φ_j et W_j. L'état du cristal est défini par l'ensemble $\{ \alpha_s \}$ des nombres d'occupation dans chaque mode de vibration s. L'énergie propre de l'état $\{ \alpha_s \}$ est $E\{ \alpha_s \} = \sum_{\{\alpha_s\}} \alpha_s \hbar\omega_s$. A l'état d'équilibre, à température T, le poids statistique de chaque état $\{ \alpha_s \}$ est $g\{ \alpha_s \}$. Dans le cas où une espèce atomique est insérée dans un réseau d'un autre constituant, ce ne sont pas les degrés de liberté de l'ensemble qui sont à considérer, mais ceux des atomes intéressés.

1. Diffusion Rayleigh atomique.

— La section efficace de diffusion d'un photon d'énergie k, impulsion $\boldsymbol{K}$ et polarisation $\boldsymbol{\epsilon}$ en un photon d'énergie k', impulsion $\boldsymbol{K}'$ et polarisation ε', le cristal étant initialement et finalement dans les états purs $\{ \alpha_s \}$ et $\{ \beta_s \}$, l'atome étant laissé dans l'état initial, est, en approximation non relativiste :

$$\begin{aligned}\frac{\mathrm{d}\sigma_R}{\mathrm{d}\Omega}(\{ \alpha_s \}\{ \beta_s \}\boldsymbol{KK}'\boldsymbol{\epsilon\epsilon}') = \Big| &< \{ \beta_s \}| \mathrm{e}^{i\boldsymbol{qu}/\hbar} | \{ \alpha_s \} > < \psi_0 \Big| \sum_{j=1}^{Z} \mathrm{e}^{i\boldsymbol{qr}_i/\hbar} \Big| \psi_0 > \boldsymbol{\epsilon\epsilon}' \\ &+ \frac{1}{m}\sum_{\{n_s\},n} \frac{< \{ \beta_s \}| \mathrm{e}^{-i\boldsymbol{K}'\boldsymbol{u}/\hbar} | \{ n_s \} > < \{ n_s \}| \mathrm{e}^{i\boldsymbol{Ku}/\hbar} | \{ \alpha_s \} > < \psi_0 | \sum \mathrm{e}^{-i\boldsymbol{K}'\boldsymbol{r}_j/\hbar} p_j' | \psi_n > < \psi_n | \sum \mathrm{e}^{i\boldsymbol{Kr}_i/\hbar} p_j | \psi_0 >}{E_p - E_0 - k + E\{n_s\} - E\{\alpha_s\} + i\gamma} \\ &+ \frac{1}{m}\sum_{\{n_s\},n} \frac{< \{ \beta_s \}| \mathrm{e}^{i\boldsymbol{Ku}/\hbar} | \{ n_s \} > < \{ n_s \}| \mathrm{e}^{-i\boldsymbol{K}'\boldsymbol{u}/\hbar} | \{ \alpha_s \} > < \psi_0 | \sum \mathrm{e}^{i\boldsymbol{Kr}_j/\hbar} p_j | \psi_n > < \psi_n | \sum \mathrm{e}^{-i\boldsymbol{K}'\boldsymbol{r}_j/\hbar} p_j | \psi_0 >}{E_n - E_0 + k' + E\{n_s\} - E\{\alpha_s\} + i\gamma} \Big|^2 \\ &\times (e^2/mc^2)^2 \, k'/k \end{aligned} \quad (1)$$

ici $\boldsymbol{q} = \boldsymbol{K} - \boldsymbol{K}'$ transfert d'impulsion

$$k' + E\{\beta_s\} = k + E\{s_x\}$$

$\boldsymbol{u}$: coordonnée du centre de gravité de l'atome considéré dans le cristal ;

$\boldsymbol{r}_j$: coordonnées des électrons atomiques dans un système lié à l'atome.

Le premier terme décrit la diffusion Thomson par les Z électrons arrangés selon la configuration ψ_0. Le facteur de forme :

$$ZF(q) = < \psi_0 | \sum \mathrm{e}^{i\boldsymbol{qr}_j/\hbar} | \psi_0 >$$

(dans le cas d'un atome sphérique) suffit généralement à rendre compte de la diffusion cohérente si l'énergie du photon est supérieure aux énergies des discontinuités d'absorption $E_n - E_0$ les plus fortes. Nous ne nous limiterons pas pour l'instant à ce terme.

Si k est très différent de $E_n - E_0$, $E_{n_s} - E_{\alpha_s}$ peut être négligé dans les dénominateurs des termes dispersifs du premier type ; si $k \simeq E_n - E_0$, cette approximation reste valable car la partie imaginaire $\gamma \simeq \frac{1}{2}\Gamma_n$, la largeur de l'état ψ_n est, pour les transitions les plus fortes, très supérieure à $E_{\{n_s\}} - E_{\{\alpha_s\}} \simeq k\Theta$, Θ étant la température de Debye du solide.

Dans les termes dispersifs du deuxième type, l'approximation est évidemment meilleure. La sommation $\sum_{\{n_s\}}$ s'effectue alors aisément puisque :

$$\sum_{\{n_s\}} |\{ n_s \} > < \{ n_s \}| = 1$$

et il vient :

$$\frac{d\sigma_R}{d\Omega}(\{\alpha_s\}\{\beta_s\}\, \boldsymbol{KK'\epsilon\epsilon'})$$
$$= |< \{\beta_s\}| e^{i\boldsymbol{qu}/\hbar} |\{\alpha_s\}>|^2$$
$$|ZF(q)\, \boldsymbol{\epsilon}.\boldsymbol{\epsilon}' + M^+ + M^-|^2 (e^2/mc^2)^2 \frac{k'}{k}. \quad (2)$$

Dans ce cas, le plus répandu, la section efficace dans un cristal est simplement le produit d'un facteur « cristallin » par la section efficace atomique. Si la section efficace varie rapidement dans des intervalles d'énergie de l'ordre de $k\Theta$, cette factorisation n'a plus lieu. C'est le cas des résonances de réaction $(n\gamma)$ [2], avec, ici, la complication supplémentaire des termes dispersifs.

Deux quantités facilement observables sont déduites de (1) : la section efficace de diffusion totale, intégrée sur tous les états finals possibles du cristal, $\frac{d\sigma_R^t}{d\Omega}(\boldsymbol{KK'\epsilon\epsilon'})$ et la section efficace de diffusion sans recul, $\frac{d\sigma_R^0}{d\Omega}(\boldsymbol{KK'\epsilon\epsilon'})$.

En nous plaçant dans les conditions de validité de (2) :

$$\frac{d\sigma_t^R}{d\Omega} = \sum_{\{\beta_s\}\{\alpha_s\}} g\{\alpha_s\}|< \{\beta_s\}| e^{i\boldsymbol{qu}/\hbar} |\{\alpha_s\}>|^2 \frac{dS_R}{d\Omega}.$$

Si nous négligeons la variation de $\frac{dS_R}{d\Omega}$ en fonction de $k' = k + E_{\{\alpha_s\}} - E_{\{\beta_s\}}$ en utilisant :

$$\sum_{\{\beta_s\}} |\{\beta_s\} > < \{\beta_s\}| = 1 \quad \text{et} \quad \sum_{\{\alpha_s\}} g\{\alpha_s\} = 1$$

nous obtenons évidemment :

$$d\sigma_R^t/d\Omega = d\sigma_R/d\Omega$$

et :

$$d\sigma_0^R/d\Omega = \sum_{\{\alpha_s\}} g\{\alpha_t\}|< \{|\alpha_s\}| e^{i\boldsymbol{qu}/\hbar} |\{\alpha_s\}>|^2\, d\sigma_R/d\Omega.$$

Pour un cristal isotrope, on trouve le facteur de Debye-Waller par un calcul immédiat calqué sur celui de Lamb :

$$\frac{d\sigma_R^0}{d\Omega} = \exp\left\{-\frac{3}{2}\cdot\frac{q^2}{2M}\frac{1}{k\Theta}\left[1 + \int_0^1 \frac{4v\, dv}{e^{vx} - 1}\right]\right\}\frac{d\sigma_R}{d\Omega} \quad (3)$$

où

$$X = \Theta/T.$$

2. **Diffusion nucléaire résonnante.** — La diffusion résonnante est un phénomène à un seul quantum ou encore cohérent, lorsque l'état du diffuseur pendant le processus n'est pas observé [4]. C'est le cas de toutes les diffusions et réactions, où le temps de vie de l'état excité étant très court, le faisceau incident (la perturbation) et le faisceau diffusé sont pratiquement établis en permanence. Cependant les expériences où un délai est introduit entre l'onde incidente et l'observation d'une particule réémise [5] détruisent cette cohérence. Notons aussi que les transformations α ou β et les cascades de γ des noyaux peuvent être envisagées sous cet aspect ; la cohérence peut être détruite simplement en isolant l'état intermédiaire s'il a une vie assez longue ou bien par une interaction extérieure telle que le couplage entre le moment quadrupolaire de l'état intermédiaire et le champ cristallin.

Puisque la cohérence et l'absence d'information sur l'état du diffuseur pendant la diffusion sont liées, on s'attendrait à ce que la proportion de diffusion sans recul soit donnée par

$$\exp\left\{-\frac{3}{2}\frac{q^2}{2M}\frac{1}{k\Theta}F(x)\right\} = \varphi$$

où figure le transfert global d'impulsion q et non par

$$\exp\left\{-3\frac{K^2}{2M}\frac{1}{k\Theta}F(x)\right\} = f^2$$

où figure le transfert d'impulsion lors de l'absorption ou de l'émission. En réalité le résultat varie entre ces deux extrêmes selon la largeur de l'état excité. En effet, en appelant

$$\frac{M(\boldsymbol{KK'\epsilon\epsilon'})}{W_1 - W_0 - k + i\Gamma/2}$$

l'amplitude de diffusion résonnante, la section efficace de diffusion sans recul est :

$$\frac{d\sigma_r}{d\Omega}(\{\alpha_s\}\{\alpha_s\}\,\boldsymbol{KK'\epsilon\epsilon'})$$
$$= \left|\sum_{\{n_s\}} \frac{< \{\alpha\}| e^{i\boldsymbol{K'u}/\hbar} |\{n_s\} > < \{n_s\}| e^{i\boldsymbol{Ku}/\hbar} |\{\alpha_s\}>}{W_1 - W_0 - k + E_{\{n_s\}} - E_{\{\alpha_s\}} + i\gamma}\right|^2$$
$$|M(\boldsymbol{KK'\epsilon\epsilon'})|^2, \quad (4)$$

Les deux cas limites sont : 1° Largeur de l'état excité φ_1 grande devant $k\Theta$; déjà examiné plus haut :

$$|E_{\{n_s\}} - E_{\{\alpha_s\}}| \ll |W_1 - W_0 - k + i\gamma|$$

et on obtient :

$$\mathrm{d}\sigma_{\mathrm{r}}^{0}/\mathrm{d}\Omega = \varphi\, \mathrm{d}\sigma_{\mathrm{r}}/\mathrm{d}\Omega.$$

2° Largeur $\Gamma \ll k\Theta$. Alors $|W_1 - W_0 - k| \simeq \Gamma$. Les transitions par des états intermédiaires du cristal $\{ n_s \} \neq \{ \alpha_s \}$ ne contribueront pas si $E_{\{n_s\}} - E_{\{\alpha_s\}} \gg \Gamma$. Il ne pourrait y avoir de contribution que de la part de transitions à un ou quelques phonons très mous : $\hbar\omega_s \to 0$. Mais leur densité $\mathrm{d}N(\omega)/\alpha\omega$ varie en ω^2/Θ^3 ; on peut donc les négliger, d'autant mieux que la température de Debye est élevée. La somme dans (5) se réduit au terme $\{ n_s \} = \{ \alpha_s \}$, la partie imaginaire γ est égale à $\Gamma/2$. On a donc :

$$\mathrm{d}\sigma_{\mathrm{r}}^{0}/\mathrm{d}\Omega = \sum_{\{\alpha_s\}} g\{\alpha_s\} |<\{\alpha_s\}| e^{-i\boldsymbol{Ku}/\hbar} |\{\alpha_s\}>|^2$$

$$|<\{\alpha_s\}| e^{i\boldsymbol{Ku}/\hbar} |\{\alpha_s\}>|^2\, \mathrm{d}\sigma_{\mathrm{r}}/\mathrm{d}\Omega$$

$$= \exp\left\{ -3 \frac{K^2}{2M} \frac{1}{k\Theta} F(X) \right\} \frac{\mathrm{d}\sigma_{\mathrm{r}}}{\mathrm{d}\Omega} = f^2 \frac{\mathrm{d}\sigma_{\mathrm{r}}}{\mathrm{d}\Omega}.$$

Dans le cas intermédiaire d'une largeur nucléaire assez importante, le résultat est plus compliqué, car la factorisation en termes dépendant du cristal et du noyau ne se fait plus.

3. **Interférence entre diffusion atomique et diffusion nucléaire résonnante.** — Dans le cas le plus fréquent, la diffusion Rayleigh est monotone, et la diffusion nucléaire a lieu sur un niveau très étroit. Nous avons dans ces conditions :

$$\frac{\mathrm{d}\sigma}{\mathrm{d}\Omega}(\{\alpha_s\}\{\beta_s\}\boldsymbol{KK'\epsilon\epsilon'})$$

$$= \Big| <\{\beta_s\}| e^{i\boldsymbol{qu}/\hbar} |\{\alpha_s\}> \frac{e^2}{mc^2} \left(\frac{k'}{k}\right)^{1/2} \mathcal{A}_{\mathrm{R}}(\boldsymbol{KK'\epsilon\epsilon'})$$

$$+ <\{\beta_s\}| e^{-i\boldsymbol{K'u}/\hbar} |\{\alpha_s\}> <\{\alpha_s\}| e^{i\boldsymbol{Ku}/\hbar} |\{\alpha_s\}>$$

$$\times \frac{M(KK'\varepsilon\varepsilon')}{W_1 - W_0 - k + i\Gamma/2} \Big|^2.$$

où :

$$\mathcal{A}_{\mathrm{R}}(\boldsymbol{KK'\epsilon\epsilon'}) = ZF(q)\, \boldsymbol{\epsilon}.\boldsymbol{\epsilon}' + \ldots$$

L'interférence entre les deux amplitudes a lieu quel que soit l'état final du cristal (l'interférence du type de Bragg ne peut avoir lieu que si le cristal est laissé dans l'état initial). Dans le premier cas :

$$\frac{\mathrm{d}\sigma^0}{\mathrm{d}\Omega} = \sum_{\{\alpha_s\}} g\{\alpha_s\} \frac{\mathrm{d}\sigma}{\mathrm{d}\Omega}(\{\alpha_s\}\{\alpha_s\} KK'\varepsilon\varepsilon')$$

$$= \varphi \frac{\mathrm{d}\sigma_{\mathrm{R}}}{\mathrm{d}\Omega} + f^2 \frac{\mathrm{d}\sigma_{\mathrm{r}}}{\mathrm{d}\Omega}$$

$$+ \sum_{\{\alpha_s\}} g\{\alpha_s\} |<\{\alpha_s\}| e^{i\boldsymbol{qu}/\hbar} |\{\alpha_s\}> <\{\alpha_s\}|$$

$$e^{i\boldsymbol{K'u}/\hbar} |\{\alpha_s\}> <\{\alpha_s\}| e^{-i\boldsymbol{Ku}/\hbar}|$$

$$\{\alpha_s\}> \frac{\mathcal{A}_{\mathrm{R}} S\, M^*}{W_1 - W_0 - k - i\Gamma/2} + C.C| \times e^2/mc^2$$

au premier ordre les éléments de matrice :

$$<\{\alpha_s\{| e^{i\boldsymbol{pu}/\hbar} |\{\alpha_s\}>$$

$$\simeq \prod_{S=1}^{3N} < \alpha_s \Big| 1 + \frac{1}{2} \frac{p_s^2}{2MN\hbar\omega_s}(2N_s + 1) \Big| \alpha_s >$$

sont réels, donc :

$$\frac{\mathrm{d}\sigma}{\mathrm{d}\Omega} = \varphi \frac{\mathrm{d}\sigma_{\mathrm{R}}}{\mathrm{d}\Omega} + f^2 \frac{\mathrm{d}\sigma_{\mathrm{r}}}{\mathrm{d}\Omega}$$

$$+ \varphi^{1/2} f \left[\frac{\mathcal{A}_{\mathrm{R}} M^*}{W_1 - W_0 - k - i\Gamma/2} + C.C. \right]$$

$\mathcal{A}_{\mathrm{R}}\, M^*$ est réel. Le terme d'interférence varie donc avec l'énergie comme :

$$\frac{W_1 - W_1 - k}{(W_1 - W_0 - k)^2 + \Gamma^2/4}.$$

Si les photons incidents proviennent d'une source de même nature émettant sans recul, l'intégration sur le spectre $\dfrac{1}{(W_1 - W_0 - k)^2 + \Gamma/4}$ fait disparaître le terme d'interférence. Celui-ci ne subsiste que si la raie incidente est dissymétrique par rapport à $W_1 - W_0$, par exemple si la source est animée d'une vitesse qui décale l'énergie de $(v/c)k$.

La diffusion totale a pour section efficace, en admettant l'approximation $k' = k$:

$$\frac{\mathrm{d}\sigma^{\mathrm{t}}}{\mathrm{d}\Omega} = \sum_{\{\alpha_s\}\{\beta_s\}} g\{\alpha_s\} \frac{\mathrm{d}\sigma}{\mathrm{d}\Omega}(\{\alpha_s\}\{\alpha_s\})$$

$$= \frac{\mathrm{d}\Omega}{\mathrm{d}\sigma_{\mathrm{R}}} + f \frac{\mathrm{d}\sigma_{\mathrm{r}}}{\mathrm{d}\Omega}$$

$$+ f \frac{2(W_1 - W_0 - k)}{(W_1 - W_0 - k)^2 + \Gamma^2/4} \mathcal{A}_{\mathrm{R}}\, Me^2/mc^2$$

à quoi s'applique la même discussion que pour $\mathrm{d}\sigma^2/\mathrm{d}\Omega$.

Conclusion. — La diffusion atomique et la diffusion résonnante nucléaire sont des processus cohérents. Les facteurs de Debye-Waller pour ces deux processus dépendent essentiellement de la largeur des niveaux vis-à-vis du spectre de vibration du cristal. Pour des raies très étroites, la diffusion procède par un état intermédiaire du cristal bien défini identique à l'état initial. Pour des raies très larges, ou une section efficace monotone, l'état intermédiaire du cristal n'est pas défini : le processus passe par tous les états intermédiaires possibles du cristal. En d'autres termes, dans le cas de raies très étroites, le temps caractéristique de diffusion est long, la configuration des positions de l'atome dans le cristal pendant la diffusion est moyennée, ce qui correspond au mélange statistique d'états à l'équilibre. Pour des raies larges, ou des temps caractéristiques très courts, la moyenne n'a pas le temps de se faire, la diffusion a lieu sur une configuration instantanée. Notons que le premier terme dans la diffusion Rayleigh décrivant la diffusion Thomson, comporte une sommation implicite sur des états intermédiaires. En effet l'expression rigoureuse de la diffusion Thomson fait apparaître des termes dispersifs de la forme :

$$\lim_{h=0} \sum_{\{n_s\} v_i} \frac{<\{\beta_s\}|\, e^{-i\boldsymbol{K}'\boldsymbol{u}/\hbar}|\,\{n_s\}><\{n_s\}|\, e^{i\boldsymbol{K}\boldsymbol{u}/\hbar}|\{\alpha\}><v_0|\boldsymbol{\alpha}\boldsymbol{A}'|v_i><v_i|\boldsymbol{\alpha}\boldsymbol{A}|v_0>}{\pm\sqrt{m^2c^4+c^2p'^2}-mc^2\pm k+E\{s_u\}-E\{s_x\}}$$

les états intermédiaires sont à énergie positive ou négative et l'ordre d'absorption et d'émission est inversé. Lorsque $k=0$, les termes relatifs aux états d'énergie positive s'annulent. Seuls les états d'énergie négative contribuent, et leurs dénominateurs sont de la forme

$$-\sqrt{m^2c^2+c^2p'^2}-mc^2+E\{n_s\}-E\{\alpha_s\} \rightarrow -2mc^2+E\{n_s\}-E\{\alpha_s\}$$

$E_{\{n_s\}}-E_{\{\alpha_s\}}$ peut être négligé, d'où la possibilité de sommer sur les états intermédiaires $\{n_s\}$.

L'interférence entre la diffusion résonnante et la diffusion atomique est à rapprocher de l'interférence entre photoélectrons et électrons de conversion [6].

L'auteur tient à remercier MM. Abragam, Barloutaud, Cotton, Picou pour les discussions qu'il a eues avec eux.

APPENDICE

Émission d'une cascade de deux photons. — Le noyau est initialement dans l'état excité d'énergie W_2, de largeur infiniment fine, et en équilibre thermique dans le réseau. Il émet un photon k_2, $\boldsymbol{K}_2$ (ou un électron de conversion E_2, $\boldsymbol{p}_2$) par transition à l'état φ_1 d'énergie W de largeur Γ puis un photon au fondamental. Le problème est de calculer la probabilité d'émission sans recul du photon k_1. Elle est proportionnelle à :

$$\sum_{\{\beta_s\}\{\alpha_s\}} g\{\alpha_s\} \left| \sum_{n_s} \frac{<\{\beta_s\}|e^{i\boldsymbol{K}_1\boldsymbol{u}/\hbar}|\{n_s\}><\{n_s\}e^{i\boldsymbol{K}_2\boldsymbol{u}/\hbar}|\{\alpha_s\}>}{W_1-W_2+k_2+E\{n_s\}-E\{\alpha_s\}+i\gamma} \right|^2 \tag{1}$$

avec

$$k_2+k_1+E\{\beta_s\}=W_2+E\{\alpha_s\}. \tag{2}$$

L'émission du photon k_1 sans recul signifie que l'état du cristal ne change pas au cours de la deuxième transition : $\{n_s\}=\{\beta_s\}$. En même temps nous nous plaçons dans l'hypothèse que l'état cristallin intermédiaire subsiste plus longtemps que $\hbar/\Gamma$ autrement dit qu'il n'y a pas de réarrangement spontané pendant le temps de vie de l'état intermédiaire. Alors (1) devient, avec l'aide de (2)

$$\sum_{\{\beta_s\}\{\alpha_s\}} g\{\alpha_s\} \frac{<\{\beta_s\}|e^{i\boldsymbol{K}_1\boldsymbol{u}/\hbar}|\{\beta_s\}><\{\beta_s\}|e^{i\boldsymbol{K}_2\boldsymbol{u}/\hbar}|\{\alpha_s\}>|^2}{(W_1-k_1)^2+\Gamma^2/4}.$$

La raie k_1 est donc émise avec sa largeur naturelle. Le terme cristallin s'évalue comme suit :

$$\sum_{\{\beta\}\{\alpha_s\}} g\{\alpha_s\} \prod_{s=1}^{3N} |<\{\beta_s\}|1 - k_{1s}^2(2N_s + 1)|\{\beta_s\}>|$$

$$|<\{\beta_s\}|1 - \frac{k_{2s}^2}{2}(2N_s + 1) + ik_{2s}(a_s + a_s^+)|\{\alpha_s\}>|^2 \qquad (3)$$

en posant

$$k_{1s} = \boldsymbol{K}_1\, \boldsymbol{\epsilon}_s(2MN\hbar\omega_s)^{-1/2}$$

$$= \sum_{\{\alpha_s\}} g\{\alpha_s\} \prod_{s=1}^{3N} |\{1 - k_{1s}^2[2(\alpha_s + 1) + 1]\}\alpha_s k_{2s}^2$$

$$+ \{1 - k_{1s}^2(2\alpha_s + 1)\}\{1 - k_{2s}^2(2\alpha_s + 1)\}$$

$$+ \{1 - k_{1s}^2[2(\alpha_s + 1) + 1]\}(\alpha_s + 1)\, k_{2s}^2] \qquad (3)$$

au premier ordre en k_{1s}^2 il ne reste que

$$\sum_{\{\alpha_s\}} g\{\alpha_s\} \prod_s [1 - k_{1s}^2(2\alpha_s + 1)]$$

qui est l'expression du facteur d'émission sans recul d'un photon k_1 égal, pour un cristal de Debye à :

$$\exp\left\{-\frac{3}{2}\frac{K_1^2}{2M}\frac{1}{k\Theta}F(X)\right\}.$$

Ceci démontre le fait expérimental reconnu que l'émission d'un photon Mössbauer a lieu indépendamment de l'histoire antérieure du système, sans qu'il soit utile pour l'expliquer de faire appel à un réarrangement du cristal après les émissions précédentes. Les états intermédiaires du cristal se comportent comme un état d'équilibre pratiquement identique à l'état d'équilibre initial $g\{\alpha_s\}$.

L'explication par le réarrangement cristallin se révèle nécessaire si le recul $K_2^2/2M$ est considérable et détruit localement le réseau.

Manuscrit reçu le 5 janvier 1961.

RÉFÉRENCES

[1] Mossbauer (R. L.), *Z. Physik*, 1958, **151**, 124.
[2] Lamb (W. E.), *Phys. Rev.*, 1939, **55**, 190.
[4] Heitler (W.), Quantum Theory of radiation, Oxford, University Press.
[5] Holland (R. E.), Lynch (F. J.), Perlow (G. J.) et Hanna (S. S.), *Phys. Rev.*, Letters, 1960, **4**, 181.
[6] Cf. Lipkin, dans « Mössbauer Effect », ed. de l'Université d'Illinois, TN, 60.698.

PHYSIQUE NUCLÉAIRE. — *Diffusion résonnante du rayonnement γ de 23,8 keV de $^{119}Sn^*$ émis sans recul.* Note (*) de MM. **Roland Barloutaud, Jean-Loup Picou** et **Christophe Tzara**, présentée par M. Francis Perrin.

Nous avons observé les photons réémis par ^{119}Sn après absorption résonnante de photons émis sans recul par $^{119}Sn^*$. La valeur du facteur de Debye-Waller, à environ 90° K, mesurée par cette méthode, est en bon accord avec celle mesurée par transmission.

De récentes expériences ont mis en évidence l'émission et l'absorption sans recul de photons par des noyaux liés dans un cristal. Cet effet découvert par Mössbauer [1] a été jusqu'à maintenant observé au moyen d'expériences de transmission à différentes températures. Nous avons étudié les rayonnements γ réémis après une absorption résonnante sans recul. Une telle expérience est en principe plus sensible qu'une expérience de transmission; en effet, les photons émis sans recul ne sont diffusés notablement que par interaction avec les électrons atomiques, les sections efficaces correspondantes étant généralement beaucoup plus petites que celles de la diffusion par résonance nucléaire.

Les meilleures conditions d'observation de ce processus sont obtenues lorsque :

1° La diffusion non résonnante est peu intense, c'est-à-dire aux grands angles où les divers facteurs de forme de la diffusion atomique sont petits.

2° La section efficace de diffusion résonnante, proportionnelle à $1/E^2(1+\alpha)$ est élevée (E étant l'énergie de la transition et α le coefficient de conversion).

3° Les facteurs de Debye-Waller, donnant la proportion des processus sans recul, sont grands.

Cette expérience a été faite avec le rayonnement γ de 23,8 keV de $^{119}Sn^*$ [2] dont le schéma de désintégration est représenté sur la figure 1. Ce noyau remplit assez bien les conditions ci-dessus et présente en outre l'avantage de n'émettre, à part le rayonnement γ intéressant, que les raies X de l'étain. Un écran de palladium dont la discontinuité K est située à 24,36 keV, absorbe sélectivement les X_K de l'étain sans atténuer fortement le rayonnement γ.

Le dispositif expérimental est schématisé sur la figure 2. Les photons sont diffusés à 70 ± 5° par un cylindre d'étain enrichi en ^{119}Sn (71,5 %) maintenu à l'intérieur d'un cylindre en mylar de 0,07 mm d'épaisseur. Un écran de plomb masque complètement la source vue du cristal. L'ensemble source diffuseur se trouve à l'intérieur d'une boîte en polyéthylène expansé et peut être porté à une température voisine de celle de l'azote liquide.

Les mesures d'intensité des photons diffusés ont été effectuées à la température ambiante et à environ 90° K. La diffusion due à la matière environnante a été déterminée par une expérience témoin faite sans diffuseur de ^{119}Sn. Les taux de comptage obtenus, corrigés de l'effet d'émission des X_K du palladium, sont respectivement :

$$N_{90^\circ K} = 13{,}9 \pm 1 \quad \text{par minute,}$$
$$N_{300^\circ K} = 4{,}65 \pm 0{,}7 \text{ par minute;}$$

d'où

$$\frac{N_{90}}{N_{300}} = 3 \pm 0{,}5.$$

Ces intensités peuvent s'exprimer en fonction des sections efficaces différentielles de diffusion résonnante et non résonnante $(d\sigma/d\omega)_r$ et

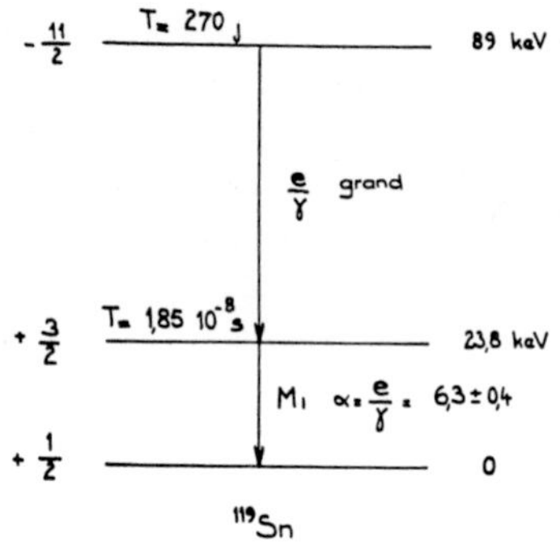

Fig. 1.

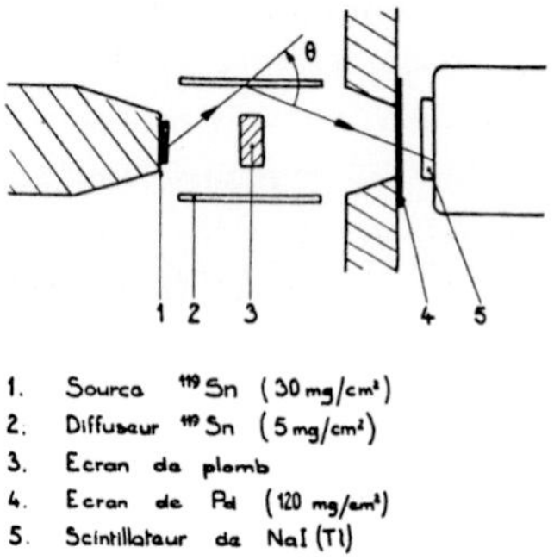

Fig. 2.

$(d\sigma/d\omega)_{n.r.}$ et de la proportion f_t du rayonnement γ émis ou absorbé sans recul à la température t en supposant que f_{300} est négligeable :

$$N_{300} \simeq n\left(\frac{d\sigma}{d\omega}\right)_{n.r.} a_{n.r}$$
$$N_{90} \simeq (1 - f_{90})\, n\left(\frac{d\sigma}{d\omega}\right)_{n.r.} a_{n.r.} + (f_{90} - \varepsilon_{90})\, S,$$

n est le nombre d'atomes d'étain par centimètre carré du diffuseur à l'incidence 35°, ε_{90} est l'autoabsorption résonnante de la source à 90° K. S est la probabilité pour qu'un photon sans recul soit diffusé par résonance dans la direction du cristal :

$$S = \frac{a_r}{\alpha + 1}\left[\frac{f_{90}}{2}(1 - \tau^2) + \left(1 - \frac{f_{90}}{2}\right)(1 - \tau)\right]\frac{\left(\dfrac{d\sigma}{d\omega}\right)_r}{\sigma_r}$$

τ étant la transmission des photons sans recul à travers l'écran à l'incidence de 35°; a_r et $a_{n.r.}$ sont les absorptions électroniques moyennes des photons diffusés dans les processus résonnants et non résonnants.

La section efficace des processus non résonnants $(d\sigma/d\omega)_{n.r.}$ a été déterminée à l'aide des facteurs de formes donnés dans ([3]); elle est égale à

19 barns/srad. La section efficace résonnante $(d\sigma/d\omega)_r$ a été calculée en supposant que la distribution angulaire des photons correspondait à une transition dipolaire magnétique pure et n'était pas atténuée par interaction quadrupolaire, une récente mesure ([4]) donnant une limite supérieure de 10^{-8} eV à $Q\ \partial^2V/\partial z^2$. Elle est égale à 6 000 barns/srad. On déduit des résultats expérimentaux :

$$f_{90} = 0{,}30 \pm 0{,}07.$$

Cette valeur est en bon accord avec celle obtenue par des mesures de transmission ($f_{90} = 0{,}32 \pm 0{,}015$) ([4]).

Il est possible d'augmenter le rapport N_{90}/N_{300} et d'améliorer ainsi la précision en opérant avec un diffuseur plus mince (~ 1 mg) et un angle de diffusion plus grand de façon à rendre pratiquement négligeable la diffusion non résonnante.

Cette méthode présente d'autres aspects intéressants. La distribution angulaire des photons diffusés est une source d'information sur le caractère de la transition et l'importance de l'interaction quadrupolaire; de plus l'étude des interférences entre les processus sans recul résonnants et non résonnants ([5]), ([6]) peut apporter une vérification de la cohérence dans la diffusion résonnante. Enfin, la raie de photons sans recul absorbés et réémis sans perte d'énergie est sensiblement plus étroite que la raie émise initialement par la source, la distribution en énergie est par exemple, pour une source et un diffuseur minces, de la forme $1/[(E-E_0)^2+\Gamma^2/4]^2$, conduisant à une raie de largeur à mi-hauteur 0,64 fois celle de la raie des photons avant diffusion.

(*) Séance du 4 avril 1960.

([1]) R. L. MÖSSBAUER, *Z. Physik*, 151, 1958, p. 124.

([2]) R. BARLOUTAUD, E. COTTON, J.-L. PICOU et J. QUIDORT, *Comptes rendus*, 250, 1960, p. 319.

([3]) A. K. COMPTON et S. K. ALLISON, *X-rays and experiment*, Van Nostrand, 2e éd. p. 781.

([4]) Sous presse.

([5]) A. KASTLER, *Comptes rendus*, 250, 1960, p. 509.

([6]) C. TZARA et R. BARLOUTAUD (sous presse).

(*Centre d'Études nucléaires de Saclay.*)

VOLUME 4, NUMBER 11 PHYSICAL REVIEW LETTERS JUNE 1, 1960

ZEEMAN EFFECT IN THE RECOILLESS γ-RAY RESONANCE OF Zn^{67}†

P. P. Craig, D. E. Nagle, and D. R. F. Cochran
Los Alamos Scientific Laboratory, University of California, Los Alamos, New Mexico
(Received May 4, 1960)

Recoil-free resonance emission and absorption (Mössbauer effect)[1] of the 93-kev γ ray in Zn^{67} gives rise to the most precise energy definition thus far reported.[2] Despite the numerous difficulties which beset the experimenter searching for the resonance,[3] a small but definite Mössbauer effect has been found.[2] This Letter reports measurements on the influence of the nuclear Zeeman effect and other perturbing factors upon the Mössbauer effect in Zn^{67} embedded in an enriched ZnO absorber lattice.

The relatively high energy of this γ ray makes it necessary to embed the source and the absorber atoms in rigid crystalline lattices, and to perform the experiments at low temperatures. The first of these requirements was met by using ZnO for both the source and the absorber lattices. The second requirement was more than satisfied by using temperatures below the helium lambda transition (2.175°K). In addition to these basic requirements, several experimental difficulties are consequences of the extreme narrowness of the line (4.84×10^{-11} ev). It is accordingly necessary to take into account the effect of various perturbing influences. Here we list the more important of these perturbations, and in the following paragraphs indicate how they enter into the design of the experiment.

One class of shifts arises from the change of nuclear mass upon γ-ray emission or absorption, with a resultant change in the phonon spectrum of the lattice. The change in energy of the emitted γ ray is given by[4]

$$\Delta E = -(E/Mc^2)\langle T\rangle, \qquad (1)$$

where E is the γ-ray energy, M is the mass of the emitting nucleus, and $\langle T\rangle$ is the expectation value for the kinetic energy per atom of the lattice. If any parameter x should differ between source and absorber lattice, the recoil-free peaks will occur at different energies in the emission spectrum and in the absorption spec-

VOLUME 4, NUMBER 11 PHYSICAL REVIEW LETTERS JUNE 1, 1960

trum. The shift is given by

$$\delta(\Delta E) = \frac{\delta}{\delta x}(\Delta E)\delta x. \qquad (2)$$

This expression predicts that a difference in Debye temperature between source and absorber of only about 1.3°K would cause a shift of one linewidth. Thus a change in the average isotopic mass number of 2% would, through the mechanism of the Debye temperature (taking $\theta = 300°K$), result in a shift of about four linewidths. Similarly, differences in chemical constitution[5] or lattice defects may be expected to produce significant shifts. We shall refer to a shift due to difference in isotopic mass between source and absorber as the isotopic mass effect.

In order for the emitted gamma radiation to remain unshifted by the recoil of the emitting nuclei, it is essential that the recoil momentum be absorbed by entire crystallites. For all previously observed resonances the minimum size of the crystallites was quite small. In the present situation this is no longer true. The recoil momentum must be taken up by at least 2×10^9 nuclei, so that the ZnO crystallites must be larger than 0.4 micron. Since commercial ZnO would normally possess average grain sizes smaller than one micron,[6] care must be exercised to ensure a grain size much larger than the above nominal requirement. A sintering process assured that this requirement was met for the source. A sample of the enriched absorber was studied under an oil immersion microscope. No grains smaller than 0.5 micron were observed, and the majority of the grains were in the range of 1 to 2 microns.

Mechanical vibrations of only 10^{-5} cm/sec would produce a Doppler broadening of about one linewidth. Since the vibration level in our building was nearly 5×10^{-4} cm/sec, the helium cryostat was shock-mounted and the pumping lines carefully decoupled. The source and the absorber were clamped rigidly in a single package, which was suspended by threads in the helium bath. The helium bath was pumped below the lambda transition and the nitrogen radiation shield was frozen to prevent vibrations from boiling liquids and also to place source and absorber in an isothermal bath.

In place of the velocity drive usually used in this type of experiment, the resonance was shifted by means of the nuclear Zeeman effect. The magnetic moment of the Zn^{67} nucleus interacting with an applied magnetic field splits the ground state into six components and the excited state into four components. Selection rules permit twelve component gamma transitions, as is shown in Fig. 1(a). Here $I_g = 5/2$, $I_e = 3/2$, and the ground-state gyromagnetic ratio $g = 0.35$.[7] For the excited state no g value has been measured; we adopt arbitrarily the value -1. (The negative sign is predicted by the shell model.) The source is shielded from the magnetic field and hence the emission spectrum is not split. For simplicity, the effect of quadrupole interactions has been omitted. Assuming a shift δE between source and absorber, resonance can occur for six values of magnetic field. Each component has a width which is compounded of the natural linewidth and the widths due to residual mechanical vibrations, quadrupole broadening, etc. Even if this width is the same for all components, the present method of studying the resonances as a function of an external magnetic field will cause the apparent or magnetic width of each resonance peak to be proportional to the field required to establish the resonance. Thus resonances occurring at low values of the applied field will appear narrower than those established at high fields, and the observed spectrum will appear distorted.

The magnetic field was produced by a small

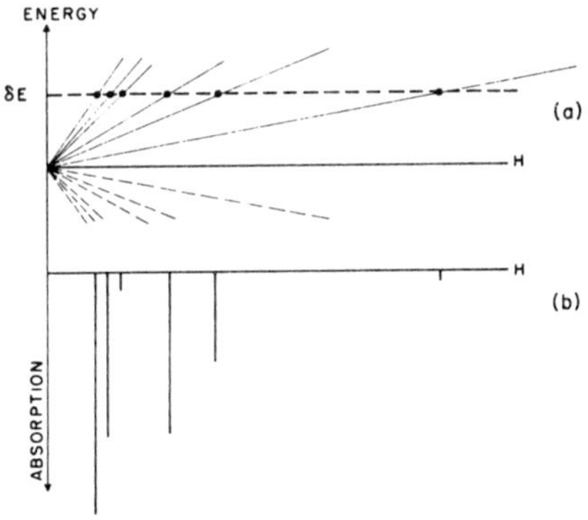

FIG. 1. (a) Zeeman splittings of the gamma ray vs an applied magnetic field. The gyromagnetic ratio of the ground state is 0.35, and a value of -1.0 has been arbitrarily chosen for the excited state. (b) Resonance pattern expected from the splittings in (a) in the presence of an energy shift δE between source and absorber. In actuality, line broadening would be expected to merge closely spaced lines into single peaks.

solenoid surrounding the absorber. Fields of up to 700 gauss could be applied to the absorber, while the source was entirely shielded (at operating temperatures) by superconducting lead foil. Stray fields at the absorber were measured to be less than 2 gauss. Fields from the solenoid were prevented from reaching the photomultiplier by a superconducting ring placed in the cryostat bottom through which the gamma rays emerged. Changes in counting rate due to changing fields at the photomultiplier were found, even without the superconducting shield, to be less than ± 0.02 %.

The absorber used in all experiments was 1.231 g of enriched ZnO (92.4 % Zn^{67} enrichment) pressed with 0.036 g of polyethylene glycol binder into a button 1.11 cm in diameter. Sources were prepared in the Los Alamos cyclotron by the reaction $Zn^{66}(d,n)Ga^{67}$ on normal sintered ZnO. Other reaction products were accounted for by a background correction. After bombardment, the sources were annealed for about one hour in air at about 1000°C in order to anneal radiation damage and to assure that the Ga^{67} atoms were correctly placed in the ZnO lattice. Such a procedure is essential, and lower temperatures or shorter times yielded erratic results, or no resonance whatever.

Measurements were made of the transmission of the absorber vs the applied magnetic field. Because of the extremely small change in counting rate and the large number of counts required (typically 10^8 per point), automation of the counting system and extreme system stability were imperative. The 93-kev gamma rays passed through thin windows in the cryostat bottom, and were detected by a NaI(Tl) scintillation crystal. The pulses were amplified and analyzed by a single-channel analyzer followed by a scaler equipped with a digital recorder. In order to eliminate the effect of source decay, all measurements were taken relative to the counting rate when one applied a magnetic field sufficient to destroy the resonance entirely. The magnetic field sequencing and the scaler were controlled by an automatic programmer. Timing was controlled by a thermostatted quartz crystal frequency standard with a stated accuracy of 3 parts in 10^7 per week. The programming was such as to make the measurements insensitive to linear drifts.

Instrument checks were performed by cycling the magnetic field (a) at room temperature, (b) at low temperature using a nonresonant gamma ray, and (c) at low temperature using as an absorber a zinc-containing material (gahnite) in which no resonance exists.[2] In each case the change in counting rate upon application of the magnetic field was found to be zero to within ± 0.02 %.

Figure 2 shows the resonance curve obtained. The points include corrections for background and unresolved nonresonant gamma rays of typically 30 %. The central features of the data are the remarkably large total area under the resonance, and the structure and total breadth present. The total area is sufficiently large that, were there no line broadening, one would estimate the resonance absorption to be several percent. Such a value implies a Debye temperature for ZnO of about 300°K, which is consistent with the results obtained from specific heats. The major structural feature of the curve lies in the fact that the maximum resonance does not occur at zero field, but is shifted to about 10 gauss. This result indicates the presence of shifts such as the isotopic mass effect mentioned above. However, the displacement of the maximum (to 10 gauss) is smaller than one would predict from this effect alone unless an unreasonably large value is assumed for the excited state g value. A plausible explanation is that chemical shifts[5] are superimposed upon the isotopic effect. The presence of such shifts is implied by the small resonance found at zero field using an unenriched absorber.[2] Since in that case no isotope effects were present, only chemical shifts or quadrupole broadening can explain the small resonance ob-

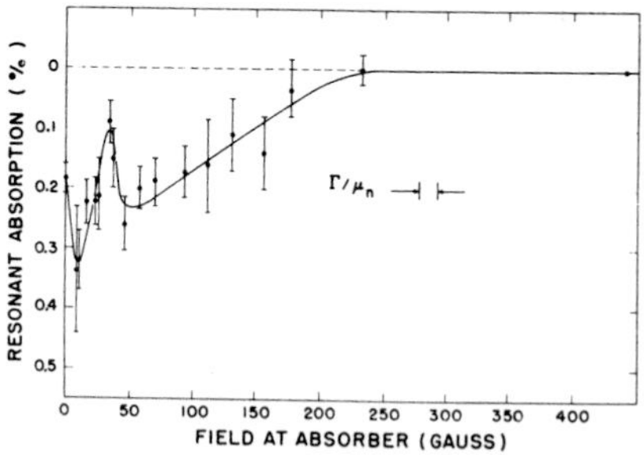

FIG. 2. Experimental resonance absorption pattern for the 93-kev line of Zn^{67} vs the magnetic field applied to an enriched ZnO absorber. The source is in zero magnetic field. Γ/μ_n is the natural level width (in ergs) divided by a nuclear magneton (in ergs per gauss).

served. In the present experiments two peaks are found separated by only about 40 gauss so that it seems unlikely that the broadening is extreme. The tail of the resonance extends to about 400 gauss with no additional structure. This may be related to the characteristic of the magnetic method that even unbroadened lines possess apparent magnetic widths which are proportional to the applied magnetic field.

Although the interpretation is admittedly incomplete, the extreme sharpness of the resonance is apparent. In further study, involving the development of a Doppler shift drive, we hope to measure a number of the energy shifts and level splittings mentioned in previous paragraphs.

We wish to thank S. D. Stoddard and R. E. Cowan for preparation of the ZnO source buttons and for compacting the enriched ZnO absorber. The generous cooperation of the cyclotron group is gratefully acknowledged. W. E. Keller and J. G. Dash each contributed a number of ideas to the experiment.

[†]Work done under the auspices of the U. S. Atomic Energy Commission.

[1]R. L. Mössbauer, Z. Physik 151, 124 (1958); Naturwissenschaften 45, 538 (1958); Z. Naturforsch. 14a, 211 (1959).

[2]D. E. Nagle, P. P. Craig, and W. E. Keller, Nature (to be published).

[3]R. V. Pound and G. A. Rebka, Phys. Rev. Letters 4, 397 (1960).

[4]R. V. Pound and G. A. Rebka, Phys. Rev. Letters 4, 337 (1960); B. D. Josephson, Phys. Rev. Letters 4, 341 (1960).

[5]O. C. Kistner and A. W. Sunyar, Phys. Rev. Letters 4, 412 (1960).

[6]G. Heiland, E. Mollwo, and F. Stöckmann, Solid-State Physics, edited by F. Seitz and D. Turnbull (Academic Press, New York, 1959), Vol. 8, p. 191.

[7]H. Kopfermann, Kernmomente (Akademische Verlagsgesellschaft, Frankfurt am Main, 1956).

Mössbauer Effect in Ferrocyanide

S. L. Ruby, L. M. Epstein, and K. H. Sun

Radiation and Nucleonics Laboratory of the Materials Laboratories, Westinghouse Electric Corporation, East Pittsburgh, Pennsylvania

(Received March 18, 1960)

In order to utilize the Mössbauer effect more conveniently, it would be desirable to have either a source or an absorber which is monoenergetic. To date, the detailed work[1,2] using Fe^{57} has employed soft iron sources and absorbers; here, the inner magnetic field creates a hyperfine splitting which is disadvantageous for some work.

During a discussion with the group at the Argonne National Laboratories, ferrocyanide was pointed out as a possible material with no hyperfine splitting. This follows from the fact that potassium ferrocyanide has no magnetic moment.[3] Roughly speaking, the electrons from the cyanogen groups completely fill the d-shell of the iron atom and eliminate the magnetic behavior.

The apparatus employs a loud speaker to vibrate the Co^{57} source at 25 cps, and a coil in an auxiliary magnetic field rigidly attached to the source is used to measure its instantaneous velocity. The 14.4-kev γ ray is detected conventionally using a thin NaI(Tl) crystal and a single channel analyzer. Its output is used to initiate a multichannel analyzer which has been modified to accept the output of the velocity transducer. Thus the complete velocity spectrum is scanned every 20 msec, while each γ ray detected is stored in the appropriate velocity channel. The source was made by plating about 300 μc of Co^{57} onto soft iron and annealing as suggested by Pound.[4] $Na_4Fe(CN)_6\cdot 10H_2O$ at 80°K was used as an absorber during the measurements reported here. The thickness of the absorber is about 100 mg/cm^2 which corresponds to 0.25 mg/cm^2 of Fe^{57}.

The result of the experiment is given in Fig. 1. For comparison purposes, a spectrum obtained in this apparatus using a soft iron absorber at room temperature is also shown. Also plotted in the figure are bars showing the position and relative size of the absorption peaks to be expected utilizing the results of Hanna *et al.*,[1] if there is *no* inner field in ferrocyanide. Our present knowledge of instrumental line shape is incomplete, and consequently, the problem of assigning an upper bound to the inner magnetic field in ferrocyanide will not be considered here. However, if not zero, it is less than 10% of the field in soft iron.

The foregoing results indicate that in a ferrocyanide source the emission from excited Fe^{57} would be monoenergetic. It would be convenient to have such a source, and particularly so if it were effective at room temperature. Accordingly, a run using the ferrocyanide absorber was made at room temperature. The same peaks are observed but with their amplitudes reduced to 60 ($\pm$10)% of their value at 80°K. An effect of this magnitude can be calculated from the formula for the resonant fraction given by Pound,[5]

$$f=\exp-\left\{\frac{3}{2}\frac{E_\gamma^2}{2Mc^2k\theta}\left[1+\frac{2}{3}\left(\frac{\pi T}{\theta}\right)^2\right]\right\},$$

with a Debye θ of 340 ($\pm$40) °K. This suggests that a ferrocyanide source will emit about 40% of the 14.4-kev γ rays without energy change as compared to 60% for soft iron.

However, there is the question of whether the excited Fe^{57} (produced from Co^{57} present as a substitutional impurity) would be present in the proper chemical state. One possibility is that cobalt in cyanide complexes tends to go to the trivalent oxidation state, whereas the divalent state is required for transmutation to ferrocyanide. In addition, there is evidence[6] that the cobalto-cyanide complex contains only five cyanide groups instead of six.

We would like to thank the members of the Argonne

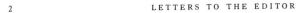

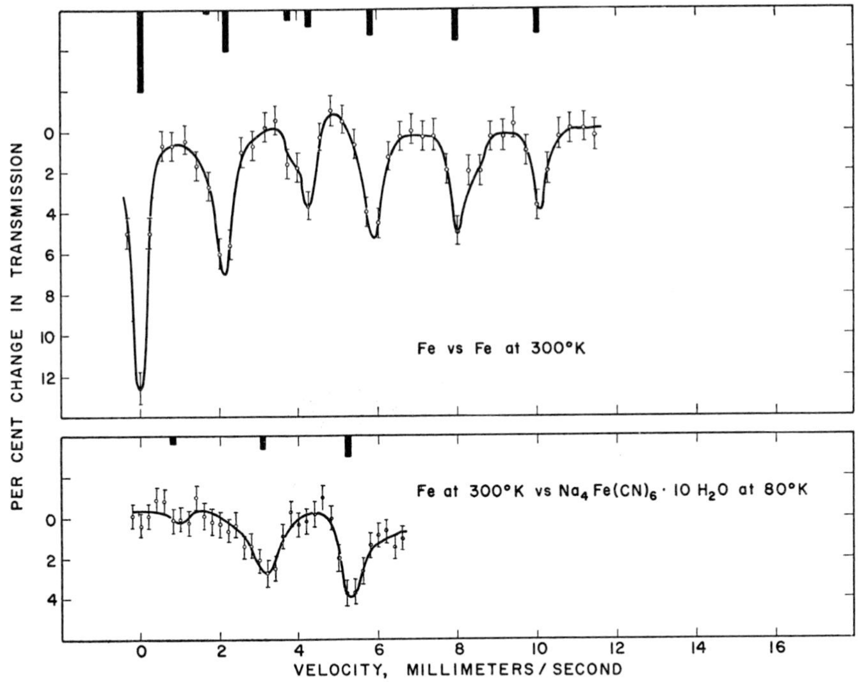

FIG. 1. Percent change in transmission of a Co^{57} (Fe^{57*}) source vs velocity of an iron absorber at room temperature and a sodium ferrocyanide absorber at 80°K.

group for their helpful advice, and also Dr. Sergio De Benedetti who first suggested the use of a multichannel analyzer as a velocity measuring device.

[1] S. S. Hanna *et al.*, Phys. Rev. Letters, **4**, 177 (1960).
[2] G. DePasquali *et al.*, Phys. Rev. Letters **4**, 71 (1960).
[3] L. Pauling, *Nature of the Chemical Bond* (Cornell University Press, Ithaca, New York, 1960), third ed., p. 166.
[4] R. V. Pound and G. A. Rebka, Jr., Phys. Rev. Letters **3**, 554 (1959).
[5] R. V. Pound and G. A. Rebka, Jr., Phys. Rev. Letters **3**, 440 (1959).
[6] A. W. Adamson, J. Am. Chem. Soc. **73**, 5710 (1951).

NUCLEAR INSTRUMENTS AND METHODS 12 (1961) 131–137; NORTH-HOLLAND PUBLISHING CO.

TRANSMISSION AND LINE BROADENING OF RESONANCE RADIATION INCIDENT ON A RESONANCE ABSORBER†

S. MARGULIES and J. R. EHRMAN

University of Illinois, Urbana, Illinois

Received 13 February 1961

The transmission of resonance radiation emitted from a source of finite thickness and passing through an external resonance absorber is discussed. The transmission integral is examined for both a linear and a Gaussian distribution of radioactive atoms in the source. Several special cases are presented, and the general case is evaluated by numerical integration. Over the range of values considered, the transmitted line shape closely approximates a Breit-Wigner curve whose width is greater than the natural width of the transition. This line broadening, caused by resonance absorption in the source and in the external absorber, is presented graphically as a function of source and absorber thickness.

1. Introduction

R. L. Mössbauer's discovery that recoilless emission and absorption of nuclear gamma radiation can occur[1]) has stimulated a host of recent investigations[2]). Interest in this process has grown rapidly because the Mössbauer effect allows the direct observation of many phenomena formerly thought unmeasurable. A terrestial measurement of the gravitational red-shift[3]), a test of the equivalence principle for rotating systems[4]), and the observation of the Zeeman splitting of excited nuclear levels[5]), are but a few of the experiments made possible by the Mössbauer effect. In addition, the effect is finding many applications in the measurement of the internal fields in solids.

When recoilless emission and absorption of gamma radiation occurs, the conditions for nuclear resonance fluorescence are inherently satisfied. The numerous applications of the Mössbauer effect follow from the fact that, in such cases, the very narrow lines resulting from transitions from metastable nuclear levels can actually be observed: resonance lines with widths in the range 10^{-10} to 10^{-5} eV, which correspond respectively to gamma transitions from levels whose half-lives vary between 10^{-5} and 10^{-10} sec, have been measured.

Although experiments involving the Mössbauer effect can be performed with either a transmission or a scattering geometry, most of the work done so far has employed the former approach[6]). A typical transmission experiment consists of measuring the resonance radiation passing through a resonance absorber, as a function of the relative velocity between source and absorber. In this manner, a resonance line shape is traced out. Since the great utility of the Mössbauer effect depends upon the measurement of such lines, a consideration of the line shape is of interest. In what follows, we will be concerned with the transmission

† This work has been supported in part by the joint program of the U.S. Office of Naval Research and the U.S. Atomic Energy Commission.

1) R. L. Mössbauer, Z. Physik **151** (1958) 124.

2) For a listing of recent experiments, see the bibliography contained in Proceedings of the Allerton Park Conference on Mössbauer Effect, University of Illinois, Urbana, Illinois, June 5–7, 1960 (unpublished).

3) R. V. Pound and G. A. Rebka, Jr., Phys. Rev. Letters **4** (1960) 337.

4) H. J. Hay, J. P. Schiffer, T. E. Cranshaw and P. A. Egelstaff, Phys. Rev. Letters **4** (1960) 165.

5) R. V. Pound and G. A. Rebka, Jr., Phys. Rev. Letters **3** (1959) 554;
G. DePasquali, H. Frauenfelder, S. Margulies and R. N. Peacock, Phys. Rev. Letters **4** (1960) 71;
S. S. Hanna, J. Heberle, C. Littlejohn, G. J. Perlow, R. S. Preston and D. H. Vincent, Phys. Rev. Letters **4** (1960) 177.

6) H. Frauenfelder, D. R. F. Cochran, D. E. Nagle and R. D. Taylor, Nuovo Cim. **19** (1961) 183.

of resonant gamma radiation emitted from a source of finite thickness†, and passing through a finite resonance absorber. In particular, we will consider two types of sources; one in which the radioactive atoms are distributed uniformly and one which has a Gaussian distribution of emitting nuclei.

2. General Formulation

In our calculation of the transmitted intensity, we will assume that a fraction f of all decays occur without recoil energy loss[7]). The resonance radiation resulting from these decays will be taken to have an emission and absorption spectrum of Breit-Wigner shape. The remaining fraction of the radiation is non-resonant, and is subject only to ordinary electronic absorption. We will consider a source having arbitrary area, and extending in depth from $x = 0$ to $x = \infty$. The distribution of emitting atoms along the x-axis will be denoted by $\rho(x)$. We will deal only with the radiation emitted normal to the area of the source, as shown in fig. 1. The distribution of the absorbing atoms in both the source and absorber will be taken to be uniform.

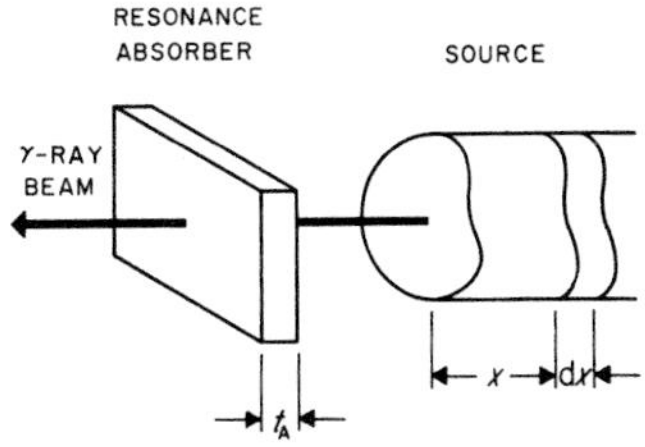

Fig. 1. Geometry used to calculate the transmission of γ-radiation through a resonance absorber moving with a velocity v relative to the source.

Under these circumstances, the transmission through a resonance absorber of thickness t_A, moving with a velocity v relative to the source, is given by

$$p(\mathscr{S}) = e^{-\mu_A t_A} \left\{ (1-f) \int_0^\infty dx\, \rho(x) e^{-\mu_S x} + f \frac{\Gamma}{2\pi} \int_{-\infty}^{\infty} dE \exp\left[-f'_A n_A a_A \sigma_0 t_A \frac{\Gamma^2/4}{(E-E_0)^2 + \Gamma^2/4} \right] \right.$$
$$\left. \times \int_0^\infty \frac{dx\, \rho(x)}{(E - E_0 + \mathscr{S})^2 + \Gamma^2/4} \exp\left[-\left(f'_S n_S a_S \sigma_0 \frac{\Gamma^2/4}{(E - E_0 + \mathscr{S})^2 + \Gamma^2/4} + \mu_S \right) x \right] \right\}. \quad (1)$$

In this equation, Γ is the full width at half-height of both the emission and absorption lines which are centered about E_0, and σ_0 is the absorption cross-section at resonance††. The subscripts S and A identify the following source and absorber quantities:

f' = probability of resonance absorption without recoil,
n = number of atoms per cubic centimeter of volume,
a = fractional abundance of the atoms which can absorb resonantly,
μ = ordinary mass attenuation coefficient, evaluated at E_0.

The quantity $\mathscr{S} = (v/c)E_0$ characterizes the Doppler shift between the source and absorber.

The first term in (1) represents the transmission of the non-resonant fraction of the radiation, and is independent of the Doppler shift $\mathscr{S}$. In the second term, which is the resonant contribution, the x-integral represents the emission and self-absorption in the source. We will neglect the μ_S appearing in the exponential of this integral, since the mass absorption is usually much smaller than the resonance absorption. The remaining factors in the second term represent the absorption in the external resonance absorber. The lower limit on the energy integral has been taken as $-\infty$ instead of zero for convenience.

[7]) W. Marshall and J. P. Schiffer, The Debye-Waller Factor in the Mössbauer Effect, A.E.R.E., Harwell (1960), (unpublished).

† The case of a beam of γ-radiation, having a Breit-Wigner energy spectrum, passing through a resonance absorber, has been considered by W. M. Visscher in The Evaluation of the Transmission Integral, Los Alamos Scientific Laboratory (1959) (unpublished). This corresponds, in effect, to the non-resonant absorbing source described in Section 5.

†† The absorption cross-section at resonance is given by

$$\sigma_0 = 2\pi\bar{\lambda}^2 \frac{2I^* + 1}{2I + 1} \frac{1}{1 + \alpha}$$

where $\bar{\lambda}$ is the wavelength of the γ-ray, I^* and I are the nuclear spins of the initial and final states, respectively, and α is the conversion coefficient for the transition.

Equation (1) can be seen to be independent of the sign of the Doppler shift $\mathscr{S}$. Since only relative motion between source and absorber is pertinent, $\mathscr{S}$ can be included in the absorber part of the transmission integral instead of the source part, if desired.

Equation (1) can easily be generalized for the case when the emission and absorption lines consist of more than one component (as when electric or magnetic splitting exists) by forming appropriate sums. In this paper we will limit ourselves to the overlap of a single emission line with a single absorption line, each centered about E_0. For convenience, we will translate the energy axis so that both lines are centered about $E = 0$ in the absence of any Doppler shift; that is, $(E - E_0)$ will be replaced by E.

Sources for Mössbauer experiments are generally prepared in either of two ways†:

1. The activity is electroplated or otherwise deposited on a source backing. The activity is then diffused into the host lattice by heating[8]).
2. The activity and the host atoms are co-plated on a backing, thereby building up a lattice containing the radioactive atoms as integral parts[9]).

The second method produces a source in which the emitting atoms are uniformly distributed in depth. The same type of distribution results from the first method if the backing is very thin and the diffusion time is very long. On the other hand, if either the backing is thick or the diffusion time is short, then the first method produces an activity distribution which is approximately Gaussian. Both types of distribution will be discussed below.

3. Uniform Source Distribution

We first consider a source of thickness t_S, having N radioactive atoms per unit length:

$$\rho(x) = \begin{cases} N \text{ atoms/cm}, & t_S \geq x \geq 0 \\ 0 & x > t_S \,. \end{cases} \tag{2}$$

Since Nt_S is the total number of radioactive atoms and $e^{-\mu_A t_A}$ represents the non-resonant electronic absorption in the external absorber, we will deal with a normalized transmission $P(\mathscr{S})$ defined by

$$P(\mathscr{S}) = p(\mathscr{S})/(e^{-\mu_A t_A} N t_S) \,. \tag{3}$$

For the distribution given in (2) the x part of the transmission integral can easily be evaluated, and we find

$$P(\mathscr{S}) = (1-f)\left[\frac{1-e^{-\mu_S t_S}}{\mu_S t_S}\right] + f\frac{2}{\pi\Gamma}\frac{1}{T_S}\int_{-\infty}^{\infty} \mathrm{d}E \exp\left(\frac{-T_A\Gamma^2/4}{E^2+\Gamma^2/4}\right) \times \left[1-\exp\left(\frac{-T_S\Gamma^2/4}{(E+\mathscr{S})^2+\Gamma^2/4}\right)\right] \,. \tag{4}$$

Here, $T_S = f'_S n_S a_S \sigma_0 t_S$ and $T_A = f'_A n_A a_A \sigma_0 t_A$ are effective source and absorber thicknesses, respectively. The first term in this equation is the non-resonant transmission, and will henceforth be denoted by $(1-f)P_{\text{non-res.}}(\text{uniform})$. As $\mu_S t_S$ approaches zero, this quantity approaches $(1-f)$. The second term in (4), containing an integral over energy, represents the resonant contribution. Before discussing the general evaluation of the integral, we will first consider two special cases.

3.1. THIN SOURCE AND ABSORBER

When both source and absorber are thin in the sense that $T_S \ll 1$, $T_A \ll 1$, we can expand both exponentials in the second term of (4) and keep only lowest-order terms in effective thickness. Integrating over energy, we obtain

† Occasionally the target foil, which has been irradiated in a pile or in an accelerator beam to produce the desired radioisotope, may serve directly as a source. In such a case, the distribution of emitting atoms can be quite complex, and will not be treated here.

[8]) R. V. Pound and G. A. Rebka, Jr., Phys. Rev. Letters **3** (1959) 554.

[9]) S. S. Hanna, J. Heberle, C. Littlejohn, G. J. Perlow, R. S. Preston and D. H. Vincent, Phys. Rev. Letters **4** (1960) 28.

$$P(\mathscr{S}) = \Big[(1-f)\underset{\text{non-res.}}{P(\text{uniform})} + f\Big(1 - \frac{T_S}{4}\Big)\Big] - f\,\frac{T_A}{2}\,\frac{1}{1 + (\mathscr{S}/\Gamma)^2}\,. \tag{5}$$

The bracketed term in this equation represents the transmission when $\mathscr{S}$, the relative Doppler shift between source and absorber, is large. This asymptotic value is less than unity because of the self-absorption in the source. The second term represents the dip in the transmission due to resonance absorption in the external absorber. It is seen that the transmitted line, in the case of thin source and absorber, has a Breit-Wigner shape, but has an apparent width Γ_a which is twice that of either the emission or absorption spectrum. This broadening results from the overlap of the emission and absorption lines.

3.2. THIN SOURCE – TRANSMISSION AT ZERO DOPPLER SHIFT

When the effective source thickness T_S approaches zero (as, for example, in a source which has little resonance absorption because $a_S \to 0$), the transmission at zero Doppler shift can be found in terms of T_A, the effective absorber thickness. Expanding the term containing T_S in (4) and keeping only the lowest-order term leads to

$$P(0) \approx (1-f)\underset{\text{non-res.}}{P(\text{uniform})} + f\,e^{-\frac{1}{2}T_A}\,J_0(\tfrac{1}{2}iT_A)\,, \qquad T_S \to 0\,, \tag{6}$$

where J_0 is the Bessel function of zero order. Because of the nature of resonance absorption, the resonant contribution to the transmission does not decrease exponentially with absorber thickness, but instead, shows a saturation behavior.

3.3. UNIFORM SOURCE – GENERAL CASE

Attempts to evaluate (4) analytically for arbitrary source and absorber thicknesses have been unsuccessful. Consequently, we have performed a numerical integration on the University of Illinois digital computer ILLIAC for values of T_S and T_A between zero and ten. It has been found empirically that over this range the transmitted line is, to a very good degree of approximation, a Breit-Wigner curve whose full width at half-height Γ_a, depends upon the value of T_S and T_A. The general variation of transmission with Doppler shift $\mathscr{S}$ is shown in fig. 2. The results of our numerical integration, in the form of the variation of Γ_a/Γ as a function of T_A with T_S as parameter, are shown in fig. 3. Note that as T_S and T_A both approach zero, Γ_a/Γ approaches the value two, since the conditions described in section 3.1 are applicable.

4. Gaussian Source Distribution

For the case of a Gaussian distribution of radioactive atoms, we will use

$$\rho(x) = (2N/\sqrt{\pi})\,e^{-x^2/t_S^2} \quad \text{atoms/cm}, \qquad x \geqslant 0\,. \tag{7}$$

Here t_S represents a characteristic diffusion depth whose value depends upon the details of the source preparation. The above distribution is normalized so that Nt_S once again represents the total number of radioactive atoms.

Substitution of this Gaussian distribution into (1) leads to the following expression, which is normalized in the sense defined by (3):

$$P(\mathscr{S}) = (1-f)\,e^{(\frac{1}{2}\mu_S t_S)^2}\,[\,1 - \Phi(\mu_S t_S/2)\,] + f\,\frac{\Gamma}{2\pi}\int_{-\infty}^{\infty} \frac{dE}{(E+\mathscr{S})^2 + \Gamma^2/4}\exp\Big(\frac{-T_A\Gamma^2/4}{E^2+\Gamma^2/4}\Big)$$
$$\times\Big[1 - \Phi\Big(\frac{T_S\Gamma^2/4}{2\,[\,(E+\mathscr{S})^2+\Gamma^2/4\,]}\Big)\Big]\exp\Big(\frac{T_S\Gamma^2/4}{2\,[\,(E+\mathscr{S})^2+\Gamma^2/4\,]}\Big)^2, \tag{8}$$

where Φ represents the error function,

$$\Phi(y) = (2/\sqrt{\pi})\int_0^y e^{-u^2}\,du\,.$$

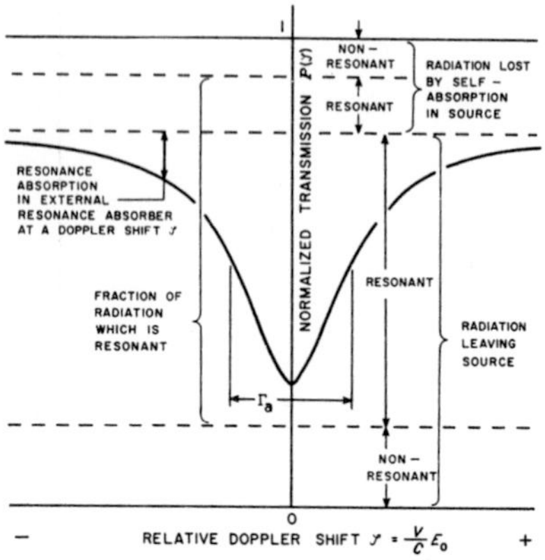

Fig. 2. Normalized transmission of γ-radiation through a resonance absorber as a function of the relative Doppler shift between source and absorber. The apparent full width at half-height of the transmitted line is denoted by Γ_a.

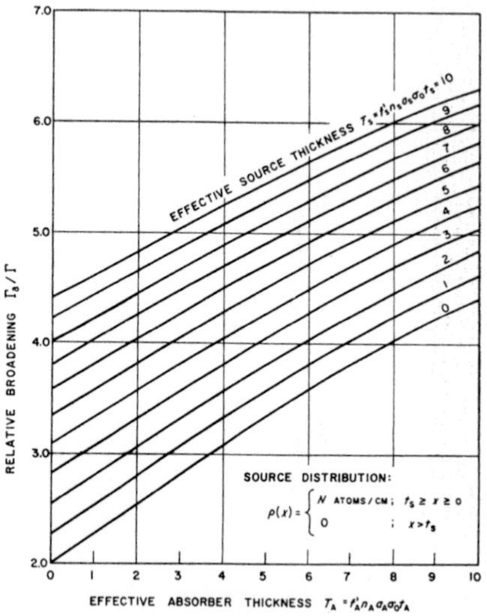

Fig. 3.

Fig. 3. Broadening of the transmitted line for a source having a uniform distribution of emitting atoms.

The first term in (8) corresponds to the transmission of the non-resonant fraction of the radiation, and will be denoted by $(1-f)P_{\text{non-res.}}(\text{Gaussian})$. Again, as $\mu_S t_S$ approaches zero, the non-resonant contribution approaches $(1-f)$. The resonant contribution to the transmission is contained in the second term of (8). Before discussing the general evaluation of this equation, we will consider two special cases.

4.1. THIN SOURCE AND ABSORBER

If both source and absorber effective thicknesses satisfy the conditions $T_S \ll 1$, $T_A \ll 1$, we can expand the exponentials and the error function in the second term of (8), and keep only first-order terms in thickness. After integrating over energy, one obtains

$$P(\mathscr{S}) = \left[(1-f)P_{\text{non-res.}}(\text{Gaussian}) + f\left(1-\frac{T_S}{2\sqrt{\pi}}\right)\right] - f\frac{T_A}{2}\frac{1}{1+(\mathscr{S}/\Gamma)^2}. \tag{9}$$

In this equation the bracketed term represents the asymptotic transmission as $\mathscr{S}\to\infty$, and differs from unity because of self-absorption in the source. The second term results from resonance absorption in the external absorber. The transmitted line shape has the Breit-Wigner form, but is twice as wide as either the emission or the absorption line. Note that (9) differs from (5) only in that the Gaussian source results in more self-absorption than the uniform source. This conclusion follows from the choice of normalization for the Gaussian distribution and is subject to the thin source approximation used to derive both equations.

4.2. THIN SOURCE – TRANSMISSION AT ZERO DOPPLER SHIFT

Expansion of the appropriate terms to lowest order when $T_S \to 0$ allows (8) to be evaluated at the point $\mathscr{S}=0$. Since both the Gaussian distribution of (7) and the uniform distribution described by (2) are normalized in the same way, it is not surprising that (6) once again follows for this special case, but with $P_{\text{non-res.}}(\text{uniform})$ replaced by $P_{\text{non-res.}}(\text{Gaussian})$.

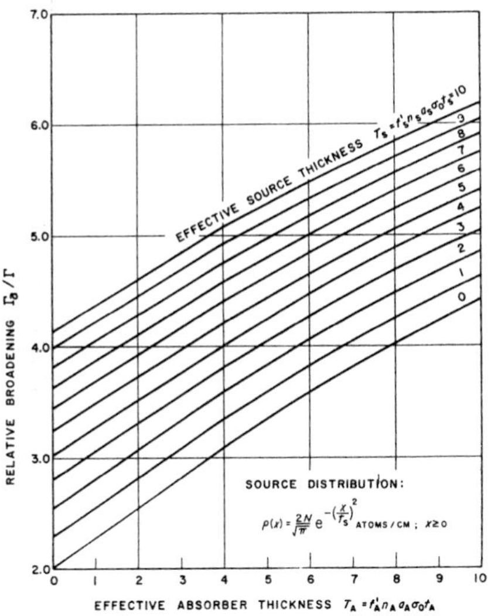

Fig. 4. Broadening of the transmitted line for a source having a Gaussian distribution of emitting atoms.

4.3. GAUSSIAN SOURCE – GENERAL CASE

Equation (8), representing the transmission from a source which has a Gaussian distribution of radioactive atoms, could not be evaluated analytically for arbitrary values of T_S and T_A. Again, we have performed a numerical integration on ILLIAC for the range $10 \geq (T_S, T_A) \geq 0$. As in the uniform case, it has been found empirically that the resulting transmitted lines differ but little from Breit-Wigner curves whose full widths at half-height vary with source and absorber thicknesses (see fig. 2). The calculated broadening of the transmitted line as a function of T_S and T_A is shown in fig. 4. As T_S and T_A approach zero, the conditions of section 4.1 apply, and Γ_a/Γ approaches the value two.

5. Non-Resonant Absorbing Sources

As has been shown, the width of the transmission curve obtained from a resonantly absorbing source of finite thickness is always greater than twice the natural width of the transition. The way to obtain the narrowest lines with any given radioisotope is to use a source backing which has zero abundance of atoms that can absorb resonantly. In this way, only the external resonance absorber contributes to the line broadening. When this is the case, the ordinary electronic absorption, neglected so far for the resonant fraction of the radiation, must be considered. The transmission under these circumstances is given by

$$p(\mathscr{S}) = e^{-\mu_A t_A} \left\{ (1-f) \int_0^\infty dx\, \rho(x)\, e^{-\mu_S x} + f \frac{\Gamma}{2\pi} \int_{-\infty}^{\infty} dE \exp\left(\frac{-T_A \Gamma^2/4}{(E-E_0)^2 + \Gamma^2/4} \right) \times \int_0^\infty \frac{dx\, \rho(x)\, e^{-\mu_S x}}{(E-E_0+\mathscr{S})^2 + \Gamma^2/4} \right\}. \tag{10}$$

The x-integral is the same in both the non-resonant and the resonant terms of this equation, and can be evaluated for the uniform distribution of (2) and the Gaussian distribution of (7). The transmission, normalized according to (3), is found to be

$$\left.\begin{aligned} P(\mathscr{S}) &= [(1-f) + fI(\mathscr{S})] \left[\frac{1 - e^{-\mu_S t_S}}{\mu_S t_S} \right] \\ &= [(1-f) + fI(\mathscr{S})] P(\text{uniform})_{\text{non-res.}} \end{aligned}\right\} \text{ uniform source} \tag{11}$$

and

$$\left.\begin{aligned} P(\mathscr{S}) &= [(1-f) + fI(\mathscr{S})] [e^{(\frac{1}{2}\mu_S t_S)^2} (1 - \Phi(u_S t_S/2))] \\ &= [(1-f) + fI(\mathscr{S})] P(\text{Gaussian})_{\text{non-res.}} \end{aligned}\right\} \text{ Gaussian source} \tag{12}$$

where

$$I(\mathscr{S}) = \frac{\Gamma}{2\pi} \int_{-\infty}^{\infty} \frac{dE}{(E+\mathscr{S})^2 + \Gamma^2/4} \exp\left(\frac{-T_A \Gamma^2/4}{E^2 + \Gamma^2/4} \right). \tag{13}$$

In either case, the shape of the transmitted line is the same, only the amplitude being affected by the electronic absorption. This behavior follows from the fact that the ordinary mass attenuation coefficients are energy independent over the width of the emission and absorption lines. The shape of the transmitted line is determined by the energy integral of (13). Since this integral corresponds to the $T_S = 0$ case for either a uniform or a Gaussian source it has, in effect, already been considered. In the results presented below, it should be remembered that $I(\mathscr{S})$ must be substituted into either (11) or (12) to obtain the transmission, $P(\mathscr{S})$.

When the resonance absorber satisfies the condition $T_A \ll 1$, the integral of (13) reduces to

$$I(\mathscr{S}) = 1 - \frac{T_A}{2} \frac{1}{1 + (\mathscr{S}/\Gamma)^2}, \tag{14}$$

again representing a Breit-Wigner curve whose width at half-height is 2Γ.

For arbitrary values of T_A, the transmission also approximates a Breit-Wigner curve, but the apparent width Γ_a varies with the absorber thickness in the manner described by the $T_S = 0$ curve in either fig. 3 or fig. 4.

When there exists no Doppler shift between source and absorber, the energy integral of (13) can be evaluated:

$$I(0) = e^{-\frac{1}{2}T_A} J_0(iT_A/2) . \tag{15}$$

In section 3.2 and 4.2, where very thin sources were considered, the evaluation of the energy integral led to the approximation given in (6). In the case of a non-resonantly absorbing source, no approximations are needed, and the result of (15) is exact. Since $I(\infty) = 1$, we can combine (15) with either (11) or (12) to get the useful result

$$\frac{P(\infty) - P(0)}{P(\infty)} = f [1 - e^{-\frac{1}{2}T_A} J_0(iT_A/2)] . \tag{16}$$

Note added in proof: Equation (16), firxt applied to the analysis of Mössbauer experiments by the Los Alamos group, is often being used when it is not applicable. It must be remembered that (16) is

1) exact only for non-resonantly absorbing sources; it is a good approximation for sources where $T_S \ll 1$;

2) derived on the assumption that the emission and absorption lines overlap exactly at zero relative velocity between source and absorber. If, as is often the case, there exists an energy shift between emission and absorption spectra, $P(0)$ must be replaced by $P(\mathscr{S}_0)$, where $\mathscr{S}_0$ is the Doppler shift required to produce coincidence;

3) valid for source and absorber half-widths equal to Γ, the natural width of the transition. It is still correct if these widths are not the natural width, provided that they are equal: $\Gamma_S = \Gamma_A$. In this case, however, the maximum absorption cross-section σ_0 must be multiplied by the factor Γ/Γ_S to keep the total absorption constant.

We wish to emphasize that (16) can be used to extract f and f' from absorption measurements only if the conditions assumed in the derivation are at least approximately satisfied.

Acknowledgement

We wish to thank Professor H. Frauenfelder as well as Dr. E. Lüscher, Dr. P. Debrunner, and Mr. J. H. Hetherington for many interesting discussions.

VOLUME 4, NUMBER 4 PHYSICAL REVIEW LETTERS FEBRUARY 15, 1960

POLARIZED SPECTRA AND HYPERFINE STRUCTURE IN Fe^{57}†

S. S. Hanna, J. Heberle, C. Littlejohn, G. J. Perlow, R. S. Preston, and D. H. Vincent
Argonne National Laboratory, Lemont, Illinois

(Received January 26, 1960)

The observation in this laboratory[1] of the polarization of the resonance radiation[2-5] emitted by the 14-kev level of Fe^{57} has led to a study of polarization in the hyperfine spectrum of the resonant absorption. The apparatus and the method of producing and detecting polarization were the same as used in reference 1 except that the source and the absorber were mounted on separate Alnico magnets. The magnet carrying the absorber was attached firmly to the bed of the lathe used in our previous work.[4] The other magnet holding the source was fastened securely to the carriage of the lathe. The detector of radiation (40-mil NaI) was mounted on the axis determined by the source and absorber and it was well shielded from magnetic fields.

The motion of the carriage provided uniform velocities of the source, and the polarized spec-

VOLUME 4, NUMBER 4 PHYSICAL REVIEW LETTERS FEBRUARY 15, 1960

tra were obtained by measuring the transmission, with crossed or parallel magnetizations in source and absorber, as a function of the velocity of the source. The operation of the lathe was made automatic so that the carriage (source) moved to and fro at a predetermined speed. During the "to" motions the pulses from the detector were recorded in the lower channels of a 256-channel analyzer; and during the "fro" motions they were accumulated in the upper channels of the analyzer. In a single run, therefore, the transmission was measured for a positive and for an equal negative velocity.

The spectra obtained in this way are shown in Fig. 1. Since no significant differences were observed for positive and negative velocities, the spectra have been folded about zero velocity. The spectrum obtained with source and absorber magnetized perpendicular to each other differs markedly from that obtained with parallel magnetizations. For comparison, a spectrum is shown for an unmagnetized source and absorber. It is seen that the hyperfine spectrum consists of six prominent lines instead of the four previously reported.[3,5] It is clear therefore that the earlier interpretation based on the existence of only four lines is incorrect.

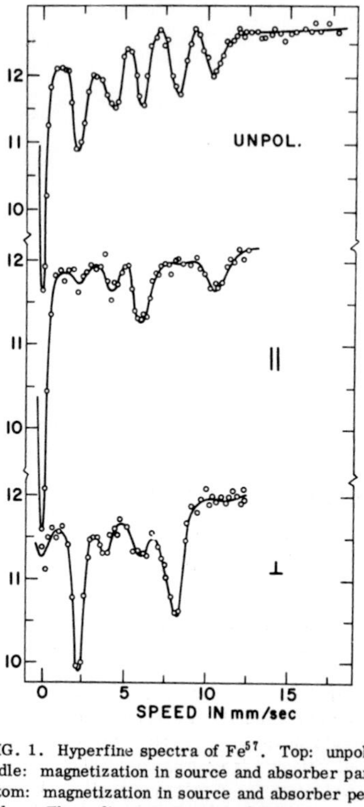

FIG. 1. Hyperfine spectra of Fe^{57}. Top: unpolarized. Middle: magnetization in source and absorber parallel. Bottom: magnetization in source and absorber perpendicular. The ordinate is in units of 2000.

The level diagram of Fe^{57} which seems to provide a satisfactory explanation of the spectra in Fig. 1 is shown on the left in Fig. 2. In the upper right are given the hyperfine components for $M1$ radiation. (We have found little need to introduce a significant amount of $E2$.) The intensities of the components are those appropriate to a random orientation of the internal magnetic fields at the nuclei. At the lower right are shown the components for the case in which the internal fields have been aligned. The intensities given are for radiations emitted perpendicular to the aligned field. The direction of polarization of each component relative to the direction of the aligned field is indicated by the symbol ∥ or ⊥.

If one takes a hyperfine pattern and moves it over itself, one obtains the hyperfine spectrum,

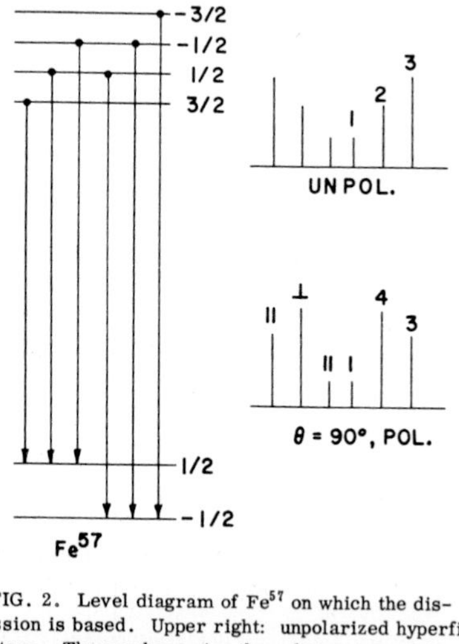

FIG. 2. Level diagram of Fe^{57} on which the discussion is based. Upper right: unpolarized hyperfine pattern. The numbers give the relative intensities. Lower right: polarized hyperfine pattern ($\theta = 90°$). The symbols ∥ and ⊥ stand for polarization parallel or perpendicular to the aligned field.

each line in the spectrum arising from the coincidence of hyperfine components in emission and absorption. At the top in Fig. 3 is shown the predicted spectrum of unpolarized radiation. In the middle is given the spectrum for the case in which the internal fields in source and absorber are aligned parallel to each other. In this case a line in the absorption spectrum will appear only if the respective hyperfine components have the same polarization. If, on the other hand, these polarizations are perpendicular, then the line will appear in the absorption spectrum only if the internal fields in source and absorber are aligned at right angles. The spectrum predicted for this case is shown at the bottom in Fig. 3. The intensities given in Fig. 3 are those nominally expected for a thin absorber. In addition it is assumed that a line which should appear only with one orientation of the fields will actually be present to the extent of about 10% with the other orientation, because of incomplete alignment of the fields in source and absorber. The spectra in Fig. 3 are in good qualitative agreement with the observations in Fig. 1.

The hyperfine pattern of six components produces, in all, eight lines in the absorption spectrum. However, the splittings in the ground state and in the excited state are such that two doublets are formed which are not resolved in the unpolarized spectrum. The resolved peaks are numbered from one to six in Fig. 3. One member of the doublet in line 2 is too weak to affect the position of the peak. Thus, the spacings between line 1 and 2, 4 and 5, and 5 and 6 should be equal to the splitting of the ground state. The spacing between lines 2 and 4 gives the splitting of the ground state. Line 3 is a doublet, one member of which should appear in the spectrum with parallel fields, the other in the spectrum with crossed fields. The separation in the doublet is equal to $2g_1 - g_0$, where g_1 and g_0 are the splittings of the excited and ground level, respectively. We have measured this doublet separation with some care by observing the shift in line 3 in going from one polarized spectrum to the other. The separation is (0.5 ± 0.1) mm/sec. We have also measured the separation between lines 1 and 2 more carefully than shown in Fig. 1 and obtained $g_1 = (2.23 \pm 0.03)$ mm/sec. Hence $g_0 = (3.96 \pm 0.10)$ mm/sec.

Ludwig and Woodbury[8] have recently obtained an accurate determination of the magnetic moment of the ground state. If we use their value of $+(0.0903 \pm 0.0007)$ nm, the above measurements give $-(0.153 \pm 0.004)$ nm for the magnetic moment of the excited state, and a value of $(3.33 \pm 0.10) \times 10^5$ oersteds for the effective magnetic field at the iron nucleus. We note the opposite sign of the magnetic moment, which is an important feature of the above interpretation.

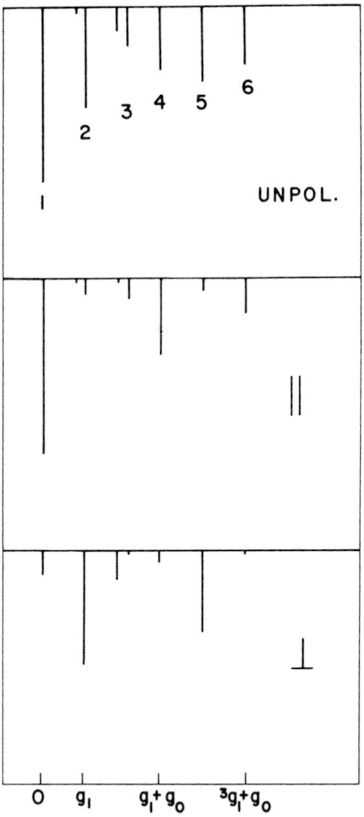

FIG. 3. Spectra predicted by the scheme in Fig. 2. Top: unpolarized. Middle: magnetizations parallel. Bottom: magnetizations perpendicular. The main peaks are numbered from one to six. The symbols g_0 and g_1 represent the gyromagnetic ratios of ground and excited levels, respectively.

We would like to thank B. F. Martinka and H. W. Ostrander for generous assistance in the mechanical aspects of our work. We are grateful to

G. W. Ludwig and H. H. Woodbury for communicating their results to us.

---

†Work performed under the auspices of the U. S. Atomic Energy Commission.

[1]G. J. Perlow, S. S. Hanna, M. Hamermesh, C. Littlejohn, D. H. Vincent, R. S. Preston, and J. Heberle, Phys. Rev. Letters 4, 74 (1960).

[2]J. P. Schiffer and W. Marshall, Phys. Rev. Letters 3, 556 (1959).

[3]R. V. Pound and G. A. Rebka, Jr., Phys. Rev. Letters 3, 554 (1959).

[4]S. S. Hanna, J. Heberle, C. Littlejohn, G. J. Perlow, R. S. Preston, and D. H. Vincent, Phys. Rev. Letters 4, 28 (1960).

[5]G. DePasquali, H. Frauenfelder, S. Margulies, and R. N. Peacock, Phys. Rev. Letters 4, 71 (1960).

[6]G. W. Ludwig and H. H. Woodbury, Phys. Rev. (to be published).

VOLUME 4, NUMBER 8 PHYSICAL REVIEW LETTERS APRIL 15, 1960

EVIDENCE FOR QUADRUPOLE INTERACTION OF Fe^{57m}, AND INFLUENCE OF CHEMICAL BINDING ON NUCLEAR GAMMA-RAY ENERGY*

O. C. Kistner and A. W. Sunyar
Brookhaven National Laboratory, Upton, New York
(Received March 30, 1960)

The recoil-free emission and resonant absorption[1] of the 14.4-kev nuclear gamma ray of Fe^{57}, has been used to determine the quadrupole coupling for the 3/2- excited state of Fe^{57} bound in Fe_2O_3, and to measure an energy shift of this nuclear gamma ray which is attributed to effects of chemical binding. This effect is corollary to the effects of chemical environment on internal conversion coefficients[2] and on electron capture disintegration rates.[3] These measurements also yield the value of the internal magnetic field at the position of the Fe^{57} nucleus when it is bound in antiferromagnetic Fe_2O_3.

The $M1$ emission line of Fe^{57} bound in ordinary metallic iron is split into six components by the magnetic hyperfine interaction.[4] The resonant absorption of this emission spectrum by Fe^{57} bound in Fe_2O_3 has been examined, as well as the much simpler absorption pattern which results when the "unsplit" emission line from Fe^{57} bound in a stainless steel lattice[5] is used. Because the interpretation of the two sets of measurements agree, only the latter measurements are presented in this Letter. The former measurements, in which a Co^{57} source co-plated with iron onto 1-mil copper was used, will only briefly be remarked upon.

The $\sim 2\text{-mg/cm}^2$ Fe_2O_3 absorber used in these measurements contained Fe^{57} enriched to $\sim 30\%$. The source consisted of Co^{57} plated onto 0.001-inch stainless steel (25% Cr, 20% Ni). After plating, this source was annealed for one hour at 900°C in a hydrogen atmosphere. All measurements were made with source and absorber at a temperature of 25°C.

In order to obtain a Doppler shift of the emission line, a uniform motion was obtained by coupling a pneumatically driven cylinder to another cylinder filled with oil, the ports of which were connected via a needle valve. A wide range of uniform velocities could be selected by adjusting this valve. The direction of source travel was reversed automatically by means of microswitches. Additional microswitches, set to exclude the region of nonuniform motion near the travel limits, were used to provide gate signals for the counters. The distance of travel between the limits of the counting gates was 0.973 cm. Source velocity was determined by counting the cycles from a 1000 cps tuning fork oscillator during the time between the gate limits.

The 14.4-kev gamma ray was detected with a NaI(Tl) scintillation counter. The phosphor was 2 mm thick and 1.5 inches in diameter. The counter face was located 5.4 cm above the upper limit of vertical travel of the source. The absorber was placed 4.7 cm from the counter face. A single-channel pulse-height analyzer selected the 14.4-kev gamma ray photopeak. The outputs of this analyzer and the 1000 cps clock were switched between two pairs of scalers so as to record counting rate and velocity separately for both directions of source motion.

Figure 1 shows the counting rate (in arbitrary units) as a function of source velocity relative to the Fe_2O_3 absorber for the stainless steel source. Absorption of the "unsplit" emission line at each of the six possible absorption energies of Fe^{57} in Fe_2O_3 is evident. The lack of symmetry of the absorption pattern about zero velocity shows immediately that one is not dealing simply with a magnetic hyperfine splitting pattern.

The velocities at which absorption peaks occur are given in Table I. Experimental values have been corrected by -2.5% to take account of the effect of geometry on our velocity scale. These absorption line velocities may be fitted precisely in terms of an energy level diagram as shown in Fig. 2. It is necessary to introduce an energy shift $\Delta E = \Delta E_1 + \Delta E_2$ between the center of gravity of the absorption lines of Fe^{57} in Fe_2O_3 and the emission line of Fe^{57} in stainless steel. In addition, an energy shift ϵ, of positive or negative sign, on the individual m states of the excited level is required. This is interpreted as being caused by a quadrupole interaction when Fe^{57} is bound in Fe_2O_3. A least-squares fit to our data yields the following splitting parameters (in "velocity units") for the two Fe^{57} nuclear states when Fe^{57} is bound in Fe_2O_3:

$$g_0' = 0.611 \pm 0.005 \text{ cm/sec},$$

$$g_1' = 0.345 \pm 0.003 \text{ cm/sec},$$

$$\Delta E = 0.047 \pm 0.003 \text{ cm/sec},$$

$$\epsilon = 0.012 \pm 0.003 \text{ cm/sec}.$$

VOLUME 4, NUMBER 8 PHYSICAL REVIEW LETTERS APRIL 15, 1960

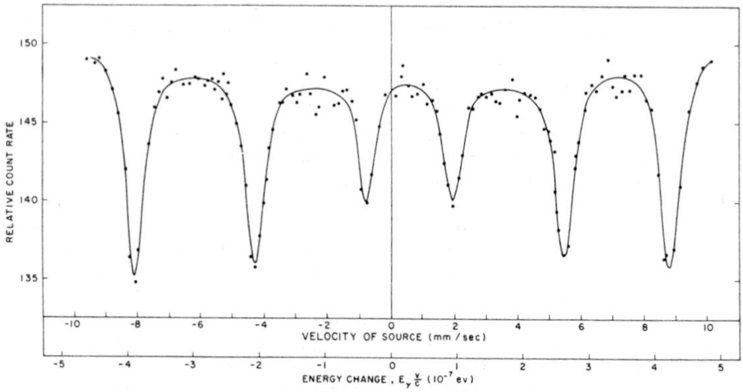

FIG. 1. The absorption by Fe^{57} bound in Fe_2O_3 of the 14.4-kev gamma ray emitted in the decay of Fe^{57m} bound in stainless steel as a function of relative source-absorber velocity. Positive velocity indicates a motion of source toward absorber.

These data indicate that the ratio g_0'/g_1' is 1.77 ± 0.02, in excellent agreement with the results of Hanna et al.,[4] and that the internal magnetic field in antiferromagnetic Fe_2O_3 is larger than in ferromagnetic iron by the factor 1.547 ± 0.022. If we take 3.33×10^5 oersteds as the value of the internal field[4] in Fe, we find a value of 5.15×10^5 oersteds at the Fe nucleus in Fe_2O_3. It is worth noting that the absorption peaks in Fig. 1 (reading from left to right) should have "thin absorber" intensity ratios of 3:2:1:1:2:3. However, the relative intensities found for the absorption peaks clearly exhibit evidence of saturation due to the rather large effective thickness of the enriched Fe_2O_3 absorber. Nevertheless, the experimental intensity ratios are such that an inverted hyperfine pattern is required for the 3/2- state, providing confirmation for this fact as previously reported.[4]

Let us now consider the effect of quadrupole

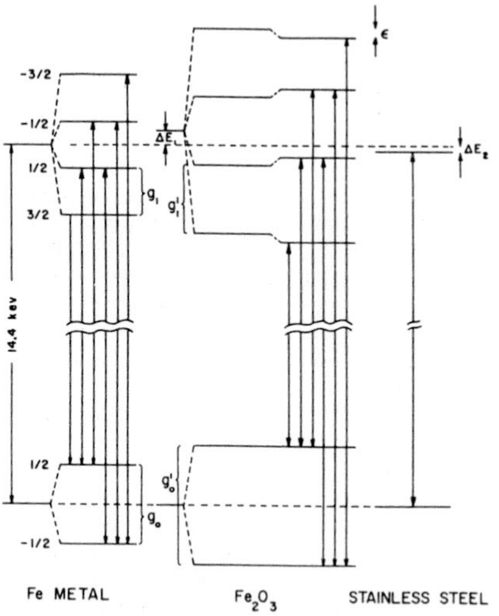

FIG. 2. Schematic representation of the ground and 14.4-kev excited states of Fe^{57} bound in ordinary iron, Fe_2O_3, and stainless steel. This diagram illustrates the details of magnetic hyperfine splitting, quadrupole interaction, and energy shifts due to chemical binding effects.

Table I. Velocities of maximum absorption (corrected for geometry) for a stainless steel source and Fe_2O_3 absorber. The negative signs indicate motions of source away from absorber.

Absorption line	Relative source-absorber velocity (cm/sec)
1/2+ → 3/2+	-0.789
1/2+ → 1/2+	-0.417
1/2+ → 1/2-	-0.076
1/2- → 1/2+	+0.192
1/2- → 1/2-	+0.536
1/2- → 3/2-	+0.859

interaction. For a pure quadrupole spectrum, in the case of axially symmetric field gradients, the shift ϵ for the substates of a spin I state is given by[6]

$$\epsilon = \frac{e^2qQ}{4I(2I-1)}[3m^2 - I(I+1)],$$

where q denotes $(1/e)(\partial^2V/\partial z^2)$. All other symbols have the conventional meanings. When Zeeman splitting is combined with quadrupole interaction, the precise energy shifts for the individual m states due to quadrupole interaction depend upon the orientation of the magnetic axis relative to the axis of symmetry for the electric field gradient, and are in general not the same for all m states.[7] However, for a case such as we deal with here, where the quadrupole interaction is small compared to the magnetic interaction, the absolute magnitude of ϵ is the same for all m states of the spin 3/2 state within the accuracy of our measurements, independent of the orientation of the crystal axes. Thus, we find $\epsilon = \frac{1}{4}|e^2qQ| = 0.012 \pm 0.003$ cm/sec (5.75×10^{-9} ev). Since our measurements indicate that the shift of magnitude ϵ is negative for the $m = \pm 3/2$ substates and positive for the $m = \pm 1/2$ substates, the product e^2qQ is negative. The absolute value is suggestive of a small quadrupole moment for Fe^{57m} although this statement cannot be amplified further without knowledge of electric field gradients in Fe_2O_3.

In our earlier absorption measurements on Fe_2O_3 using the emission lines of Fe^{57} bound in ordinary iron, we find an energy shift upward (see Fig. 2) of $\Delta E_1 \cong 0.04$ cm/sec. Within the accuracy of our measurements, the splitting parameters g_0', g_1', and ϵ remain the same. A separate measurement of the absorption by Fe^{57} bound in stainless steel of the emission lines of Fe^{57} in ordinary iron confirms the implied existence of an energy shift downward (see Fig. 2) of $\Delta E_2 = 0.01$ cm/sec in this case.

The existence of an energy shift $\Delta E = (2.26 \pm 0.15) \times 10^{-8}$ ev between stainless steel and Fe_2O_3 has been definitely established. We will now discuss the ways in which differences in chemical environment may produce such a shift. (1) Source and absorber will in general have different Debye temperatures. Since the nucleus in its excited state has a slightly greater rest mass than when it is in its ground state, the energy difference between the nuclear states will decrease from its value for an "unbound" system by different amounts because of the difference in the zero-point energies. This reduction in energy is larger for the substance having the higher Debye temperature. (2) In addition, when a lattice is at a finite temperature, the energy difference between the nuclear states is reduced further by virtue of the previously reported temperature effect.[8] Since the magnitude of this reduction depends upon the integral of the specific heat of the lattice up to the temperature of the substance, it will be larger for the substance having the lower Debye temperature. We expect this temperature effect to be small, although it should be noted that it acts to reduce the energy shift between different substances which results from zero-point energy differences. The sign and magnitude of the observed shift between stainless steel and Fe_2O_3 would require that Fe_2O_3 have a considerably lower Debye temperature than stainless steel or ordinary iron. Were this the case, the Debye-Waller factor would materially depress the recoil-free resonant yield in Fe_2O_3, a result which is not indicated by the data. (3) When chemical environment is altered, a nuclear isotope shift may result. This effect has its origin in the change in the electronic wave functions over the region of space occupied by the nucleus. s electrons may be expected to contribute most to this effect. Since s electrons are in effect removed in going from Fe in metal to Fe in Fe_2O_3, a smaller charge radius for Fe^{57m} than for Fe^{57} in its ground state would produce a shift in the observed direction. The direction of the observed energy shift ΔE requires the presence of the nuclear isotope shift, since the zero-point energy shift is in the opposite direction. This nuclear isotope shift is similar to the isomeric isotope shift[9] observed in the optical spectrum of Hg^{197}.

We wish to emphasize two additional points about recoil-free emission and absorption experiments when source and absorber are chemically different. First, the existence of energy shifts introduces asymmetries into the absorption pattern which make it essential not to combine data taken at equal velocities of opposite sense. Second, any recoil-free absorption at zero velocity is accidental. In general, therefore, a search for this effect by comparing absorption at zero velocity with absorption at a large relative velocity between source and absorber will not yield significant results unless source and absorber are identical chemically. It is amusing to note that in the absorption by Fe_2O_3 of the emission lines of Fe^{57} in ordinary iron, two such accidental coincidences do indeed occur to give substantial absorption at zero velocity.

We wish to thank many of our colleagues, particularly M. Goldhaber and J. Weneser, for interesting discussions, and G. K. Wertheim for providing us with a sample of the particular stainless steel used in his measurements.[5]

---

*Work done under the auspices of the U. S. Atomic Energy Commission.

[1]R. L. Mössbauer, Z. Physik 151, 124 (1958).

[2]K. T. Bainbridge, M. Goldhaber, and E. Wilson, Phys. Rev. 90, 430 (1953).

[3]R. F. Leininger, E. Segrè, and C. Wiegand, Phys. Rev. 76, 897 (1949).

[4]S. S. Hanna, J. Heberle, C. Littlejohn, G. J. Perlow, R. S. Preston, and D. H. Vincent, Phys. Rev. Letters 4, 177 (1960).

[5]G. K. Wertheim (private communication) has informed us that Fe^{57} in stainless steel exhibits a single absorption line. [See G. K. Wertheim, this issue, Phys. Rev. Letters 4, 403 (1960).]

[6]T. P. Das and E. L. Hahn, Nuclear Quadrupole Resonance Spectroscopy, Solid State Physics, Suppl. 1 (Academic Press Inc., New York, 1958).

[7]P. M. Parker, J. Chem. Phys. 24, 1096 (1956).

[8]R. V. Pound and G. A. Rebka, Jr., Phys. Rev. Letters 4, 274 (1960).

[9]A. C. Melissinos and S. P. Davis, Phys. Rev. 115, 130 (1959).

VOLUME 6, NUMBER 2 PHYSICAL REVIEW LETTERS JANUARY 15, 1961

ELECTRIC QUADRUPOLE SPLITTING AND THE NUCLEAR VOLUME EFFECT IN THE IONS OF Fe^{57}†

S. DeBenedetti, G. Lang, and R. Ingalls*
Carnegie Institute of Technology, Pittsburgh, Pennsylvania
(Received December 19, 1960)

A study of the Mössbauer spectra of Fe^{57} in chemical compounds has revealed some striking regularities. Typical transmission curves for Fe^{++} and Fe^{+++} ionic compounds relative to an unsplit room-temperature stainless steel source are shown in Figs. 1 and 2, respectively. Both patterns exhibit a shift of the center of gravity from the zero of velocity, and the curve of Fe^{++} shows the two absorption lines characteristic of a pure nuclear electric quadrupole interaction. The quantities δ and ΔE, which characterize these effects, are defined in the figures; their values for various compounds are shown in Table I. It is noteworthy that the value of δ and the low-temperature value of ΔE are, for a given iron ion, relatively independent of the chemical combination.

The center of gravity displacement, or chemical shift,[1] arises from two mechanisms: (a) the second order Doppler shift,[2,3] which is caused by lattice vibrations, and is a function $A(T_s,T_a,\theta_s,\theta_a)$ of the source and absorber temperatures and Debye temperatures, and (b) the nuclear volume effect,[4,5] which represents the change, from source to absorber, in the modification of the nuclear transition energy caused by electrons overlapping the finite nucleus. The total shift in a Mössbauer spectrum may be written:

$$\delta \approx A(T_s, T_a, \theta_s, \theta_a) + B(R_e^{2\rho} - R_g^{2\rho})[\Psi_a^2(0) - \Psi_s^2(0)], \quad (1)$$

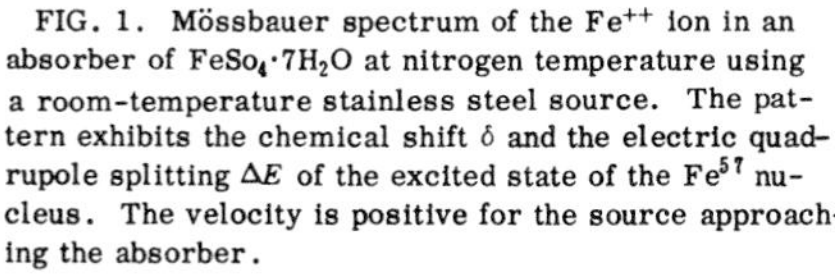

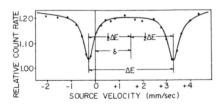

FIG. 1. Mössbauer spectrum of the Fe^{++} ion in an absorber of $FeSo_4 \cdot 7H_2O$ at nitrogen temperature using a room-temperature stainless steel source. The pattern exhibits the chemical shift δ and the electric quadrupole splitting ΔE of the excited state of the Fe^{57} nucleus. The velocity is positive for the source approaching the absorber.

where R_e and R_g are the charge radii of the nuclear excited and ground states. $\Psi^2(0)$ is the s-electron density at the position of the nucleus. B is a constant which is 1.76×10^9 cm/sec for iron when $R^{2\rho}$ and $\Psi^2(0)$ are expressed in atomic units. $\rho = (1 - \alpha^2 Z^2)^{1/2}$ is a relativistic factor[5] equal to 0.982 for iron.

An estimate of R_g/R_e may be made if one neglects the influence of the crystalline surroundings and uses wave functions[6] for the free iron ions. Using (1) and the room-temperature shifts (which are less sensitive to differences in θ than are the low-temperature shifts), we obtain

$$\delta_{++} - \delta_{+++} \approx B(R_e^{2\rho} - R_g^{2\rho})[\Psi_{++}^2(0) - \Psi_{+++}^2(0)]. \quad (2)$$

We have neglected the small difference $A_{++} - A_{+++}$. Watson's wave functions yield $\Psi_{++}^2(0) < \Psi_{+++}^2(0)$; the extra electron in Fe^{++} apparently shields the $3s$ electrons slightly. Equation (2) yields $R_g/R_e = 1.001$.

Watson[6,7] has also calculated wave functions for the outer electron configurations $3d^6 4s^2$ and $3d^8$ for iron. Using an equation similar to (2) one obtains the shifts expected for each case:

$$\delta_{Fe} = -0.178 \text{ cm/sec for } 3d^4 4s^2,$$

$$\delta_{Fe} = +0.182 \text{ cm/sec for } 3d^8.$$

When metallic iron is used as an absorber with the stainless steel source at room temperature, a shift of +0.01 cm/sec results. Since this value is midway between the above calculated values,

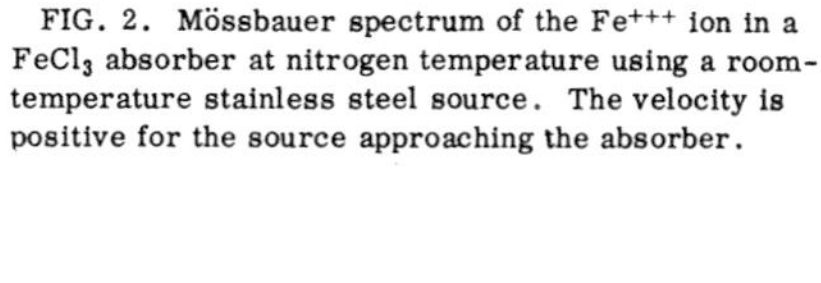

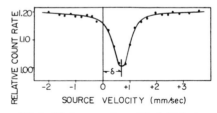

FIG. 2. Mössbauer spectrum of the Fe^{+++} ion in a $FeCl_3$ absorber at nitrogen temperature using a room-temperature stainless steel source. The velocity is positive for the source approaching the absorber.

Table I. A list of quadrupole splittings ΔE and chemical shifts δ relative to the emission line from a stainless steel source at room temperature.

Absorber	Temperature	ΔE(cm/sec)	δ(cm/sec)	References
Fe_2O_3	Room	0.024 ± 0.003	0.047 ± 0.003	a
Fe_2O_3	Room	0.024	0.050	b
$Fe_2(SO_4)_3$	Room	0	0.064	b
$Fe_2(SO_4)_3$	Room	0	0.055 ± 0.005	this work
$Fe_2(SO_4)_3$	Nitrogen	0	0.065 ± 0.005	this work
$FeCl_3$	Room	0	0.045 ± 0.005	this work
$FeCl_3$	Nitrogen	0	0.065 ± 0.005	this work
$FeCl_2\cdot 4H_2O$	Room	0.300 ± 0.005	0.135 ± 0.005	this work
$FeCl_2\cdot 4H_2O$	Nitrogen	0.310 ± 0.005	0.145 ± 0.005	this work
$FeSO_4\cdot 7H_2O$	Room	0.320 ± 0.005	0.140 ± 0.005	this work
$FeSO_4\cdot 7H_2O$	Nitrogen	0.360 ± 0.005	0.150 ± 0.005	this work
$Fe(NH_4)_2(SO_4)_2\cdot 6H_2O$	Room	0.175 ± 0.005	0.140 ± 0.005	this work
$Fe(NH_4)_2(SO_4)_2\cdot 6H_2O$	Nitrogen	0.270 ± 0.005	0.150 ± 0.005	this work
FeF_2	Room	0.268		c

[a]See reference 4.

[b]I. Solomon, Proceedings of the Allerton Park Conference on Mössbauer Effect, University of Illinois, Urbana, Illinois, June 5-7, 1960 (unpublished), Sec. IIc.

[c]G. K. Wertheim, Phys. Rev. 121, 63 (1961).

it strongly suggests that metallic iron has an outer electron configuration equivalent to $3d^7 4s^1$.

Although the electric quadrupole splitting seems to be temperature dependent, it is roughly the same at low temperatures for all the Fe^{++} compounds listed in Table I. This suggests that the relevant field gradient is mainly caused by the ion alone. The free Fe^{++} ion has an outer electron configuration of $3d^6$ and is in a ^5D state. Five of these $3d$ electrons have their spins aligned and together form a spherically symmetric distribution of charge. The sixth electron has opposite spin and also a choice of the five possible values of m_l. The crystal symmetry dictates the m_l combination the ion will actually take. For sufficiently low symmetry the lowest energy state will be a linear combination of the two states with m_l equal to 2 and -2. Assuming this, and neglecting all other possible effects of the crystalline environment, it is possible to calculate the ionic field gradient at the nucleus to within the factor $(1-\gamma)$, where γ is the Sternheimer antishielding factor. Taking ΔE to be 0.3 cm/sec one obtains $|Q(1-\gamma)| \approx 0.1$ b, where Q is the nuclear electric quadrupole moment for the excited state of Fe^{57}.

The temperature dependence of the quadrupole splitting could be caused by thermal excitation of the Fe^{++} ion into a state which yields a lower field gradient at the nucleus. For sufficiently rapid ionic transitions, the nucleus will respond to the time average of the field gradient. This interpretation indicates that the level splitting of the Fe^{++} ion in $Fe(NH_4)_2(SO_4)_2\cdot 6H_2O$ is sufficiently small that significant excitation occurs at room temperature.

It is noted that there is very little quadrupole splitting in the case of Fe^{+++}. Presumably there is negligible field gradient from this ion, since its $3d^5$ electron configuration gives a ^6S state. The splitting that does occur[4] is therefore caused by field gradients from the neighboring ions rather than from the Fe^{+++} ion itself.

We are grateful to Professor J. Michael Radcliffe for some very helpful discussions.

†This work was supported by the Office of Naval Research.

*Submitted by R. Ingalls in partial fulfillment of the requirements for the degree of Doctor of Philosophy at the Carnegie Institute of Technology.

[1]O. C. Kistner, Proceedings of the Allerton Park Conference on Mössbauer Effect, University of Illinois, Urbana, Illinois, June 5-7, 1960 (unpublished), Sec. II*c*.

[2]R. V. Pound and G. A. Rebka, Jr., Phys. Rev. Letters 4, 274 (1960).

[3]B. D. Josephson, Phys. Rev. Letters 4, 341 (1960).

[4]O. C. Kistner and A. W. Sunyar, Phys. Rev. Letters 4, 412 (1960).

[5]G. Breit, Revs. Modern Phys. 30, 507 (1958).

[6]R. E. Watson, Technical Report No. 12, Solid-State and Molecular Theory Group, Massachusetts Institute of Technology (unpublished).

[7]R. E. Watson, Phys. Rev. 119, 1934 (1960).

VOLUME 6, NUMBER 3 PHYSICAL REVIEW LETTERS FEBRUARY 1, 1961

INTERPRETATION OF THE Fe^{57} ISOMER SHIFT

L. R. Walker, G. K. Wertheim, and V. Jaccarino
Bell Telephone Laboratories, Murray Hill, New Jersey
(Received January 3, 1961)

We have made a systematic study of the Mössbauer effect[1] of Fe^{57} in di- and tri-valent iron compounds and in d-group metals. The observed "isomer shift"[2] measures the total s-electron density at the nucleus. The shift in compounds is shown to depend mainly upon the $3d$ configuration of iron involved and to a lesser extent upon the "chemical" bond. The Hartree-Fock calculations of Watson[3] on the various $3d$ configurations of iron are combined with the data on the shifts in the most ionic compounds to obtain a calibration of the shift in terms of s-electron density. This enables us to estimate the difference in charge radius of the ground state and isomeric state of Fe^{57}. We associate the shift of an Fe solute ion in a d-group metal with the addition of some fraction of a $4s$ electron to an Fe $3d^7$ configuration; an estimate of the $4s$-electron wave function density at the nucleus from the Fermi-Segrè-Goudsmit (FSG) formula[4] enables this fraction to be determined.

Kistner and Sunyar[5] first observed in the recoil-free emission and resonant absorption of the 14.4-kev nuclear gamma ray of Fe^{57}, that the energies of the emitted and absorbed gamma rays were noticeably different if the emitter and absorber were two dissimilar lattices containing iron. The origin of this effect is as follows.

The ground and isomeric levels of the nucleus have different effective charge radii; the electrostatic interaction with the electronic charge is then different in the two states and the gamma-ray energy is consequently changed (relative to its value for a point nucleus) by an amount proportional to the s-electron density at the nucleus. If the s-electron density is different for the absorber and emitter, the difference in gamma-ray energies, $E_a - E_e$, is defined as the isomer shift.

$$E_a - E_e = \tfrac{2}{5}\pi Z e^2 [R_{\mathrm{is}}^2 - R_{\mathrm{gr}}^2][|\psi(0)_a|^2 - |\psi(0)_e|^2], \quad (1)$$

where R_{is} and R_{gr} are the radii of the isomeric and ground states and $|\psi(0)_a|^2$ and $|\psi(0)_e|^2$ are the total s-electron densities at the nucleus for absorber and emitter, respectively.[6] It is to be noted that the sign of the shift has its origin in the fact that the level energy is lower the more compact the charge distribution.

An examination of the restricted Hartree-Fock calculations of Watson[3] shows that there are significant differences in the value of $|\psi_{3s}(0)|^2$ for different $3d$ configurations of iron; the change in $|\psi_{1s}(0)|^2$ and $|\psi_{2s}(0)|^2$ is substantially smaller.

It is perhaps worthwhile to point out that unrestricted Hartree-Fock calculations, which exhibit the imbalance of up and down spin density (exchange polarization effect), appear to give the same total density at the nucleus as the restricted procedure.[7] The variation of $|\psi_{3s}(0)|^2$ is such as to correspond to different degrees of shielding of $3s$ by $3d$ electrons. To calibrate the observed shifts in terms of total s-electron density, we associate the difference in the shifts for the most ionic Fe^{2+} and Fe^{3+} compounds with the difference in Watson's values of $\sum_{n=1}^{3}|\psi_{ns}(0)|^2$ for $3d^6$ and $3d^5$ configurations. When an Fe atom is introduced into a d-group host metal, $\sum_n|\psi_{ns}(0)|^2$ will also contain a contribution from $4s$ conduction electrons. Hartree-Fock calculations do not exist for single $4s$ electrons outside $3d^n$ configurations, but the FSG[4] formula, combined with the known term value of $3d^n4s$ configurations,[8] provides an entirely adequate estimate of $|\psi_{4s}(0)|^2$.

In Fig. 1 is shown a possible interpretation of the observed shifts making use of the above ideas. The total s-electron density in atomic units is plotted as ordinate. Watson's values for $2\sum_{n=1}^{3}|\psi_{ns}(0)|^2$ for the Fe $3d^n$ configurations from $n=4$ to $n=8$ are indicated on the left. The scale on the right for Mössbauer center-of-gravity shifts relative to stainless steel is established by identifying the shifts in the most ionic Fe^{2+} and Fe^{3+} with Watson's densities for $3d^6$ and $3d^5$, respectively. The solid straight lines represent s-electron densities for hypothetical $3d^n4s^x$ configurations. They are drawn on the assumption that the density for such a configuration is of the form $|\psi(3d^n)|^2+x|\psi_{4s}(0)|^2$, where $|\psi_{4s}(0)|^2$ is calculated from the FSG formula for a single $4s$ electron outside the $3d^n$ configuration. This assumes no screening of inner s electrons by the single $4s$ electron.[9] Curves for the configurations $3d^{8-x}4s^x$ and $3d^{7-x}4s^x$ are indicated by dashed lines and were obtained by extrapolation and interpolation of the FSG formula. The experimental data are given in Table I.

The shifts for Fe in various metals have been represented as horizontal lines of a length sufficient to cover what appear to be the most plausible configurations. Since for Fe in Fe metal there are certainly 8 electrons to be accounted

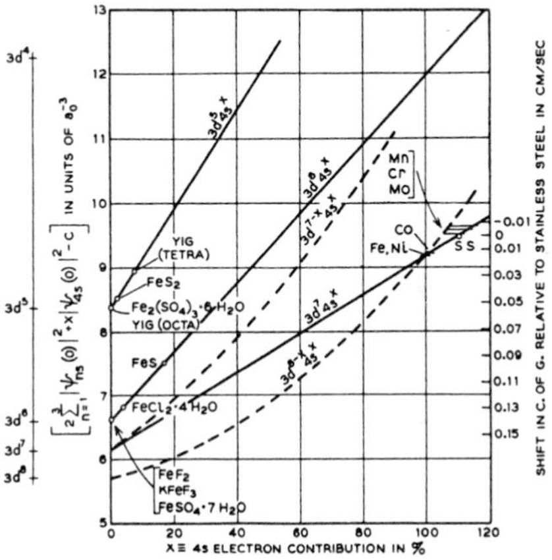

FIG. 1. A possible interpretation of the Fe^{57} Mössbauer isomer shifts in various solids. The total s-electron density is plotted as a function of the percentage of $4s$ character for various d-electron configurations. The reasons for placing the experimental data on given theoretical curves are discussed in the text. The constant $C = 11\,873\ a_0^{-3}$.

for, the evidence seems to point clearly to the configuration $3d^74s$ for this case. The smallness of the spread in shifts between the different metals indicates strongly that the configuration of the solute Fe is substantially the same in the metals investigated. For the Fe^{2+} and Fe^{3+} compounds, the experimental data are entered upon the $3d^64s^x$ and $3d^54s^x$ curves, respectively. This is consistent with the idea that in these covalent compounds the $4s$ atomic orbitals are partially occupied by electrons from the ligand ions (bonding orbitals).[10,11] The data for the "ferro" and "ferri" cyanides of potassium have not been plotted since it is not clear how to fit them into the above scheme. Indeed, since they have ground states which do not follow Hund's rule, it is unlikely that Watson's calculations are applicable to them. The fact that the isomer shifts in both cyanides are very small relative to each other and to stainless steel appears to be fortuitous.

From the observed isomer shift and the calculated difference in $|\psi(0)|^2$ for the d^5 and d^6 free-ion configurations we may compute the difference of the excited and ground-state charge

VOLUME 6, NUMBER 3 PHYSICAL REVIEW LETTERS FEBRUARY 1, 1961

Table I. Observed shifts in gamma-ray energy in various iron compounds and d-group metals measured relative to type 310 stainless steel. (Source and absorber at room temperature.) The measured shifts contain contributions from the second-order Doppler shift and the zero-point energy shift in addition to the isomer shift discussed here. Measurements at 77°K[a] indicate that the second-order Doppler shift contributions are small compared to the total shift. Moreover, since the Doppler shifts are likely to be of similar magnitudes in the compounds considered, they will cancel, since we are ultimately concerned only with differences in the shifts between similar materials. The same is true of the zero-point energy shift. The uncertainty in comparing metals with salts is considerably greater. To convert the shifts from cm/sec to Mc/sec, one should multiply the values by 116. The errors indicated reflect the uncertainty in the last significant figure.

		Shift (cm/sec)
$3d^6$	FeF_2 (single crystal)	0.140 ±5
$3d^6$	$KFeF_3$	0.139 ±5
$3d^6$	$FeSO_4 \cdot 7H_2O$	0.140 ±5
$3d^6$	$FeCl_2 \cdot 4H_2O$	0.130 ±5
$3d^6$	FeS	~0.11 ±1
$3d^5$	$Fe_2(SO_4)_3 \cdot 6H_2O$	0.052 ±5
$3d^5$	Fe_2O_3[b]	0.047 ±5
$3d^5$	Yttrium-iron garnet, octahedral	0.057 ±5
$3d^5$	Yttrium-iron garnet, tetrahedral	0.026 ±5
	FeS_2 (pyrites)[c]	0.048 ±5
	FeS_2 (marcasite)	0.048 ±5
Metals	Fe[b]	0.015 ±5
	Co	0.012 ±5
	Ni	0.015 ±5
	Mn	-0.008 ±2
	Cr	-0.005 ±2
	Mo	-0.001 ±2
Cyanides	$K_4Fe(CN)_6 \cdot 3H_2O$	0.0083 ±10
	$K_3Fe(CN)_6$	0.0000 ±10

[a]R. L. Ingalls, G. Lang, and S. DeBenedetti, Bull. Am. Phys. Soc. 5, 429 (1960).
[b]See reference 5.
[c]See reference 6.

radii using Eq. (1), assuming the usual charge radius dependence on mass number, i.e., $R = 1.20A^{1/3} \times 10^{-13}$ cm. We obtain $\delta R/R = 1.8 \times 10^{-3}$ as the fractional change in the charge radius, with the effective radius of the ground state larger than that of the excited state. This result is not unexpected[12] in sign and magnitude. The shell model predicts that the ground state for 3 odd neutrons outside a closed shell (28 neutrons), corresponding to a hole in the $2p_{3/2}$ shell, is one for which $I = 3/2$, as is the case for the 14-kev excited state. The large spin-orbit coupling precludes the possibility of a $2p_{1/2}$ configuration being the ground state.

Using the radial moments for an isotropic square well[13] and even assuming a proton excitation corresponding to $\Delta l = 3$ or 4, one still obtains a value of only 2×10^{-3} for $\delta R/R$. (The more likely case of a neutron excitation would leave the charge radius unchanged in a first approximation.) It is most unlikely therefore that the ground state is a simple shell state. It is interesting to note that the charge radius change expected for the addition of one particle (isotope shift at $A = 57$) is $\delta R/R \equiv \frac{1}{3}(\delta A/A) = 5.9 \times 10^{-3}$.

In the isomeric transition of Hg^{197} ($I_{gr} = 1/2 \rightarrow I_{ex} = 13/2$), it was estimated[2] that the charge redistribution corresponded to an increase of one-fourth to one-fifth of that observed experimentally for the addition of one neutron at $A = 157$. (The excited state has the larger charge distribution in this case.) Since both states are identifiable as single-particle neutron states, it is clear that a general charge redistribution accompanies the isomeric transition.

We would like to thank W. E. Blumberg, A. M. Clogston, and M. Goldhaber for several critical discussions.

[1]R. L. Mössbauer, Z. Physik 151, 124 (1958).

[2]Isomer shift was first observed in the optical spectra of Hg^{197} (ground state $I = 1/2$, excited state $I = 13/2$); A. C. Melissinos and S. P. Davis, Phys. Rev. 115, 130 (1959). If one accepts "isotope shift" to be the proper name for charge redistribution effects resulting from addition of particles, the name "isomer shift" is the logical choice for the effect discussed herein. Unfortunately, the phrase "chemical shift" has been used to describe Mössbauer isomer shifts in the past.

[3]R. E. Watson, Solid State and Molecular Theory Group, Technical Report No. 12, Massachusetts Institute of Technology, June 15, 1959 (unpublished).

[4]E. Fermi and E. Segrè, Z. Physik 82, 729 (1933); S. A. Goudsmit, Phys. Rev. 43, 636 (1933).

[5]O. C. Kistner and A. W. Sunyar, Phys. Rev. Letters 4, 412 (1960). A temperature-dependent shift had been

previously observed and identified as a second-order Doppler shift resulting from the thermal motion of the atoms. See R. V. Pound and G. A. Rebka, Jr., Phys. Rev. Letters 4, 274 (1960).

[6]I. Solomon, Compt. rend. 250, 3828 (1960). Apart from the numerical constant which was not given in this reference, our Eq. (1) is the same as the result given there.

[7]R. E. Watson and A. J. Freeman, Phys. Rev. 120, 1125 (1960).

[8]C. E. Moore, Atomic Energy Levels, National Bureau of Standards Circular No. 467 (U. S. Government Printing Office, Washington, D. C. 1952), Vol. 2.

[9]R. E. Watson, Phys. Rev. 119, 1934 (1960). An estimate of the charge $|\psi_0(0)|^2$ for the inner s electron was made from this reference in which the configurations $3d^{n-2}4s^2$ are considered.

[10]J. S. Van Wieringen, Discussions Faraday Soc. No. 19, 118 (1955).

[11]The effect of covalency on the occupation of d orbitals is neglected.

[12]M. Goldhaber (private communication).

[13]J. Eisinger and V. Jaccarino, Revs. Modern Phys. 30, 528 (1958).

PHYSICAL REVIEW
LETTERS

VOLUME 4 APRIL 1, 1960 NUMBER 7

APPARENT WEIGHT OF PHOTONS*

R. V. Pound and G. A. Rebka, Jr.
Lyman Laboratory of Physics, Harvard University, Cambridge, Massachusetts
(Received March 9, 1960)

As we proposed a few months ago,[1] we have now measured the effect, originally hypothesized by Einstein,[2] of gravitational potential on the apparent frequency of electromagnetic radiation by using the sharply defined energy of recoil-free γ rays emitted and absorbed in solids, as discovered by Mössbauer.[3] We have already reported[4] a detailed study of the shape and width of the line obtained at room temperature for the 14.4-kev, 0.1-microsecond level in Fe^{57}. Particular attention was paid to finding the conditions required to obtain a narrow line. We found that the line had a Lorentzian shape with a fractional full-width at half-height of 1.13×10^{-12} when the source was carefully prepared according to a prescription developed from experience. We have also investigated the 93-kev, 9.4-microsecond level of Zn^{67} at liquid helium and liquid nitrogen temperatures using several combinations of source and absorber environment, but have not observed a usable resonant absorption. That work will be reported later. The fractional width and intensity of the absorption in Fe^{57} seemed sufficient to measure the gravitational effect in the laboratory.

As a preliminary, we sought possible sources of systematic error that would interfere with measurements of small changes in frequency using this medium. Early in our development of the instrumentation necessary for this experiment, we concluded that there were asymmetries in, or frequency differences between, the lines of given combinations of source and absorber which vary from one combination to another. Thus it is absolutely necessary to measure a change in the relative frequency that is produced by the perturbation being studied. Observation of a frequency difference between a given source and absorber cannot be uniquely attributed to this perturbation. More recently, we have discovered and explained a variation of frequency with temperature of either the source or absorber.[5] We conclude that the temperature difference between the source and absorber must be accurately known and its effect considered before any meaning can be extracted from even a change observed when the perturbation is altered.

The basic elements of the apparatus finally developed to measure the gravitational shift in frequency were a carefully prepared source containing 0.4 curie of 270-day Co^{57}, and a carefully prepared, rigidly supported, iron film absorber. Using the results of our initial experiment, we requested the Nuclear Science and Engineering Corporation to repurify their nickel cyclotron target by ion exchange to reduce cobalt carrier. Following the bombardment, in a special run in the high-energy proton beam of the high-current cyclotron at the Oak Ridge National Laboratory, they electroplated the separated Co^{57} onto one side of a 2-in. diameter, 0.005-in. thick disk of Armco iron according to our prescription. After this disk was received, it was heated to 900°-1000°C for one hour in a hydrogen atmosphere[6] to diffuse the cobalt into the iron foil about 3×10^{-5} cm.

The absorber made by Nuclear Metals Inc., was composed of seven separate units. Each unit consisted of about 80 mg of iron, enriched in Fe^{57} to 31.9%, electroplated onto a polished side of a 3-in. diameter, 0.040-in. thick disk of beryllium. The electroplating technique required considerable development to produce films with absorption lines of width and strength that satisfied our tests. The films finally accepted, resonantly absorbed about 1/3 the recoil-free γ rays from our source. Each unit of the absorber was mounted over the 0.001-in. Al window of a 3 in. $\times$ 1/4 in. NaI(Tl) scintillation crystal integrally mounted on a Dumont 6363 multiplier phototube. The multiplier supply voltages were separately adjusted to equalize their conversion gains, and their outputs were mixed.

The required stable vertical baseline was conveniently obtained in the enclosed, isolated tower of the Jefferson Physical Laboratory.[7] A statistical argument suggests that the precision of a measurement of the gravitational frequency shift should be independent of the height. Instrumental instability but more significantly the sources of systematic error mentioned above are less critical compared to the larger fractional shifts obtained with an increased height. Our net operating baseline of 74 feet required only conveniently realizable control over these sources of error.

The absorption of the 14.4-kev γ ray by air in the path was reduced by running a 16-in. diameter, cylindrical, Mylar bag with thin end windows and filled with helium through most of the distance between source and absorber. To sweep out small amounts of air diffusing into the bag, the helium was kept flowing through it at a rate of about 30 liters/hr.

The over-all experiment is described by the block diagram of Fig. 1. The source was moved sinusoidally by either a ferroelectric or a moving-coil magnetic transducer. During the quarter of the modulation cycle centered about the time of maximum velocity the pulses from the scintillation spectrometer, adjusted to select the 14.4-kev γ-ray line, were fed into one scaler while, during the opposite quarter cycle, they were fed into another. The difference in counts recorded was a measure of the asymmetry in, or frequency-shift between, the emission and absorption lines. As a precaution the relative phase of the gating pulses and the sinusoidal modulation were displayed continuously. The data were found to be insensitive to phase changes much larger than the drifts of phase observed.

A completely duplicate system of electronics, controlled by the same gating pulses, recorded

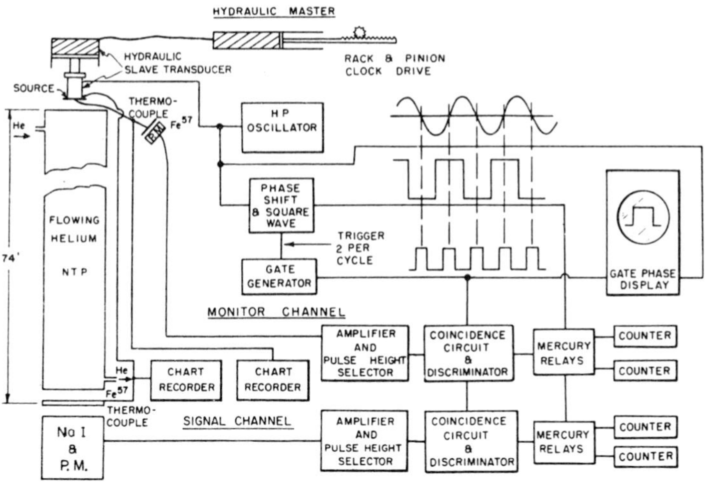

FIG. 1. A block diagram of the over-all experimental arrangement. The source and absorber-detector units were frequently interchanged. Sometimes a ferroelectric and sometimes a moving-coil magnetic transducer was used with frequencies ranging from 10 to 50 cps.

VOLUME 4, NUMBER 7 PHYSICAL REVIEW LETTERS APRIL 1, 1960

data from a counter having a 1-in. diameter, 0.015-in. thick NaI(Tl) scintillation crystal covered by an absorber similar to the main absorber. This absorber and crystal unit was mounted to see the source from only three feet away. This monitor channel measured the stability of the over-all modulation system, and, because of its higher counting rate, had a smaller statistical uncertainty.

The relation between the counting rate difference and relative frequency shifts between the emission and absorption lines was measured directly by adding a Doppler shift several times the size of the gravitational shift to the emission line. The necessary constant velocity was introduced by coupling a hydraulic cylinder of large bore carrying the transducer and source to a master cylinder of small bore connected to a rack-and-pinion driven by a clock.

Combining data from two periods having Doppler shifts of equal magnitude, but opposite sign, allowed measurement of both sensitivity and relative frequency shift. Because no sacrifice of valuable data resulted, the sensitivity was calibrated about 1/3 of the operating time which was as often as convenient without recording the data automatically. In this way we were able to eliminate errors due to drifts in sensitivity such as would be anticipated from gain or discriminator drift, changes in background, or changes in modulation swing.

The second order Doppler shift resulting from lattice vibrations required that the temperature difference between the source and absorber be controlled or monitored. A difference of 1°C would produce a shift as large as that sought, so the potential difference of a thermocouple with one junction at the source and the other at the main absorber was recorded. An identical system was provided for the monitor channel. The recorded temperature data were integrated over a counting period, and the average determined to 0.03°C. The temperature coefficient of frequency which we have used to correct the data, was calculated from the specific heat of a lattice having a Debye temperature of 420°K. Although at room temperature this coefficient is but weakly dependent on the Debye temperature, residual error in the correction for, or control of, the temperature difference limits the ability to measure frequency shifts and favors the use of a large height difference for the gravitational experiment.

Data typical of those collected are shown in Table I. The right-hand column is the data after correction for temperature difference. All data are expressed as fractional frequency shift $\times 10^{15}$. The difference of the shift seen with γ rays rising and that with γ rays falling should be the result of gravity. The average for the two directions of travel should measure an effective shift of other origin, and this is about four times the difference between the shifts. We confirmed that this shift was an inherent property of the particular combination of source and absorber by measuring the shift for each absorber unit in turn, with temperature correction, when it was six inches from the source. Although this test was not exact because only about half the area of each absorber was involved, the weighted mean shift from this test for the combination of all absorber units agreed well with that observed in the main experiment. The individual fractional frequency shifts found for these, for the monitor absorber, as well as for a 11.7-mg/cm^2 Armco iron foil, are displayed in Table II. The considerable variation among them is as striking as the size of the weighted mean shift. Such shifts could result from differences in a range of about 11% in effective Debye temperature through producing differences in net second order Doppler effect. Other explanations based on hyperfine structure including electric quadrupole interactions are also plausible. Although heat treatment might be expected to change these shifts for the iron-plated beryllium absorbers, experience showed that the line width was materially increased by such treatment, probably owing to interdiffusion. The presence of a significant shift for even the Armco foil relative to the source, both of which had received heat treatments, suggests that it is unlikely one would have, without test, a shift of this sort smaller than the gravitational effect expected in even our "two-way" baseline of 148 feet. The apparently fortuitous smallness of the shift of the monitor absorber relative to our source corresponds to the shift expected for about 30 feet of height difference.

Recently Cranshaw, Schiffer, and Whitehead[8] claimed to have measured the gravitational shift using the γ ray of Fe^{57}. They state that they believe their 43% statistical uncertainty represents the major error. Two much larger sources of error apparently have not been considered: (1) the temperature difference between the source and absorber, and (2) the frequency difference inherent in a given combination of source and absorber. From the above discussion, only 0.6°C of temperature difference would produce a shift

Table I. Data from the first four days of counting. The data are expressed as fractional frequency differences between source and absorber multiplied by 10^{15}, as derived from the appropriate sensitivity calibration. The negative signs mean that the γ ray has a frequency lower than the frequency of maximum absorption at the absorber.

Period	Shift observed	Temperature correction	Net shift
	Source at bottom		
Feb. 22, 5 p.m.	-11.5 ± 3.0	-9.2	-20.7 ± 3.0
	-16.4 ± 2.2[a]	-5.9	-22.3 ± 2.2
	-13.8 ± 1.3	-5.3	-19.1 ± 1.3
	-11.9 ± 2.1[a]	-8.0	-19.9 ± 2.1
	-8.7 ± 2.0[a]	-10.5	-19.2 ± 2.0
Feb. 23, 10 p.m.	-10.5 ± 2.0	-10.6	-21.0 ± 2.0
			Weighted average = -19.7 ± 0.8
	Source at top		
Feb. 24, 0 a.m.	-12.0 ± 4.1	-8.6	-20.6 ± 4.1
	-5.7 ± 1.4	-9.6	-15.3 ± 1.4
	-7.4 ± 2.1[a]	-7.4	-14.8 ± 2.1
	-6.5 ± 2.1[a]	-5.8	-12.3 ± 2.1
	-13.9 ± 3.1[a]	-7.5	-21.4 ± 3.1
	-6.6 ± 3.0	-5.7	-12.3 ± 3.0
Feb. 25, 6 p.m.	-6.5 ± 2.0[a]	-8.9	-15.4 ± 2.0
	-10.0 ± 2.6	-7.9	-17.9 ± 2.6
			Weighted average = -15.5 ± 0.8
			Mean shift = -17.6 ± 0.6
			Difference of averages = -4.2 ± 1.1

[a]These data were taken simultaneously with a sensitivity calibration.

Table II. Data on asymmetries of various absorbers in apparent fractional frequency shift multiplied by 10^{15}. In the third column we tabulate the Debye temperature increase of the absorber above that of the source which could account for the shift.

Absorber	$(\Delta\nu/\nu)\times 10^{15}$	$\Delta\theta_D$ in °K
No. 1	-8.4 ± 2.5	+15 ± 4
No. 2	-24 ± 3.5	+41 ± 6
No. 3	-28 ± 3.5	+48 ± 6
No. 4	-19 ± 3.5	+33 ± 6
No. 5	-24 ± 3.5	+41 ± 6
No. 6	-17 ± 2.5	+29 ± 4
No. 7	-19 ± 3.5	+33 ± 6
Weighted mean of No. 1-No. 7	-19 ± 3.0	+33 ± 5
Monitor absorber	+0.55 ± 0.15	-0.95 ± 0.26
Armco foil	+10 ± 3.5	-17 ± 6

as large as the whole effect observed. Their additional experiment at the shortened height difference of three meters does not, without concomitant temperature data, resolve the question of inherent frequency difference. Their stated disappointment with the over-all line width observed would seem to add to the probability of existence of such a shift. They mention this broadening in connection with its possible influence on the sensitivity, derived rather than measured, owing to a departure from Lorentzian shape. Clearly such a departure is even more important in allowing asymmetry.

Our experience shows that no conclusion can be drawn from the experiment of Cranshaw et al.

If the frequency-shift inherent in our source-absorber combination is not affected by inversion of the relative positions, the difference between shifts observed with rising and falling γ rays measures the effect of gravity. All data collected since recognizing the need for temperature correction, yield a net fractional shift, $-(5.13 \pm 0.51) \times 10^{-15}$. The error assigned is the rms statistical deviation including that of independent sensitivity calibrations taken as representative of their respective periods of operation. The shift observed agrees with -4.92×10^{-15}, the predicted gravitational shift for this "two-way" height difference.

VOLUME 4, NUMBER 7 PHYSICAL REVIEW LETTERS APRIL 1, 1960

Expressed in this unit, the result is

$$(\Delta\nu)_{\rm exp}/(\Delta\nu)_{\rm theor} = +1.05 \pm 0.10,$$

where the plus sign indicates that the frequency increases in falling, as expected.

These data were collected in about 10 days of operation. We expect to continue counting with some improvements in sensitivity, and to reduce the statistical uncertainty about fourfold. With our present experimental arrangement this should result in a comparable reduction in error in the measurement since we believe we can take adequate steps to avoid systematic errors on the resulting scale. A higher baseline or possibly a narrower γ ray would seem to be required to extend the precision by a factor much larger than this.

We wish to express deep appreciation for the generosity, encouragement, and assistance with details of the experiment accorded us by our colleagues and the entire technical staff of these laboratories during the three months we have been preoccupied with it.

---

*Supported in part by the joint program of the Office of Naval Research and the U. S. Atomic Energy Commission and by a grant from the Higgins Scientific Trust.

[1]R. V. Pound and G. A. Rebka, Jr., Phys. Rev. Letters 3, 439 (1959).

[2]A. Einstein, Ann. Physik 35, 898 (1911).

[3]R. L. Mössbauer, Z. Physik 151, 124 (1958); Naturwissenschaften 45, 538 (1958); Z. Naturforsch. 14a, 211 (1959).

[4]R. V. Pound and G. A. Rebka, Jr., Phys. Rev. Letters 3, 554 (1959).

[5]R. V. Pound and G. A. Rebka, Jr., Phys. Rev. Letters 4, 274 (1960).

[6]We wish to thank Mr. F. Rosebury of the Research Laboratory of Electronics, Massachusetts Institute of Technology, for providing his facilities for this treatment.

[7]See E. H. Hall, Phys. Rev. 17, 245 (1903), first paragraph.

[8]T. E. Cranshaw, J. P. Schiffer, and A. B. Whitehead, Phys. Rev. Letters 4, 163 (1960).

VOLUME 4, NUMBER 4 PHYSICAL REVIEW LETTERS FEBRUARY 15, 1960

MEASUREMENT OF THE RED SHIFT IN AN ACCELERATED SYSTEM USING THE MÖSSBAUER EFFECT IN Fe^{57}

H. J. Hay, J. P. Schiffer,* T. E. Cranshaw, and P. A. Egelstaff
Atomic Energy Research Establishment, Harwell, England
(Received January 27, 1960)

In an adjoining paper[1] an experiment is described in which the change of frequency in a photon passing between two points of different gravitational potential has been measured. Einstein's principle of equivalence states that a gravitational field is locally indistinguishable from an accelerated system. It therefore seemed desirable to measure the shift in the energy of 14-kev gamma rays from Fe^{57} in an accelerated system. In order to do this we have plated a Co^{57} source on to the surface of a 0.8-cm diameter iron cylinder. This cylinder was rigidly mounted between two Dural plates which also held a cylindrical shell of Lucite, 13.28 cm in diameter and 0.31 cm thick, concentric with the iron cylinder. An iron foil 3.5 mg/cm^2 thick and enriched in Fe^{57} to 50% was glued to the inside surface of the Lucite. This assembly was mounted in a neutron chopper drive unit[2] and rotated at angular velocities up to 500 cycles per second. The gamma rays passing through the absorber were detected in a xenon-filled proportional counter. A schematic diagram of the apparatus is shown in Fig. 1.

The expected shift can be calculated in two ways. One can treat the acceleration as an effective gravitational field and calculate the difference in potential between the source and absorber, or one can obtain the same answer using the time dilatation of special relativity. The expected fractional shift in the energy of the gamma ray is $(R_1^2 - R_2^2)\omega^2/2c^2 = 2.44 \times 10^{-20}\omega^2$.

The number of gamma rays as a function of angular velocity is shown in Fig. 2. In a separate measurement the counting rate as a function of radial velocity was determined for this same source and absorber. It was found that with the source moving rapidly the counting rate was 1.29 times what it was with the source stationary. The measured full width of the resonance was 0.38 mm/sec. The curve calculated from these parameters is also shown in Fig. 2. The sensitivity of the equipment to vibrations was tested by vibrating the shaft of the rotor with frequencies corresponding to the rotational frequencies involved, and negligible effect was observed. Changes in counting rate due to forces on the absorber were also found to be negligible.

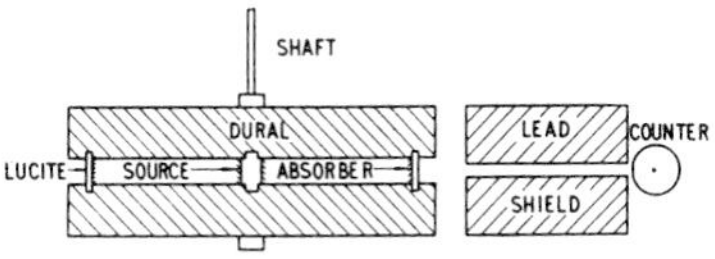

FIG. 1. Schematic diagram of the experimental equipment.

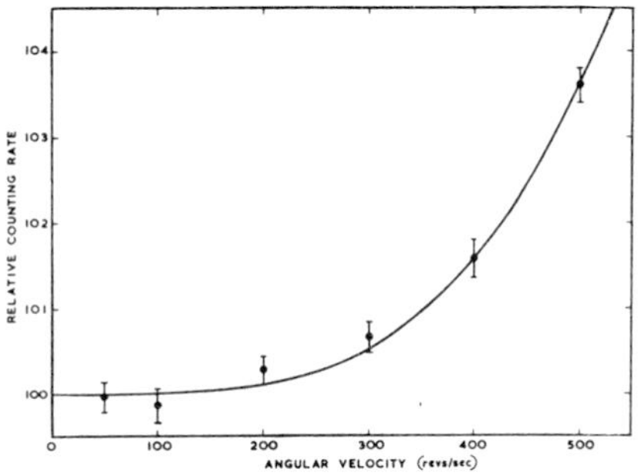

FIG. 2. Comparison of the calculated curve with experimental points. The statistical errors of each point are indicated. The curve was calculated from the parameters given in the text.

It appears that the observed effect is in reasonable agreement with expectations. The size of the shift of the gamma-ray energy in the effective gravitational field of a rotating system is in agreement with that due to the terrestrial gravitational field, within the accuracy of the measurements. The present experiment is expected to be improved when a more pure source is available for reasons stated in the previous paper. It will also be necessary to study further the factors which could influence the absorption process, including changes in the magnetic hyperfine fields due to the high velocities.

We would like to acknowledge helpful and illuminating discussions with Dr. J. S. Bell, Dr. W. Marshall, and Dr. T. Skyrme. We would also like to thank Dr. E. Bretscher for his support and encouragement.

*John Simon Guggenheim fellow, on leave from

Argonne National Laboratory, Lemont, Illinois.

[1]T. E. Cranshaw, J. P. Schiffer, and A. B. Whitehead, preceding Letter [Phys. Rev. Letters 4, 163 (1960)].

[2]Egelstaff, Hay, Holt, Raffle, and Pickles, J. Inst. Elec. Engrs. (London) (to be published).

Absence of Doppler Shift for Gamma Ray Source and Detector on Same Circular Orbit

By D. C. CHAMPENEY and P. B. MOON
Department of Physics, University of Birmingham

MS. received 29th August 1960

Abstract. An experiment is described showing that for a source and absorber of ^{57}Fe placed at opposite ends of a rotor the Mössbauer absorption is unaffected by rotation. This is contrary to the situation with the source at the centre when relativistic effects cause a frequency shift between source and absorber.

REPORTING a test of the effect of circular motion on the resonant frequency of the gamma-ray transition in ^{57}Fe, Hay, Schiffer, Cranshaw and Egelstaff (1960) point out that one can treat the acceleration as an effective gravitational field and calculate the frequency shift from the difference of potential between source and absorber, or one can obtain the same answer by using the time dilatation of special relativity.

For their arrangement, with the source at the centre and the absorber at the periphery of the rotating system, the same result also follows from the argument that since source and absorber have relative velocity v ($\ll c$) in a direction perpendicular to the line joining them, there exists a transverse Doppler effect giving a fractional frequency shift $v^2/2c^2$.

It is perhaps surprising that the naïve use of this formula, without any account being taken of acceleration, should give the correct answer; an indication of the subtleties that may be involved is obtained by considering source and absorber to move on the same circle, e.g. at opposite points on the periphery. Their pseudo-gravitational potentials are equal, so are their time-dilatations, yet their relative velocity is $2v$.

We are indebted to several of our colleagues for interesting comments on this problem, involving such matters as Coriolis forces on photons and the difference between the lines-of-flight of photons and the line joining instantaneous positions of source and absorber.

Since in this laboratory we were undertaking a 'source at centre' experiment similar to that of Hay *et al.*, we decided also to make an experimental test of the 'peripherally opposite' arrangement. A null result, besides confirming the consensus of theoretical opinion, would give an important check on the absence of Doppler effect due to mechanical vibration of the rotor.

The source of ^{57}Co in a matrix of ^{56}Fe, was in the form of a slightly convex foil F, 0·001 in. thick, hard-soldered to a short thin steel cylinder C which fitted inside the tubular steel rotor (Fig. 1) against the rim R; the absorber was a similar foil of natural iron (2% ^{57}Fe) in the other tip of the rotor. This assembly was spun within an evacuated glass vessel provided with a thin window, behind which was a proportional counter for the 14 kev gamma radiation (Fig. 2). Two standard speeds were chosen: 100 rev/sec and 600 rev/sec and in separate experiments two different methods were used to restrict the counting of gamma rays to those few degrees of the rotor's azimuthal position within which the counter could 'see' the source through the absorber.

In the first method, the counts were displayed on the screen of a 100-channel kicksorter by a device that caused each gamma ray to deliver to the kicksorter an impulse proportional to the azimuth of the rotor at the instant in question; the counts in the four channels corresponding most nearly to the 'seeing' position were totalled. A typical record is shown in Fig. 3.

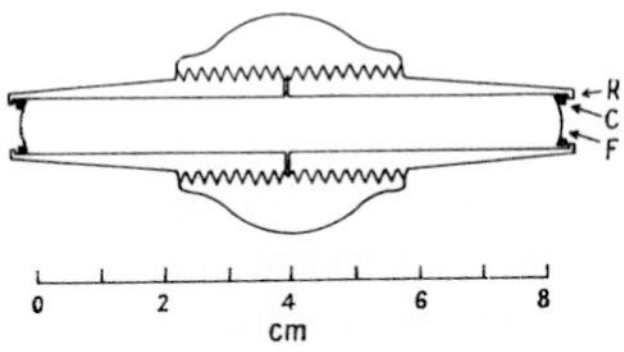

Fig. 1. Diagram of the rotor.

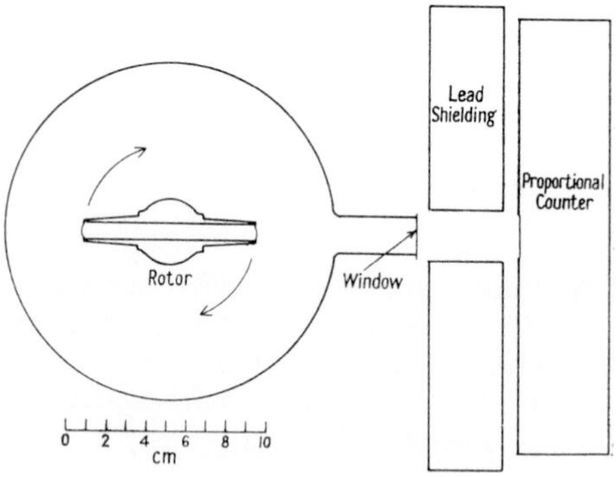

Fig. 2. Plan of the rotor, vacuum vessel, shielding and counter.

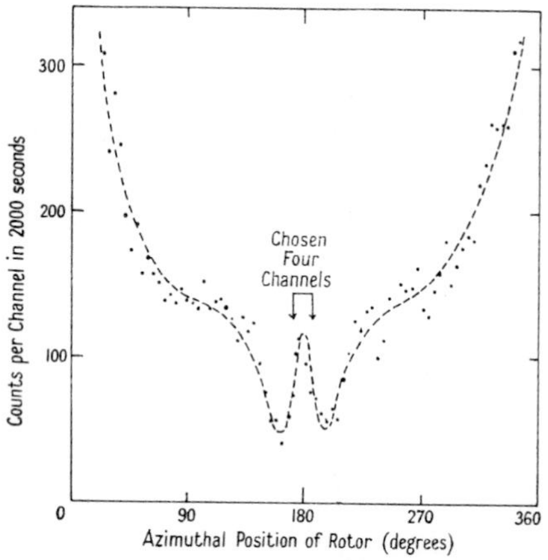

Fig. 3. Plot of typical kicksorter record. The channel number is expressed in terms of the angular position of the rotor.

In the second method, the successive interception of two light beams by one arm of the rotor opened and closed an electronic gate; a scale-of-two device prevented the gate from responding to the other arm of the rotor.

After subtraction of background (measured by placing $\frac{1}{8}$ in. aluminium over the window) the events recorded at 600 rev/sec were found by the first method to be $(0{\cdot}4 \pm 3)\%$ less and by the second method to be $(2{\cdot}0 \pm 2{\cdot}5)\%$ more than those at 100 rev/sec; combining these two results we obtain $(+0{\cdot}8 \pm 2{\cdot}0)\%$.

The width of the resonance was measured for the actual source and absorber by the method described by Cordey-Hayes, Dyson and Moon (1960); it was thence calculated that a fractional shift $\frac{1}{2}(2v)^2/c^2$ would have given a 9·4% higher counting rate at the higher speed. In comparison with this figure, our result with its associated probable error may be taken as satisfactory evidence in favour of a null result.

As an incidental check that the null result was not due to instrumental deficiencies, an experiment with the source at the centre gave an increase in counting rate of $(7{\cdot}1 \pm 1{\cdot}7)\%$ at 900 rev/sec in agreement with an expected increase of 5·4%.

References

Cordey-Hayes, M., Dyson, N. A., and Moon, P. B., 1960, *Proc. Phys. Soc.*, **75**, 810.

Hay, H. J., Schiffer, J. P., Cranshaw, T. E., and Egelstaff, P. A., 1960, *Phys. Rev. Letters*, **4**, 165.

Ruderfer, M., 1960, *Phys. Rev. Letters*, **5**, 191.

Note added in proof.—It may be pointed out that the experiment is equivalent to that proposed by Ruderfer (1960) to test for the effects of other drift. No special care was taken to obtain readings in more than one direction, but when our results are interpreted according to Ruderfer's ideas they indicate an average value for $v \sin \theta$, over the six days of experimentation, of 17 ± 43 m sec^{-1}, where v is the magnitude of the component of the ether drift velocity in the plane of rotation of the rotor and θ is the angle between this component and the counting axis.

VOLUME 4, NUMBER 6 PHYSICAL REVIEW LETTERS MARCH 15, 1960

VARIATION WITH TEMPERATURE OF THE ENERGY OF RECOIL-FREE GAMMA RAYS FROM SOLIDS*

R. V. Pound and G. A. Rebka, Jr.
Harvard University, Cambridge, Massachusetts
(Received February 17, 1960)

The 14.4-kev γ ray emitted without recoil by 0.1-μsec Fe^{57} in metallic iron[1-4] excited great interest as the most precisely defined electromagnetic frequency yet discovered. It may be adequately well defined to allow measurement of the influence of a gravitational potential on frequency[5] and of other small effects hitherto beyond the sensitivity available in the laboratory. As a preliminary step in the operation of an experimental system designed to measure the gravitational effect, we have been making tests to find out whether other influences than the one intended might lead to systematic errors by introducing important frequency shifts not taken into account.

So far the largest such effect found is that of temperature. That temperature should influence the frequency exactly as we observe is very simply explained. Thermally excited vibrations cause little broadening through first order Doppler effect under the conditions obtaining in the solid because the value of any component of the nuclear velocity averages very nearly to zero over the nuclear lifetime. The precision of the γ ray of Fe^{57} requires the second order Doppler effect also to be considered. A shift to lower frequency with increased temperature results from this because the also well-defined average of the square of the velocity of the particle increases in direct proportion to the average kinetic energy. As a consequence one would expect a temperature coefficient of frequency in a homogeneous solid,

$$(\partial\nu/\partial T) = -\nu C_L/2Mc^2,$$

where C_L is the specific heat of the lattice and M is the gram atomic weight of iron. In the high-temperature classical limit where $C_L = 3R$,

$$(\partial\nu/\partial T)_{T\to\infty} = -2.44\times10^{-15}\nu \text{ per }^\circ\text{K}.$$

At lower temperatures one would expect a coefficient reduced by the value of the appropriate normalized Debye specific heat function. For iron, at 300°K one should find about 0.9 times, and at 80°K about 0.3 times, the above classical value.

The temperature dependence has been measured by counting the γ rays from our 0.4-curie Co^{57} source transmitted through enriched Fe^{57} absorbing films (0.6 mg Fe^{57}/cm^2). The Co^{57} of the source is distributed in about 3×10^{-5} cm thickness below the surface of a 2-in. diameter iron disk, made in the manner described earlier.[1] Small frequency shifts that result when the source and absorber are held at different temperatures were measured by using a transducer to move the source sinusoidally at ten cps toward and away from the absorber at a peak speed of about 0.01 cm/sec. A gate pulse and mercury relays were used to make one counter record during 25 milliseconds of the modulation period symmetrically disposed about the time of maximum velocity toward the absorber. Another counter recorded the corresponding counts with the source going away from the absorber. The difference of the counts in the two registers should be proportional to the relative frequency shift of the absorber and source for shifts small compared to the line width. Quantitative knowledge of the parameters of the system that are involved in determining the constant of proportionality is rendered unnecessary by adding through a clock-driven hydraulic system a continuous relative motion of 6.3×10^{-4} cm/sec directed oppositely during each of the two halves of the time for a given datum point. In this way the sensitivity to frequency shift originating in the Doppler effect is measured simultaneously with the shift sought. The algebraic sum of the counting rate differences for the two halves of the run are proportional to the shift and the difference to the sensitivity.

The shift at liquid nitrogen relative to room temperature is comparable to the line width and for that point the two counting rates were recorded at a series of values of the sinusoidal modulation amplitude. From these a value of the shift and of the apparent line width could be obtained although difficulties of calibration under the conditions of operation have contributed strongly to the uncertainties. There is evidence that the line appears to broaden with such a temperature difference by perhaps a factor of 2.3 which might be evidence that the hyperfine structure splittings are temperature sensitive to some extent, as must be expected.

The data are plotted in Fig. 1. A solid line representing the effect expected with a Debye temperature of 420°K is also drawn. The agreement can be regarded as an experimental demonstration of the second order Doppler effect using thermal velocities rather than a centrifuge. It might be remarked that crystalline anisotropy might make this source of high velocities useful for experiments to the end of detecting such spatial anisotropies as might accompany ether drift or an inertial frame.

The temperature sensitivity at room temperature [experimentally $(-2.09\pm0.24)\times10^{-15}$ per degree C, theoretically -2.21×10^{-15} per degree C] is highly relevant to the interpretation of data

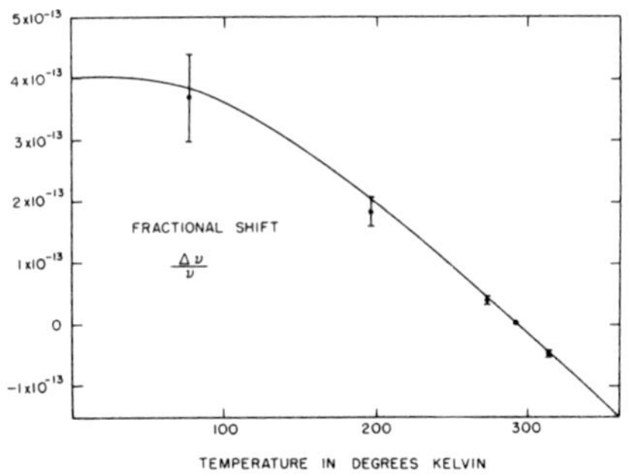

FIG. 1. Fractional shift of energy of 14.4-kev gamma-ray absorption of Fe^{57} vs absolute temperature of the metal. The solid line is derived from assuming a Debye temperature of 420°K.

from our experiment on the effect of gravitational potential. A temperature difference of 1°C between the top and the bottom of our 22-meter tower would result in a shift about equal to that predicted by the principle of equivalence. For smaller height differences correspondingly smaller temperature differences would be required. It is now clear that correction for or control of the temperature difference and perhaps other parameters must be included in the instrumentation of experiments intending to utilize the extreme frequency discrimination available with gamma rays of this type.

*Supported in part by the joint program of the Office of Naval Research and the U. S. Atomic Energy Commission.

[1]R. V. Pound and G. A. Rebka, Jr., Phys. Rev. Letters 3, 554 (1959).

[2]J. P. Schiffer and W. Marshall, Phys. Rev. Letters 3, 556 (1959).

[3]S. S. Hanna, J. Heberle, C. Littlejohn, G. J. Perlow, R. S. Preston, and D. H. Vincent, Phys. Rev. Letters 4, 28 (1960).

[4]G. DePasquali, H. Frauenfelder, S. Margulies, and R. N. Peacock, Phys. Rev. Letters 4, 71 (1960).

[5]R. V. Pound and G. A. Rebka, Jr., Phys. Rev. Letters 3, 439 (1959).

TEMPERATURE-DEPENDENT SHIFT OF γ RAYS EMITTED BY A SOLID

B. D. Josephson
Trinity College, Cambridge, England
(Received March 11, 1960)

Recent experiments by Mössbauer[1] have shown that when low-energy γ rays are emitted from nuclei in a solid a certain proportion of them are unaffected by the Doppler effect. It is the purpose of this Letter to show that they are nevertheless subject to a temperature-dependent shift to lower energy which can be attributed to the relativistic time dilatation caused by the motion of the nuclei.

Let us regard the solid as a system of interacting atoms with the Hamiltonian

$$H = \sum p_i^2/2m_i + V(r_1, r_2, \cdots).$$

The Mössbauer effect is due to those processes in which the phonon occupation numbers do not change. It might appear that in such cases the energy of the solid is unaltered, but this is not so, as the nucleus which emits the γ ray changes its mass, and this affects the lattice vibrations. Suppose the nucleus of the ith atom emits a γ ray of energy E, its mass changing by $\delta m_i = -E/c^2$.

The change in energy, δE, of the solid is given by

$$\delta E = \langle \Delta H \rangle = \delta \langle p_i^2/2m_i \rangle = -\delta m_i \langle p_i^2/2m_i^2 \rangle$$
$$= (\delta m_i/m_i)T_i = (E/m_i c^2)T_i,$$

where T_i is the expectation value of the kinetic energy of the ith atom. The energy of the γ ray must accordingly be reduced by δE so there is a shift of relative magnitude $\delta E/E = T_i/m_i c^2$. The same formula can be deduced by regarding the shift as due to a relativistic time dilatation.

To estimate T_i we make the following assumptions: (i) The atoms all have the same mass, and the kinetic energy is equally distributed among them. (ii) The kinetic energy is half the total lattice energy, i.e., we assume that the forces coupling the atoms are harmonic. Under these assumptions $T_i/m_i = \frac{1}{2}U$, where U is the lattice energy per unit mass. The relative shift is thus given by $\delta E/E = U/2c^2$. For Fe at 300°K this has the value 8×10^{-13}. Clearly a compensating shift would occur for absorption provided source and absorber were identical and at the same temperature. A small difference in temperature between source and absorber leads to a relative shift per degree given by $\delta E/E = C_p/2c^2$ where C_p is the specific heat. For Fe at 300°K this is 2.2×10^{-15}/°K. This is sufficient for it to be necessary to take it into account in accurate experiments using the resonance absorption of γ rays, such as those to measure the gravitational red shift.[2,3]

I would like to thank Dr. Ziman, Professor O. R. Frisch, and Dr. W. Marshall for helpful discussions.

[1]R. L. Mössbauer, Z. Physik 151, 124 (1958).
[2]R. V. Pound and G. A. Rebka, Phys. Rev. Letters 3, 554 (1959).
[3]T. E. Cranshaw, J. P. Schiffer, and A. B. Whitehead, Phys. Rev. Letters 4, 163 (1960).

ACOUSTICALLY MODULATED γ RAYS FROM Fe^{57}

S. L. Ruby and D. I. Bolef
Westinghouse Electric Corporation, Pittsburgh, Pennsylvania
(Received June 13, 1960)

The relationship between the emission of γ rays by nuclei bound in a crystal and the creation (or destruction) of phonons has been discussed by Visscher,[1] and suggests that a careful study of the "off-resonance" line shape in a Mössbauer-type experiment may be used to observe the frequency distribution of lattice vibrations in the crystal. Unfortunately, a direct attempt at such a study seems difficult since it requires the measurement of nuclear γ-ray absorption cross sections much smaller than the photoelectric cross sections for the same atom. In an attempt to investigate the interactions between phonons and emitting nuclei, therefore, it was decided to generate low-energy phonons acoustically, and to study their effect on the γ-ray spectrum.

Source and absorber were one-mil thick 321 stainless steel (18% chromium, 8% nickel) foils. The source, into which had been diffused Co^{57}, could be driven by either or both of two methods: (1) a low-frequency (15 cps) drive utilizing a loud speaker, and (2) a piezoelectric quartz crystal drive mounted on the rear of the source foil. The quartz crystal is driven by a radiofrequency oscillator whose frequency and amplitude are continuously adjustable. The counting rate for the 14.4-kev γ ray, as a function of loudspeaker velocity, is measured by using the output of a single-channel analyzer to "command" a multichannel analyzer to measure the velocity at a particular instant. This is accomplished by feeding the amplified output of the velocity pickup coil (rigidly attached to the source) to the appropriate place in the analog-to-digital converter section of the analyzer.

The experiment was planned on the assumption that the density of ultrasonic phonons in a narrow frequency band could be markedly increased over that corresponding to 300°K, and that this should lead to pairs of satellite peaks, symmetrically located relative to the main Mössbauer peak, with a spacing in energy units of $\Delta E = \hbar q$ or, in velocity units, $v_s = (c/E_0)\Delta E$. ($q/2\pi$ = ultrasonic frequency, $E_0 = 14.4$ kev.) This corresponds to the creation or destruction of acoustic phonons with the emission of the γ ray. A similar discrete Doppler effect has been observed in optical light diffracted by acoustic "gratings." The optical effect is extremely small, of the order of 10^{-4} A for an optical wavelength of 5460 A and an ultrasonic frequency of 10 Mc/sec. The effect has been observed for both traveling and stationary sound waves.[2] A theory of this optical effect has been given by Raman and Nagendra Nath.[3]

Since the source foil is thin (approximately one-tenth the wavelength of sound at 20 Mc/sec), one can alternatively consider the quartz transducer as simply vibrating the foil with a sinusoidal velocity, $v_s = v_m \cos qt$. This corresponds merely to a sinusoidal motion of the center of mass of the foil. The "instantaneous" frequency of the 14.4-kev γ ray may therefore be expressed as

$$\nu = \nu_0 + \Delta\nu \sin qt, \qquad (1)$$

where

$$\nu_0 = E_0/h = 3.48 \times 10^{18} \text{ cycles/sec},$$

and the maximum frequency deviation is $\Delta\nu = \nu_0(v_m/c)$. Expressed in the language of frequency modulation, this corresponds to a carrier of frequency ν_0, modulated sinusoidally at a frequency $q/2\pi$. The modulation index is $m = (v_m/c) \times (2\pi\nu_0/q)$. The frequency spectrum can be shown[4] to consist of the carrier and an infinite set of side-bands, with the nth side frequency separated from the $(n+1)$th side frequency by the modulating frequency, $q/2\pi$. The maximum amplitude of the nth side frequency is given by $J_n^2(m)$, where $J_n(m)$ is the Bessel function of the first kind of order n.

In Fig. 1 the solid lines in curves a-e show the result of calculations for five values of m, with $q/2\pi = 20$ Mc/sec. The vertical scale of the drawing is based on curve a. Also shown in the figure are the experimental results, using a 20-Mc/sec

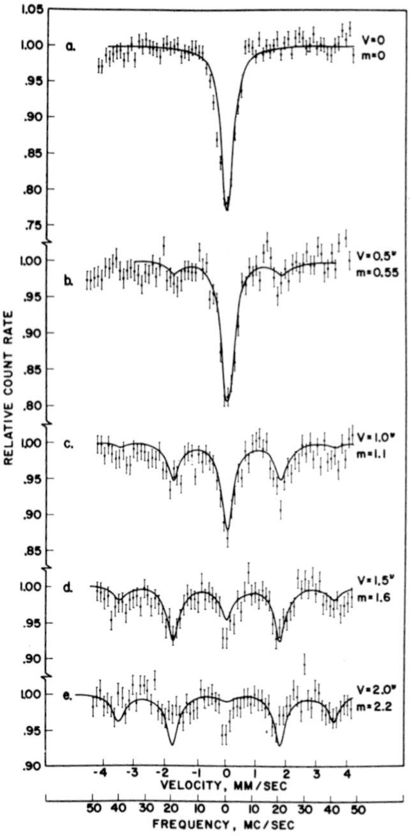

FIG. 1. Mössbauer pattern for Fe^{57} γ ray emitted by a stainless steel source driven by a 20-Mc/sec x-cut quartz transducer. The experimental points are shown in a-e for values of the driving voltage, V, from 0 to 2.0 volts rms. The solid curves are calculated on the basis of FM theory, using a single proportionality constant between m and V_{rms} which best fits the data.

x-cut quartz transducer, taken at five different transducer driving voltages. The maximum velocity of the iron atoms resulting from the ultrasonic vibration has not been measured directly, but is expected to be proportional to the driving voltage; the proportionality constant has been chosen so as to fit the solid curves as well as possible to the experimental points. Using $m = 1.1\, V_{rms}$, one finds $v_m = 0.29$ cm/sec for $1.5\, V_{rms}$ across the transducer. This value for v_m is consistent with the value calculated from the piezoelectric properties of the quartz transducer. The velocity at 20 Mc/sec corresponds to the rather small maximum displacement of approximately 2×10^{-9} cm.

The progressive disagreement between the calculated and experimental curves with higher drive voltage, especially near the carrier frequency, suggests that all of the iron atoms did not have the same velocities. A new source foil was then prepared, care being taken to preserve flatness of the foil and uniformity of the acoustic bond. In Fig. 2, a plot of the amplitude of the carrier (unshifted γ ray) vs the 20-Mc/sec driving voltage is given, together with a plot of $[1 - 0.24 J_0^2(m)]$ with $m = 0.6\, V_{rms}$. The calculated curve assumes that all the Fe^{57} atoms have the same maximum velocity v_m. The pattern using the new foil, however, still suggests a continuous range of velocities with perhaps 50% of the Fe^{57} nuclei moving considerably more slowly than the remainder. Such an effect could be caused by bonding defects, such as air bubbles trapped in the cement between foil and quartz. Velocity blurring also results from the fact that the thickness of the foil is not negligible compared to the wavelength of the sound waves.

Since the energy shift of the γ ray is determined solely by the frequency of the ultrasonic drive, this discrete Doppler technique offers a precise method for adding or subtracting known quantities of energy to the γ ray. This may be useful in providing a monochromatic calibration of energy or velocity in the measurement of line splittings (such as Fe^{57} in iron) or line shifting

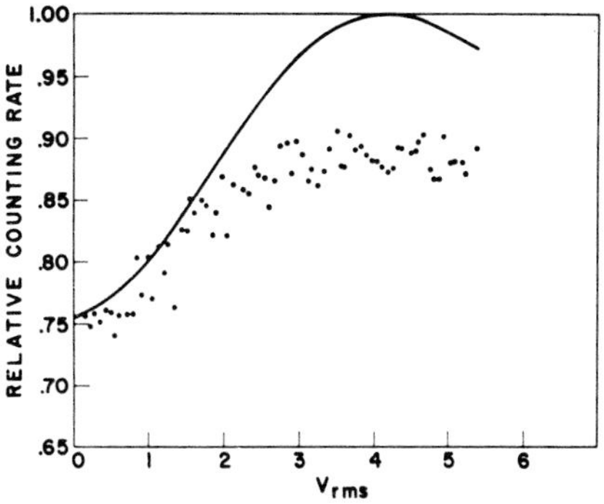

FIG. 2. Relative intensity of carrier (unshifted γ ray) vs voltage on quartz transducer. The solid line represents the theoretically predicted function $[1 - 0.24 J_0^2(m)]$, where $m = 0.6\, V_{rms}$ for this case. This prediction assumes that all the Fe^{57} atoms have the same maximum velocity v_m.

(such as temperature shifts of the Mössbauer peak due to zero-point vibration). This method for Doppler shifting may also be applicable at low temperatures when more conventional drives are inconvenient to use. For this purpose, broadbanding of the transducer frequency response will be desirable.

We wish to thank Dr. L. Epstein for help in the preparation of the source, Mr. John Hicks for his careful and ingenious help throughout the experiment, and Dr. Meir Menes, who first suggested the FM approach.

[1]W. M. Visscher, Ann. Phys. 9, 194 (1960).

[2]For a review of this work see L. Bergmann, Ultrasonics (John Wiley & Sons, New York, 1951), pp. 66 ff.

[3]C. V. Raman and N. S. Nagendra Nath, Proc. Indian Acad. Sci. (A)2, 406, 413 (1935); and (A)3, 75 (1936).

[4]S. Goldman, Frequency Analysis, Modulation and Noise (McGraw-Hill Book Company, New York, 1948).

PHYSICAL REVIEW VOLUME 124, NUMBER 3 NOVEMBER 1, 1961

Measurement of the Refractive Index of Lucite by Recoilless Resonance Absorption*

L. GRODZINS AND E. A. PHILLIPS
Laboratory for Nuclear Science, Massachusetts Institute of Technology, Cambridge, Massachusetts
(Received June 20, 1961)

A method of frequency-modulating a monochromatic electromagnetic wave by varying the optical path length between the source and detector is described. The method has been applied to the measurement of the refractive index of Lucite for the 0.86 A radiation emitted from Co^{57}; the small frequency shift was detected by recoilless resonance absorption. The refractive index was found to be $1-n=(1.29\pm0.03)\times10^{-6}$, in agreement with classical theory.

THIS paper describes a method of frequency-modulating a monochromatic electromagnetic wave by varying the optical path length between the source and detector. The method has been applied to, and is described in terms of, the measurement of the refractive index of Lucite for the 14.4-kev radiation emitted from Co^{57}. The measured refractive index agrees, within the 2% experimental uncertainty, with the simple theory applicable when the radiation energy is much greater than the binding energy of the electrons in the refractive medium, as in this case. The technique is in principle applicable to the nearly monochromatic radiation emitted from optical-frequency masers.

It is instructive to consider the method from two points of view, first in terms of frequency modulation and then in terms of a Doppler shift. Consider a source S and an observer (in our case a recoilless resonance absorber) A separated by a distance x [Fig. 1(a)]. A wave of angular frequency ω emitted by S will have the form $e^{i\omega(t-x/c)}$ at A. If a length L of material with refractive index n is placed in the optical path, the wave becomes $e^{i\omega(t-x/c)+i\phi}$, where the phase advance

$$\phi=(1-n)\omega L/c. \qquad (1)$$

If ϕ changes with time, the instantaneous frequency seen by A will be $(\omega+d\phi/dt)$. This is done by moving a wedge-shaped piece of material to produce a frequency shift

$$\frac{1}{2\pi}\frac{d\phi}{dt}=\Delta\nu=\nu\frac{(1-n)}{c}\frac{dL}{dt}. \qquad (2)$$

An equivalent point of view considers the radiation as being Doppler-shifted during the refraction by the moving wedge [Fig. 1(b)]. As it leaves the wedge the radiation is deflected (toward the normal, since $n<1$) by an angle

$$\Delta\theta=(1-n)\tan\alpha.$$

The change in momentum of the photon is $\Delta p=p\Delta\theta$, and since the wedge is moving at a speed V it does work on the photon, increasing its energy by

$$\Delta E=V\Delta p=Vp(1-n)\tan\alpha=E[(1-n)/c]V\tan\alpha,$$

which is equivalent to Eq. (2) above.

For 14.4-kev radiation, the refractive index of Lucite is (see below)

$$(1-n)=1.29\times10^{-6},$$

so that

$$(\Delta\nu/\nu)_{14\text{ kev}}=4\times10^{-17}dL/dt.$$

The frequency shift thus obtained for reasonable values of dL/dt can be detected by recoilless resonance scattering.[1]

A schematic drawing of the experimental arrangement is shown in Fig. 2(a). The recoilless resonance

* This work is supported in part through a U. S. Atomic Energy Commission contract, by funds provided by the U. S. Atomic Energy Commission, the Office of Naval Research, and the Air Force Office of Scientific Research.

[1] R. L. Mössbauer, Z. Physik 151, 124 (1958); R. V. Pound and G. A. Rebka, Jr., Phys. Rev. Letters 4, 337 (1960).

apparatus has been described previously.[2] The 14.4-kev gamma rays from a Co^{57} source diffused into Armco iron passed through a rotating wheel, shown in profile in Fig. 2(b), then through a movable 0.5-mil Armco Fe absorber to the Be-window NaI(Tl) detector.

To construct the wheel, 12-in. diam. pieces of $\frac{1}{16}$-in. brass and $\frac{1}{4}$-in. Lucite were clamped together and 120 radial slots $\frac{1}{16}$ in. wide were cut through both at an angle of 60°. Since the gamma rays are stopped by the brass, they are allowed to pass through only one side of each Lucite tooth. As the wheel rotates, every gamma ray which passes through it does so when the thickness of Lucite in the tooth is changing in the same direction. Thus all the gamma rays detected undergo a frequency shift of the same direction and magnitude.

The absorption line profiles for four wheel speeds are shown in Fig. 3. The shift in the line position is evident. The high-speed runs, 1500 rpm clockwise and counterclockwise, show a broader line which we attribute to vibration transmitted through the air from the rotating wheel to the source and absorber. This effect diminished rapidly with decrease of angular speed and no attempt was made to alleviate it. At speeds below 1000 rpm, line broadening resulted in an error of less than 2% in the determination of the line shift.

The shift in the position of an accurately known line profile is most efficiently determined by measuring the

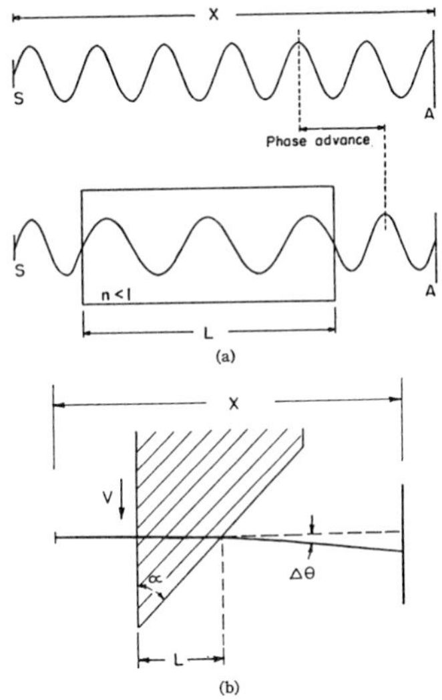

FIG. 1. (a) The phase advance produced by interposition of a length L of refractive material between source S and observer A. (b) The deflection $\Delta\theta$ of the beam when the refractive material of Fig. 1(a) is wedge-shaped.

[2] L. Grodzins and F. Genovese, Phys. Rev. **121**, 228 (1961).

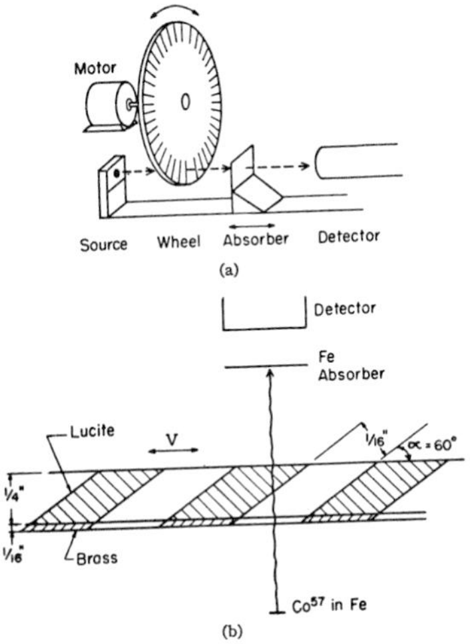

FIG. 2. (a) Schematic diagram of experimental arrangement. (b) Detail of the slotted wheel; not to scale.

change in counting rate at the maximum slope points of the absorption line profile, 0.013 cm/sec in this case. The counting rates for absorber speeds towards and away from the source were separately recorded for each of a set of speeds of the Lucite wheel; the resulting line shift as a function of wheel speed is shown in Fig. 4. A least-squares fit of the data (from 4 to 12×10^6 counts per point) between 900 rpm clockwise and 900 rpm counterclockwise yields a slope

$$\frac{\Delta v}{\Delta\omega_{\text{wheel}}}=c\frac{\Delta\nu}{\nu}\frac{1}{\Delta\omega_{\text{wheel}}}=(3.32\pm0.05)\times10^{-6}\frac{\text{cm/sec}}{\text{rpm}},\quad(3)$$

where $\Delta\nu/\nu$ is the relative frequency shift.

The effective radius from the axis of the wheel to the gamma ray path was 14.2 cm so that

$$\frac{(dL/dt)}{\Delta\omega_{\text{wheel}}}=2.58\frac{\text{cm/sec}}{\text{rpm}}.\quad(4)$$

A combination of Eqs. (2)–(4), yields the refractive index:

$$(1-n)=\frac{c(\Delta\nu/\nu)}{(dL/dt)}=\frac{3.32\times10^{-6}}{2.58}=(1.29\pm0.04)\times10^{-6}.$$

The stated error includes uncertainties in the effective radius, the absorption line depth, and the absorber velocity.

This result is in agreement with the theoretical value obtained for the refractive index of a gas in which the binding energy of the electrons is much less than the energy of the radiation. This condition holds for 14.4-kev radiation on Lucite ($C_5H_8O_2$) since E_K(oxygen) $=0.53$ kev. The result is[3]

$$(1-n)=N_0\frac{\rho Z}{2A}\frac{e^2}{m\omega^2\epsilon_0},$$

where the symbols have their conventional meaning; i.e., N_0 is Avogadro's number, ρ is the density, etc. For the case of Lucite and 14.4-kev radiation, Z/A

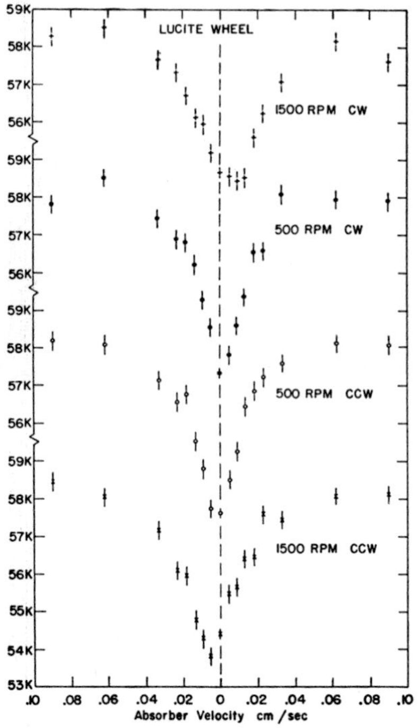

FIG. 3. Absorption line profile versus wheel speed.

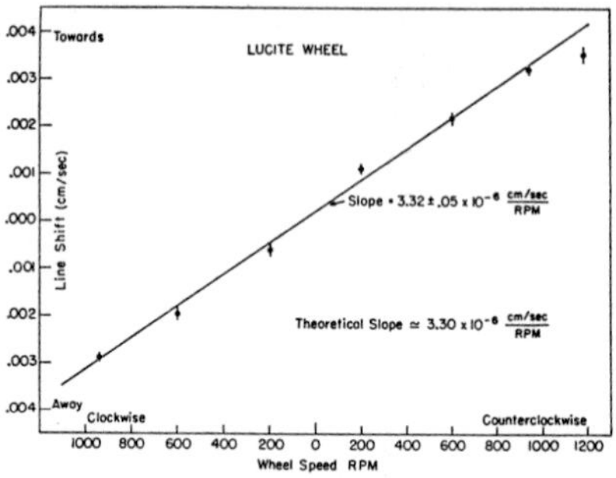

FIG. 4. Reduced data: Line shift versus wheel speed; the theoretical slope contains an uncertainty in the wheel radius. (See text.)

$=0.54$, $\rho=1.185$, and $\omega=2.185\times10^{19}$. Then

$$1-n=1.285\times10^{-6}.$$

The exact theory of the index of refraction, which takes into account the binding energies of the electrons,[4,5] yields a result differing from the above number by about 0.1%.

The measurement of the index of refraction at x-ray wavelengths is, of course, not new.[3] Indeed, Bearden[4] measured the refractive index of diamond at 1.39 A to an accuracy of 1 part in 10^4. The phase modulation technique can, if desirable, be made as accurate for those wavelengths observed by recoilless nuclear gamma emission.

We have shown that the frequency of a nearly monochromatic electromagnetic wave may be shifted by modulating the optical path between source and observer. The application to an optical-frequency maser where $\Delta\nu/\nu\lesssim10^{-9}$ is evident. Since $(1-n)$ is $\sim10^6$ times as large for optical frequencies as for x rays, frequency modulation may be observed by varying either n or L. For example, L may be varied by vibrating a mirror [$1-n=2$ in Eq. (2)] from which the light is reflected. The corresponding experiment for recoilless gamma radiation has been reported by Ruby and Bolef,[6] who acoustically vibrated the source.

[3] F. K. Richtmeyer and E. H. Kennard, *Introduction to Modern Physics* (McGraw-Hill Book Company, New York, 1947), 4th ed., pp. 522–527.

[4] J. A. Bearden, Phys. Rev. **54**, 698 (1938).

[5] J. A. Prins, A. Physik **47**, 479 (1928).

[6] S. L. Ruby and D. I. Bolef, Phys. Rev. Letters **5**, 5 (1960).

Time Dependence of Resonantly Filtered Gamma Rays from Fe^{57}†

F. J. LYNCH, R. E. HOLLAND, AND M. HAMERMESH
Argonne National Laboratory, Argonne, Illinois
(Received June 6, 1960)

The time dependence of gamma rays emitted by the 14.4-kev state of Fe^{57} has been studied by delayed-coincidence measurements between a 123-kev gamma ray preceding formation of the state and the 14.4-kev gamma ray from the state. When no filter was used, the number of gamma rays decreased exponentially with the known half-life of 0.1 μsec. When a foil of Fe^{57} (which was resonant to 14.4-kev radiation) was used as a filter, the number of gamma rays observed through the filter did not decrease exponentially. Instead, the filter absorbed almost none of the gamma rays first emitted by the 14.4-kev state; at later times the absorption increased. Data were taken with three different thicknesses of absorber and with emission and absorption peaks separated by 0 to 11 times the width of the resonance. The energy separation resulted from the Doppler shift associated with a constant velocity between source and absorber. These data were, for the most part, in good accord with the prediction of a theory based on a classical model for absorber and source. In particular, the results verified the theoretical prediction that at certain times the intensity of radiation observed would be greater with the filter than without it.

I. INTRODUCTION

IN an earlier paper,[1] we showed that the intensity of the gamma rays transmitted through an absorber which is resonant to the incident gamma radiation does not decrease exponentially with time. Instead, the transmitted beam appears initially to decay faster than the rate corresponding to the life-time τ of the emitting state. The intuitive picture which led us to undertake the initial experiments was that the resonance absorption tends to reduce the intensity at the center of the emitted line relative to the intensity in the wings. Thus the width at half maximum of the remaining peak is greater than the value $\Gamma=\hbar/\tau$ of the original peak; and the lifetime of the state appears to be correspondingly shorter.

A quantitative theoretical treatment was developed by describing the emitted radiation as a damped electromagnetic wave.[2] On passing through a medium filled with resonators, the frequency spectrum of the radiation is altered, so that its time dependence is no longer exponential. The theoretical analysis, which is presented in Sec. II, suggested some of the experiments which are described in Sec. III.

The 14.4-kev state of Fe^{57} provides a convenient source for observation of this effect. The formation of the 14.4-kev state is announced by a 123-kev gamma ray in the decay[3] of Co^{57}, the Mössbauer effect is large[4] (about 60% of the radiation is emitted without recoil at room temperature), the half-life[3] is 0.1 μsec, and the gamma ray is highly converted[5] ($\alpha=15$) so that imprisonment of the resonance radiation need not be considered.

II. THEORY

The time dependence of the 14-kev radiation of Fe^{57} as observed in transmission through an Fe^{57} absorber can be explained on a simple classical theory. As in standard treatments of emission and dispersion, the medium is assumed to consist of damped oscillators with natural frequency ω_0 and decay constant λ. The radiation emitted by the Fe^{57} source has an electric field

$$a(t)=\exp[i\omega_0 t-\tfrac{1}{2}\lambda t]=\frac{1}{2\pi i}\int_{-\infty}^{+\infty}d\omega\frac{e^{i\omega t}}{\omega-\omega_0-\frac{1}{2}i\lambda}$$
$$=\int_{-\infty}^{+\infty}d\omega\, a(\omega)e^{i\omega t}. \quad (1)$$

The constant λ is just the reciprocal of the mean life of the excited state. In the case of the 14-kev line of Fe^{57}, 93% of the radiation is internally converted; the quantity λ contains contributions from all types of decay (radiation and internal conversion).

The effect of transmission through the Fe^{57} absorber can be found by standard methods.[6] Each monochromatic component $a(\omega)e^{i\omega t}$ excites forced oscillations of the resonators in the medium. The complex dielectric constant is

$$\epsilon(\omega)=1+r(\omega_0'^2-\omega^2+i\omega\lambda)^{-1}. \quad (2)$$

We have written ω_0' for the resonant frequency of the absorber to take account of a possible Doppler shift due to motion relative to the source.

† Work performed under the auspices of the U. S. Atomic Energy Commission.
[1] R. E. Holland, F. J. Lynch, G. J. Perlow, and S. S. Hanna, Phys. Rev. Letters 4, 181 (1960).
[2] M. Hamermesh, Argonne National Laboratory Report ANL-6111, February, 1960 (unpublished), p. 6.
[3] *Nuclear Data Sheets*, National Academy of Sciences, National Research Council, 1959 (U. S. Government Printing Office, Washington, D. C.).
[4] R. L. Mössbauer, Z. Physik **151**, 124 (1958); J. P. Schiffer and W. Marshall, Phys. Rev. Letters **3**, 556 (1959); R. V. Pound and J. A. Rebka, Jr., Phys. Rev. Letters **3**, 554 (1959).
[5] H. R. Lemmer, O. J. A. Segaert, and M. A. Grace, Proc. Phys. Soc. (London) **A68**, 701 (1955).
[6] J. A. Stratton, *Electromagnetic Theory* (McGraw-Hill Book Company, Inc., New York, 1941), p. 321.

From Eq. (2), the propagation vector in the medium is found to be

$$k=(\omega/c)[1+r(\omega_0'^2-\omega^2+i\omega\lambda)^{-1}]^{\frac{1}{2}}. \tag{3}$$

The wavelength of the radiation is about 10^{-8} cm and, as in the x-ray case, we can expand Eq. (3) and retain only the first term. The effect of passage through the absorber is to change $a(\omega)$ to $a'(\omega)$, where

$$a'(\omega)=a(\omega)\exp\{-2ib\omega[\omega_0'^2-\omega^2+i\omega\lambda]^{-1}\}, \tag{4}$$

in which b is a constant.

At $\omega=\omega_0'$, $a'(\omega_0')=a(\omega_0')\exp[-2b/\lambda]$, so the transmission at the center of the line is $\exp[-4b/\lambda]$.

By combining Eqs. (1) and (4), the time dependence of the transmitted amplitude is found to be

$$a'(t)=\frac{1}{2\pi i}\int_{-\infty}^{+\infty} d\omega\frac{e^{i\omega t}}{\omega-\omega_0-\frac{1}{2}i\lambda}\exp\left[\frac{2ib\omega}{\omega^2-\omega_0'^2-i\omega\lambda}\right]. \tag{5}$$

This integral is evaluated in the Appendix with the result expressed as either

$$a'(t)=\exp[i\omega_0't-\tfrac{1}{2}\lambda t]\times\sum_{n=0}^{\infty}\left[\frac{i\{\omega_0-\omega_0'\}}{b}\right]^n(bt)^{\frac{1}{2}n}J_n(2b^{\frac{1}{2}}t^{\frac{1}{2}}), \tag{6a}$$

or

$$a'(t)=\exp\left[i\omega_0't-\frac{\lambda}{2}t\right]\left\{-\exp i\left[\frac{b}{\omega_0-\omega_0'}+(\omega_0-\omega_0')t\right]+\sum_{n=1}^{\infty}\left(\frac{ib}{\omega_0-\omega_0'}\right)^n(bt)^{-n/2}J_n(2b^{\frac{1}{2}}t^{\frac{1}{2}})\right\}. \tag{6b}$$

The time dependence of the transmitted intensity is given by $|a'(t)|^2$. Setting $\omega_0-\omega_0'=\Delta\omega$, $\beta=4b/\lambda$, and

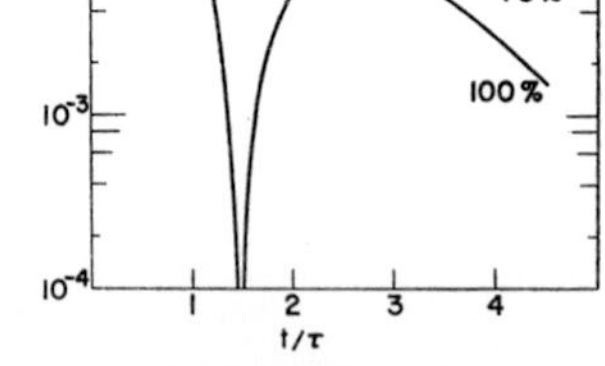

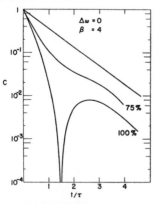

FIG. 1. Time dependence of radiation after transmission through a resonant filter according to Eq. (7), assuming all radiation is recoilless or 75% is recoilless ($\beta=4$, $\Delta\omega=0$). The straight line represents an exponential decay for comparison.

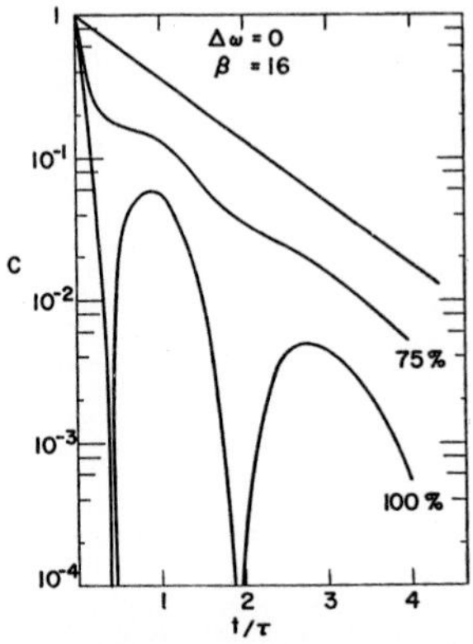

FIG. 2. Time dependence of radiation after transmission through a resonant filter according to Eq. (7), assuming all radiation is recoilless or 75% is recoilless ($\beta=16$, $\Delta\omega=0$). The straight line represents an exponential decay for comparison.

$T=\lambda t$ in Eq. (6a) yields

$$|a'(T)|^2=e^{-T}\left|\sum_{n=0}^{\infty}\left[i\frac{4}{\beta}\frac{\Delta\omega}{\lambda}\right]^n\left[\frac{\beta T}{4}\right]^{\frac{1}{2}n}J_n(\beta^{\frac{1}{2}}T^{\frac{1}{2}})\right|^2. \tag{7}$$

In particular, for $\Delta\omega=0$ this reduces to

$$|a'(T)|^2=e^{-T}[J_0(\beta^{\frac{1}{2}}T^{\frac{1}{2}})]^2. \tag{6}$$

For large values of $\Delta\omega$, the series (7) converges very slowly. In this region, we use Eq. (6b) for $a'(t)$. The transmitted intensity is

$$|a'(T)|^2=e^{-T}\left|-\exp i\left[\frac{\Delta\omega}{\lambda}T+\frac{\lambda}{\Delta\omega}\frac{\beta}{4}\right]+\sum_{n=1}^{\infty}\left[i\frac{\beta}{4}\frac{\lambda}{\Delta\omega}\right]^n\left[\frac{\beta T}{4}\right]^{-\frac{1}{2}n}J_n(\beta^{\frac{1}{2}}T^{\frac{1}{2}})\right|^2. \tag{9}$$

In computing the time behavior of the transmitted intensity, Eq. (7) converges rapidly for

$$\frac{2}{\beta}\frac{\Delta\omega}{\lambda}(\beta T)^{\frac{1}{2}}<1,$$

while Eq. (9) gives rapid convergence for

$$\frac{2}{\beta}\frac{\Delta\omega}{\lambda}(\beta T)^{\frac{1}{2}}>1.$$

The detailed comparison of the theoretical formulas with the experimental results is quite complicated. Here we only indicate some of the points to be considered.

Only some fraction of the 14-kev radiation is recoilless, while the remainder is shifted far from resonance and decays exponentially. In Figs. 1 and 2 we show the time dependence of the transmitted beam for two different absorber thicknesses when $\Delta\omega=0$, for the pure resonance radiation and for the case when 75% of the radiation is recoilless.

The effect of relative motion of source and absorber on the time dependence of the transmitted beam is shown in Fig. 3 ($\Delta\omega=\frac{1}{2}\lambda$) and Fig. 4 ($\Delta\omega=4\lambda$).

Figure 4 shows the surprising behavior which should occur as the source and absorber frequency are separated more and more: the intensity oscillates about the exponential curve. Thus, *at certain times* more gamma rays are received *through* the absorber than would have arrived if the absorber were absent. The medium behaves like a resonant filter and appears to "ring" in response to the incident damped oscillation. As $\Delta\omega$ is increased the oscillations shown in Fig. 4 are shifted toward shorter and shorter times so that, for very large $\Delta\omega$, the normal exponential decay is approached.

The transmitted intensity given by Eq. (7) or (9) can be written as

$$|a'(t)|^2=\exp(-\lambda t)F(\beta,t),$$

where $\lambda=1/\tau$. The deviations from exponential behavior are more easily seen if one plots the product of the counting rate with the factor $\exp(\lambda t)$. For the emitted line this product is a constant. For the transmitted line, the theory predicts that the product will vary as $F(\beta,t)$.

The theory given above assumes that there is a single emission (and absorption) line. However, the 14.4-kev line of Fe^{57} has a hyperfine structure of six lines.[7] Since the separation of the hyperfine components is large compared to the linewidth, we assume that

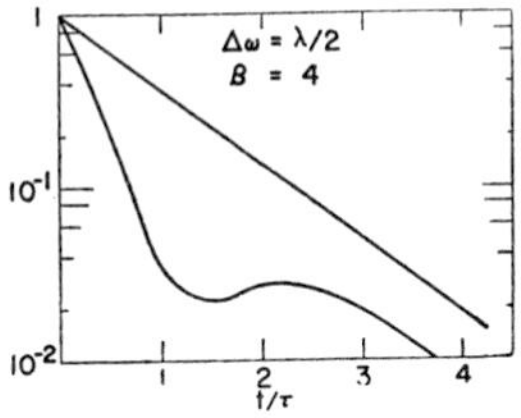

FIG. 3. Effect of relative motion on time dependence of transmitted radiation according to Eq. (7) ($\beta=4$, $\Delta\omega=\frac{1}{2}\lambda$). For comparison, the straight line represents an exponential decay.

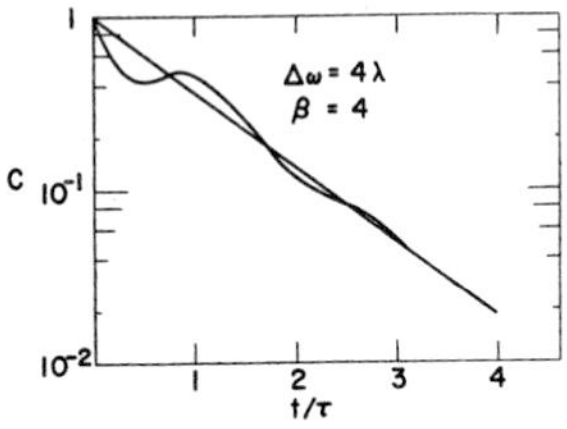

FIG. 4. Effect of relative motion on time dependence of transmitted radiation according to Eq. (7) ($\beta=4$, $\Delta\omega=4\lambda$). For comparison, the straight line represents an exponential decay.

[7] S. S. Hanna, J. Heberle, C. Littlejohn, G. J. Perlow, R. S. Preston, and D. H. Vincent, Phys. Rev. Letters 4, 177 (1960).

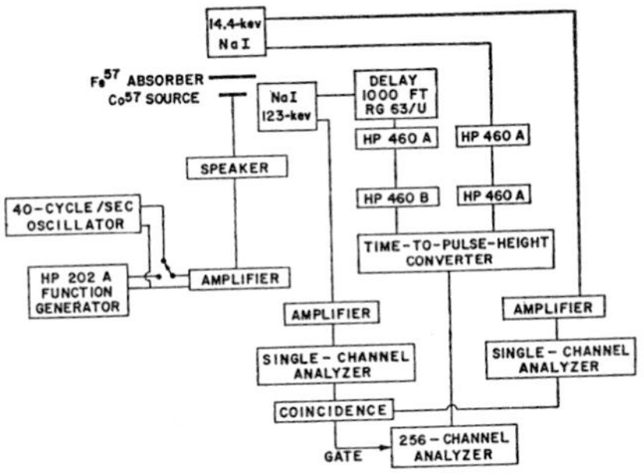

FIG. 5. Schematic diagram of equipment.

each emitted hyperfine component is absorbed only in the corresponding transition in the absorber. By use of the values for the intensities of the hyperfine components, the time dependence of the transmitted radiation is found to be

$$|a'(t)|^2=\exp(-\lambda t)\left[1-f+f\{\tfrac{1}{2}F(\tfrac{1}{4}\beta,t)+\tfrac{1}{3}F(\tfrac{1}{6}\beta,t)+\tfrac{1}{6}F(\tfrac{1}{12}\beta,t)\}\right], \quad (10)$$

where f is the fraction of gamma rays emitted without recoil and β is the thickness of the absorber expressed in mean free paths at the peak of the absorption curve. Although in principle β is measurable, it is difficult to determine it accurately. We have used β as a parameter in fitting the theoretical formula to the experimental data. Equation (10) was evaluated on an IBM-704 computer for various values of β and the other parameters, and the calculated curve giving the best visual fit was plotted with the data. One should expect that β would be given by $N\sigma_0 f'$, where f' is the fraction of Fe^{57} nuclei which can absorb without recoil, N is the number of atoms of Fe^{57} per cm², $\sigma_0=4\pi\lambda\!\!\!^{-2}/(1+\alpha)$, $\lambda\!\!\!^{-}$ is the wavelength of the 14.4-kev gamma ray divided by 2π, and α is the internal conversion coefficient.

III. EQUIPMENT AND PROCEDURE

The measurements were made with a source of Co^{57} (25 000 disintegrations of Co^{57} per sec) co-plated[8] with Fe^{56} on a thin copper foil and annealed in vacuum at 800°C. Absorbers consisted of rolled foils of Fe^{57} (enriched to 75% in Fe^{57}) or normal Armco iron rolled foils annealed at 800°C. The geometric arrangement of source, absorber, and detectors is shown schematically in Fig. 5. The source, $\frac{3}{8}$ in. in diameter, was mounted on an extension of the speaker diaphragm which could be used to shift the resonant frequency of the source by the Doppler effect. The absorber foil (1 in. in diameter) was clamped between two Lucite disks mounted $\frac{3}{8}$ in. above the source. The detector for the 14.4-kev gamma

[8] S. S. Hanna, J. Heberle, C. Littlejohn, G. J. Perlow, R. S. Preston, and D. H. Vincent, Phys. Rev. Letters 4, 28 (1960).

ray consisted of a NaI(Tl) scintillator 1 in. in diameter and 0.006 in. thick mounted on a Lucite light pipe and an RCA 7265 photomultiplier tube. A second NaI(Tl) scintillator, 1 in. in diameter and $\frac{1}{4}$ in. thick, served as a detector for the 123-kev gamma ray and was mounted $\frac{1}{2}$ in. from the source on a line making an angle of 120° with the line connecting the centers of the other detector and the source.

The speaker coil was driven with a peak-to-peak amplitude of $\frac{1}{8}$ in. by the amplified signal coming alternately from a triangular wave generator[9] and from a 40-cps sinusoidal signal. The triangular wave caused the source to move with a constant velocity either toward or away from the absorber, except during the short interval of reversal of direction. This constant velocity produced a small constant increase or decrese in gamma-ray energy through the Doppler effect. On the other hand, the sinusoidal signal, because of its much higher frequency, produced a wide range of energy shifts; most of the time the gamma rays were not resonant nor even nearly resonant with the absorber. Other sources of absorption, such as the photoelectric effect, would be scarcely affected by the energy shift. Thus we observed the effect of both nonresonant and resonant absorption for small energy shifts with the triangular wave applied to the voice coil and we observed the effect of nonresonant absorption alone with the sinusoidal voltage applied to the voice coil.

Because the average geometric arrangement was slightly different for the two signals, measurements were taken without an absorber, and the sinusoidal signal was adjusted slightly to bring the coincidence counting rate within 1% of the counting rate with the triangular drive.

It is desirable that the triangular wave of voltage should move the source with constant speed. The degree to which this condition holds is determined by the linearity of speaker movement with current, the linearity of the triangular wave voltage, the duration of the transient vibration occurring during reversal of the direction of motion, and the isolation of the system from mechanical vibrations conducted by the air or by the building.

We investigated the movement of the voice coil as a function of current and found the relationship to be linear within the accuracy of measurement (2%). The duration of the transient at the peaks of the triangular wave from the generator was known to be small. From the observed duration of the transient voltage induced by a sudden displacement of the voice coil, the effect due to the inertia of the voice coil and source holder was estimated to be less than 25 msec. At the frequencies we used (<0.2 cps), this corresponded to less than 1% of the period.

The transmission of noise to the speaker was greatly reduced by mounting the assembly consisting of speaker, source, absorber, and detectors in a box lined with sound-absorbing material and acoustically isolated from the floor. With these precautions, the observed vibration of the voice coil because of acoustic noise was less than 0.0004 in. per sec, which should be compared to the velocity of 0.0037 in. per sec needed to produce a Doppler shift of one resonance width. The over-all performance of the system was investigated by observing the width of the central dip in transmission. This was 20% wider than expected for the thickest absorber and 40% wider for the thinnest.

The circuits for measuring the coincidence rate as a function of time delay after formation of the 14.4-kev state are shown schematically in Fig. 5 and were the same (except for slight modifications) as those used previously to measure the lifetimes of excited states of nuclei.[10] The output of the time-to-pulse-height converter was stored in the right half of the 256-channel analyzer when the voice coil was driven with the triangular wave and in the left half when the voice coil was driven with the sinusoidal voltage. During a run, the triangular wave and sinusoidal voltages were applied alternately for 4-min intervals by a timing mechanism, and data were accumulated over a 24-hr period. Signals from slow amplifiers and single-channel analyzers set on the photopeaks of the two gamma rays were required in order to record an event.

Because of the method of recording data, slow drifts were not important. The calibration of the time-to-pulse-height converter (as obtained by using the data from the sinusoidal run to measure the lifetime of the 14.4-kev state of Fe^{57}) remained constant within 1.5% over a period of 1 month. A slow drift of the peak channel was also observed (about $\frac{1}{4}$ channel per day). The converter was linear to within 1% in the region of interest.

IV. RESULTS AND DISCUSSION

The results of a typical measurement for the thickest absorber foil (2.7 mg/cm² of Fe^{57}, isotopic enrichment 75%) is shown in Fig. 6. The upper part of the figure shows a conventional semilogarithmic plot of the data after subtraction of background due to accidental coincidences. This background was determined from the counting rate at times preceding the peak shown in Fig. 6(a). In general it was less for the part of the run in which the source was moved at constant velocity than for the part in which the source was vibrated sinusoidally because the counting rate in the 14.4-kev detector was less in the former condition. The total number of accidental coincidences was 2.5% of the total number of true coincidences for the data with vibrated source shown in Fig. 6. The steep rise at the left side of the figure represents the time resolution of the fast circuit; it corresponds to a resolution curve

[9] Model 202A function generator, manufactured by Hewlett-Packard Company, Palo Alto, California.

[10] F. J. Lynch and R. E. Holland, Phys. Rev. **114**, 825 (1959); R. E. Holland and F. J. Lynch, Phys. Rev. **113**, 903 (1959).

with a full width at half maximum of 25 mμsec. The curve obtained with vibrated source shows the exponential decay with a half-life of 0.10 μsec in agreement with previous measurements.[3] The curve obtained with the stationary source demonstrates the effect we expected.

The lower portion of Fig. 6 shows the same data plotted in such a way as to exhibit the deviations from exponential decay predicted in Sec. II. Here the count in each time channel has been multiplied by $e^{\lambda t}$, where λ is the decay constant and t is the time, and the resulting numbers have been adjusted so that the average value of the vibrated data was equal to unity after the initial rise. Data in several adjacent channels were averaged when the counting rate was low. Vertical bars give the standard deviations as calculated from the number of counts. The solid curve shown was calculated for this absorber from the prescription given at the end of Sec. II, with the thickness parameter β adjusted for best fit to the data. This value of β was twice that expected from the thickness of the absorber.

Figure 7 gives typical results for a number of runs in which the source was moved at constant velocity alternately toward and away from the absorber, and data were accumulated without distinguishing the direction of motion. This motion of the source produced

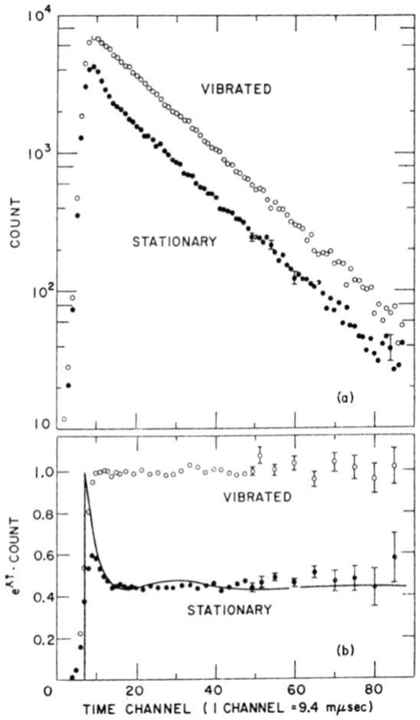

FIG. 6. (a) Semilogarithmic plot of delayed time spectra taken with source and absorber (2.7 mg/cm² of Fe^{57}, isotopic abundance 75%) stationary and with source and absorber vibrated relative to one another; (b) Data of Fig. 6(a) replotted with ordinate multiplied by $e^{\lambda t}$ in order to compare with theoretical expression given by the solid line.

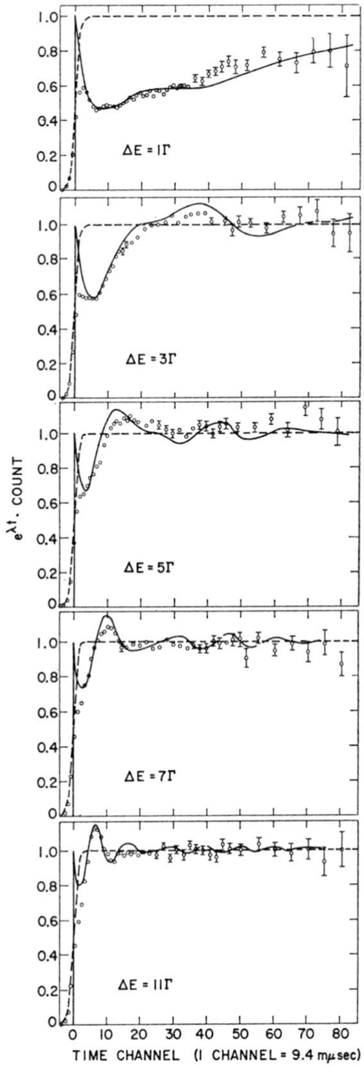

FIG. 7. Time spectra obtained with various energy shifts of the emitted gamma ray. The absorber was the same as in Fig. 6. The energy shift ΔE is given in terms of the linewidth deduced from the mean life of the state, $\Gamma = \hbar/\tau$. The dashed curves give the time spectra when the source is vibrated; the solid curves are the theoretical predictions.

a shift in energy of the emitted gamma ray. The amount of the shift, ΔE, is given on the figure in terms of $\Gamma=\hbar/\tau$, the expected full width at half maximum of the emitted line. The data taken with the source vibrated has been represented in these figures by the light dashed line in order to keep the number of data points from becoming so large as to be confusing. The solid curve is as before a theoretical curve calculated according to Sec. II, with the foil thickness parameter the same as that used in Fig. 2. Similar data for a thinner foil (1.27 mg/cm^2 of Fe^{57} in an enriched foil) is shown in Fig. 8 and for a still thinner foil (0.22 mg/cm^2 of Fe^{57} in a normal isotopic concentration) in Fig. 9.

Not shown are data which were obtained to verify the prediction of the theory that the delayed time spectrum depends only on the magnitude of the shift in gamma-ray energy and not on its sign. A run was made in which data were accumulated only during travel of the source in one direction and the result was compared with that obtained when data were accumulated during travel in both directions. No difference could be observed between the two runs.

All of the data have been compared to the theoretical

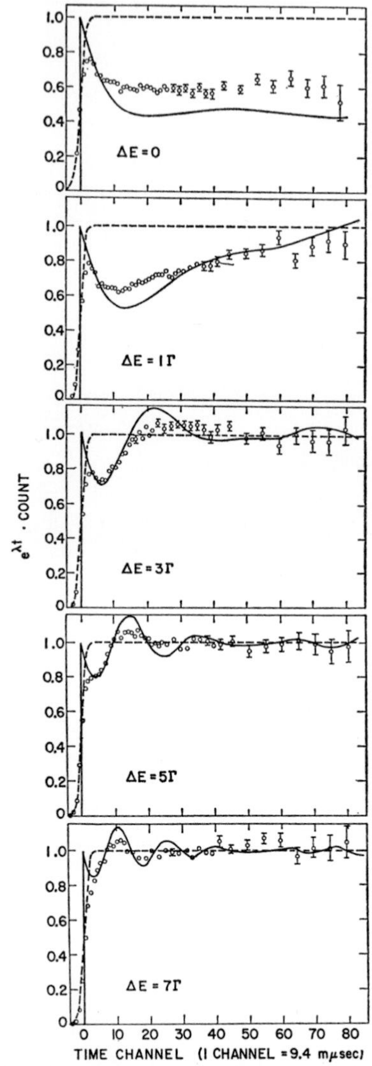

FIG. 8. Time spectra obtained with various energy shifts of the emitted gamma ray. The absorber was a rolled foil (1.27 mg/cm^2 of Fe^{57}, isotopic abundance 75%). The energy shift ΔE is given in terms of the line width deduced from the mean life of the state, $\Gamma=\hbar/\tau$. The dashed curves give the time spectra when the source was vibrated; the solid curves are the theoretical predictions.

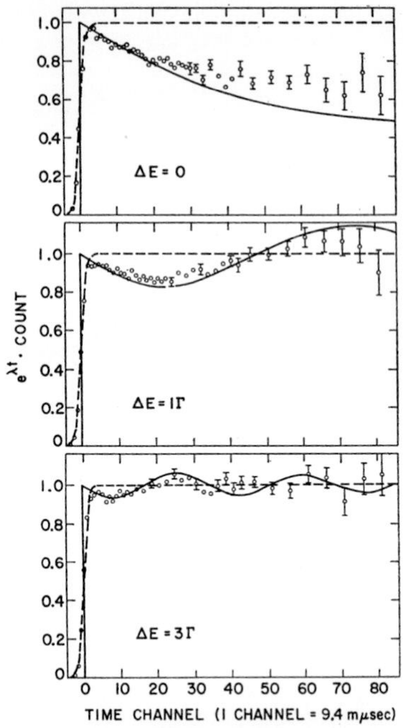

FIG. 9. Time spectra obtained with various energy shifts of the emitted gamma ray. Absorber was rolled foil (0.20 mg/cm^2 of Fe^{57}, natural isotopic abundance). The energy shift ΔE is given in terms of the linewidth deduced from the mean life of the state, $\Gamma=\hbar/\tau$. The dashed curves give the time spectra when the source was vibrated; the solid curves are the theoretical predictions.

expression at the end of Sec. II, the values of parameters given in Table I being used. These are all as expected except β; all theoretical curves are plotted for a value of β twice that obtained from the weight of the absorber foil. With this reservation and when allowance is made for the effect of finite resolution time, the fit between theory and experiment is fairly good. In particular, the predicted overshoot was observed; this is most noticeable in Fig. 7, where the curves for 5Γ, 7Γ, and 11Γ show that, at certain times, a higher intensity is obtained with the absorber than without it.

We have chosen to plot the relative transmission as a function of time, using the energy shift ΔE as a parameter to label the various curves. This has the advantage of allowing a direct estimate of the effect of time resolution. One could, of course, plot the transmission as a function of ΔE with the time as a parameter. This is done in Fig. 10 which shows the theoretical and experimental transmission (relative to that of the vibrated condition) vs ΔE for the times $t=\tau/2$ and $t=4\tau$ after the formation of the excited state. Note that the apparent half-width at half maximum decreases from about 3Γ at $t=\tau/2$ to about 0.7Γ at $t=4\tau$. The half-width measured without consideration of time was about 1.6Γ for this particular absorber (1.27 mg/cm² Fe^{57}).

In some cases the discrepancies are larger than experimental error. A number of possible sources of deviation from the theory were investigated. First, the theory assumes that no scattered radiation was detected. However, the geometric arrangement we used in order to keep the coincidence rate high was such that any appreciable scattering would have been detected. We made a crude check of this by increasing the distance from the source to detector from $\frac{3}{4}$ in. to 2 in. The fact that no change in the time spectra other than the reduced counting rate was observed indicates that scattered radiation was not contributing to the effect. Second, the source and detector might be polarized (because of permanent magnetization or by stray magnetic field) and thus change the relative intensities and polarizations of the hyperfine lines. To

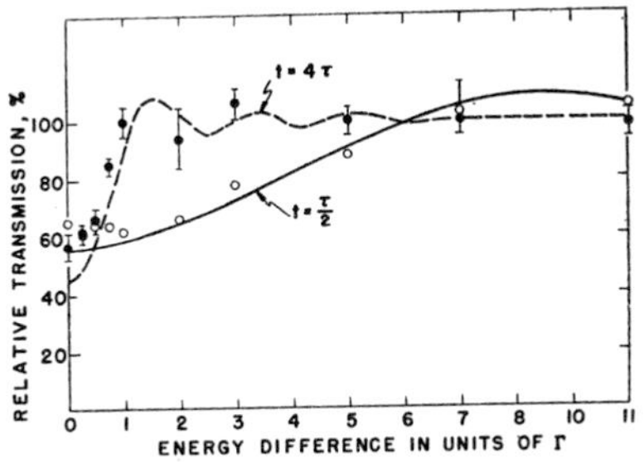

FIG. 10. Transmission (relative to the vibrated condition) of enriched Fe^{57} absorber obtained at $\frac{1}{2}\tau$ and 4τ after formation of the 14.4-kev state. The solid and dashed curves represent the theoretical predictions; the circles the experimental data points.

test for static polarization of source and detector, transmission measurements were made with various orientations of the clamped source and absorber. No effect larger than the statistical accuracy of 1% was found. In another measurement, an upper limit of 5 gauss was put on the local magnetic field, with a probable value close to the earth's field. These two observations make it unlikely that the source or absorbers were polarized. Third, because the measured linewidths were somewhat greater than they should have been, one should perhaps average over a range of energy shifts in the region of the nominal displacement ΔE. A series of curves were calculated by averaging the curves for a given ΔE over a Gaussian distribution of ΔE. Although the agreement between theory and experiment could be improved in some cases in this way, it was worse in other cases and no net improvement resulted.

TABLE I. Values of parameters used with theory of Sec. II to fit data in Figs. 6, 7, 8, and 9.

Parameter	Value	Comment
f	0.6	Fraction of 14.4-kev gamma rays emitted without recoil.
f'	0.6	Fraction of Fe^{57} nuclei absorbing without recoil.
α	15	Internal conversion coefficient.
σ_0	1.48×10^{-18} cm²	Peak absorption cross section for no hyperfine splitting.
β	$2N\sigma_0 f'$	Thickness parameter of theory. (This value is twice the expected value.)
N	...	Number of Fe^{57} nuclei per cm² in absorber. (Obtained from weight of foil.)

ACKNOWLEDGMENTS

We are indebted to Dr. G. J. Perlow and Dr. S. S. Hanna for suggesting the original problem and for supplying the proper sources and absorbers for performing the experiments. J. B. Baumgardner and A. Vandergust built most of the special electronic circuits used.

APPENDIX

The integral

$$a'(t)=\frac{1}{2\pi i}\int_{-\infty}^{+\infty} d\omega \frac{e^{i\omega t}}{\omega-\omega_0-\frac{1}{2}i\lambda}\exp\left[\frac{2ib\omega}{\omega^2-\omega_0'^2-i\omega\lambda}\right], \quad \text{(A1)}$$

can be evaluated by completing the contour on a semicircle in the upper half of the complex ω plane and finding the residues of the integrand. Since $\omega_0'\gg\lambda$, the exponent has singularities at $\omega=\pm\omega_0'+\frac{1}{2}i\lambda$. It is easily shown that the contribution from $\omega=-\omega_0'+\frac{1}{2}i\lambda$ contains a factor λ/ω_0', so this term can be neglected.

We are then left with

$$a'(t)=\frac{1}{2\pi i}\oint d\omega\frac{e^{i\omega t}}{\omega-\omega_0-\frac{1}{2}i\lambda}$$
$$\times\exp[ib(\omega-\omega_0'-\tfrac{1}{2}i\lambda)^{-1}]\equiv\frac{1}{2\pi i}\oint Gd\omega$$
$$=\frac{1}{2\pi i}\left[\oint_{\omega_0+\frac{1}{2}i\lambda}Gd\omega+\oint_{\omega_0'+\frac{1}{2}i\lambda}Gd\omega\right]. \quad (A2)$$

In the first integral we let $z=\omega-\omega_0-\frac{1}{2}i\lambda$ so that

$$I_1=\frac{1}{2\pi i}\oint_{\omega_0+\frac{1}{2}i\lambda}Gd\omega=\frac{1}{2\pi i}\exp(i\omega_0t-\tfrac{1}{2}\lambda t)$$
$$\times\oint_{z=0}\frac{dz}{z}e^{itz}\exp[ib(z+\omega_0-\omega_0')^{-1}]$$
$$=\exp[i\omega_0t-\tfrac{1}{2}\lambda t+ib/(\omega_0-\omega_0')]. \quad (A3)$$

In the second integral we set $z=\omega-\omega_0'-\frac{1}{2}i\lambda$ so that

$$I_2=\frac{1}{2\pi i}\oint_{\omega_0'+\frac{1}{2}i\lambda}Gd\omega=\frac{1}{2\pi i}\exp[i\omega_0't-\tfrac{1}{2}\lambda t]$$
$$\times\oint_{z=0}\frac{dz}{z+\omega_0'-\omega_0}\exp\left[i\left(tz+\frac{b}{z}\right)\right]$$
$$=-\frac{1}{2\pi i}\exp[i\omega_0't-\tfrac{1}{2}\lambda t]$$
$$\times\oint\sum_{n=0}^{\infty}dz\frac{z^n}{(\omega_0-\omega_0')^{n+1}}\exp\left[i\left(tz+\frac{b}{z}\right)\right]. \quad (A4)$$

From the formula for generating Bessel functions,

$$\exp[\tfrac{1}{2}x(u-1/u)]=\sum_{m=-\infty}^{+\infty}u^mJ_m(x), \quad (A5)$$

we find

$$\exp\left[i\left(tz+\frac{b}{z}\right)\right]=\sum_{m=-\infty}^{\infty+}i^m(t/b)^{\frac{1}{2}m}z^mJ_m(2b^{\frac{1}{2}}t^{\frac{1}{2}}). \quad (A5a)$$

Substitution in Eq. (A4) yields

$$I_2=\frac{1}{2\pi i}\oint_{\omega_0'+\frac{1}{2}i\lambda}Gd\omega$$
$$=-\exp[i\omega_0't-\tfrac{1}{2}\lambda t]\sum_{n=0}^{\infty}\left(\frac{ib}{\omega_0-\omega_0'}\right)^{n+1}$$
$$\times(bt)^{-\frac{1}{2}(n+1)}J_{n+1}(2b^{\frac{1}{2}}t^{\frac{1}{2}}) \quad (A6)$$
$$=-\exp[i\omega_0't-\tfrac{1}{2}\lambda t]\sum_{n=1}^{\infty}\left[\frac{ib}{\omega_0-\omega_0'}\right]^n$$
$$\times(bt)^{-n/2}J_n(2b^{\frac{1}{2}}t^{\frac{1}{2}}) \quad (A6a)$$
$$=-\exp[i\omega_0't-\tfrac{1}{2}\lambda t]\left[\sum_{n=-\infty}^{\infty}S_n-\sum_{n=-\infty}^{0}S_n\right], \quad (A6b)$$

where S_n is the summand in Eq. (A6a).

We use the generating function (A5) in the first sum and find a term which cancels I_1, so we are left with

$$a'(t)=\exp[i\omega_0't-\tfrac{1}{2}\lambda t]\sum_{n=-\infty}^{0}\left[\frac{ib}{\omega_0-\omega_0'}\right]^n$$
$$\times(bt)^{-n/2}J_n(2b^{\frac{1}{2}}t^{\frac{1}{2}})$$
$$=\exp[i\omega_0't-\tfrac{1}{2}\lambda t]\sum_{n=0}^{\infty}\left[\frac{i(\omega_0-\omega_0')}{b}\right]^n$$
$$\times(bt)^{n/2}J_n(2b^{\frac{1}{2}}t^{\frac{1}{2}}). \quad (A7)$$

For large values of $(\omega_0-\omega_0')$ it is convenient to obtain $a'(t)$ from the sum of (A3) and (A6a). Then we have

$$a'(t)=\exp[i\omega_0't-\tfrac{1}{2}\lambda t]\left\{-\exp i\left[\frac{b}{\omega_0-\omega_0'}+(\omega_0-\omega_0')t\right]\right.$$
$$\left.+\sum_{n=1}^{\infty}\left(\frac{ib}{\omega_0-\omega_0'}\right)^n(bt)^{-n/2}J_n(2b^{\frac{1}{2}}t^{\frac{1}{2}})\right\}. \quad (A8)$$

Effect of Radiofrequency Resonance on the Natural Line Form (*).

M. N. HACK and M. HAMERMESH

Argonne National Laboratory - Argonne, Ill.

(ricevuto l'11 Ottobre 1960)

Summary. — The form of Zeeman lines in the presence of a resonant rotating r.f. magnetic field is determined. The spontaneous emission distributions are obtained from the steady-state solutions, leading to a prediction of the splitting of Zeeman lines at rotation frequencies corresponding to well separated single- and multiple-quantum resonance frequencies, as well as at the resonance frequency in the Majorana case.

1. – Introduction.

Some time ago BITTER (1) and PRYCE (2) indicated the possibility of a new method of detecting radiofrequency resonance, by means of certain changes in the radiation emitted by an atom when it is subjected to a radiofrequency field at a resonance frequency between its Zeeman levels in a constant magnetic field. At that time the observation of such an effect appeared difficult to perform, since it would require large radiofrequency field amplitudes and high resolution of the emitted radiation in order to detect the changes produced by applying the radiofrequency field. However, the possibility of an experiment on the nuclear Zeeman lines by means of the Mössbauer effect has renewed interest in this problem (3).

(*) Work performed under the auspices of the U. S. Atomic Energy Commission.

(1) F. BITTER: *Phys. Rev.*, **76**, 833 (1949).

(2) M. H. L. PRYCE: *Phys. Rev.*, **77**, 136 (1950). We are indebted to Professor A. ABRAGAM for bringing references (1) and (2) to our attention when we informed him of our results.

(3) A preliminary experimental attempt was reported by E. C. AVERY, C. LITTLEJOHN, G. J. PERLOW and B. SMALLER at the Allerton Park Conference, University of Illinois (June 1960).

In the present note we study the influence of radiofrequency resonance on the natural line form of the emitted radiation. The general theory is closely related to the steady-state solutions found in the study of multiple-quantum transitions ([4]).

2. – The two-level case.

We first consider a system undergoing radiative decay from a pair of levels α and β to levels α' and β' respectively, in the presence of a rotating r.f. field which produces transitions between α and β (Fig. 1). We wish to study the effect on the emitted spectral lines when the angular frequency of rotation ω is close to the resonance frequency $\omega_{\alpha\beta} = (E_\alpha - E_\beta)/\hbar$ between the upper states, and the amplitude of the rotating field is sufficiently large to produce an appreciable probability of transfer between α and β during their mean life-time. We shall assume that both states decay at the same rate.

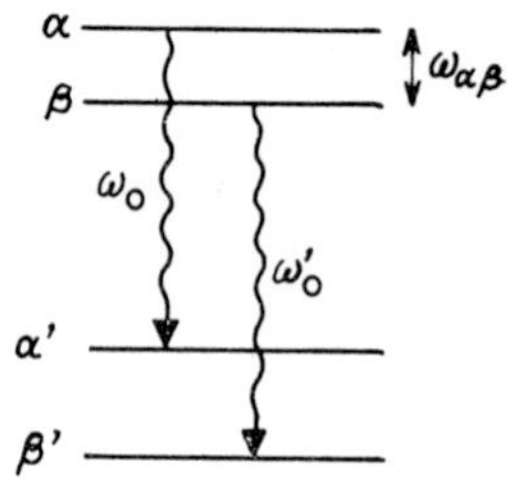

Fig. 1. – Decay transitions in the presence of a r.f. field.

For the present we neglect the influence of other levels on the resonance $\alpha \leftrightarrow \beta$. In the following section the possibility of transitions to other levels will be taken into account, leading to corresponding results also at the resonance frequencies associated with well separated single- and multiple-quantum transitions, as well as at the single resonance frequency in the case of equally spaced levels.

To investigate the effect of the radiofrequency resonance on the natural line form, we study the solution of the system of equations

$$(1a)\qquad i\dot{b}_{\alpha 0} = H \exp[i(\omega_{\alpha\beta} - \omega)t]\, b_{\beta 0} + \sum_\lambda H_{\alpha 0|\alpha' 1_\lambda} \exp[i(\omega_{\alpha\alpha'} - \omega_\lambda)t]\, b_{\alpha' 1}\,,$$

$$(1b)\qquad i\dot{b}_{\alpha' 1_\lambda} = H_{\alpha' 1_\lambda|\alpha 0} \exp[i(\omega_\lambda - \omega_{\alpha\alpha'})t]\, b_{\alpha 0}\,,$$

$$(1c)\qquad i\dot{b}_{\beta 0} = H \exp[i(\omega - \omega_{\alpha\beta})t]\, b_{\alpha 0} + \sum_\sigma H_{\beta 0|\beta' 1_\sigma} \exp[i(\omega_{\beta\beta'} - \omega_\sigma)t]\, b_{\beta' 1}\,,$$

$$(1d)\qquad i\dot{b}_{\beta' 1_\sigma} = H_{\beta' 1_\sigma|\beta 0} \exp[i(\omega_\sigma - \omega_{\beta\beta'})\, t]\, b_{\beta 0}\,,$$

subject to the condition that initially no photons are in the radiation field,

$$(2)\qquad b_{\alpha' 1_\lambda}(0) = b_{\beta' 1_\sigma}(0) = 0\,.$$

([4]) M. N. Hack: *Phys. Rev.*, **100**, 975 (A) (1955); **104**, 84 (1956); H. Salwen: *Phys. Rev.*, **99**, 1274 (1955); C. Besset, J. Horowitz, A. Messiah and J. M. Winter: *Journ. Phys. et Rad.*, **15**, 251 (1954); J. M. Winter: *Ann. Phys.*, **4**, 745 (1959).

For $H = 0$, *i.e.*, for zero amplitude of the radiofrequency field, these equations reduce to the equations of Weisskopf and Wigner [5] for describing the radiative decay of excited states. For vanishing matrix elements of the interaction with the radiation field, $H_{\alpha 0|\alpha' 1_\lambda} = 0$, etc., they would reduce to the equations describing the transitions produced by the radiofrequency field alone.

In general eqs. (1) are too complicated to solve exactly. Nevertheless, for the cases of practical interest a satisfactory approximate solution can be obtained. For this purpose we look for solutions of the form

$$b_{\alpha 0} = C_\alpha \exp[-ipt]\,, \tag{3a}$$

$$b_{\beta 0} = C_\beta \exp[-i(p + \omega_{\alpha\beta} - \omega)t]\,. \tag{3b}$$

Substituting (3*a*) into (1*b*) and integrating, subject to the initial condition (2), and inserting the result

$$b_{\alpha'} = H_{\alpha'\alpha} C_\alpha \frac{\exp[-i(\omega_{\alpha\alpha'} + p - \omega_\lambda)t] - 1}{\omega_{\alpha\alpha'} + p - \omega_\lambda}\,, \tag{4a}$$

and eqs. (3) into (1*a*) gives

$$pC_\alpha = HC_\beta + C_\alpha \sum_\lambda |H_{\alpha\alpha'}|^2 \frac{1 - \exp[i(\omega_{\alpha\alpha'} + p - \omega_\lambda)t]}{\omega_{\alpha\alpha'} + p - \omega_\lambda}\,. \tag{5}$$

(For simplicity photon occupation numbers have been suppressed.)

It is now important to note that for the times of actual interest, *i.e.*, during a long time interval which includes the mean lifetime of the decaying states, by virtue of the smallness of the decay constant (line width) compared to the line frequency, the last term in eq. (5) is practically constant [6]. Denoting

---

[5] V. Weisskopf and E. Wigner: *Zeits. Phys.*, **63**, 54 (1930).

[6] V. Weisskopf and E. Wigner: ref. [5]. One can estimate the upper limit of the interval to be of the order of a few times $\Gamma^{-1} \ln(\omega_0/\Gamma)$, for $\Gamma \ll \omega_0$. At the same time one obtains an estimate for the lower limit (non-linear decay contribution to the change in probability of remaining in the initial state at very early times) as being at most of the order of the period $2\pi/\omega_0$. These results follow already in the Weisskopf-Wigner approximation, even with the usual neglect of the frequency variation of the matrix element and density of states. In this case the second term in the sum in eq. (5) leads to a factor

$$\int_0^\infty \frac{[\exp[i(\varpi - \omega_\lambda - \frac{1}{2}i\Gamma)t]}{\varpi - \omega_\lambda - \frac{1}{2}i\Gamma}\, d\omega_\lambda = 2\pi i + \exp[\tfrac{1}{2}\Gamma t] I\,,$$

its value by $-(i/2)\Gamma\cdot C_\alpha$ (7), we have

(6a) $$\left(p+\frac{i}{2}\Gamma\right)C_{\dot\alpha}=HC_\beta\,.$$

In the same way we get

(4b) $$b_{\beta'}=H_{\beta'\beta}C_\beta\,\frac{\exp\left[-i(\omega_{\alpha\beta'}+p-\omega-\omega_\sigma)t\right]-1}{\omega_{\alpha\beta'}+p-\omega-\omega_\sigma}\,,$$

and

(6b) $$HC_\alpha=\left(p+\frac{i}{2}\Gamma+\omega_{\alpha\beta}-\omega\right)C_\beta\,,$$

where by the restriction to the case of equal lifetimes Γ has the same value as in (6a).

The simple eigenvalue problem, eqs. (6a, b), has the solutions

(7a) $$p_\pm=\frac{1}{2}(\omega-\omega_{\alpha\beta})+w_\pm-\frac{i}{2}\Gamma\,,$$

where

(7b) $$w_\pm=\pm\tfrac{1}{2}[(\omega-\omega_{\alpha\beta})^2+4H^2]^{\frac{1}{2}}\,,$$

and

(8a) $$C_{\pm,\alpha}=\pm\frac{H}{|H|}\,\frac{1}{\sqrt{2}}\left[1\pm\frac{\omega_{\alpha\beta}-\omega}{[(\omega-\omega_{\alpha\beta})^2+4H^2]^{\frac{1}{2}}}\right]^{\frac{1}{2}},$$

(8b) $$C_{\pm,\beta}=\frac{1}{\sqrt{2}}\left[1\mp\frac{\omega_{\alpha\beta}-\omega}{[(\omega-\omega_{\alpha\beta})^2+4H^2]^{\frac{1}{2}}}\right]^{\frac{1}{2}}.$$

---

where $\Gamma>0$, (7) and the last term furnishes the deviations. For all $t>0$ we have $|I|\leqslant 1/\overline{\omega}t$, and for $t\gg 1/\overline{\omega}$, $I\sim\{\exp[i\overline{\omega}t]\}/i(\overline{\omega}-i\Gamma/2)t$. More refined estimates taking into account the frequency variation of the matrix element and density of states lead to similar results. The dependence of the decay constant on the r.f. quantities in our case ($\omega-\omega_{\alpha\beta}$, H) is also weak since these are very small, of the order of the line width, compared to the frequency of the line. Decay theory has been discussed from a different viewpoint, based on the characteristic functions of the total-energy operator, by L. A. KHALFIN: *Sov. Phys. Journ. Exp. Theor. Phys.*, **6**, 1053 (1958).

(7) We suppose the imaginary parts of the decay constants to be absorbed into the energies E_α and E_β. Then Γ is purely real and moreover, as one readily verifies, $\geqslant 0$. We take Γ strictly positive, since we naturally are not interested in cases where selection rules forbid the decay.

The particular superposition satisfying the initial condition that the system is in the state $\alpha 0$ at time $t=0$ is given by

$$(9)\quad \begin{cases} b_{\alpha 0} = C^2_{+\alpha} \exp[-ip_+ t] + C^2_{-\alpha} \exp[-ip_- t]\,, \\ b_{\beta 0} = (C_{+\alpha} C_{+\beta} \exp[-ip_+ t] + C_{-\alpha} C_{-\beta} \exp[-ip_- t]) \exp[-i(\omega_{\alpha\beta} - \omega)t]\,. \end{cases}$$

The probabilities of finding the system subsequently, at time t, in the states $\alpha 0$ or $\beta 0$ are therefore

$$(10)\quad \begin{cases} |b_{\alpha 0}(t)|^2 = (1-P)\exp[-\Gamma t]\,, \\ |b_{\beta 0}(t)|^2 = P \exp[-\Gamma t]\,, \end{cases}$$

where

$$(11)\quad P = \frac{4H^2}{(\omega - \omega_{\alpha\beta})^2 + 4H^2} \sin^2 \frac{1}{2} [(\omega - \omega_{\alpha\beta})^2 + 4H^2]^{\frac{1}{2}}\, t\,,$$

i.e., the Rabi transition probabilities multiplied by the exponential decay factor $\exp[-\Gamma t]$.

The probability amplitudes for finding the system in the lower levels after decay, with a photon of frequency ω_λ or ω_σ respectively in the radiation field, are (7)

$$(12)\quad \begin{cases} b_{\alpha'}(\infty) = H_{\alpha'\alpha}\left(\eta_+ C_{+\alpha} \dfrac{1}{\omega_\lambda - \omega_{\alpha\alpha'} - p_+} + \eta_- C_{-\alpha} \dfrac{1}{\omega_\lambda - \omega_{\alpha\alpha'} - p_-}\right), \\ b_{\beta'}(\infty) = H_{\beta'\beta}\left(\eta_+ C_{+\beta} \dfrac{1}{\omega_\sigma - \omega_{\alpha\beta'} - p_+ + \omega} + \eta_- C_{-\beta} \dfrac{1}{\omega_\sigma - \omega_{\alpha\beta'} - p_- + \omega}\right), \end{cases}$$

where the constants $\eta_\pm$ $(|\eta_+|^2 + |\eta_-|^2 = 1)$ determine the particular superposition satisfying an arbitrary initial condition.

For the initial condition corresponding to (9), $\eta_+ = C_{+,\alpha}$ and $\eta_- = C_{-,\alpha}$. For

$$(13)\quad \omega = \omega_{\alpha\beta} \quad \text{(r.f. resonance)},$$

the corresponding emission probabilities are therefore

$$(14)\quad \begin{cases} |b_{\alpha\to\alpha'}(\infty)|^2_{\text{res}} = |H_{\alpha\alpha'}|^2 \dfrac{(\omega_\lambda - \omega_0)^2 + \Gamma^2/4}{[(\omega_\lambda - \omega_0)^2 - \Gamma^2/4 - H^2]^2 + \Gamma^2(\omega_\lambda - \omega_0)^2}\,, \\ |b_{\alpha\to\beta'}(\infty)|^2_{\text{res}} = |H_{\beta\beta'}|^2 \dfrac{H^2}{[(\omega_\sigma - \omega_0')^2 - \Gamma^2/4 - H^2]^2 + \Gamma^2(\omega_\sigma - \omega_0')^2}\,, \end{cases}$$

where

$$(15)\quad \omega_0 = \omega_{\alpha\alpha'}\,, \qquad \omega_0' = \omega_{\beta\beta'}\,.$$

Similarly for the condition that the system is initially in the state $\beta 0$ at time $t=0$,

$$(16)\quad \begin{cases} |b_{\beta\to\alpha'}(\infty)|^2_{\text{res}} = |H_{\alpha\alpha'}|^2 \dfrac{H^2}{[(\omega_\lambda-\omega_0)^2-\Gamma^2/4-H^2]^2+\Gamma^2(\omega_\lambda-\omega_0)^2}\,, \\ |b_{\beta\to\beta'}(\infty)|^2_{\text{res}} = |H_{\beta\beta'}|^2 \dfrac{(\omega_\sigma-\omega_0')^2+\Gamma^2/4}{[(\omega_\sigma-\omega_0')^2-\Gamma^2/4-H^2]^2+\Gamma^2(\omega_\sigma-\omega_0')^2}\,. \end{cases}$$

The effects of the r.f. field on the emitted spectral lines are readily seen in the solutions (14) and (16). They persist and take an even simpler form in the case of equal populations (and random phase difference) in the levels α and β. In this case the emission distribution is the superposition with equal weights of the distributions for the pure steady-state solutions where the components are displaced without change of shape.

Averaging over the inital states and summing over all the final photon states at the energy $\hbar\omega_\lambda$, we obtain for the line $\alpha\to\alpha'$ the photon frequency distribution

$$(17)\qquad P(\omega_\lambda)_{\text{res}} = \frac{\Gamma}{4\pi}\,\frac{(\omega_\lambda-\omega_0)^2+H^2+\Gamma^2/4}{[(\omega_\lambda-\omega_0)^2-\Gamma^2/4-H^2]^2+\Gamma^2(\omega_\lambda-\omega_0)^2}\,.$$

The similar distribution for the line $\beta\to\beta'$ is obtained by replacing ω_0 by ω_0'.

The corresponding results in general, *i.e.*, not restricted to r.f. resonance, are

$$(18)\qquad P(\omega_\lambda) = \frac{\Gamma}{4\pi}\,\cdot$$

$$\cdot\frac{\left(\omega_\lambda-\omega_0-\dfrac{\omega-\omega_{\alpha\beta}}{2}\right)^2+\dfrac{\Gamma^2}{4}+\dfrac{1}{4}(\omega-\omega_{\alpha\beta})^2+H^2-(\omega-\omega_{\alpha\beta})\left(\omega_\lambda-\omega_0-\dfrac{\omega-\omega_{\alpha\beta}}{2}\right)}{\left[\left(\omega_\lambda-\omega_0-\dfrac{\omega-\omega_{\alpha\beta}}{2}\right)^2-\dfrac{\Gamma^2}{4}-\dfrac{1}{4}(\omega-\omega_{\alpha\beta})^2-H^2\right]^2+\Gamma^2\left(\omega_\lambda-\omega_0-\dfrac{\omega-\omega_{\alpha\beta}}{2}\right)^2}$$

and the similar relation for the line $\beta\to\beta'$ obtained by replacing ω_0 by $\omega_{\alpha\beta'}-\omega$ and changing the sign of the last term in the numerator.

Fig. 2 shows the behavior of the emission distribution at resonance, for increasing values of the radiofrequency field amplitude. When the field amplitude is sufficiently large that the angular frequency of oscillation between α and β is comparable to the decay rate, the spectral lines $\alpha\to\alpha'$ and $\beta\to\beta'$ each exhibit two peaks. The distribution $P(\omega_\lambda)_{\text{res}}$ is the superposition of two Lorentzian [8] components of equal intensity, and widths equal to Γ, centered at $\omega_0\pm H$.

---

[8] The frequency dependence of the factor $\int|H_{\alpha\alpha'}|^2\varrho(\omega_\lambda)\,d\Omega$ leads to asymmetry of the normal line [5]. For the frequencies of interest, however, because of $\Gamma\ll\omega_0$, we make a negligible error by replacing this factor for simplicity by its value at the

One verifies further that the splitting of the spectral lines appears only for ω close to resonance. As the relative deviation of ω from resonance increases, both lines tend to their natural forms (the intensity of the off-frequency component drops to zero). The emission distribution near resonance in the two-level case is illustrated in Fig. 3.

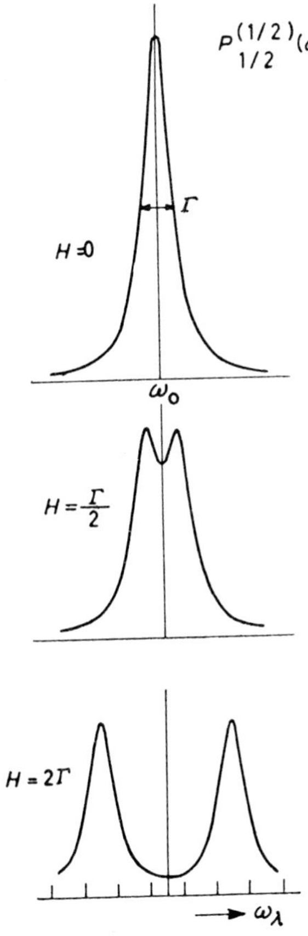

Fig. 2. – Emission distribution $P^{(\frac{1}{2})}_{\frac{1}{2}}(\omega_\lambda)$ at resonance for increasing r.f. amplitude.

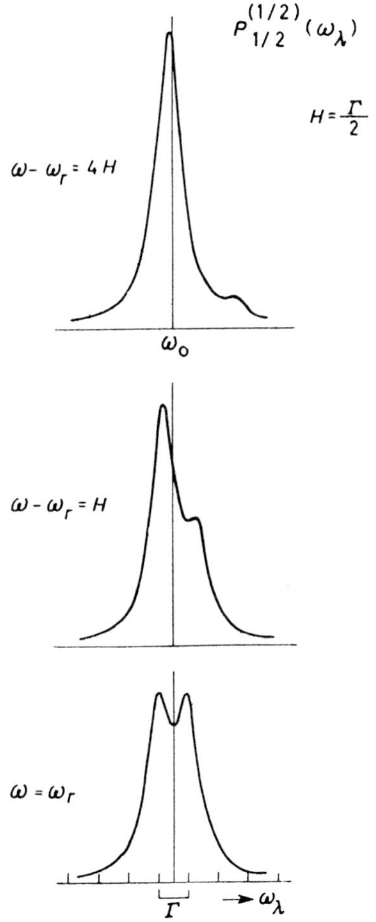

Fig. 3. – Emission distribution $P^{(\frac{1}{2})}_{\frac{1}{2}}(\omega_\lambda)$ for fixed $H=\frac{1}{2}\Gamma$ and varying deviation from resonance.

---

line center. At large ω_λ it tends to zero by virtue of the retardation, as required for convergence of the total radiated energy. For small ω_λ (frequencies up to and even beyond the line frequency) it has the approximate value $\Gamma\omega_\lambda/\omega_0$.

3. – Arbitrary number of levels.

The preceding treatment of the decay from two levels can readily be extended to the case of an arbitrary number of decaying states (9). We will show that the splitting of spectral lines by r.f. fields also occurs at distinct multiple-quantum resonance frequencies, as well as at the resonance frequency in the case of equally spaced levels.

For this purpose we consider a rotationally invariant system which interacts, through magnetic moments $\gamma_1 \boldsymbol{J}_1$ and $\gamma_2 \boldsymbol{J}_2$, with an external magnetic field consisting of a constant field $\mathscr{H}_0$ and a perpendicular rotating field of constant amplitude $\mathscr{H}$ and angular velocity ω, which causes transitions between the levels of the system in the constant field.

Omitting for the moment the interaction with the radiation field, and choosing the z direction along the constant field and the x axis along the direction of the rotating field at time $t=0$, we have for the Hamiltonian of the system

$$\hat{H} = H_0 + H' , \tag{19}$$

where

$$H' = (\gamma_1 \boldsymbol{J}_1 + \gamma_2 \boldsymbol{J}_2)\cdot[(\mathscr{H}\cos\omega t)\boldsymbol{i} + (\mathscr{H}\sin\omega t)\boldsymbol{j}] . \tag{20}$$

H_0 contains the interaction with the constant field and the $\boldsymbol{J}_1\cdot\boldsymbol{J}_2$ interaction, and commutes with the z component of the total angular momentum $J_z = J_{1z} + J_{2z}$.

The Schrödinger equation takes on a more convenient form if we transform to the co-ordinate system of the rotating magnetic field (10) by means of the unitary operator $U = \exp[iJ_z\omega t/\hbar]$. Then

$$\varphi = U\psi = \exp[iJ_z\omega t/\hbar]\psi \tag{21}$$

satisfies

$$i\hbar\frac{\mathrm{d}\varphi}{\mathrm{d}t} = W\varphi , \tag{22}$$

(9) When the calculation is extended in addition to an arbitrary number of lower levels to which a given state can decay, the decay constants combine additively to give the total width (5). It is this summation which leads in practice to the (approximate) equality of lifetimes of the decaying states. When several states decay to the same level, cross terms appear which are rapidly oscillating for $\omega \gg \Gamma$.

(10) I. I. Rabi, N. F. Ramsey and J. Schwinger: *Rev. Mod. Phys.*, **26**, 167 (1954).

where the transformed Hamiltonian

$$W = H_0 - \omega J_z + V \tag{23}$$

with

$$V = \gamma_1 J_{1x} \mathscr{H} + \gamma_2 J_{2x} \mathscr{H} \tag{24}$$

is independent of the time.

The transformed Schrödinger equation (22) has steady-state solutions

$$\varphi = u \cdot \exp[-iwt]\,. \tag{25}$$

By means of this transformation, the problem is reduced to the solution of an eigenvalue problem. As in the two-level case treated in the previous section, the introduction of the decay transitions effectively changes w according to

$$w \to w - \frac{i}{2}\Gamma, \tag{26}$$

where Γ is the decay constant. Here, as before, we consider the case where all levels decay at the same rate. In this case the eigenvalue problem is the same as in the absence of decay. (In the general case, the effect of decay is to introduce constants $\frac{1}{2}i\Gamma_1$, $\frac{1}{2}i\Gamma_2$, ... into the diagonal terms of the eigenvalue equations. In the case treated here, all the Γ's are equal).

For well separated resonance frequencies and for ω in the neighborhood of a resonance frequency, it has been shown (4) that the eigenvalue problem can be reduced to a two-level problem, even in the case of the higher order multiple-quantum transitions.

Equations (1) then apply directly, with H replaced by an expression of the type of higher order perturbation theory, (11) and $\omega - \omega_{\alpha\beta}$ replaced by a quantity Ω' (12). The splitting of the spectral lines thus occurs for each of the resonance frequencies, including the ones corresponding to multiple-quantum transitions. Only the two lines emanating from the particular initial and final levels of the given resonance transition are split by the application of the r.f. field. This follows from the fact that only these levels have appreciable components in the corresponding steady-state solutions which become almost degenerate at the given resonance.

The opposite case of equally spaced levels, where several resonance frequencies coincide, can be treated by similar methods. Apart from the field-

(11) M. N. HACK: reference (4), eq. (51) for δ.

(12) M. N. HACK: reference (4), eq. (42), (50), (51).

independent term of w, the steady-state solutions for this case (Majorana case) can be expressed in the form [13]

$$C^{(j)}_{\mu m} = d^{(j)}_{\mu m}(\theta)\,, \tag{27}$$

$$w^{(j)}_{\mu} = \mu[(\omega-\omega_r)^2+4H^2]^{\frac{1}{2}}\,, \tag{28}$$

where

$$\cos\theta = \frac{\omega_r-\omega}{[(\omega-\omega_r)^2+4H^2]^{\frac{1}{2}}} \tag{29a}$$

$$\sin\theta = \frac{2H}{[(\omega-\omega_r)^2+4H^2]^{\frac{1}{2}}}\,, \tag{29b}$$

$\omega_r=\gamma_J\mathscr{H}_0$, $2H=\gamma_J\mathscr{H}$, and the $d^{(j)}_{\mu m}$ are representations of the rotation group. Applied to the decay problem, they lead to the probability amplitudes

$$b^{(j)}_{um} = d^{(j)}_{\mu m}\exp\{-i(m[\omega-\omega_r]+\mu[(\omega-\omega_r)^2+4H^2]^{\frac{1}{2}}-\tfrac{1}{2}i\Gamma)t\}\,, \tag{30}$$

$$b'^{(j)}_{\mu m}(\infty) = d^{(j)}_{\mu m}H_{\text{rad}}\frac{1}{\omega_\lambda-(\omega_0+m[\omega-\omega_r]+\mu[(\omega-\omega_r)^2+4H^2]^{\frac{1}{2}})+\frac{1}{2}i\Gamma}\,. \tag{31}$$

In the case of equal populations and random phases, this gives

$$P^{(j)}_m(\omega_\lambda) = \frac{1}{2j+1}\frac{\Gamma}{2\pi}\sum_\mu|d^{(j)}_{\mu m}(\theta)|^2\cdot \frac{1}{\{\omega_\lambda-(\omega_0+m[\omega-\omega_r]+\mu[(\omega-\omega_r)^2+4H^2]^{\frac{1}{2}})\}^2+\Gamma^2/4}\,, \tag{32}$$

i.e., a superposition of normal components with widths Γ, centers at

$$\omega_0+m[\omega-\omega_r]+\mu[(\omega-\omega_r)^2+4H^2]^{\frac{1}{2}}, \qquad \mu=-j,\,-j+1,\,\ldots j\,,$$

and intensities proportional to the squares of the coefficients of the rotation matrices.

In this case, each line thus splits in general into a number of components equal to the multiplicity $2j+1$. However, in certain cases fewer components may appear, because some of the intensity coefficients vanish. At resonance ($\omega=\omega_r$), this occurs when the multiplicity is odd, for the central level (the next to last and alternate components are absent) and besides the central

---

(13) H. Salwen: reference (4), eq. (38), (39).

level for all the alternate levels starting from the next to last (the central component is absent).

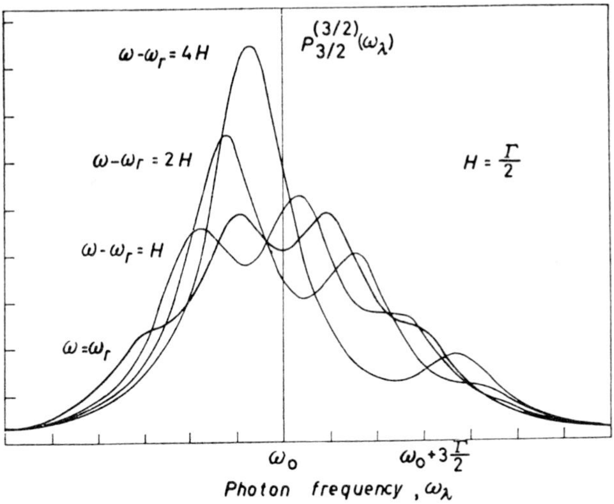

a)

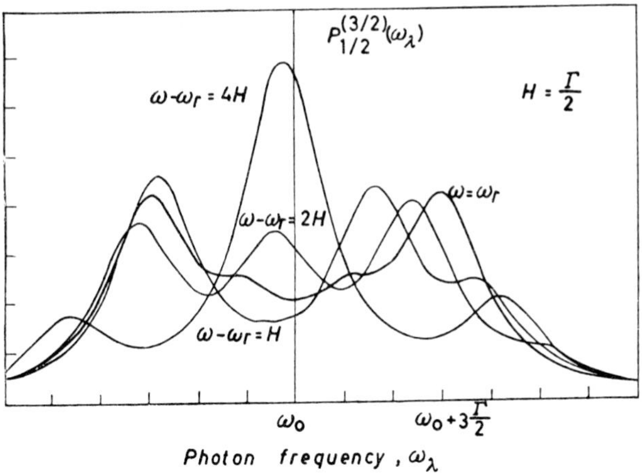

b)

Fig. 4. – Emission distribution $P_m^{(\frac{3}{2})}(\omega_\lambda)$ for fixed $H=\frac{1}{2}\Gamma$ and varying $\omega \geqslant \omega_r$. (*a*) $m=\frac{3}{2}$; (*b*) $m=\frac{1}{2}$. The corresponding curves for $\omega \leqslant \omega_r$ are obtained by reflection in the vertical axis through ω_0. The curves for negative m are obtained by reflection in the same axis and displacement to the corresponding mean emission frequency.

In the particular case of $j=\frac{1}{2}$, eq. (32) reduces to eq. (18) ff. (Figs. 2 and 3). The graphs of $P_m^{(j)}(\omega_\lambda)$ for the case of $j=\frac{3}{2}$ are shown in Fig. 4*a* and *b* for fixed $H=\Gamma/2$.

RIASSUNTO (*)

Si determina la forma delle linee di Zeeman in presenza di un campo magnetico rotante risonante a r.f. Le distribuzioni della emissione spontanea vengono ottenute dalle soluzioni per lo stato continuo, e portano alla predizione della scissione delle linee di Zeeman sia per frequenze di rotazione pari alle ben distinte frequenze di risonanza quantistiche singole e multiple, sia per la frequenza di risonanza nel caso di Majorana.

(*) *Traduzione a cura della Redazione.*

VOLUME 4, NUMBER 8 PHYSICAL REVIEW LETTERS APRIL 15, 1960

RECOILLESS RAYLEIGH SCATTERING IN SOLIDS

C. Tzara and R. Barloutaud
Centre d'Études Nucléaires de Saclay, Gif-sur-Yvette (Seine-et-Oise), France
(Received March 21, 1960)

Using the Mössbauer effect, photon sources and analyzers extremely selective in energy are now available. We study here with such an analyzer the recoilless Rayleigh scattering by atoms in solids.

This effect is related to the x-ray diffraction by crystals as follows. The interference at the exact Bragg angles occurs when the scattering is elastic with respect to the lattice as a whole, that is, without any phonon exchange. Debye and Waller have calculated the reduction in intensity of x rays scattered at the Bragg angles in a solid at temperature T,[1]

$$\varphi_T = \exp\left\{-\frac{3}{2}\frac{E_R}{k\theta}\left[\frac{1}{4}+\frac{1}{x}\int_0^x \frac{u\,du}{e^u - 1}\right]\right\}, \qquad (1)$$

where $x = T/\theta$, θ is the Debye temperature, and $E_R = (E^2/Mc^2)(1-\cos\theta)$ is the recoil energy given to the free atom by a photon of energy E scattered at the angle θ.

In the present work, where we detect the elastic scattering directly by an energy selection instead of analyzing a diffraction pattern, the factor φ_T is the relative number of photons scattered without energy change. It is clearly the same factor which gives the proportion of recoilless γ rays in the Mössbauer effect[2]; in that case $E_R = E^2/2Mc^2$ in Eq. (1).

In order to measure the factor φ_T, we have studied the Rayleigh scattering for several materials: Pt, Al, graphite, and paraffin. The 23.8-kev photons emitted by Sn^{119*} were scattered at $50° \pm 5°$ and absorbed by a Sn^{119} foil 40 mg cm^{-2} thick (almost completely black for the recoilless photons[3]) (Fig. 1). The scatterers' thicknesses were such that the transmission of the γ rays was of the order of 10%.

The Rayleigh-scattered photons are accompanied by inelastically scattered photons (Raman, Compton), considerably shifted in energy, so that the selective absorption in Sn^{119} occurs only

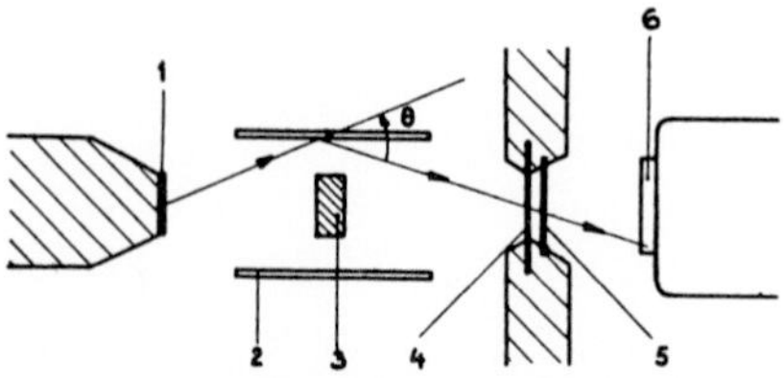

FIG. 1. (1) Sn^{119*} source; (2) scatterer; (3) bismuth stopper; (4) 40 mg cm^{-2} Sn^{119} foil (71.5% Sn^{119}); (5) 62 mg cm^{-2} Pd foil absorbing Sn x rays; (6) 1.5 mm NaI(Tl) scintillator and photomultiplier.

for a fraction α of all the scattering processes; α is extracted from the form factors given by Compton and Allison.[4]

We have measured the relative decrease Δ of counting rate between room temperature $T_1 = 300°K$ and $T_2 = 80°K$. The recoilless scattering proportion at T_2 is approximately

$$\varphi_{T_2} = \frac{1}{\alpha}\frac{\Delta - \epsilon}{f_2 - \epsilon},$$

where f_2 is the ratio of recoilless emission of the Sn^{119*} source and ϵ is its self-absorption at T_2. Here $f_2 = 0.32 \pm 0.015$ and $\epsilon = 0.05 \pm 0.01$. We neglect the small recoilless emission at 300°K which introduces a negligible correction for φ_{T_2}.

The results are given in Table I. The agreement between the calculated and experimental values of φ is reasonably good, especially when

Table I. Experimental and calculated values of φ_{T_2}.

	$1/\alpha$	Δ	φ_{T_2}	φ_{calc}
Pt	1.05	0.27 ± 0.03	0.72 ± 0.09	0.80
Al	2.15	0.19 ± 0.016	0.92 ± 0.09	0.62
C	4.13	0.10 ± 0.01	0.79 ± 0.09	0.68
CH_2	5.30	0.020 ± 0.01	0	

we notice that the Debye temperatures are deduced from specific heat measurements rather than from x-ray diffraction.

We have also, using a thin Sn^{119} foil as a scatterer, observed at low temperature the resonant Mössbauer scattering.[5]

This method extends the range of solids which can be studied by means of the Mössbauer effect or by x-ray diffraction.

It is a pleasure to acknowledge interesting discussions with Dr. Abragam, Dr. Cotton, and Dr. Jacrot.

[1] I. Waller, Ann. Physik 79, 261 (1926).
[2] R. L. Mössbauer, Z. Physik 151, 124 (1958).
[3] R. Barloutaud, E. Cotton, J. L. Picou, and J. Quidort, Compt. rend. 250, 319 (1960).
[4] A. K. Compton and S. K. Allison, X-Rays in Theory and Experiment (D. Van Nostrand Company, Inc., Princeton, New Jersey, 1947), 2nd ed., p. 781.
[5] C. Tzara and R. Barloutaud, Compt. rend. (to be published).

PHYSIQUE NUCLÉAIRE. — *Sur la possibilité de mettre en évidence la cohérence de phase dans la diffusion de résonance des rayons γ par des noyaux atomiques.* Note de M. **Alfred Kastler**, présentée par M. Gustave Ribaud.

Lorsque la diffusion de résonance des rayons γ par des noyaux atomiques d'un réseau se fait sans recul du noyau, la cohérence des radiations diffusées doit se manifester par une répartition d'intensité analogue à celle de la diffraction des rayons X par les électrons d'un cristal.

La découverte faite par Mössbauer (1) que des rayons γ de faible énergie peuvent être émis ou absorbés par des noyaux situés dans un réseau cristallin sans perte d'énergie due au recul du noyau, a soulevé un intérêt considérable. La finesse extraordinaire des rayons γ obtenus dans ces conditions permet d'aborder des investigations nouvelles : L'étude de la largeur de raie par analyse cinétique grâce à l'effet Doppler, l'étude par ce même procédé de la structure Zeeman et de la structure hyperfine de la raie, la mise en évidence par une expérience de laboratoire de l'effet Einstein, c'est-à-dire de la différence de fréquence entre deux étalons identiques liée à la différence de potentiel gravifique (2). D'autres études, confinées jusqu'à présent au domaine optique vont pouvoir être étendues au domaine des rayons γ. Citons à titre d'exemples les mesures de variation de fréquence dans la diffusion des ondes électromagnétiques par les ondes d'agitation thermique (effet Brillouin), les études des effets de polarisation et d'anisotropie spatiale des radiations de résonance lorsque émetteur et absorbant sont soumis à des champs magnétiques de directions variées (3), enfin les applications des méthodes optiques de spectroscopie des radiofréquences (4).

Une autre question intéressante va pouvoir recevoir maintenant une réponse expérimentale, celle de savoir si les radiations de résonance électromagnétiques diffusées par des centres résonnants présentent des effets de cohérence de phase. Une telle cohérence a été explicitement admise par Weisskopf (5). Si la radiation de résonance diffusée est totalement incohérente, sa répartition spatiale doit être continue et conforme aux relations de corrélation angulaire qui ne font entrer en jeu que le caractère multipolaire de la transition spectrale et les nombres de spin des niveaux qui bordent la transition. Si, au contraire, la radiation diffusée est partiellement cohérente, comme on peut le supposer pour la composante Zeeman qui ramène le noyau au niveau magnétique initial, il faut s'attendre à observer des effets d'interférence. Une diffraction sélective doit se faire dans les directions de von Laue-Bragg, ou dans celles des anneaux de Debye-Scherrer, suivant que la matière diffusante est mono- ou polycristalline.

(2)

Dans le domaine optique, lorsqu'il y a diffusion résonnante de la lumière par les atomes d'une vapeur sous faible densité, la lumière diffusée ne présente pas de caractères de cohérence. Dans ce cas, l'irrégularité des positions des centres diffusants et les fluctuations de densité masquent complètement la cohérence (si elle existe) de l'acte de diffusion élémentaire (tout comme l'irrégularité des mouvements de translation de ces centres masque la finesse « naturelle » de la raie). L'apparition, aux fortes densités de vapeur, d'une réflexion régulière sur la face d'entrée de la vapeur ([6]) révèle la cohérence.

Dans le cas de la diffusion résonnante de rayons γ par des noyaux, le caractère quantique du phénomène est prédominant. Ce caractère n'exclut pas les propriétés de cohérence. Dans le cas de la diffusion de photons γ par les noyaux d'un réseau, le noyau diffusant devient identifiable lorsqu'il recule (par exemple, il peut quitter un nœud du réseau pour se mettre en position interstitielle). Dans ce cas, la faculté d'interférence du photon diffusé se trouve détruite. Mais lorsqu'il n'y a pas de recul nucléaire, lorsque c'est le réseau tout entier qui encaisse la quantité de mouvement du recul, le noyau diffusant n'est pas identifiable. Dans ce cas, la cohérence de phase du rayonnement liée à l'arrangement spatial périodique des centres diffusants doit se manifester.

Il faut remarquer que la cohérence n'est que difficilement observable lorsque les noyaux diffusants sont ceux d'un isotope irrégulièrement répartis dans un mélange isotopique. L'observation de la cohérence parfaite nécessite un arrangement spatial régulier des noyaux diffusants, donc l'emploi d'un cristal formé d'un isotope pur ou fortement concentré. Lorsqu'on ajoute à cet isotope actif des proportions croissantes d'isotopes inactifs dans le réseau, l'intensité des raies de diffraction diminue au profit du fond continu incohérent et le contraste se trouve affaibli.

Il faut pouvoir distinguer la diffusion de résonance nucléaire cohérente de la diffusion normale, également cohérente, par les électrons des atomes du réseau. Dans le cas de ^{57}Fe, ce dernier phénomène est d'ailleurs d'intensité négligeable ([7]). Les deux effets sont séparables en comparant l'intensité diffusée avec une source immobile et une source mobile. Le mouvement de la source permet de supprimer la résonance nucléaire, il ne modifie pas l'intensité de la diffusion des rayons γ par les électrons. Il est à prévoir que la diffraction nucléaire donne des raies de diffraction beaucoup plus fines que la diffraction électronique à cause de la grande finesse spectrale des radiations de résonance nucléaire. La localisation précise des noyaux dans le réseau donne lieu à des caractères particuliers : les franges d'interférence d'ordres élevés doivent être intenses.

Il faut noter qu'un cristal émetteur de substance-fille (^{57}Fe) contenant des noyaux émetteurs de substance-mère (^{57}Co) donne lieu au phénomène d'autodiffusion dont la cohérence peut se manifester par des lignes de Kossel ([8]).

(3)

([1]) R. J. Mössbauer, *Z. Physik*, 151, 1958, p. 124; *Naturwissenschaften*, 45, 1958, p. 538; *Z. Naturforschung*, 14 *a*, 1959, p. 538.

([2]) Craig, Dash, Mc Guire, Nagle et Reiswig, *Phys. Rev. Lett.*, 3, 1959, p. 221; Lee, Meyer-Schutzmeister, Schiffer et Vincent, *Phys. Rev. Lett.*, 3, 1959, p. 223; R. V. Pound et G. A. Rebka, *Phys. Rev. Lett.*, 3, 1959, p. 439 et 554; J. P. Schiffer et W. Marshall, *Physik. Rev. Lett.*, 3, 1959, p. 556.

([3]) A. C. Mitchell et M. W. Zemansky, *Resonance Radiation and Excited Atoms*, Cambridge, University Press, 1934; P. Pringsheim, *Fluorescence and Phosphorescence*, Interscience, 1949.

([4]) A. Kastler, *Nuovo Cimento*, 6, 1957, Supplemento n° 3, p. 1148.

([5]) V. Weisskopf, *Ann. Phys.*, 9, 1939, p. 23 (*voir* particulièrement p. 25-26).

([6]) R. W. Wood, *Physical Optics*, Mac Millan, New-York, 3e éd., 1934, p. 534; J. L. Cojan, *Thèse*, Paris, 1953, *Ann. Phys.*, 9, 1954, p. 385.

([7]) S. S. Hanna et coll., *Phys. Rev. Lett.*, 4, 1960, p. 28.

([8]) W. Kossel et H. Voges, *Ann. Physik*, 23, 1935, p. 677.

(*Laboratoire de Physique de l'École Normale Supérieure, 24, rue Lhomond, Paris, 5e.*)

Resonant Scattering of the 14-keV. Iron-57 γ-Ray, and its Interference with Rayleigh Scattering

WHEN radiation is scattered by a resonator, the question of its identity of frequency and coherence of phase with the incident radiation is not simply answered except for an infinitely narrow incident line, when the scattering is fully coherent (see, for example, the discussion by Heitler[1], written in the context of atomic resonances but equally relevant to nuclear ones).

Coherence may be experimentally proved by observing interference between the resonance radiation and some other form of scattering that is known to be coherent; for γ-rays, one would naturally look for interference with the Rayleigh (elastic electronic) scattering. In the long-studied 411 keV. resonance of mercury-198, such interference is unobservable[2], because of the thermal broadening of the line as well as for other reasons. It might just be observable in samarium-152, where the natural width of the 961-keV. line is not completely negligible[3,4] in comparison with the thermal; but the best conditions appear to be provided by the very narrow low-energy lines discovered by Mössbauer[5] in which a substantial part of the radiation is unaffected by recoil or thermal broadening.

After preliminary experiments in collaboration with Dr. B. S. Sood, in which the resonant scattering in metallic iron of the 14-keV. line of iron-57 was found to have the expected intensity, we decided that a foil of 65 per cent iron-57, electroplated on thin copper by the Isotope Division, Atomic Energy Research Establishment, Harwell, would give comparable amplitudes of resonant and Rayleigh scattering at convenient angles. We in fact chose an angle of $43 \pm 2°$, which would include the (211) Bragg reflexion. The geometry of the apparatus is indicated in Fig. 1; the source[6], about 20 mc. of cobalt-57 in a matrix of iron-56, was mounted on a 30 c.p.s. vibrator so that the exact energy of the emitted radiation could be oscillated through the resonant energy. Auxiliary apparatus enabled the intensity of transmission through, or scattering from, the foil to be plotted automatically as a function of speed, the abscissæ of the resultant graphs extending over

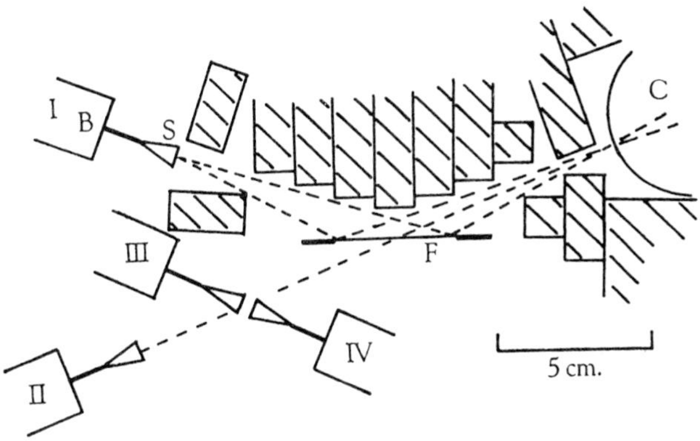

Fig. 1. Diagram of experimental arrangement. *B*, vibrator; *S*, source; *C*, proportional counter; *F*, iron foil. The shaded blocks are heavy alloy shielding. The different positions of the source and vibrator are: I, for scattering; II, for transmission; III and IV, for checking absence of shift in transmission

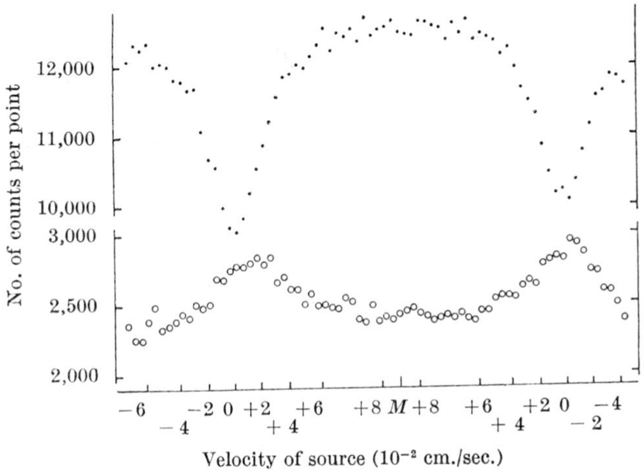

Fig. 2. Plots of intensity versus velocity for transmission (dots) and scattering (circles). The zero of the velocity scale is fixed only by the position of the transmission minima. Positive velocities are for the source approaching the foil. The position *M* on the velocity scale is the point at which the acceleration reverses

rather more than half a cycle of vibration, so that passages through zero velocity in both senses of acceleration were displayed.

Fig. 2 shows the transmission minima and scattering maxima obtained; it will be seen that the scattering peaks are somewhat broader and slightly nearer to one another than are the absorption minima.

The reduced separation of the peaks was, however, due entirely to the shift of one of them; presumably the whole pattern had suffered an instrumental drift

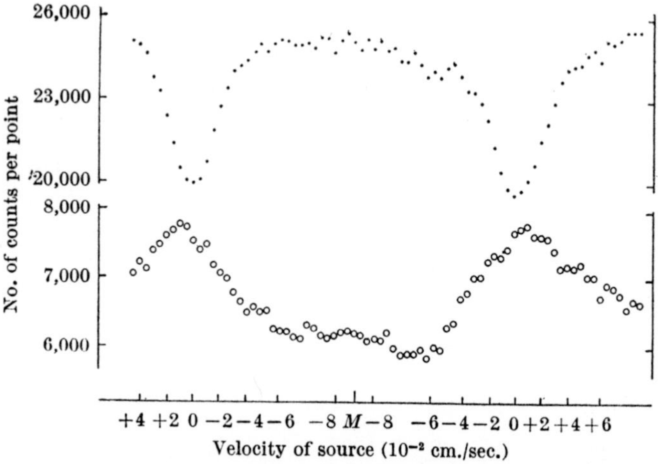

Fig. 3. Plots of intensity versus velocity for a separate experiment in which, as indicated on the velocity scale, negative velocities are displayed in the centre

during the long periods of operation that were necessary. We repeated the measurements with the apparatus set to display negative, instead of positive, speeds at the centre, alternating transmission and scattering measurements and adding the results of all sets of each kind. Fig. 3 shows that the peaks now appeared, as expected, more widely spaced than the dips, with no evidence of general drift. Thus, assuming the transmission dips to occur at exactly zero velocity, we can say that the maximum scattering occurs when the source is approaching the scatterer with a velocity corresponding to a fraction of the line-width.

It remains to verify that the dips correspond precisely to zero velocity ; this need not be so if source and scatterer materials are not identical. This point was checked at the suggestion of Mr. D. A. O'Connor, by successive transmission experiments with the source assembly set in the positions marked III and IV in Fig. 1 ; this amounts to reversing the velocity-scale about the true zero. No change in the dip position was found.

If there is some coherence of phase between resonant and Rayleigh scattering, we should expect them to be in quadrature at exact resonance, moving towards coincidence of phase on the high-frequency side. Thus, on top of the constant intensity of the Rayleigh and the sharply peaked contour of the resonant scattering, there should be added a dispersion-type curve representing the interference between them, with its maximum a fraction of a line-width to the positive side of zero velocity. The observed shift and broadening are probably to be explained in terms of such coherence, but the measurements are not yet detailed enough to show clearly the asymmetry of line-shape that is also to be expected or to determine what percentage of coherence exists ; full coherence is not to be expected when the incident line is of similar breadth to that of the resonance.

We have also observed the resonant scattering from ordinary iron (2·2 per cent iron-57) at a mean angle of 90°, in the presence of a relatively large intensity of Rayleigh scattering. We found neither shift nor broadening of the scattering resonance, which is consistent with the expectation that, at this angle of scattering in a magnetic dipole transition, the resonant component will be polarized at right angles to the Rayleigh.

It is to be expected that the narrow-line resonance radiation will show, in its scattering from crystals containing iron-57, interference phenomena similar to those of X-rays. Interesting differences may arise from the resonant absorption which accompanies the scattering, from the narrowness of the line as compared with X-ray lines, and from the simple way in which the exact energy, and with it the phase of the resonant scattering, may be varied.

P. J. Black
P. B. Moon

Department of Physics,
University of Birmingham.

[1] Heitler, W., "The Quantum Theory of Radiation", chap. 3 (Oxford Univ. Press, 1944).
[2] Moon, P. B., *Proc. Phys. Soc.*, A, **63**, 1189 (1950).
[3] Grodzins, L., *Phys. Rev.*, **109**, 1014 (1958).
[4] Moon, P. B., and Sood, B. S., *Proc. Roy. Soc.*, A, **257**, 44 (1960).
[5] Mössbauer, R. L., *Z. Phys.*, **151**, 124 (1958); *Naturwiss.*, **45**, 538 (1958).
[6] Chackett, G. A., Chackett, K. F., and Singh, B., *J. Inorg. Nucl. Chem.*, **14**, 138 (1960).

The Mössbauer Effect in Tin from 120°K to the Melting Point

By A. J. F. Boyle, D. St. P. Bunbury, C. Edwards and H. E. Hall

The Physical Laboratories, University of Manchester

Communicated by B. H. Flowers; MS. received 18*th June* 1960

Abstract. Measurements have been made of the intensity of the recoilless resonance absorption of the 24 kev γ-ray from the decay of $^{119}Sn^{m}$ in metallic tin from 120°K to the melting point. Values of the Debye–Waller factor deduced from these results tend towards the values calculated for a Debye Θ of 142°K at low temperatures; the behaviour of the Debye–Waller factor at higher temperatures indicates considerable anharmonicity of the lattice vibrations. Comparison with evidence from the thermal expansion and specific heat suggests that the quartic term in the interatomic potential is positive, and that the ratio of quartic to cubic terms is of the same order as the ratio of cubic to quadratic terms.

In the last few degrees below the melting point the resonance absorption shows a rapid drop accompanied by an increase in line width. It is suggested that this effect is due to enhanced self-diffusion in the solid, and it is estimated that the diffusion coefficient reaches a value of $10^{-8}\,cm^2\,sec^{-1}$ about 0·6°K below the melting point.

§ 1. Introduction

The primary purpose of the experiments to be described in this paper was to investigate the way in which the recoilless γ emission discovered by Mössbauer (1958) is affected by the transition from solid to liquid; for this purpose the 24 kev γ-ray of $^{119}Sn^{m}$ in metallic tin was used. The experiments show that the effect disappears continuously in the last few degrees below the melting point, and this result is attributed to self-diffusion in the solid. In addition, measurements of the intensity of the effect down to liquid air temperatures have yielded some information about the nature of the atomic vibrations in tin.

For the purpose of this paper it is convenient to express the emission of γ-rays from a solid in a way analogous to the elegant result derived by Van Hove (1954) for the scattering of X-rays or neutrons by an assembly of atoms. Van Hove shows that the differential cross section for scattering with momentum change $\hbar\boldsymbol{\kappa}$ and energy change $\hbar\omega$ is proportional to a quantity $S(\boldsymbol{\kappa}, \omega)$ which is the Fourier transform in space and time of a time dependent pair correlation function. $S(\boldsymbol{\kappa}, \omega)$ is given by

$$S(\boldsymbol{\kappa}, \omega)=\frac{1}{2\pi}\int_{-\infty}^{\infty} e^{i\omega t}dt \sum_{ij}\langle \exp[-i\boldsymbol{\kappa}.\mathbf{r}_i(0)]\exp[i\boldsymbol{\kappa}.\mathbf{r}_j(t)]\rangle, \quad \ldots\ldots(1)$$

where $\mathbf{r}_i(t)$ is the Heisenberg position operator of the ith atom and the symbol $\langle\,\rangle$

denotes an average value in thermal equilibrium. For emission of a γ-ray from a given atom the equivalent result (Marshall and Schiffer, private communication) is that the probability of the emitted γ-ray having wave number k is

$$p(k)=\frac{1}{2\pi}\int_{-\infty}^{\infty}\exp[ic(k-k_0)t]\exp(-\tfrac{1}{2}\Gamma_\gamma|t|)\langle\exp[-i\mathbf{k}.\mathbf{r}(\mathbf{t})]\exp[i\mathbf{k}.\mathbf{r}(0)]\rangle dt, \qquad \ldots\ldots(2)$$

where $\hbar ck_0$ is the energy of the γ transition and Γ_γ its width. The correlations in $\langle e^{-i\mathbf{k}.\mathbf{r}(t)}e^{i\mathbf{k}.\mathbf{r}(0)}\rangle$ at small times give the emission of γ-rays with recoil; at large times this factor tends asymptotically to

$$\exp(-2W)=\exp(-k^2\overline{x^2}), \qquad \ldots\ldots(3)$$

where $\overline{x^2}$ is the mean square displacement of the atom (assumed Gaussian) in the direction of emission of the γ-ray. The factor (3) is the Debye–Waller factor, familiar in x-ray crystallography, and from Eqn (2) we see that this fraction of the γ-rays is emitted as a sharp line with the energy and width of the nuclear transition. The cross section for resonance absorption is likewise multiplied by this factor. For a Debye solid

$$2W=\frac{3E_\gamma^2}{Mc^2\boldsymbol{k}\Theta}\left[\frac{1}{4}+\left(\frac{T}{\Theta}\right)^2\int_0^\Theta\frac{x\,dx}{e^x-1}\right], \qquad \ldots\ldots(4)$$

where E_γ is the energy of the γ-ray and M the mass of the emitting atom.

§ 2. Experimental Method

The resonance absorption was measured by moving the source so as to destroy the resonance by the Doppler effect. The source was driven by a flat-topped saw-tooth waveform, so that it was stationary and moving for equal periods of time; a feedback amplifier was used to ensure that the motion of the source followed the driving waveform. Pulses from a scintillation counter were passed through a single-channel pulse height analyser and then gated into separate counting channels for the stationary and moving periods; the counting rate was obtained by simultaneously gating pulses from a standard oscillator. The velocity in the moving part of the waveform was such as to shift the emission line off resonance by about ten half-widths. This velocity was calculated from the frequency of the driving waveform and the amplitude of motion (about 0·2 mm, measured with a micrometer-eyepiece microscope).

To obtain maximum recoilless emission the source was maintained within a few degrees of liquid air temperature throughout the experiments, by enclosing it in a chamber surrounded by liquid air. The absorber was situated in the vacuum space below this liquid air vessel. It was held between graphite disks clamped in an aluminium ring; the graphite disks were machined so as to preserve the shape of the absorber when it was melted. Palladium foils placed on either side of the absorber served both to absorb unwanted x-rays and as thermal radiation shields. Absorber temperatures above room temperature were obtained by electrical heating; for temperatures below room temperature the absorber was connected thermally to the liquid air vessel, and electrical heating was again used to obtain temperatures up to room temperature. The temperatures of source and absorber were measured by copper–constantan thermocouples in contact with them; the thermocouples were calibrated in liquid nitrogen and at the melting point of tin.

Since the temperatures of source and absorber were normally different, a small correction had to be made to the results to allow for the thermal shift reported previously (Boyle *et al.* 1960); this never amounted to more than 7%. The apparent absorption actually measured was less than the true absorption because of the finite source velocity used; this factor was allowed for in the subsequent reduction of the results.

§ 3. The Debye–Waller Factor

To convert the measured absorptions into values of the Debye–Waller factor it was necessary to know the fraction of recoilless γ-rays emitted by the source. To this end measurements were made with three absorber thicknesses of approximately 0·001 in., 0·003 in. and 0·008 in. After correcting for background to the 24 kev photopeak passed by the single-channel analyser and for the thermal shift, the values of absorption as a function of absorber thickness were plotted on double logarithmic graph paper for six selected temperatures. These six sets of three points could then be compared with a calculated curve of apparent fraction of recoilless γ-rays absorbed as a function of $n\sigma_0 e^{-2W}$, where n is the number of atoms per cm^2, and σ_0 is the absorption cross section at resonance. In this way six values of the fraction of recoilless γ-rays emitted by the source were obtained; they agreed within the experimental error and had a mean value of 19·4%. All the results could then be expressed as fractions of recoilless γ-rays absorbed, and using the known value of σ_0 and the measured values of n, e^{-2W} could be found from the theoretical absorption curve. The results are shown as a function of temperature in Fig. 1. A slight extrapolation of these results yields an expected Debye–Waller factor for the source of 40%; after correction for self-absorption due to finite source thickness we expect a recoilless emission of 23%. The presence of ^{113}In K x-rays in the source could account for the difference between this value and the directly measured value of 19·4%; this latter estimate is probably about 10% too low, however, because of broadening

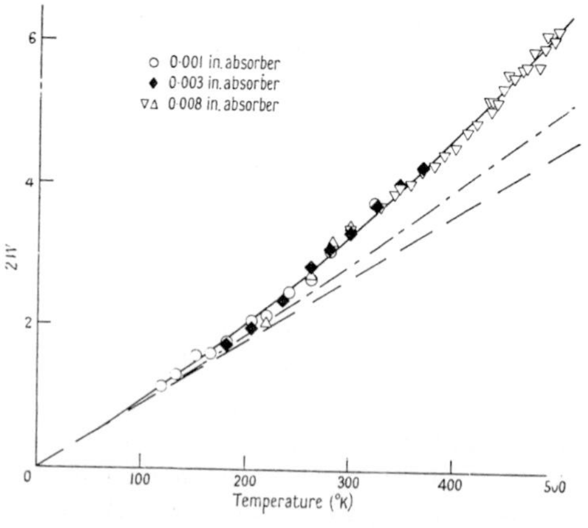

Fig. 1. Temperature dependence of the Debye–Waller factor. Broken line, Eqn (5) for $\Theta = 142°$K; chain curve, corrected for change in Θ due to thermal expansion; full curve, corrected for change in Θ due to thermal expansion, and for the effect of anharmonicity at constant volume.

of the emission line by self-absorption. Fortunately, the corresponding error in our values of the Debye–Waller factor for the absorber is of second order in the source and absorber broadenings, and is probably less than 1%.

For $T > \frac{1}{2}\Theta$ the high temperature approximation to Eqn (4) is not in error by more than 7%, and we may put

$$2W = k^2\overline{x^2} = \frac{3E_\gamma{}^2 T}{Mc^2 \boldsymbol{k}\Theta^2}. \qquad \ldots\ldots(5)$$

The broken line in Fig. 1 represents Eqn (5) with $\Theta = 142\,^\circ\mathrm{K}$. Measurements of the specific heat of tin indicate a Debye Θ of 195 °K below 2 °K, but the effective value of Θ falls rapidly to a minimum of 125 °K at about 12 °K. In view of these large deviations from the Debye law, an effective Θ of 142 °K for the Debye–Waller factor does not seem unreasonable. But the experimental results deviate more and more from the linear law of Eqn (5) as the temperature rises. The result $\overline{x^2} \propto T$ at high temperatures depends only on the assumption of harmonic forces; an explanation of the non-linear relation between W and T shown in Fig. 1 must therefore be sought in terms of anharmonicity of the lattice vibrations.

Anharmonicity can affect $\overline{x^2}$ in two ways. First, the effective Debye Θ will be altered by thermal expansion; this is the effect considered by Zener and Bilinsky (1936). If we assume that all lattice frequencies are changed in the same proportion by expansion

$$\frac{\partial \ln \Theta}{\partial \ln V} = \frac{V\beta}{C_V K}, \qquad \ldots\ldots(6)$$

where β is the coefficient of cubic expansion and K is the isothermal compressibility. From Eqn (6) we have

$$\frac{d \ln \Theta}{dT} = \frac{V\beta^2}{C_V K}, \qquad \ldots\ldots(7)$$

and if we further assume Gruneisen's law that $\beta \propto C_V$

$$\ln\left(\frac{\Theta}{\Theta_0}\right) = \frac{V}{K}\left(\frac{\beta}{C_V}\right)^2 \int_0^T C_V dT$$

$$\simeq \frac{V\beta^2}{3RK}\left(T - \frac{3}{8}\Theta\right), \qquad \ldots\ldots(8)$$

since the specific heat is almost classical in the temperature range with which we are concerned. If we insert numbers into Eqn (8) we find that the value of $\overline{x^2}$ given by Eqn (5) has to be increased by a fraction $(2{\cdot}63 \times 10^{-4})(T - \frac{3}{8}\Theta)$; values thus corrected are shown by the chain line in Fig. 1. It can be seen that this correction is too small by a factor of more than 3 to account for the experimental results. The correction is not very certain because we have, for example, ignored the very large anisotropy in the thermal expansion of tin; but it seems most unlikely that our estimate could be in error by so large a factor, and there is indeed a second mechanism by which anharmonicity can increase $\overline{x^2}$. Even at constant volume $\overline{x^2}$ is not proportional to T at high temperatures if the forces are anharmonic. To estimate the magnitude of this effect consider a particle bound in the one-dimensional potential

$$V(x) = \tfrac{1}{2}ax^2 + bx^3 + cx^4; \qquad \ldots\ldots(9)$$

it is then easily shown that in classical conditions (cf. Peierls 1956) the specific heat is, including only the lowest order corrections,

$$C_V = \boldsymbol{k}T\left\{1+\frac{\boldsymbol{k}T}{a}\left[15\left(\frac{b}{a}\right)^2-6\left(\frac{c}{a}\right)\right]\right\}, \qquad \ldots\ldots(10)$$

and the mean square displacement is

$$\overline{x^2} = \frac{\boldsymbol{k}T}{a}\left\{1+\frac{\boldsymbol{k}T}{a}\left[45\left(\frac{b}{a}\right)^2-12\left(\frac{c}{a}\right)\right]\right\}. \qquad \ldots\ldots(11)$$

This model therefore leads us to expect a fractional deviation in $\overline{x^2}$ about three times that in the specific heat; more or less according to the sign and magnitude of the quartic term in the potential. The measured expansion coefficient and specific heat of tin show that the fractional excess in C_V at high temperatures, excluding the electronic specific heat, is moderately well represented by

$$\frac{\Delta C_V}{C_V} = 1{\cdot}38\times10^{-4}(T-50). \qquad \ldots\ldots(12)$$

If a correction of 4·5 times this amount is added to the previous correction to the value of W calculated from Eqn (5) we obtain the full curve of Fig. 1, which is in excellent agreement with the experimental results. This factor of 4·5 implies that in Eqn (9)

$$\frac{c}{a} = 1{\cdot}5\left(\frac{b}{a}\right)^2. \qquad \ldots\ldots(13)$$

In view of the grossly over-simplified model used to derive this result too much significance should not be attached to it; but it is perhaps worth pointing out that for a 12–6 interatomic potential $ac/b^2 = 1{\cdot}26$.

§ 4. Diffusion near the Melting Point

Experimental values of absorption in the 0·008 in. absorber near the melting point are shown in Fig. 2. The full line corresponds to the full curve of Fig. 1. It is clear that there is a significant decrease in resonance absorption below the value expected from the Debye–Waller factor in the last few degrees below the melting point. Measurements of line width were also made at temperatures approximately 0·8 and 8°K below the melting point, by taking additional readings with a source velocity corresponding approximately to the half-width; it was found that 0·8°K below the melting point the width of the absorption line had increased by a factor of $1{\cdot}97^{+0{\cdot}75}_{-0{\cdot}54}$.

To see how such an effect might arise, consider the effect of diffusion on the factor $\langle e^{-i\mathbf{k}.\mathbf{r}(t)}e^{i\mathbf{k}.\mathbf{r}(0)}\rangle$ in Eqn (2). In an ideal lattice this tends asymptotically to e^{-2W} at infinite time, but if any diffusion occurs this is no longer true. In fact, the wavelength of 24 kev γ-rays is sufficiently short that if the atom has jumped to another lattice site at time t, $\langle e^{-i\mathbf{k}.\mathbf{r}(t)}\rangle$ is effectively zero. The value of $\langle e^{-i\mathbf{k}.\mathbf{r}(t)}e^{i\mathbf{k}.\mathbf{r}(0)}\rangle$ is thus the value in the absence of diffusion multiplied by the chance that the atom concerned has not diffused from its original lattice site, i.e.

$$\langle e^{-i\mathbf{k}.\mathbf{r}(t)}e^{i\mathbf{k}.\mathbf{r}(0)}\rangle \simeq e^{-2W}\exp[-\Gamma_D|t|], \qquad \ldots\ldots(14)$$

where Γ_D is the mean jump frequency of the atoms in the diffusion process. Eqn (2) thus becomes

$$p(k) = \frac{1}{2\pi}\int_{-\infty}^{\infty}\exp\left[ic(k-k_0)t\right]\exp\left[(\tfrac{1}{2}\Gamma_\gamma+\Gamma_D)|t|\right]e^{-2W}dt. \quad \ldots\ldots(15)$$

The effect of diffusion is thus to increase the width of the absorption line by a factor $(\Gamma_\gamma+2\Gamma_D)/\Gamma_\gamma$ and thus to reduce its maximum height by the same factor. When this absorption line is folded with the emission line of width $\frac{1}{2}\Gamma_\gamma$, we find that the actual reduction in resonant absorption is by a factor $(\Gamma_\gamma+\Gamma_D)/\Gamma_\gamma$.

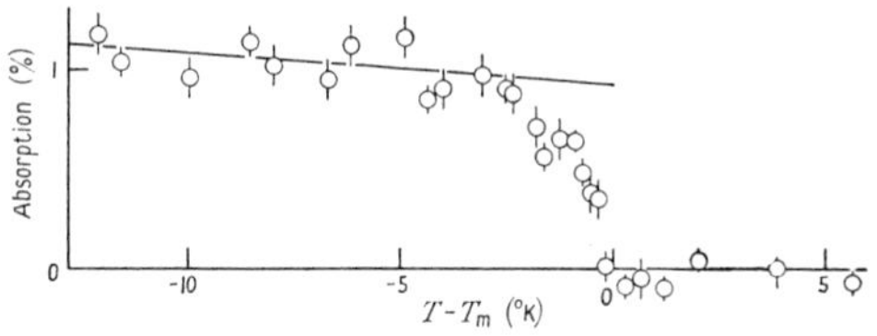

Fig. 2. Resonance absorption in the 0·008 in. absorber near the melting point. The full line corresponds to the full curve in Fig. 1.

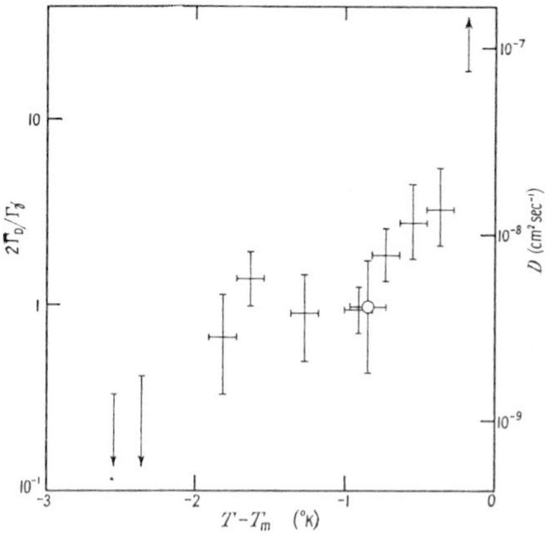

Fig. 3. Diffusion near the melting point. The point marked by a circle was deduced from the width of the resonance absorption, and the other points from its amplitude (Fig. 2).

Values of $2\Gamma_D/\Gamma_\gamma$ calculated from the measured reduction in absorption are shown in Fig. 3; a point calculated from the change in line width is also shown; the agreement with the other points provides some confirmation of Eqn (15). The diffusion coefficient D may be estimated from the relation for a random walk in three dimensions

$$\Gamma_D = 6D/\delta^2, \qquad \ldots\ldots (16)$$

where δ is the step length. A tin atom has four nearest neighbours at 3·02 Å, and two others at 3·16 Å. We therefore have taken a mean value of 3·1 Å to obtain the approximate values of diffusion coefficient indicated on the right-hand ordinate of Fig. 3. Measurements of self-diffusion in tin (Fensham 1950) only extend up to 223·1 °K (8·8 °K below the melting point), where $D=2{\cdot}65\times10^{-10}$ cm² sec⁻¹ along the tetrad axis and $D=0{\cdot}93\times10^{-10}$ cm² sec⁻¹ perpendicular to it. Our results could reasonably be extrapolated to join these smoothly, but they indicate a greatly accelerated rise in diffusion near the melting point. Such an effect has been found by conventional methods in indium close to the melting point by Eckert and Drickamer (1951). This encourages us to believe that our proposed explanation of the behaviour of the Mössbauer effect near the melting point is indeed correct. We may also mention that very rapid recrystallization of an unmelted absorber foil was observed at temperatures where the Mössbauer effect was reduced.

§ 5. Conclusion

Our experiments show that the intensity of the Mössbauer effect is essentially determined by the mean square displacement of the emitting atom during the lifetime of the excited state, in accordance with Eqn (2). The effect of diffusion may be thought of crudely as defining rather precisely the time at which the γ-ray was emitted, and thereby broadening its energy. It is essentially because of diffusion that the effect is not observed in the liquid; but there seems to be no reason in principle why it should not be observed in a liquid if the diffusion coefficient were sufficiently low and the lifetime sufficiently short.

Our analysis in § 3 shows that measurements of the Debye–Waller factor may give useful information about lattice anharmonicity, if a more thorough theoretical analysis can be given. For this purpose the Mössbauer effect has the advantage over x-ray diffraction that it readily yields absolute values of the Debye–Waller factor.

Acknowledgments

We should like to thank Dr. S. F. Edwards, Dr. A. Herzenberg and Dr. J. O. Newton for a number of helpful discussion, and Mr. J. R. Rook for computing the theoretical absorption integrals. One of us (C.E.) is indebted to the Department of Scientific and Industrial Research for financial support.

References

Boyle, A. J. F., Bunbury, D. St. P., Edwards, C., and Hall, H. E., 1960, *Proc. Phys. Soc.*, **76**, 165.
Eckert, R. E., and Drickamer, H. G., 1951, *J. Chem. Phys.*, **20**, 13.
Fensham, P. J., 1950, *Aust. J. Sci. Res.* A, **3**, 91; **4**, 229.
Mössbauer, R. J., 1958, *Z. Phys.*, **151**, 124.
Peierls, R. E., 1956, *Quantum Theory of Solids*, § 2.3 (Oxford: University Press).
Van Hove, L., 1954, *Phys. Rev.*, **95**, 249.
Zener, C., and Bilinsky, S., 1936, *Phys. Rev.*, **50**, 101.

Mössbauer Effect: Applications to Magnetism

G. K. Wertheim
Bell Telephone Laboratories, Inc., Murray Hill, New Jersey

The Mössbauer effect, the resonant absorption of nuclear gamma rays in solids, may be used to obtain the hyperfine structure of Fe^{57} in magnetic materials. Experiments are performed by observing the absorption by *stable* Fe^{57} of the 14.4-kev gamma ray coming from a source which contains *radioactive* Fe^{57} produced by the decay of Co^{57}. The experiments are not limited to naturally iron-bearing materials; other substances can be studied, provided only, that small amounts of cobalt can be introduced into lattice sites of interest. The magnetic moments of the ground and first excited states of Fe^{57} are known and make possible direct determination of the field at the iron nucleus once the hyperfine structure has been measured. The magnetic field at iron nuclei has been determined in the ferromagnetic transition metals (Fe 3.42×10^5 oe, Co 3.12×10^5 oe, Ni 2.80×10^5 oe at 0°K), but no hyperfine structure has been observed down to 4°K in the antiferromagnetic transition metals, Mn and Cr. In the case of yttrium-iron garnet the fields at the iron atoms in the two types of sites have been obtained (tetrahedral 3.9×10^5 oe, octahedral 4.7×10^5 oe). The most complete analysis so far has been made in FeF_2 where the magnetic field in the antiferromagnetic state ($H_{T=0}=3.40\times10^5$ oe) and the quadrupole splitting in the paramagnetic state (31.2 Mc/sec) have been obtained. Other materials under investigation are the iron oxides and some ferrites, where, for trivalent iron, fields in the vicinity of 5.0×10^5 oe have generally been found.

INTRODUCTION

THE realization by R. L. Mössbauer[1] that the nuclear recoil associated with gamma emission may be absent when the decaying atom is bound in a crystal lattice has led to a number of interesting experiments in nuclear physics. It also has considerable promise as a tool in solid-state physics, and in particular in magnetism. The connection between these usually unrelated fields arises from the narrowness of the linewidth of the emitted gamma rays, which makes it possible to resolve the hyperfine splitting of the nuclear energy levels.[2–4] These, of course, reflect the magnetic field at the nucleus as well as the electric field gradient tensor, both of which are of immediate interest to the solid-state physicist.

The statement that the nuclear recoil is absent does not imply a violation of the law of conservation of momentum. In the recoil-free emission process the crystal containing the decaying atom recoils as a unit. As a consequence of the large mass of the recoiling unit, the energy associated with the recoil is vanishingly small, and the nuclear gamma ray has an energy which is very closely equal to that of the nuclear transition. It is this fact (which we will discuss further below) that in turn makes possible the resonant reabsorption of the gamma ray by another atom of the same species, which is an essential part of all Mössbauer experiments.

The fraction of decays which take place without recoil depends on the ratio of the free-atom recoil energy to the Debye energy $k\theta_D$, the characteristic energy of a phonon. An atom in the solid may be thought of as being free to emit zero, one, or many phonons, but as being unable to recoil with an arbitrary energy.[5] (This statement is true only as long as the recoil energy is sufficiently small so that the atom is not displaced from its lattice site by the recoil.) When many decay processes are considered it is found that the average energy of the emitted phonons per decay is still the free-atom recoil energy. From this it is immediately apparent that when the free-atom recoil energy is smaller than $k\theta_D$, there will be a high probability of emitting no phonon at all. These facts are contained in the familiar Debye-Waller

[1] R. L. Mössbauer, Z. Physik **151**, 124 (1958); Naturwissenschaften **45**, 538 (1958); Z. Naturforsch. **14a**, 211 (1959).
[2] L. L. Lee, L. Meyer-Schutzmeister, J. P. Schiffer, and D. Vincent, Phys. Rev. Letters **3**, 223 (1959).
[3] R. V. Pound and G. A. Rebka, Jr., Phys. Rev. Letters **3**, 554 (1959).
[4] I. Ya Barit, M. I. Podgoretskii, and F. L. Shapiro, Zhur. Eksptl. i Teoret. Fiz. **38**, 301 (1960).
[5] For a fuller discussion see: W. M. Visscher, Ann. Phys. (N. Y.) **9**, 194 (1960); H. J. Lipkin, *ibid.* **9**, 332 (1960); K. S. Singwi and A. Sjolander (to be published).

factor expressing the fraction of recoil-free events

$$f=\exp\left\{-\frac{3}{2}\frac{E_r}{k\theta_D}\left[1+\frac{2}{3}\left(\frac{\pi T}{\theta_D}\right)^2\right]\right\}.$$

The usefulness of the zero-phonon gamma rays arises from their unusually narrow linewidths. The natural linewidth of a gamma ray is determined by the widths of the states involved in the decay process. Here we will consider only decays from an excited state to the ground state of a stable isotope, in which the width is entirely determined by the excited state. The natural width of the excited state is determined through the uncertainty principle by the lifetime of the state; a lifetime of 10^{-7} sec, characteristic of the widely used Mössbauer isotope Fe^{57}, leads to a level width of 4.6×10^{-9} ev (equivalent to 1.13 Mc/sec), which is smaller than characteristic hyperfine or quadrupole interaction energies in many solids.

Other sources of line broadening must also be considered. The thermal motion of the emitting atoms could be a serious limitation in a gaseous or liquid source, but since the zero-phonon process takes place to a measurable extent only in solids, we will consider only this case. Lattice vibration frequencies are characteristically 10^{13} sec^{-1}. If an isotope is considered whose excited state has a lifetime long compared to the period of the lattice vibration, there will be no first-order Doppler broadening or shift from this cause. There will, however, be a second-order Doppler shift[6,7] which depends only on the average of the square of the velocity, i.e., on the kinetic energy, of the lattice atoms. This shift is small and does not affect the resolution since it is of the same magnitude and in the same direction for all emitting atoms. Broadening can also arise if the environment of the emitting atoms varies, as it might in an alloy, or if the crystalline fields at the emitting atoms have frequencies comparable to the lifetime of the excited nuclear state.

The existence of recoil-free emission and resonant absorption is best demonstrated in a simple transmission experiment in which gamma rays from a source pass through an absorber to a detector. If the resonant absorption is destroyed, the counting rate at the detector will increase. This is most simply accomplished by giving the source a velocity sufficient to Doppler-shift the energy of the emitted gamma rays by more than their natural linewidth; velocities of the order of a small fraction of 1 cm/sec are required. A simple extension of this idea produces a "Mössbauer spectrometer" with which an absorption spectrum is obtained simply by observing the counting rate at the detector as a function of the Doppler velocity of the source.

After the original demonstration of resonant absorption by Mössbauer using the isotope Ir^{191}, and its subsequent verification by a number of other groups,[2,8] attention has shifted to other suitable isotopes. One of the first to be used, and one which remains of particular interest for solid-state work, is Fe^{57}.[9-12] This isotope offers a combination of desirable properties which have already made possible experiments ranging from a verification of the gravitational red shift to the determination of magnetic fields in solids. The cobalt parent of Fe^{57} has a 270-day half-life, convenient for most work. The decay is by electron capture, and the neutrino which accompanies this process has an energy of ~0.6 Mev. The iron is left in a fairly low state of excitation (134 kev), from which it makes a 120-kev gamma transition to the first excited state whose lifetime is 10^{-7} sec. The low energy (14.4 kev) of the transition to the ground state used in the experiment leads to a large fraction of zero-phonon decays. In addition, Fe^{57} has the advantage that iron is a component of many interesting magnetic materials.

EXPERIMENTAL

Experiments always involve a source which contains the radioactive species, an absorber which contains the stable isotope, and a radiation detector (Fig. 1). The substance under study may be used as either the source or the absorber. If a substance is naturally iron-bearing there are a number of advantages to using it as an absorber. One of these is that the iron is in a normal lattice site, rather than in a site characteristic of cobalt; another is that there is no preceding electron-capture decay, which could result in a displaced or multiply ionized atom. The concentration or iron in the material should be high enough so that an absorber of areal density 0.1 mg/cm^2 of Fe^{57} can be made. Since the natural abundance of Fe^{57} is only 2.14%, the use of enriched isotope may be desirable. (It has also been possible to use as absorbers substances not normally iron-bearing into which Fe^{57} obtained as separated isotope was introduced in amounts less than 1 atom-percent.)

Substances which do not normally contain iron may be studied by incorporating small amounts of Co^{57} into them and using them as sources. Such studies yield information on the fields at isolated impurity atoms. This general approach is of course also applicable to iron-bearing substances. In the case of metallic iron no difference has been found between experiments using the iron as an absorber in the pure form and those using it as a source containing trace amounts of Co^{57}. In insulators, however, major differences between these two types of experiment have been observed.

---

6 R. V. Pound and G. A. Rebka, Jr., Phys. Rev. Letters 4, 227 (1960).

7 B. D. Josephson, Phys. Rev. Letters 4, 341 (1960).

8 P. P. Craig, J. G. Dash, A. D. McGuire, D. Nagle, and R. D. Reiswig, Phys. Rev. Letters 3, 221 (1959).

9 R. V. Pound and G. A. Rebka, Jr., Phys. Rev. Letters 3, 439 (1960).

10 J. P. Schiffer and W. Marshall, Phys. Rev. Letters 3, 556 (1959).

11 S. S. Hanna *et al.*, Phys. Rev. Letters 4, 28 (1960).

12 G. DePasquali, H. Frauenfelder, S. Margulies, and R. N. Peacock, Phys. Rev. Letters 4, 71 (1960).

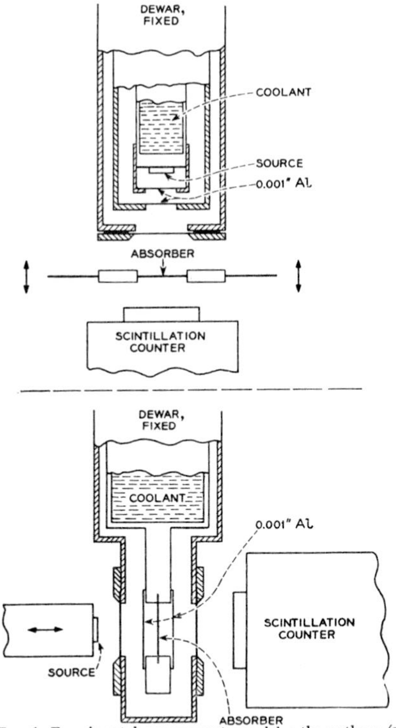

FIG. 1. Experimental arrangements used by the author: (a) Stationary source and moving, unsplit absorber. (b) Moving, unsplit source and stationary absorber.

One of the components of the experiment, either the source or the absorber, should have an unsplit line in order for the hyperfine spectrum of the other to be observed directly. A number of substances have already been used for this purpose. The first to be proposed were the ferrocyanides,[13] which are diamagnetic and have no hyperfine field at the iron atom. In general, these suffer from the disadvantage that they do not contain much iron for use as absorbers. Considerable improvement can be obtained with a ferrocyanide made with separated Fe^{57} isotope.[14] Even at room temperature this substance, used as an absorber, is by far the most successful we have yet used, the criteria of excellence being the linewidth and the ratio of resonant absorption to photoelectric absorption. Unfortunately, all attempts to make sources by incorporating Co^{57} into a ferrocyanide have failed[13] because the structure of the cobaltocyanide is different from that of the ferrocyanide.

[13] S. L. Ruby, L. M. Epstein, and K. H. Sun, Rev. Sci. Instr. **31**, 580 (1960).

[14] The author is indebted to J. D. Struthers of this laboratory or the preparation of this material.

A second group of substances that has been widely used is the stainless steels.[15] Most of the experiments described in this paper were done with sources made by incorporating Co^{57} into type 310 stainless. Here it has proved to be easy to prepare sources by simply evaporating $Co^{57}Cl_2$ solution to dryness on stainless steel and diffusing at 950°C in a carefully evacuated quartz capsule.

The linewidth of the absorption or emission line in stainless steel has been examined in some detail, and has generally been found to be considerably larger than the natural linewidth. Any or all of the following mechanisms may contribute.

(1) The environment of the various iron atoms in an alloy is necessarily different. Since it is known that the chemical environment can shift the energy of the nuclear levels, it is possible that there is inhomogeneous broadening due to this effect.

(2) The existence of a single line of natural width is predicated on an electron spin correlation time sufficiently short to destroy the hyperfine interaction. For a broadening of less than 10%, a spin correlation time less than 3×10^{-12} sec is required. The actual correlation time is not known, but values of 10^{-12} or 10^{-13} sec do not seem unreasonable. Some indication of a temperature-dependent linewidth, which would confirm that this mechanism is operative, has been obtained.

(3) Broadening can also arise from the finite thickness of the source or absorber, and begins to be appreciable (30%) when the radiation traverses one absorption length of material. The importance of this effect in stainless steel of the thickness generally used as an absorber has been investigated. A series of experiments have been conducted using as a source Co^{57} diffused into chromium metal, the combination which produces the narrowest unsplit line found so far, and using as absorbers type 310 stainless in a variety of thicknesses. The linewidth was 0.045 cm/sec, or more than two times the natural linewidth. No difference in linewidth was found with absorbers ranging from 0.00025 in. to 0.0010 in., the latter being the thickness usually used in experiments. It was noted that the frac-

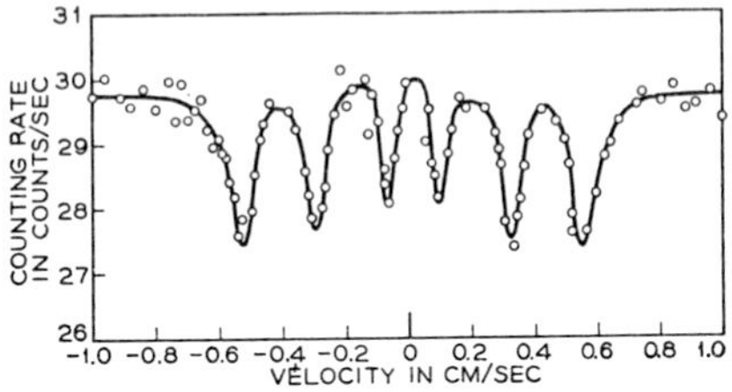

FIG. 2. The hyperfine spectrum of Fe^{57} in iron metal, obtained with a stainless steel source and a natural iron absorber 0.001 in. thick.

[15] G. K. Wertheim, Phys. Rev. Letters **4**, 403 (1960).

tional absorption in these experiments was not proportional to absorber thickness. This fact might be considered evidence that the absorber is thick, i.e., longer than one absorption length, but the effect could equally well be caused by the increase in the degraded 120-kev radiation falling into the energy selection channel. The deterioration of the gamma-ray scintillation spectrum with increasing absorber thickness is in accord with the latter interpretation.

These difficulties, inherent in the use of an alloy, have not prevented the widespread use of stainless steel, but there is a continuing interest in other substances. One of the most promising is $KFeF_3$, a cubic material with perovskite structure, used as an absorber at room temperature where it is paramagnetic. Its spin correlation time at room temperature is short enough to result in a relatively narrow line, while its cubic nature assures the absence of quadrupole interaction. Its use as a source is being studied.

Experimentally, two distinct methods for taking data have emerged. The first uses motion at a constant velocity, usually symmetrical in the forward and backward directions; different velocities are obtained by changing frequency or amplitude. As the source of motion, electromechanical transducers, cams, lathes, and constant-velocity servos have been used. The experiments reported here were done with a system of this type employing a loudspeaker voice coil driven at constant velocity by dc coupled transistors from the symmetrical sawtooth wave output of a Hewlett-Packard function generator. In the second method, all desired velocities are included in the motion, and the counts are sorted according to instantaneous velocity of the source relative to the absorber. This is generally done by using a sinusoidal motion, or more advantageously a double parabola, which has the feature that equal time is spent at each velocity increment. The instantaneous velocity is determined by a pickup coil rigidly attached to the moving source and placed in a uniform magnetic field. The resulting signal is either fed directly into the address logic in a multichannel analyzer or else used to modulate the amplitude of the energy-selected counts, which can then be sorted by an unmodified multichannel analyzer.

The first method places somewhat higher demands on counting rate stability and requires a motion which is more difficult to obtain, especially at high velocities. On the other hand, it is more flexible, since part of an absorption spectrum can be examined without sweeping through the whole range. The second method requires a normalization of the data if a sinusoidal motion is used, since more time is spent at high velocities than near zero. However, this problem is absent when a double parabola is used, and for many experiments this may be the most attractive approach. It might be noted, however, that the multichannel analyzer system does *not* collect data any faster than the constant velocity system.

EFFECTIVE MAGNETIC FIELDS IN THE TRANSITION METALS

The first substance in which the field at an iron atom was determined by the Mössbauer effect was metallic iron itself.[16] The experiment was originally done with an iron source as well as an iron absorber. In addition to the field at the nucleus (3.33×10^5 oe at 300°K), the magnetic moment of the first excited state was obtained. In subsequent experiments in which an external magnetic field was superposed, it was shown that the direction of the field at the nucleus is opposite to the external magnetization,[17] a result contrary to theoretical expectations.[18]

The use of an iron source and absorber gives rise to an extremely complicated pattern. If a source emitting an unsplit line is used instead, the hyperfine pattern of Fe^{57} can be obtained directly (Fig. 2). This type of experiment can readily be adapted to determine the field at an iron impurity atom in the other transition metals.[15] Such experiments have actually been done by using an unsplit absorber, such as stainless steel, and making a source by diffusing the radioactive species, Co^{57}, into rolled foils of the material under study.[19] Results for cobalt and nickel at room temperature are shown in Fig. 3. The fields at room temperature are found to be $3.10\pm0.05\times10^5$ oe and $2.65\pm0.05\times10^5$ oe; when these are extrapolated to 0°K using the known magnetization curve, values of $3.12\pm0.05\times10^5$ oe and $2.80\pm0.05\times10^5$ oe for cobalt and nickel, respectively, are obtained.

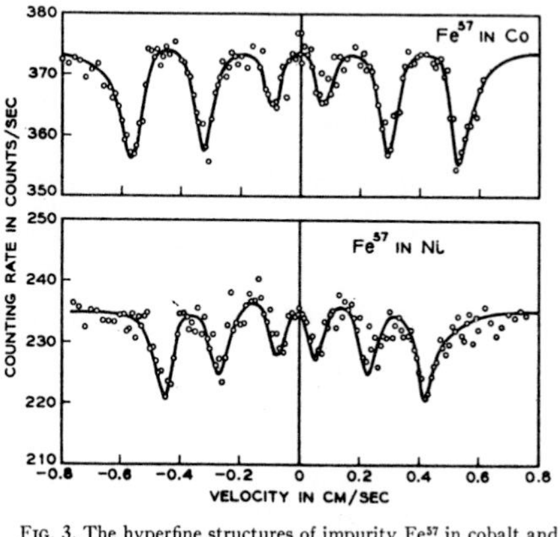

FIG. 3. The hyperfine structures of impurity Fe^{57} in cobalt and nickel metal, obtained with a stainless steel absorber 0.001 in. thick. Radioactive Co^{57} was diffused into thin cobalt and nickel foils which were then used as sources.

[16] S. S. Hanna *et al.*, Phys. Rev. Letters 4, 177 (1960).
[17] S. S. Hanna *et al.*, Phys. Rev. Letters 4, 513 (1950).
[18] W. Marshall, Phys. Rev. **110**, 1280 (1958).
[19] The foils of type 310 stainless steel, high-purity iron, and nickel were supplied by K. M. Olsen of this laboratory.

TABLE I. Magnetic fields (in units of 10^5 oe) at transition metal nuclei located in transition metals.

Nuclei at which field is measured	Lattice atoms Fe	Co	Ni
Fe	3.42[a]	3.12[b]	2.80[b]
Co	3.20[c]	2.20[c] 2.134[d]	0.80[c]
Ni	...	...	1.70[e]

[a] See footnote 16. [b] See footnote 15. [c] See footnote 20. [d] See footnote 21. [e] See footnote 22.

These values should be compared with the results obtained for cobalt and nickel atoms in the transition metals, using a variety of other techniques. The fields at cobalt in a range of Fe-Co and Ni-Co alloys were determined by Arp, Edmonds, and Petersen[20] from the measurement of the nuclear contribution to the heat capacity. Their results gave a value of 3.20×10^5 oe at a cobalt atom in iron and 2.20×10^5 oe at a cobalt atom in cobalt. An independent measure of the field at a cobalt atom in cobalt has also been obtained by Gossard and Portis[21] using nuclear resonance techniques. For fcc cobalt, they found a value of 2.134×10^5 oe at 0°K. Most recently a value for the field at a nickel atom in nickel has been similarly determined.[22] These results are summarized in Table I.

It may be noted that the field at the iron nucleus in a given metal is in every case larger than the field at the host lattice nucleus, and that fields at all the iron nuclei are of similar magnitude. This suggests that the field at an iron nucleus is due largely to its own electrons and depends only slightly on the host lattice magnetization, an idea which is borne out by a recent experiment on a CoPd alloy,[23] in which isolated impurity iron atoms were found to have fields similar to those in other metals studied. This property of the iron atom indicates that it is not a good field probe, and to some extent lessens the interest in impurity experiments. However, the present results do help to elucidate the various contributions to the field at the nucleus in a ferromagnet, and for that reason remain of interest.

In spite of this limitation on the utility of iron atoms, some interesting results have been obtained by the extension of experiments of the type described above to the antiferromagnetic transition metals, manganese and chromium. These experiments were quite analogous to those for the ferromagnetic case. The source was made by diffusing Co^{57} into electrolytically deposited Cr and Mn; the absorber was isotopically enriched potassium ferrocyanide.

[20] V. Arp. D. Edmonds, and R. Petersen, Phys. Rev. Letters 3, 212 (1959).
[21] A. C. Gossard and A. M. Portis, Phys. Rev. Letters 3, 164 (1959); A. M. Portis and A. C. Gossard, J. Appl. Phys. 31, 205S (1960). See also W. A. Hardy, J. Appl. Phys. 32, 122 (1960), this issue.
[22] L. J. Bruner, J. I. Budnick, and R. J. Blume, (to be published).
[23] D. E. Nagle *et al.*, Phys. Rev. Letters 5, 364 (1960).

It would not be surprising to find that the iron exhibits a splitting characteristic of a field of 3×10^5 oe when the host lattice is below its Néel temperature, but actually, in the case of chromium, data taken between 4°K and 370°K show an unsplit line whose width decreases uniformly with increasing temperature (Fig. 4) without discontinuity of any sort even at 308°K, the Néel temperature. The data for α-manganese are similar, except that the change in linewidth is much less pronounced. These results suggest that the exchange coupling between iron and chromium or manganese is sufficiently small so that the iron atoms are not aligned by the host lattice atoms. This conclusion is consistent with the results obtained from low-temperature susceptibility measurements in dilute iron-chromium alloys,[24] which also indicate that the iron is not aligned by the antiferromagnetic Cr system.

FERROUS FLUORIDE

As an illustration of the application of the Mössbauer effect to a naturally iron-bearing antiferromagnet, let us consider the determination of the hyperfine structure of Fe^{57} in ferrous fluoride.[25] This material is antiferromagnetic, with a transition temperature of 79°K. It has the rutile structure; thus the symmetry around the iron atoms is no higher than that characterized by three mutually perpendicular reflection planes. The electric field gradient (EFG) tensor at the iron atoms

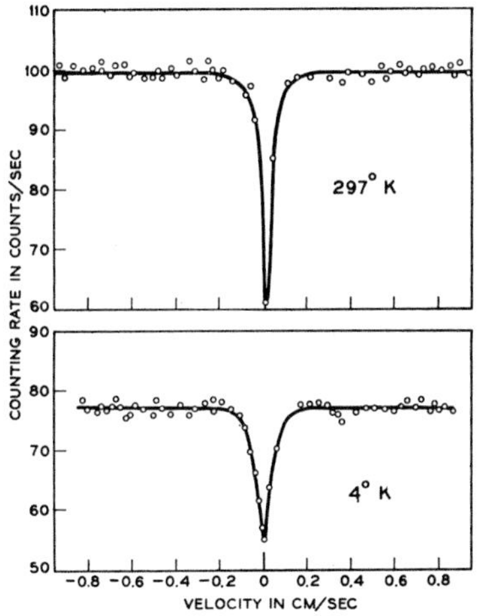

FIG. 4. The line shape of the 14.4-kev gamma ray of Fe^{57}, produced by the decay of Co^{57} diffused into chromium metal. The data were taken with an absorber of potassium ferrocyanide made with enriched Fe^{57}.

[24] M. M. Newman and K. W. H. Stevens, Proc. Phys. Soc. (London) 74, 290 (1959).
[25] G. K. Wertheim, Phys. Rev. 121, 63 (1961).

therefore does not have axial symmetry and may be characterized by two independent parameters, usually chosen to be the largest diagonal element of the tensor and a parameter which describes the deviation from axial symmetry.

The experiment was done using two 0.005-in. thick single-crystal slabs of the material as absorbers.[26] One slab had the *c* axis normal to its plane, the other parallel. A radioactive source, consisting of Co^{57} diffused into type 310 stainless steel, was mounted on a loudspeaker voice coil driven with a constant-velocity sawtooth wave as described above.

In the paramagnetic state, at room temperature, two well-defined absorption lines were obtained [Fig. 5(a)]. Their spacing indicates a quadrupole splitting of 31.2 Mc/sec due to the interaction of the *excited state* quadrupole moment with the crystalline electric field gradient. A large displacement of the centroid of the absorption from zero velocity, i.e., the energy of the gamma ray emitted by iron atoms in stainless steel, is also observed. Only a small part of this displacement can arise from a difference in the second-order Doppler shift[6] in the two materials. The major part is due to a nuclear isotope shift[27] arising both from the removal of 4*s* electrons in going from metallic binding in stainless steel to ionic binding in ferrous fluoride, and from the exchange polarization of the inner *s* electrons by the *d* shell, which causes a charge rearrangement of the *s* electron wave function at the nucleus.[28] The effect arises from the electrostatic interaction of the nucleus with the electronic wave functions,[27] and is observable provided that the strength of the interaction is different for the ground and the excited states of the nucleus, so that the corresponding energy levels are shifted by different amounts. This will be the case if the nuclear size is different in the two states.

In the antiferromagnetic state, six hyperfine components are resolved [Fig. 5(b),(c)]. (In the case where the magnetic *c* axis is prependicular to the plane of the absorber two lines, corresponding to the $\Delta m=0$ transitions, are missing. This is in accord with the radiation pattern for these transitions, which has zero intensity in the direction of the axis of quantization.) The spacing of these lines may be analyzed in terms of excited and ground-state splitting. The energy levels of the excited state are given as functions of three parameters, the magnetic hyperfine interaction $g\beta H$, the z component of the electric field gradient tensor eq, and an asymmetry parameter

$$\eta=\left(\frac{\partial^2 V}{\partial y^2}-\frac{\partial^2 V}{\partial x^2}\right)\Big/\frac{\partial^2 V}{\partial z^2},$$

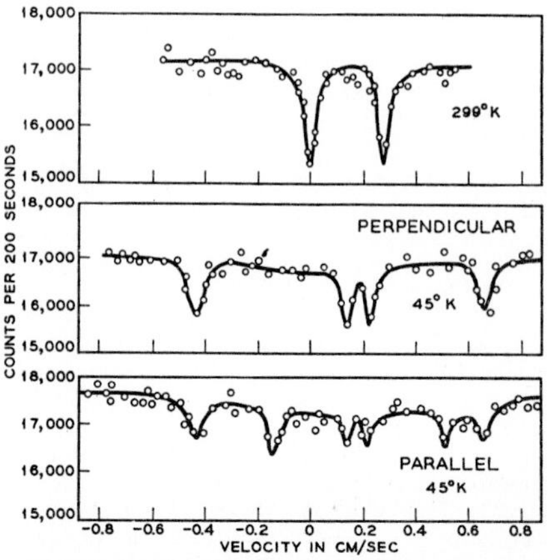

FIG. 5. Resonant absorption in 0.005-in. single-crystal ferrous fluoride absorbers (a) above the Néel temperature; (b) below the Néel temperature with magnetization along the direction of observation; and (c) below the Néel temperature with magnetization perpendicular to the direction of observation.

as follows:

$$E_{1,3}=\tfrac{1}{2}g\beta H\pm\frac{e^2Qq}{4}\left[\left(1+\frac{4g\beta H}{e^2Qq}\right)^2+\frac{\eta^2}{3}\right]^{\frac{1}{2}}$$

$$E_{2,4}=-\tfrac{1}{2}g\beta H\pm\frac{e^2Qq}{4}\left[\left(1-\frac{4g\beta H}{e^2Qq}\right)^2+\frac{\eta^2}{3}\right]^{\frac{1}{2}}.$$

The analysis yields two independent measures of the magnetic field at the iron nucleus, in terms of the ground and excited state moments, respectively. The average of these measurements gives a value of 3.13×10^5 oe at 45°K, the temperature of the measurements. Extrapolated to 0°K this becomes 3.40×10^5 oe. The quadrupole interaction deduced from the antiferromagnetic state data is consistent with that determined from the paramagnetic state, but it is found in addition that the direction of the major axis of the EFG tensor is perpendicular to the axis of magnetic alignment and that the asymmetry parameter is 0.33.

YTTRIUM-IRON GARNET

One of the more complex systems which has recently been investigated[29] is yttrium-iron garnet, $Y_3Fe_2(FeO_4)_3$. The structure of this material is well known,[30] and for the present purposes it suffices to point out that iron atoms are located in two nonequivalent sites, those with tetrahedral symmetry and those with octahedral

[26] The oriented slabs of ferrous fluoride were obtained from V. Jaccarino.
[27] O. C. Kistner and A. W. Sunyar, Phys. Rev. Letters **4**, 412 (1960).
[28] V. Heine, Phys. Rev. **107**, 1002 (1957); W. E. Blumberg and V. Jaccarino (private communication).

[29] This work was done in collaboration with Miss C. Alff of Columbia University, during a summer appointment at this laboratory. A fuller account will be published.
[30] S. Geller and M. A. Gilleo, J. Phys. Chem. Solids **3**, 30 (1957); S. Geller and M. A. Gilleo, Acta Cryst. **10**, 239 (1957); F. Bertaut and F. Forrat, Compt. rend. **242**, 382 (1956).

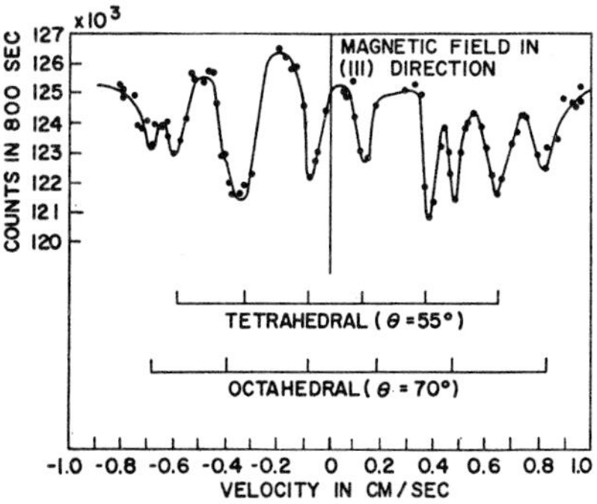

FIG. 6. Resonant absorption in an 0.002-in. single-crystal yttrium-iron garnet absorber with magnetization in the [111] direction. The source was stainless steel.

symmetry. The relative number of these is 3:2. Both sites have axes of symmetry sufficiently high to assure that the electric field gradient tensors are axially symmetric. The tetrahedral sites have fourfold rotary inversion axes in [100] directions, while the octahedral sites have threefold axes in [111] directions. The [111] directions are the directions of easy magnetization, but in a thin slab without an externally applied field the magnetization tends to be normal to the surface.

The experiments were performed using as an absorber a thin slab of the material cut normal to a [110] direction from a single crystal grown by Nielsen of this laboratory.[31] The slab was cut and lapped to a thickness of 0.002 in. according to the process described by Dillon.[32] Data were taken at room temperature with a magnetic field applied in either the [111] or the [100] direction in the plane of the slab. It should be pointed out that when the field is in the [111] direction the symmetry axes of all the tetrahedral sites make the same angle (54°44′) with the applied field, while the axes of the octahedral sites make angles of either 0° or 70°32′, in the proportion of 1 to 3. Similarly, when the field is in the [100] direction, the [111] symmetry axes of all the octahedra make an angle of 54°44′ with the field, while the axes of the tetrahedra make angles of 0° or 90° in the proportion of 1 to 2. (This information is summarized in Table II.) Three hyperfine patterns are thus to be expected in each experiment.

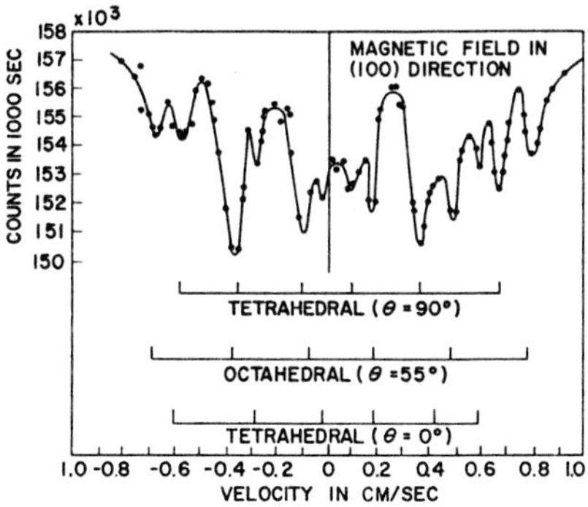

FIG. 7. Resonant absorption in the absorber of Fig. 6 with the magnetization in the [100] direction.

TABLE II. Characteristics of iron sites in yttrium-iron garnet for the two cases used in the experiment.

	Field direction			
	111		100	
Iron site	Angle[a]	Intensity[b]	Angle[a]	Intensity[b]
Tetrahedral	54°44′	6	90°	4
			0°	2
Octahedral	70°32′	3	54°44′	4
	0°	1		

[a] Angle between direction of magnetization and axis of electric field gradient tensor.
[b] Relative number of iron atoms occupying sites characterized by the given angle.

The experimental results obtained at room temperature are shown in Figs. 6 and 7. In the [100] case (Fig. 7) all three hyperfine spectra are resolved, while in the [111] case (Fig. 6) only the two stronger ones are seen. The identification of lines belonging to a given hyperfine spectrum was made partially on the basis of the intensities of the absorption lines and partially on the basis of some simple properties of the hyperfine patterns. The resulting groupings were in every case unambiguous.

The magnetic fields at the iron nuclei in each case were obtained directly from the distance separating the second and fourth or third and fifth absorption lines in the pertinent hyperfine spectrum. This distance depends only on the *ground-state* magnetic moment, and is independent of the quadrupole coupling. Values were obtained of $3.92\pm0.05\times10^5$ oe for the tetrahedral sites and $4.74\pm0.06\times10^5$ oe for the octahedral sites. The agreement between the independent determinations made for the [100] and [111] cases was satisfactory.

Further analysis was based on a direct comparison of the experimental hyperfine spectrum with spectra computed for the known angles between the magnetic field and the axis of the EFG tensor. The computations were based on the tabulations of Parker,[33] which are applicable to the excited state and give the hyperfine splitting as a function of the parameter $\lambda=e^2Qq/4\mu H$ measuring the strength of the quadrupole coupling relative to the magnetic hf coupling. The best value for λ was 0.10 ± 0.02 in each case. The large uncertainty arises from a weak dependence of the hfs on λ, which is particularly pronounced in the 54°44′ case. The resulting

[31] The YIG was obtained from J. F. Dillon.
[32] J. F. Dillon and H. E. Earl, Am. J. Phys. 27, 201 (1959).
[33] P. M. Parker, J. Chem. Phys. 24, 1096 (1956).

quadrupole couplings, expressed as the quadrupole transition energies in the absence of a magnetic field, are 9 and 11 Mc for the tetrahedral and octahedral sites respectively, with an uncertainty of 20%.

Further experiments are being done to obtain the temperature dependence of the field at the iron nucleus.

OXIDES AND FERRITES

Of the iron oxides only the simplest, Fe_2O_3, in which all the atoms are in equivalent sites, has so far produced conclusive results. Kistner and Sunyar[27] have shown that the field at the iron atom is 5.15×10^5 oe at room temperature; a small quadrupole component has also been observed.

Stoichiometric FeO probably does not exist because of the strong tendency of iron to be trivalent. Attempts to prepare this compound by the decomposition of ferrous oxalate in an inert atmosphere have produced a material which exhibits two absorption lines of unequal intensity at room temperature. These may be identified with di- and trivalent iron, since their unequal intensity and the fact that FeO is cubic rule out quadrupole splitting as a possible interpretation.

In Fe_3O_4 there exist both A sites, with tetrahedral oxygen coordination, and B sites, with octahedral oxygen coordination. Moreover, the iron occurs with two valences which are distributed over the sites in such a way that three types of iron are found in equal concentration: trivalent iron in A sites, trivalent iron in B sites, and divalent iron in B sites. As a result, three separate six-line hyperfine patterns are to be expected. In practice these patterns appear superposed in such a way that analysis is at best difficult. However, it is clear from the data in Fig. 8 that the field at the nucleus is approximately 5×10^5 oe in every case.

Among the ferrites the simplest results should be obtained from those with a structure like that of nickel ferrite; that is, like $FeO\cdot Fe_2O_3$ in which all the divalent iron atoms are replaced by divalent atoms of another metal and all the remaining iron is trivalent. Results obtained with a thin polycrystalline absorber of $NiO\cdot Fe_2O_3$[34] indicate that the field at the iron nucleus is about 5.1×10^5 oe, but the linewidths are found to be broad compared to those of the simple oxides. A number of ferrites have also been studied by Kistner and Sunyar[35] with generally similar results.

CONCLUSIONS

The Mössbauer effect of Fe^{57} has proved to be a useful tool for the investigation of magnetic fields and electric field gradients at iron nuclei in ferromagnetic and antiferromagnetic materials. The fact that the field at an iron atom depends largely on its own electronic shell and only weakly on its environment is itself interesting but lessens the usefulness of isolated iron atoms as field probes. A few generalizations have begun to emerge from the results now available: (1) the field at iron nuclei in ferromagnetic metals is close to 3×10^5 oe. (2) The field in oxides, ferrites, and yttrium iron garnet at trivalent iron atoms in octahedral coordinations is in the vicinity of 5×10^5 oe. These generalizations are as yet tentative and subject to further confirmation.

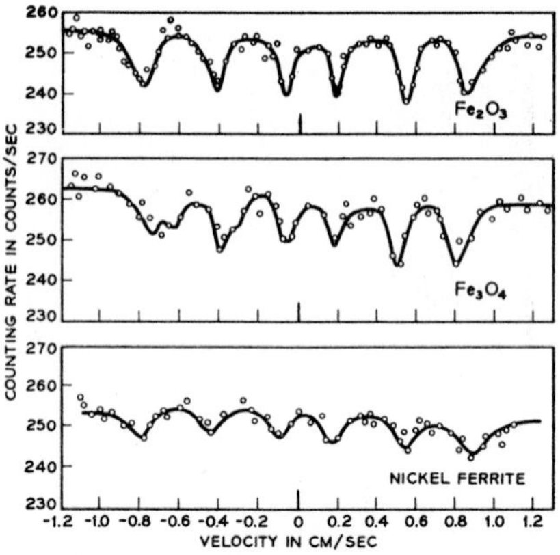

FIG. 8. Resonant absorption at room temperature in powdered iron oxides and polycrystalline nickel ferrite. The source is stainless steel.

While Fe^{57} is without doubt the most attractive isotope for Mössbauer effect studies, and the only one considered in this paper, there are a number of others which will make it possible to extend the range of materials which can be investigated. The most useful of these is Sn^{119}, an isomer with a 250-day half-life and a linewidth only five times greater than that of Fe^{57}. Other possible isotopes are Dy^{161}, W^{182}, Ir^{193}, and Au^{197}. The maximum absorption that can be expected with these is very much smaller, because of higher gamma energy or lower Debye temperature than Fe^{57}, and the linewidth is larger by a considerable factor.

ACKNOWLEDGMENTS

Conversations with V. Jaccarino, J. F. Dillon, W. E. Blumberg, S. Geschwind, and a number of other members of this laboratory have been of great assistance to the author by providing many valuable ideas and fruitful insights into the field of magnetism. The cooperation of Mrs. M. H. Read and W. M. Augustyniak in specific phases of the work, and the general technical aid of D. N. E. Buchanan are also gratefully acknowledged.

[34] The nickel ferrite was prepared by F. J. Schnettler of this laboratory.
[35] O. C. Kistner and A. W. Sunyar (unpublished).

DIRECTION OF THE EFFECTIVE MAGNETIC FIELD AT THE NUCLEUS IN FERROMAGNETIC IRON†

S. S. Hanna, J. Heberle, G. J. Perlow, R. S. Preston, and D. H. Vincent
Argonne National Laboratory, Argonne, Illinois
(Received April 28, 1960)

In a recent experiment[1] it was shown that in ferromagnetic iron the effective magnetic field at the iron nucleus is strongly correlated with the magnetization. The sense of the correlation, however, was not determined, i.e., it was not known whether the effective field was parallel or antiparallel to the magnetization. The sense of the correlation has now been established by observing the change in the hyperfine splitting of the nuclear energy levels of Fe^{57} on application of an external field of 17 to 20 koe.

In an earlier paper[2] we presented the hyperfine spectrum obtained in the resonant Mössbauer[3] absorption in Fe^{57}. The interpretation given to the spectrum has since been confirmed in detail. Several groups have shown the correctness of the hyperfine pattern by observing the spectrum when different alloys and compounds of iron are used.[4] Gossard, Portis, and Sandle[5] have observed the nuclear magnetic resonance in the ground state of Fe^{57} at a frequency corresponding to a value of the effective field in close agreement with the value of 333 koe deduced in reference 2. In addition, Ewan, Graham, and Geiger[6] have found that the $E2$ admixture in the $M1$ radiation is less than 10^{-4}, which confirms that the effect of $E2$ radiation in the spectrum is indeed negligible.[2]

Experimentally it was feasible to apply a large magnetic field only to the source of the resonant radiation. The absorber was either in the fringing field of the electromagnet holding the source or in a small parallel magnetic field of its own, applied to produce a definite magnetization in the absorber. At the top of Fig. 1 is shown the velocity spectrum which is applicable if the hyperfine splittings in source and absorber are identical. The intensities are appropriate to the emission of polarized radiation from the source but to an unpolarized absorption process. If, on the other hand, the hyperfine splittings in the emitter are about 10% greater (for example) than those in the absorber, then the complex spectrum at the bottom of Fig. 1 is obtained. It is clear that a study of the singlet line 6 affords the best means of determining the change that an external field produces in the hyperfine splitting.

For the effective field at the nucleus we write

$$\vec{H}_n = H_{n0}\vec{M}_0 + \vec{H}_{ext}, \qquad (1)$$

where $\vec{M}_0$ is a unit vector along the direction of magnetization in a ferromagnetic domain, and H_{n0} is the magnitude of the effective field in the absence of the external field $\vec{H}_{ext}$. The latter quantity includes the demagnetizing field which is negligible for the planar samples used. Since $H_{ext}/H_{n0} << 1$ in the present experiment, it is assumed in Eq. (1) that H_{n0} is not appreciably influenced by $\vec{H}_{ext}$. The quantity of interest is the sign of H_{n0}. Since $\vec{M}_0$ and $\vec{H}_{ext}$ are parallel under saturation conditions, the sign can be determined by observing whether the hyperfine splitting increases or decreases on application of a field. With a field of 17.6 koe a shift of $\pm 2.65\%$ is expected in line 6.

The experimental technique was similar to that in our earlier work.[1,2,7] The carriage of a lathe was used to provide velocities by means of which the spectrum was scanned. The source was mounted in the narrow gap of an electromagnet capable of producing fields up to 20 koe. The magnet was attached rigidly to the end of the lathe and the absorber was mounted on the carriage. The result obtained for line 6 is shown in Fig. 2. On application of the field to the source, a shift to lower energy is unmistakable. The correlation

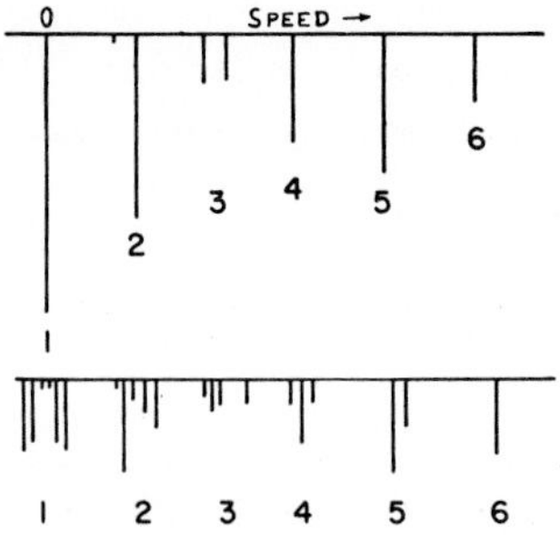

FIG. 1. Theoretical absorption spectra of 14.4-kev resonance radiation from Fe^{57}. Top: metallic source and absorber with identical hyperfine splittings. Bottom: same source and absorber but with the splitting in the source increased by 10%.

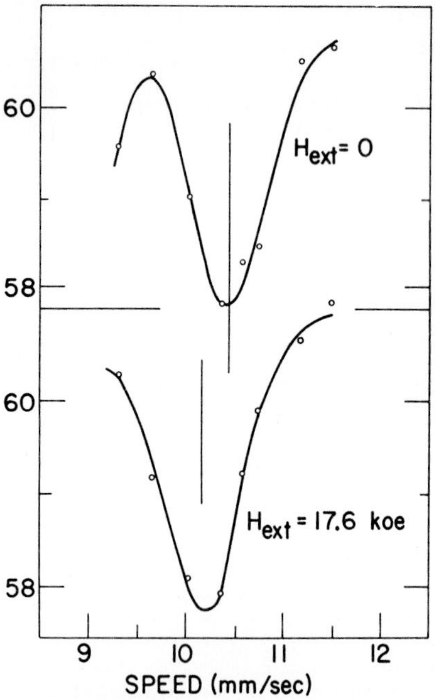

FIG. 2. Line 6 observed with $H_{ext} = 0$ and $H_{ext} = 17.6$ koe, where H_{ext} is the external field applied to the source of resonance radiation. The ordinate is in units of 10^3 counts.

is therefore negative. The magnitude of the observed shift is (2.7 ± 0.4)% which is compatible with the linear relation $H_n = H_{n0} - H_{ext}$. A negative shift of about the correct magnitude was also observed in line 4. The multiplet structure in line 4 is symmetrical (Fig. 1) and so does not seriously interfere with the observation of a shift of its central member.

The effective field at the iron nucleus has now been determined both in sign and magnitude. The existence of such a large negative field (-333 koe) was unexpected. Marshall[8] has discussed a number of sources of the effective nuclear field. These consist mainly of direct effects of the 3*d* electrons and indirect effects of polarization of the various *s* electrons, which then contribute to the field via the Fermi contact interaction. The polarization of inner shells of electrons results in negative contributions to the field. In view of the experimental result these negative terms must completely dominate the other contributions.

We are grateful to S. Raboy for loan of the magnet. We wish also to thank M. R. Perlow for preparation of the source; F. J. Karasek for continuing to supply us with thin rolled iron foils; and E. Kowalski for assistance in taking the data. We have profited from a stimulating discussion with W. Marshall.

---

†This work was performed under the auspices of the U. S. Atomic Energy Commission.

[1]G. J. Perlow, S. S. Hanna, M. Hamermesh, C. Littlejohn, D. H. Vincent, R. S. Preston, and J. Heberle, Phys. Rev. Letters 4, 74 (1960).

[2]S. S. Hanna, J. Heberle, C. Littlejohn, G. J. Perlow, R. S. Preston, and D. H. Vincent, Phys. Rev. Letters 4, 177 (1960).

[3]R. L. Mössbauer, Z. Physik 151, 124 (1958).

[4](Ferrocyanide) S. L. Ruby, L. M. Epstein, and K. H. Sun (to be published); (ferrocyanide, stainless steel) G. K. Wertheim, Phys. Rev. Letters 4, 403 (1960); (Fe_2O_3) O. C. Kistner and A. W. Sunyar, Phys. Rev. Letters 4, 412 (1960).

[5]A. C. Gossard, A. M. Portis, and W. J. Sandle (to be published).

[6]G. T. Ewan, R. L. Graham, and J. S. Geiger (to be published).

[7]S. S. Hanna, J. Heberle, C. Littlejohn, G. J. Perlow, R. S. Preston, and D. H. Vincent, Phys. Rev. Letters 4, 28 (1960).

[8]W. Marshall, Phys. Rev. 110, 1280 (1958), and private communication.

TEMPERATURE DEPENDENCE OF THE INTERNAL FIELD IN FERROMAGNETS*

D. E. Nagle, H. Frauenfelder,† R. D. Taylor, D. R. F. Cochran, and B. T. Matthias‡
Los Alamos Scientific Laboratory, University of California, Los Alamos, New Mexico
(Received September 22, 1960)

The saturation magnetization of a ferromagnet varies with temperature in a characteristic and well-investigated manner; it reaches a limiting value at temperatures well below the Curie temperature T_C and vanishes at and above T_C. The behavior of the internal magnetic field, however, is much less well known. Because the theories of internal fields in ferromagnets are still far from satisfactory,[1] accurate and detailed measurements of these internal fields over a wide temperature range are important; the effects near the Curie point are particularly revealing. Preliminary work on such problems has been discussed by the Argonne group.[1] In the present Letter, we report a determination of the temperature variation of the internal magnetic field in Fe ($T_C = 1043°K$) and in a CoPd alloy ($T_C = 275°K$) by means of the Mössbauer effect.

That the Mössbauer effect is well suited for the investigation of internal fields no longer needs any justification.[1] The radioisotope Fe^{57} is very convenient for such experiments, since Fe itself is a ferromagnet and since the Mössbauer spectrum of its 14.4-kev gamma ray is well known.[2] The emission spectrum of an Fe source at room temperature consists of six lines, well separated by the Zeeman effect due to the internal magnetic field. With an Fe absorber of identical internal field, these lines give rise to a Mössbauer spectrum consisting of a prominent central absorption line and five strong satellites on either side, two of them doublets. The internal field has been deduced from the splitting of these lines.[2]

Complications arise when the source and the absorber have different internal fields. The six emission and six absorption lines of different spacing then give rise to as many as 36 lines; the Mössbauer spectrum becomes harder to find and harder to identify. There are three ways to circumvent this difficulty. One can employ a source having no effective internal field where the six emission lines are collapsed into one,[3] one can utilize a single line absorber,[4,5] or one can reduce the number of lines by selecting plane[2] or circularly[6] polarized gamma rays. The best method will depend on the particular problem. We have chosen the first approach for Fe and the third one, with selection of circularly polarized gamma rays, for CoPd.

A CoPd source was prepared by electroplating Co^{57} onto a CoPd alloy (92 % Pd, 8 % Co) and heating the CoPd foil in a vacuum furnace at 1000°C for two hours. The source was then placed in a cryostat which allowed the source temperature to be varied from 88°K to room temperature. The Mössbauer spectrum was observed with an Fe absorber, enriched to 75 % Fe^{57} and of equivalent thickness 2.2 mg/cm^2. This absorber was mounted on a Jensen 8-inch Flexair woofer and moved sinusoidally at a frequency of 11 sec^{-1}. The output pulses from a scintillation counter were energy selected by a single-channel analyzer and modulated with a saw tooth voltage, which was locked in with the speaker drive. The modulated pulses were displayed on a 400-channel RIDL analyzer and thus yielded directly the desired Mössbauer spectrum,[4] as shown in Fig. 1. Due to the sinusoidal drive and linear display, the velocity scale in Fig. 1 is sinusoidal. The slight drop to the right in each spectrum is caused by dead-time effect in the 400-channel analyzer.

A series of measurements was taken in which the temperature of the CoPd source was varied and the temperature of the Fe absorber was 24°C.

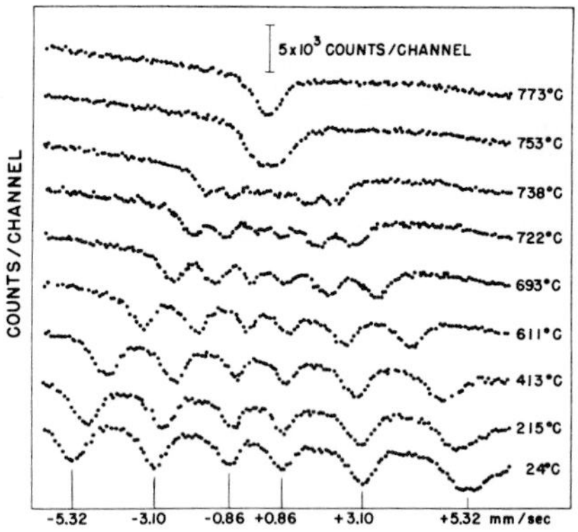

FIG. 1. Mössbauer spectra of a CoPd source at 24°C and an Fe absorber as functions of the absorber temperature. Positive velocity is taken to mean source moving away from absorber.

When the CoPd was above its Curie point of 275°K, the six-line spectrum was obtained, similar to the lowest curve of Fig. 1; such a spectrum is typical of a single-line source with an Fe absorber. Thus CoPd above its Curie point possesses only a very small effective magnetic field: From the position of the lines and from the line widths, an upper limit of 2000 oersteds is obtained. Below the Curie point, the splitting pattern changes rapidly, indicating the appearance of an internal magnetic field. At 88°K, astonishingly enough, the pattern is typical of source and absorber with identical fields. Hence at 88°K, the field at the Fe^{57} nucleus in CoPd is 3.3×10^5 oersteds,[2] the same as that of Fe^{57} in Fe at temperatures well below the Curie point. Details of these measurements will be published elsewhere.[7]

The single emission line of the CoPd source above its Curie point now offers a convenient tool for the investigation of the internal field in Fe. For this experiment, an absorber (5 mg/cm^2 Fe^{57}, 75% enriched) was placed in a furnace equipped with thin entrance and exit windows and containing an atmosphere of hydrogen. The CoPd source was mounted on the speaker and the transmission spectrum recorded as a function of the absorber temperature. Some typical spectra obtained in this way are shown in Fig. 1.

The curves in Fig. 1 show the decrease in the internal magnetic field, the temperature shift[8,9] of the center of the spectrum, the decrease in Mössbauer absorption due to the Debye-Waller factor, and finally the disappearance of the effective magnetic field in the Fe absorber at the Curie point.

The relative magnetic field at the Fe^{57} nucleus, as deduced from the curves in Fig. 1 and some additional data, is plotted in Fig. 2 as a function of T/T_C. For comparison, the relative saturation magnetization[10] is indicated by the solid line.

We thank Dr. R. M. Bozorth for determining the Curie point of our CoPd alloy, Dr. C. E. Olsen for the preparation of the CoPd alloy and the annealing of the source, and Dr. W. E. Keller for the loan of his DYNA amplifier. We are grateful to Dr. P. P. Craig and Dr. J. G. Dash for stimulating discussions and to Mr. R. Hanft for his tireless efforts during the experiment.

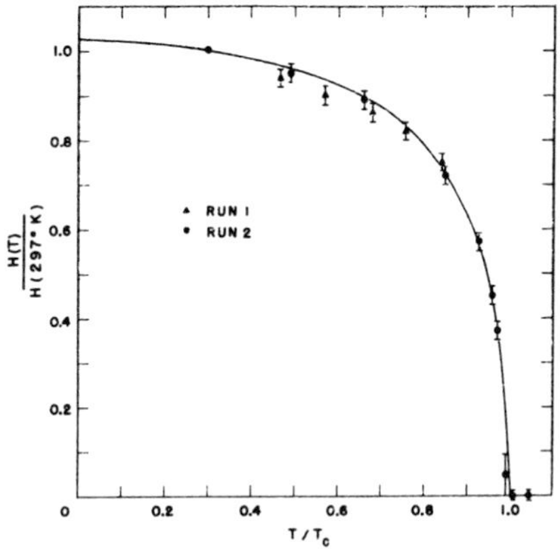

FIG. 2. Relative internal magnetic field $H(T)/H(297°K)$ at the Fe^{57} nuclei in an Fe absorber, as deduced by Mössbauer effect. The solid line indicates the relative saturation magnetization, $\sigma(T)/\sigma(297°K)$, of Fe.

*Work done under the auspices of the U. S. Atomic Energy Commission.

†Consultant, University of Illinois, Urbana, Illinois.

‡Consultant, Bell Telephone Laboratories, Murray Hill, New Jersey.

[1]Mössbauer Effect, Allerton House Conference, edited by H. Frauenfelder and H. Lustig (University of Illinois, Urbana, 1960).

[2]S. S. Hanna, J. Heberle, C. Littlejohn, G. J. Perlow, R. S. Preston, and D. H. Vincent, Phys. Rev. Letters 4, 177 (1960).

[3]O. C. Kistner and A. W. Sunyar, Phys. Rev. Letters 4, 412 (1960).

[4]S. L. Ruby, L. M. Epstein, and K. H. Sun, Rev. Sci. Instr. 31, 580 (1960).

[5]G. K. Wertheim, Phys. Rev. Letters 4, 403 (1960).

[6]H. Frauenfelder, D. E. Nagle, R. D. Taylor, D. R. F. Cochran, and W. M. Visscher (to be published).

[7]R. D. Taylor, D. E. Nagle, H. Frauenfelder, and D. R. F. Cochran (to be published).

[8]R. V. Pound and G. A. Rebka, Jr., Phys. Rev. Letters 4, 274 (1960).

[9]B. D. Josephson, Phys. Rev. Letters 4, 341 (1960).

[10]American Institute of Physics Handbook (McGraw-Hill Book Company, New York, 1957), p. 5-208.

POLARIZATION OF THE CONDUCTION ELECTRONS IN THE FERROMAGNETIC METALS*

A. J. F. Boyle, D. St. P. Bunbury, and C. Edwards
The Physical Laboratories, University of Manchester, Manchester, England
(Received November 15, 1960)

It has recently been proposed[1] that the polarization of the 4s conduction electrons in Fe, Co, and Ni is antiparallel to that of the electrons in the unfilled 3d shell; this is the reverse of the usual assumption. There are few ways in which this polarization is manifested. One, however, is in the effective magnetic field at a nucleus, which acts through the contact interaction with the 4s electrons. The magnitude of this field has been given by Marshall[2] as

$$H_c = (8\pi/3)\xi_s |\psi(0)|_A^2 \mu n p, \qquad (1)$$

where μ is the Bohr magneton, $\xi_s|\psi(0)|_A^2$ is the average probability density of a 4s conduction electron evaluated at the nucleus [$|\psi(0)|_A^2$ being the free atom value], n is the number of conduction electrons per atom, and p is their polarization. The sign of the field is positive, i.e., parallel to the direction of magnetization, if the polarization of the 4s electrons is parallel to the 3d polarization.

Hanna et al.[3,4] have measured the magnitude and sign of the field at the Fe nucleus in iron by observing the Zeeman splitting of the 14-kev transition in Fe^{57} and obtain the value -3×10^5 koe. In this case, however, there are other contributions to the field beside H_c; mainly those due to the electrons of the same atom, i.e., the polarized 3d electrons. These other contributions almost certainly outweigh the effect of the field H_c alone (H_c is probably of the order of 50 to 100 koe), and it is therefore difficult to draw any conclusion concerning its sign.

In an attempt to measure H_c directly, dilute (1%) solid solutions of Sn in the ferromagnetic metals (Fe, Co, and Ni) have been prepared. Since Sn is basically diamagnetic, we expect that there will be no contribution to the field at the Sn nucleus from its own inner electrons and that the field will be given simply by

$$H_s = (4\pi/3)M + H_c, \qquad (2)$$

where $|\psi(0)|_A^2$ in (1) is the appropriate value for a Sn atom. Since H_c is due to an over-all polarization of the conduction electrons, the other terms should remain those appropriate to the solvent atoms.[5]

The Zeeman splitting of the 24-kev transition in Sn^{119} was observed[6] using the Mössbauer effect.[7,8] The transmission through the absorber (the alloy) of the radiation emitted by a moving source was measured as a function of the velocity of the source. The velocity spectrometer has been described in detail elsewhere.[9] The temperature of both the source and absorber were maintained around 100°K. Figures 1, 2, and 3 show the transmission spectra obtained for Fe and Ni and Co. Each member of the doublet is an unresolved triplet caused by the splitting of the excited $\frac{3}{2}^+$ state, while the doublet separation is due mainly to the splitting of the ground $\frac{1}{2}^+$ state. The field strengths H_S listed in Table I were derived using the known values of the magnetic moments. (The excited state moment has been measured as 0.83 ± 0.03 nuclear magneton.[9])

The shifts listed in the table refer to the displacement of the spectra towards negative velocity and are almost entirely due to the chemical shift.[10] In this case, where the source was metallic tin, the magnitude of the shift should be proportional to $(\xi_S - \xi_{Sn})|\psi(0)|_{Sn}^2$; ξ_{Sn} and ξ_S refer to metallic tin and the solvent metal, respectively.

Table I. Results derived from the velocity spectra of the absorption of 24-kev γ rays from Sn^{119m} in absorbers containing 1% of Sn^{119} dissolved in Fe, Co, and Ni. The shift is the displacement of the spectra towards negative velocity due to chemical effects, H_S is the field at the Sn nucleus, and $(4\pi/3)M$ is the usual Lorentz field.

Solvent	Shift (mm/sec)	H_S (koe)	$(4\pi/3)M$	$H_S - (4\pi/3)M$
Fe	1.1	-81 ± 4	7.5	-88
Co	1.1	-20.5 ± 1.5	6.1	-26.5 ± 1.5
Ni	1.1	$+18.5 \pm 1$	2.0	$+16.5 \pm 1$

The sign of H_S was determined by placing each absorber in a transverse magnetic field of about 7 koe; the magnetization direction is now parallel to the external field. A positive field was observed only in the case of Ni. The final values

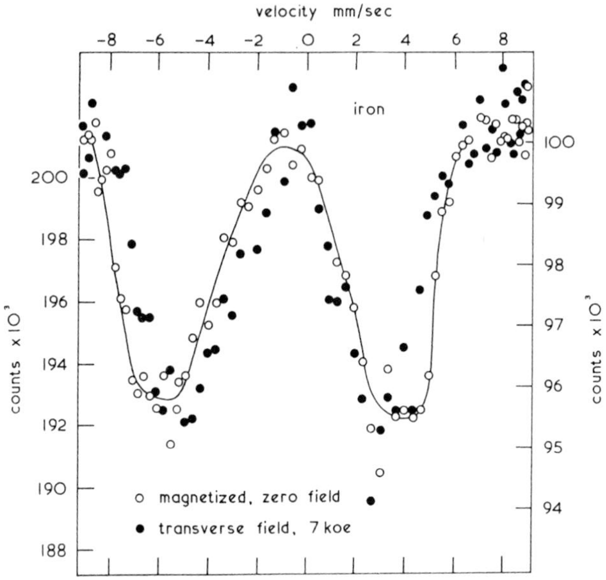

FIG. 1. The absorption spectra obtained with 1% Sn^{119} in Fe. Left scale, o ; right scale, •.

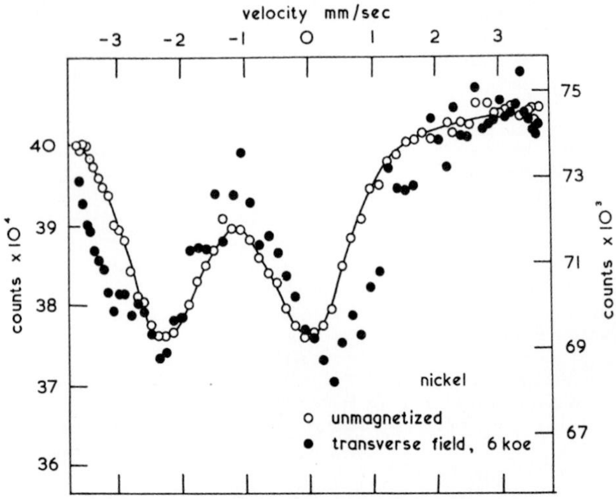

FIG. 2. The absorption spectra obtained with 1 % Sn^{119} in Ni. Left scale, o; right scale, •.

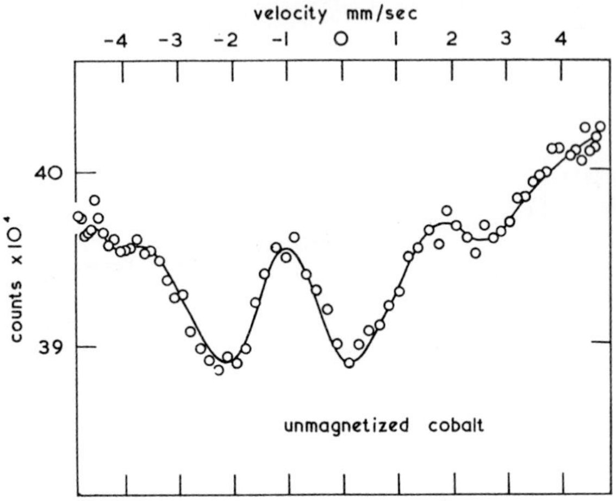

FIG. 3. The absorption spectrum obtained with 1 % Sn^{119} in Co.

of $[H_S - (4\pi/3)M]$ are listed in the table, where the values of M have been corrected for the quenching of the atomic moments by the added valence electrons of Sn. This is most significant in Ni, and, since it will occur predominantly amongst the nearest neighbors, will undoubtedly result in a lowered value of the observed field.

The results are obviously inconsistent with the existence of the single field H_c; firstly because of the different signs and secondly because of the relative magnitudes of the fields. Since p is very closely proportional to M,[2] the expression (1) for H_c can be written simply, $H_c = \text{const}\ \xi_s M$. Further, we can conclude from the chemical shifts that ξ_s is practically constant for Fe, Co, and Ni, and therefore H_c will be roughly proportional to M.

There is another mechanism[11] by which an effective field might be produced at the Sn nucleus in this situation. The wave function for the 4s electrons of the Sn atom will overlap with those of the 3d electrons of the surrounding solvent atoms, and the polarization of the latter will result in a change in the relative spatial distribution of the 4s electrons in respect of their spin orientation. In the region of the Sn nucleus, electrons with spin antiparallel to the 3d polarization will predominate, producing a negative effective field H_p.

Evidence for the existence of such a field is provided by the results for Co (Fig. 3) which indicate the presence of a second field of -50 koe with the same chemical shift. X-ray analysis of the sample showed that both cubic and hexagonal structures were present in the rough proportion 40:60. Since neither ξ_s nor p depends on the structure, the two values of the field cannot be associated with H_c; however, since the distribution of the 3d orbitals will probably differ for the two structures,[12] H_p would also differ.

We have no estimate of H_p, but its magnitude should depend not only on M but also on the mean radius of the 3d shell and thus will decrease more rapidly from Fe to Ni than does the field H_c which depends only on M. In the absence of any further contributions, combination of such a field H_p with a positive value of H_c would therefore provide a qualitative interpretation of the present results.

It is interesting to compare the present results for the field at a Sn nucleus in Fe with those of Samoilov et al.[13] From measurements of the nuclear polarization these authors obtain values of 250 koe and 280 koe, respectively, for the field at In^{114} and Sb^{122} dissolved in Fe.

We are indebted to Dr. C. Johnson for drawing our attention to the results of Samoilov et al. and we are grateful to many people for valuable discussion, particularly Dr. Lomer, Dr. W. Marshall, Dr. S. F. Edwards, and Dr. H. E. Hall. Much helpful advice in the preparation of the alloys has been given by Dr. J. Stubbles. We would also like to thank Dr. J. Zussman for performing the x-ray analysis.

---

*Supported financially by the Department of Scientific and Industrial Research.

[1]For a review article see C. Herring, Suppl. J. Appl. Phys. 31, 3S (1960).

[2]W. Marshall, Phys. Rev. 110, 1280 (1958).

[3]S. S. Hanna, J. Heberle, C. Littlejohn, G. J. Perlow, R. S. Preston, and D. H. Vincent, Phys. Rev. Letters 4, 177 (1960).

[4]S. S. Hanna, J. Heberle, G. J. Perlow, R. S. Preston, and D. H. Vincent, Phys. Rev. Letters 4, 513 (1960).

[5]D. R. Teeters, thesis, University of California, Berkeley, 1955 (unpublished).

[6]Separated Sn^{119} used in the preparation of the alloys was supplied by the Chemistry Division, Atomic Energy Research Establishment, Harwell.

[7]R. L. Mössbauer, Z. Physik 151, 125 (1959).

[8]A. J. F. Boyle, D. St. P. Bunbury, C. Edwards, and H. E. Hall, Proc. Phys. Soc. (London) (to be published).

[9]A. J. F. Boyle, D. St. P. Bunbury, and C. Edwards (to be published).

[10]O. C. Kistner and A. W. Sunyar, Phys. Rev. Letters 4, 412 (1960).

[11]D. A. Goodings and V. Heine, Phys. Rev. Letters 5, 370 (1960).

[12]J. B. Goodenough, Phys. Rev. 120, 67 (1960).

[13]V. N. Samoilov, V. V. Skliarevsky, and E. P. Stepanov, Soviet Phys.—JETP 11(38), 261 (1960).

Volume 6, Number 9 PHYSICAL REVIEW LETTERS May 1, 1961

HYPERFINE FIELD AND ATOMIC MOMENT OF IRON IN FERROMAGNETIC ALLOYS

C. E. Johnson, M. S. Ridout, T. E. Cranshaw, and P. E. Madsen
Atomic Energy Research Establishment, Harwell, England
(Received February 1, 1961; revised manuscript received April 10, 1961)

Mott and Stevens[1] and Lomer and Marshall[2] have proposed models of the ferromagnetic alloys of the iron group metals, based on the assumption that for dilute alloys a rearrangement of electrons occurs around solute atoms only, while to a first approximation the electronic structure of the matrix atoms remains unaltered from that in the pure metal. Each atom carries a localized magnetic moment which contributes directly to the total saturation moment and to the magnetic part of the neutron scattering cross section, and indirectly to the hyperfine field H_n. Marshall[3] has shown that the hyperfine field in a pure ferromagnetic metal should be proportional to the magnetization. This has been confirmed experimentally for cobalt[4] and for iron[5] by varying the temperature, but the absolute agreement between theory and measurement is poor.[6] The Mössbauer effect[7] provides a method for measuring H_n for iron in alloys which may be used to test the localized models and to investigate the relation between hyperfine field and atomic moment.

We have measured the Mössbauer absorption spectrum at room temperature over the whole range of Fe-Co and Fe-Ni alloys for the 14.4-kev γ radiation of Fe^{57}. The source was prepared by electroplating Co^{57} onto copper foil, followed by diffusion by annealing. Rapid electron spin exchange resulted in a single line which had the natural width associated with the lifetime of the emitting state: The line was shifted by 0.20 mm/sec with respect to the center of the iron spectrum. The alloys were prepared by arc-casting spectroscopically standardized materials supplied by Johnson Matthey, Ltd., and were cold rolled into foils about 1 mil thick. Alloys containing 30% or less iron were enriched in Fe^{57} by plating and annealing. Data for pure cobalt and nickel were obtained with Co^{57} sources plated onto foils of each metal, using stainless steel as a monoenergetic absorber.[8] Motion of the source was provided by a moving coil vibrator driven by an amplifier and a triangular wave generator. A moving iron transducer gave a voltage proportional to the source velocity, and this waveform was fed back to the input of the amplifier, so that the velocity of the source closely followed the input waveform. Counts were fed into a single-channel pulse-height analyzer to select the 14.4-kev radiation, and the output pulses were modulated with the velocity waveform and fed into a 100-channel kicksorter. The resulting spectrum[9] showed six lines arising from the Zeeman splitting of the nuclear levels of Fe^{57}, and the hyperfine field was computed from their separations. The spectra for the alloys showed no appreciable line broadening or shifts compared with the pure iron spectrum. Hence, the variations in hyperfine field due to local inhomogeneities are small (less than 3%), and there is no large change in s-electron density at the iron nuclei due to alloying.

The variation of the magnetic field at iron nuclei in the alloys, expressed as a fraction of the field in metallic iron, is shown in Fig. 1, where $H_n(x)/H_n(0)$ is plotted against the excess electron number x over that of iron. A remarkable feature is the general similarity in form with the corresponding region of the Slater-Pauling curve[10] for the saturation moments: For both alloy systems H_n and the saturation moment show a maximum near $x = 0.3$. Even for small additions of solute it seems that large changes in the hyperfine field of the iron atoms result, in contrast to the localized theories.

If it is assumed that the hyperfine field is proportional to the atomic moment in the alloys, then the moment on iron is given by $\mu(\mathrm{Fe}) = 2.22 H_n(x)/H_n(0)$ Bohr magnetons. The field on cobalt nuclei in Fe-Co alloys has been determined from low-temperature specific heat measurements by Arp, Edmonds, and Petersen,[11] and in contrast to the field on iron nuclei it shows no maximum but increases steadily from 217×10^3 gauss in pure cobalt to about 320×10^3 gauss in iron. From these data a curve for $\mu(\mathrm{Co})$ may be derived, taking the moment in pure cobalt to be 1.71 Bohr magnetons. If these moments are averaged so that $\bar{\mu} = (1-c)\mu(\mathrm{Fe}) + c\mu(\mathrm{Co})$, where c is the cobalt concentration, $\bar{\mu}$ is found to lie on a curve which is close to the Slater-Pauling curve.

There are no data on the hfs of nickel in Fe-Ni alloys, but Shull and Wilkinson[12] have measured the atomic moments in some of these alloys by neutron diffraction. For ordered Ni_3Fe they find $\mu(\mathrm{Fe}) = 2.8$, whereas our data, combined with the

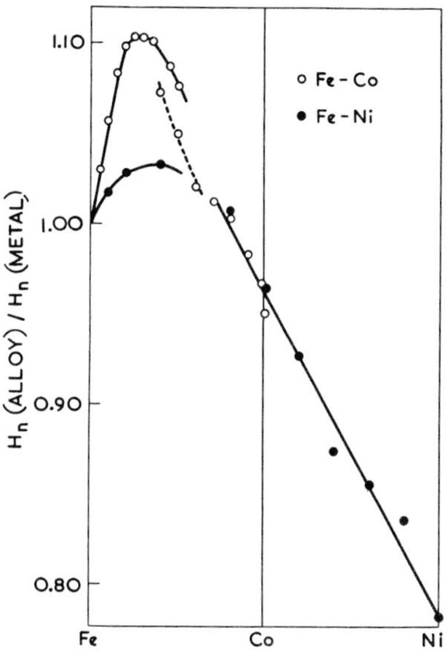

FIG. 1. The magnetic field at iron nuclei in Fe-Co and Fe-Ni alloys relative to the field in metallic iron, plotted as a function of electron number. The data in the range $Fe_{0.8}Ni_{0.2}$ to $Fe_{0.5}Ni_{0.5}$ where the Curie points are low have been corrected to take account of incomplete saturation at room temperature. Points for Co and Ni agree well with the results given by Wertheim.[8] Alloys near $Fe_{0.5}Co_{0.5}$ are very brittle and difficult to roll and the points on the dashed curve were taken with small and cracked specimens. Alloys were also prepared in this range by electroplating and they gave higher values for H_n which lie on the continuous curve.

assumption that atomic moment is proportional to H_n, give about 1.8. This implies that the proportionality between atomic moment and H_n is not strictly valid in alloys. The discrepancy could be explained by a contribution to H_n which depends on the nickel as well as the iron moments, e.g., if the component due to the conduction electron polarization were a function of the average moment $\bar{\mu}$. Since $\bar{\mu}$ for Ni_3Fe is smaller than that for iron and H_n is negative,[13] this explanation requires the polarization to be negative in accord with a suggestion of Anderson and Clogston[14] and with measurements of the field at tin nuclei in alloys with iron.[15] An estimate of the effect of such a term in the Fe-Co alloys shows that, owing to the smaller variation of $\bar{\mu}$ throughout the series, it would not destroy the agreement between $\bar{\mu}$ derived from hfs and saturation magnetization data.

We thank Dr. W. Marshall and Dr. W. M. Lomer for many valuable discussions, Dr. J. H. Stephen for performing the electroplating, and Dr. E. Bretscher for his generous support.

[1]N. F. Mott and K. W. H. Stevens, Phil. Mag. 2, 1364 (1957).

[2]W. M. Lomer and W. Marshall, Phil. Mag. 3, 185 (1958).

[3]W. Marshall, Phys. Rev. 110, 1280 (1958).

[4]A. M. Portis and A. C. Gossard, J. Appl. Phys. 31, 205S (1960).

[5]D. E. Nagle, H. Frauenfelder, R. D. Taylor, D. R. F. Cochran, and B. T. Matthias, Phys. Rev. Letters 5, 364 (1960).

[6]S. S. Hanna, J. Heberle, G. J. Perlow, R. S. Preston, and D. H. Vincent, Phys. Rev. Letters 4, 513 (1960).

[7]R. L. Mössbauer, Z. Physik 151, 124 (1958).

[8]G. K. Wertheim, Phys. Rev. Letters 4, 403 (1960).

[9]S. L. Ruby, L. M. Epstein, and K. H. Sun, Rev. Sci. Instr. 31, 580 (1960).

[10]See, e.g., C. Kittel, Introduction to Solid-State Physics (John Wiley & Sons, Inc., New York, 1953), Chap. XII.

[11]V. Arp, D. Edmonds, and R. Petersen, Phys. Rev. Letters 3, 212 (1960).

[12]C. G. Shull and M. K. Wilkinson, Phys. Rev. 97, 304 (1955).

[13]In collaboration with Dr. G. J. Perlow we have shown that the sign of the field is negative for $Fe_{0.2}Ni_{0.8}$ as well as for iron.

[14]P. W. Anderson and A. M. Clogston, Bull. Am. Phys. Soc. 6, 124 (1961).

[15]A. J. F. Boyle, D. St. P. Bunbury, and C. Edwards, Phys. Rev. Letters 5, 553 (1960).

PHYSICAL REVIEW VOLUME 122, NUMBER 6 JUNE 15, 1961

Internal Magnetic Fields in Manganese-Tin Alloys*

LUISE MEYER-SCHÜTZMEISTER, R. S. PRESTON, AND S. S. HANNA
Argonne National Laboratory, Argonne, Illinois

(Received February 13, 1961)

The hyperfine fields at the tin sites in two manganese-tin alloys have been studied as a function of temperature to above the Curie points. In addition to the Zeeman splittings, observed and analyzed previously, a possible quadrupole interaction of about 27 Mc/sec is observed in Mn_2Sn. In Mn_4Sn the hyperfine field is small and negative, about −45 koe; in Mn_2Sn it is large and positive, about +200 koe. As in the case of the pure ferromagnetic transition elements, it seems necessary to invoke a positive term associated with conduction-electron polarization and a negative one arising from core polarization to explain these results.

THE ferromagnetic alloys of manganese and tin, which were used previously[1] in observing the Zeeman splitting of the nuclear levels of Sn^{119} by means of resonant absorption,[2] have now been studied more extensively to determine the nature of the internal magnetic field at the tin nucleus. The magnitude of the field has been measured as a function of temperature, and the measurements have been carried above the Curie point in order to observe possible quadrupole or other interactions in the absence of complications produced by magnetic splitting. In addition, the sign of the field in each alloy was established by observing the change in the hyperfine structure on application of a large external magnetic field, as in our earlier work with iron.[3]

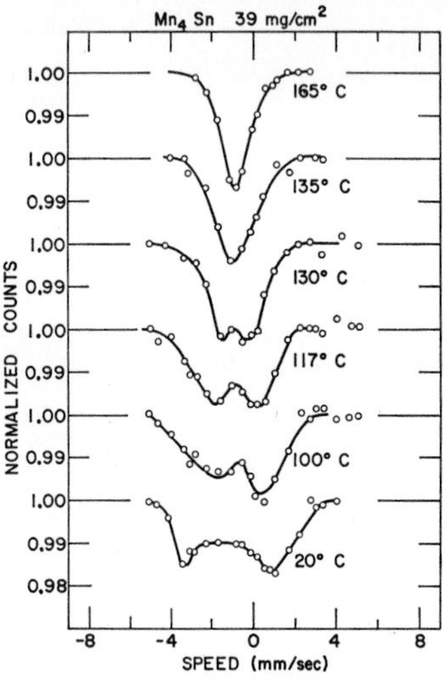

FIG. 1. Resonant absorption in Mn_4Sn, with a metallic Sn^{119} source at 77°K, for various absorber temperatures above and below the Curie point. Absorber thickness is 39 mg/cm².

Except as noted below, the experimental technique was the same as used in I. In Fig. 1 are shown measurements on Mn_4Sn at several temperatures from room temperature to above the Curie point at about 150°C.[4] For these observations the Mn_4Sn absorbing sample was clamped in vacuum in a frame which was warmed by an electrically heated coil of tungsten wire. The temperature was measured by a thermocouple in contact with the absorber. The Sn^{119} source, which emits an unsplit line, was maintained at the temperature of liquid nitrogen. It will be recalled from I that the basic resonant absorption spectrum for Mn_4Sn (with unsplit Sn source) consists of a doublet, each member of which is an unresolved triplet. The doublet separation is approximately equal to the magnetic splitting of the ground state. In Fig. 1 we can see this splitting decrease

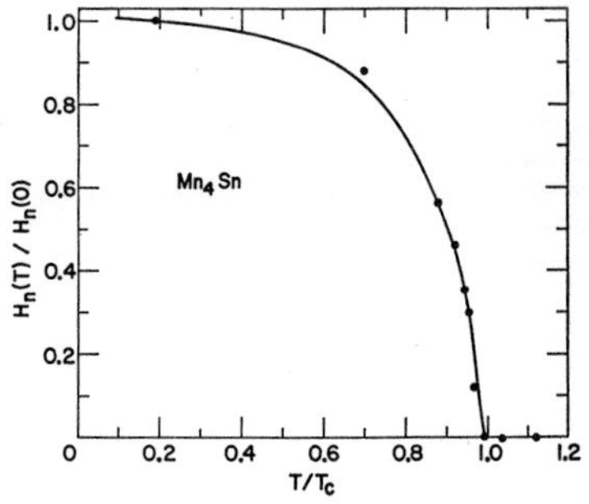

FIG. 2. Temperature variation of the internal field at the tin nucleus in Mn_4Sn. A Curie temperature T_c of 423°K has been assumed. Data taken from Fig. 1.

* Work performed under the auspices of the U. S. Atomic Energy Commission.

[1] S. S. Hanna, L. Meyer-Schützmeister, R. S. Preston, and D. H. Vincent, Phys. Rev. **120**, 2211 (1960), hereafter referred to as I.

[2] R. L. Mössbauer, Z. Physik **151**, 124 (1958).

[3] S. S. Hanna, J. Heberle, G. J. Perlow, R. S. Preston, and D. H. Vincent, Phys. Rev. Letters **4**, 513 (1960).

[4] H. H. Potter, Phil. Mag. **12**, 261 (1931). The Curie temperature is given as 178°C by Ochsenfeld (reference 5). We continue to call this alloy Mn_4Sn in accordance with much of the literature. However, the structure is close-packed hexagonal of the Ni_3Sn type (DO_{19}). Actually, single phase samples appear to have a composition intermediate between Mn_3Sn and Mn_4Sn. We are greatly indebted to M. V. Nevitt for this information.

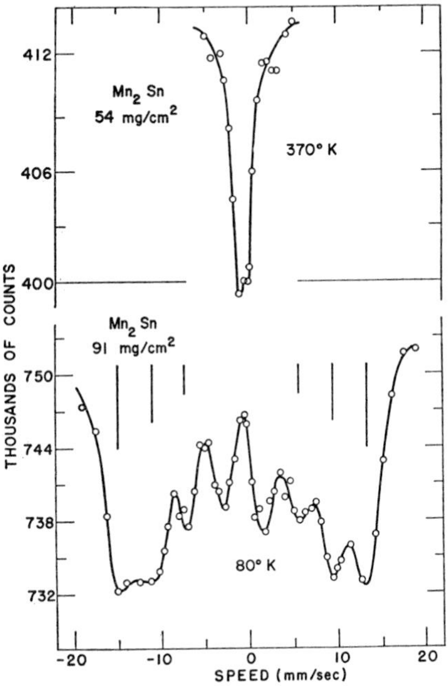

FIG. 3. Resonant absorption in Mn_2Sn, with a metallic Sn^{119} source at 77°K, at absorber temperatures below and above the Curie point. At 370°K the absorber thickness is 54 mg/cm²; at 80°K it is 91 mg/cm².

and then vanish as the temperature is raised to the Curie point. At these relatively high temperatures the absorption is very small and high precision has not been achieved in the data. The temperature variation of the internal field, as obtained from these and similar measurements, is displayed in Fig. 2. The data are normalized to the point obtained in I at the temperature of liquid nitrogen. The solid curve in the figure is a theoretical Weiss curve which is in rather good qualitative agreement with the experimental points. The value of the field at 0°K is estimated to be roughly 45 koe.

In Fig. 3 the absorption spectrum of Mn_2Sn is shown at two temperatures, one well below and the other well above the Curie point at −11°C.[5] At the lower temperature one observes the Zeeman spectrum analyzed in I. The value of the internal field at 0°K is estimated to be about 200 koe. Above the Curie point the spectrum collapses into a strong central absorption. Actually there is possibly a doublet structure in this central line as shown on an expanded velocity scale in Fig. 4. This structure is not strongly temperature dependent and would correspond to a quadrupole splitting of about 10^{-7} ev or 27 Mc/sec.

To obtain the sign of the internal field in these alloys, the powder sample, deposited on beryllium (0.010 in. thick), was clamped between two pieces of Lucite (each $\frac{1}{16}$ in. thick) and mounted in the gap ($\frac{1}{4}$ in.) of an electromagnet capable of producing fields up to 20 koe. A 0.001-in. foil of Pd was also inserted to reduce the 25-kev x ray from tin. The magnetic splittings in the absorption spectrum were then compared with the field off and on. Because of the small aperture provided by the absorber in the gap it was desirable in obtaining the absorption spectra to have the source oscillate as close as possible to the absorber in order to increase the counting rate. Since it was essential to keep the source cold, it was mounted in vacuum on a horizontal copper bar attached to a horizontal reservoir of liquid nitrogen. With this arrangement it was possible to bring the source to within about 1 in. of the absorber mounted vertically in the gap. The value of the fringing field at the average position of the source was about one sixth the field in the gap.

In the case of Mn_4Sn the measurements could be carried out with the absorber at room temperature, at which temperature the internal field at the tin nucleus has a value of about 40 koe.[1] Relative to this field the

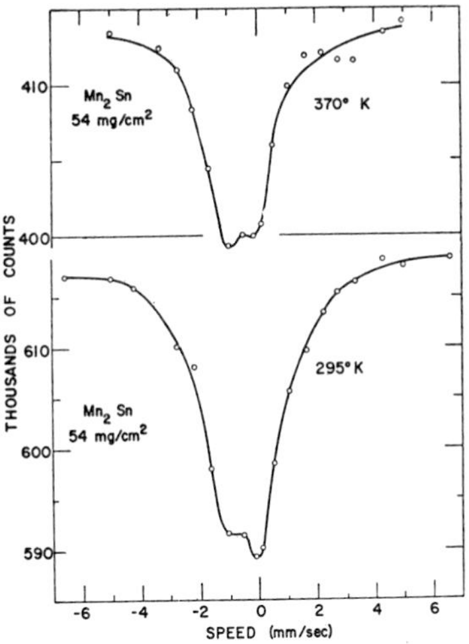

FIG. 4. Resonant absorption in Mn_2Sn, with a metallic Sn^{119} source at 77°K, at two absorber temperatures above the Curie point. The velocity scale is expanded over that in Fig. 3. Absorber thickness is 54 mg/cm².

[5] C. Guillaud, thesis, Strasbourg, 1943; quoted in R. M. Bozorth, *Ferromagnetism* (D. Van Nostrand Company, Inc., Princeton, New Jersey), p. 340; R. Ochsenfeld, Z. Metallkunde **49**, 472 (1958). This alloy is reported to have a structure of the filled NiAs type, W. Hume-Rothery and G. V. Raynor, *The Structure of Metals and Alloys* (The Institute of Metals, London, England).

applied external field of about 17 koe should produce an easily detectible shift. The observations are shown in Fig. 5. On application of the external field the doublet separation is seen to decrease. Hence the internal field at the nucleus in Mn_4Sn is negative. The amount of the shift is compatible with the linear relation,

$$H_n = H_{n0} - H_{ext},$$

where H_n and H_{n0} are the hyperfine fields with and without the external field H_{ext}.

In the case of Mn_2Sn it was necessary to cool the absorber below the Curie point (−11°C) while keeping it in the gap of the electromagnet. To produce a convenient internal field of about 40 koe the absorber was maintained at a temperature of about −23°C. This was accomplished by allowing a stream of nitrogen gas, cooled by passage through a coil immersed in liquid nitrogen, to strike each side of the Lucite holder containing the absorber. It was found that the temperature, measured with a thermocouple, could be held constant to within about 1° by carefully regulating the stream of cold nitrogen gas. It was necessary, however, to enclose the complete assembly (source, absorber, and pole pieces) in a plastic sheet in order to prevent moisture from condensing on the cold surfaces. The measurements were made by alternating many runs with field on and field off. The final averages are shown in Fig. 6. In this case the doublet separation is seen to increase on application of the field. Hence the hyperfine field at the tin nucleus in Mn_2Sn is *positive*. The amount

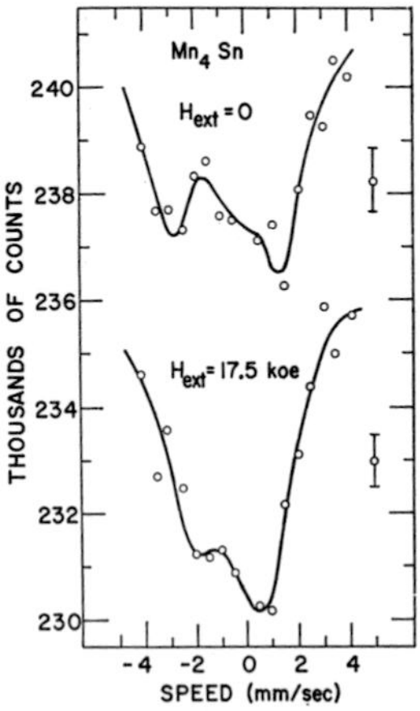

FIG. 5. Resonant absorption in Mn_4Sn at room temperature (∼300°K) without an external magnetic field (above) and with an applied field of 17.5 koe (below). The splitting is decreased by application of the field. Absorber thickness is 42 mg/cm². Source temperature is 77°K.

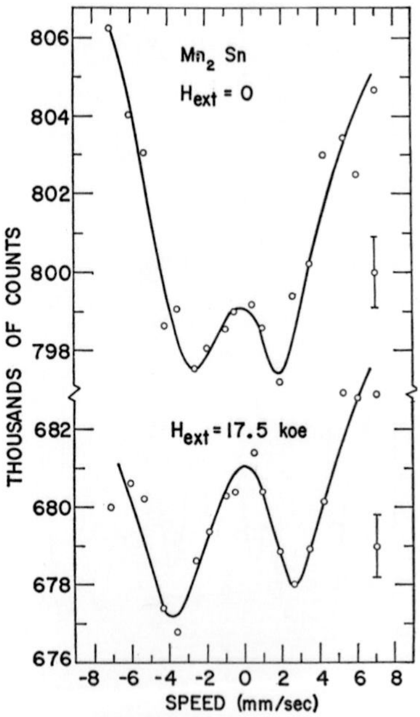

FIG. 6. Resonant absorption in Mn_2Sn at approximately 250°K without an external magnetic field (above) and with an applied field of 17.5 koe (below). The splitting is increased by application of the field. Absorber thickness is 45 mg/cm². Source temperature is 77°K.

of shift is compatible with the relation,

$$H_n = H_{n0} + H_{ext}.$$

Thus, a possible demagnetizing effect of the applied field in the sample is not noticeable in the above measurements.

Since the hyperfine field is large and negative (∼−300 koe) in the pure ferromagnetic transition elements,[3,6,7] it is of considerable interest to find such a large positive field (+200 koe) at the tin site in the case of Mn_2Sn. Moreover, this field is very sensitive to the Mn:Sn ratio, since it changes sign in going to Mn_4Sn. It is significant, perhaps, that the saturation magnetization is some four times as great in Mn_2Sn as in Mn_4Sn.[4] The hyperfine field produced by the conduction electrons is given by Marshall[8] in the form

$$H_c = (8\pi/3)n|\psi(0)|^2\mu p,$$

[6] A. C. Gossard and A. M. Portis, Phys. Rev. Letters 3, 164 (1959).

[7] S. S. Hanna, J. Heberle, C. Littlejohn, G. J. Perlow, R. S. Preston, and D. H. Vincent, Phys. Rev. Letters 4, 177 (1960).

[8] W. Marshall, Phys. Rev. 110, 1280 (1958).

where n is the number of conduction electrons per atom, $|\psi(0)|^2$ is the probability density of a conduction electron at the nucleus, μ is the Bohr magneton, and p is the polarization of the conduction electrons. It would appear that $n|\psi(0)|^2$ is roughly the same in the two alloys, since they show about the same isomer shift[9] (see Figs. 1 and 3).[9a] If, on the other hand, the polarization of conduction electrons (produced by the adjacent magnetic electrons) increases with saturation magnetization, then the polarization and so also H_c is greater numerically in Mn_2Sn than in Mn_4Sn. The simplest explanation of the large positive field in Mn_2Sn is that H_c is a *positive* field.

As for the pure transition elements,[3,10,11] it is necessary to postulate, in addition to H_c, the presence of a negative field, presumably associated with polarization of the core electrons of tin. In Mn_4Sn this field predominates. That this field is smaller, if different at all, in Mn_2Sn is consistent with the fact that the Weiss field is smaller, since the Curie temperature is lower and the magnetization larger in Mn_2Sn than in Mn_4Sn.

These effects observed in the manganese-tin alloys are somewhat analogous to those obtained by Boyle *et al.*[12] in dilute solutions of tin in the ferromagnetic transition elements. It is gratifying that essentially the same mechanisms[12] can be invoked to explain qualitatively the observations on all these tin alloys.

---

[9] O. C. Kistner and A. W. Sunyar, Phys. Rev. Letters 4, 412 (1960).

[9a] *Note added in proof.* We are indebted to V. Jaccarino for pointing out that equality of the isomer shifts does not necessarily insure the above argument, since the polarization effect is localized at the top of the conduction band.

[10] D. A. Goodings and V. Heine, Phys. Rev. Letters 5, 370 (1960).

[11] A. J. Freeman and R. E. Watson, Phys. Rev. Letters 5, 498 (1960).

[12] A. J. F. Boyle, D. St. P. Bunbury, and C. Edwards, Phys. Rev. Letters 5, 553 (1960).

PHYSICAL REVIEW VOLUME 122, NUMBER 3 MAY 1, 1961

Study of the Internal Fields Acting on Iron Nuclei in Iron Garnets, Using the Recoil-Free Absorption in Fe^{57} of the 14.4-kev Gamma Radiation from Fe^{57m}†

R. BAUMINGER, S. G. COHEN, A. MARINOV, AND S. OFER
Department of Physics, The Hebrew University, Jerusalem, Israel
(Received December 22, 1960)

The shape of the recoil-free absorption spectrum obtained in iron garnet absorbers has been investigated, using, as a source, a Co^{57} source embedded in stainless steel. The results confirm the existence of two iron sublattices each showing a Zeeman structure characterized by different parameters. No significant differences have been detected between the Zeeman structure in yttrium iron garnet and dysprosium iron garnet. The values obtained for the effective magnetic field at the Fe^{57} nuclei at room temperature are 3.90×10^5 oe and 4.85×10^5 oe for the *d* and *a* iron lattice sites, respectively. At liquid air temperature the corresponding fields are 4.6×10^5 oe and 5.4×10^5 oe, respectively. The mean value of the chemical shift for the *d* sites relative to stainless steel is about 0.04 ± 0.005 cm/sec and about 0.06 ± 0.005 cm/sec for the *a* sites.

INTRODUCTION

THE phenomenon of recoil-free resonance absorption (Mössbauer effect)[1] of nuclear gamma rays has already been shown to constitute a powerful tool for investigating the properties of the internal fields acting on nuclei in solids. In particular, the 14.4-kev gamma rays of Fe^{57m} have been employed in a striking way to study the internal fields at iron nuclei in ferro and antiferromagnetic materials.[2–4]

In these cases the Zeeman splitting patterns obtained in the absorption spectra can be simply interpreted.[5] From a knowledge of the nuclear magnetic moment of the nuclear ground state, values for the effective magnetic fields at the iron nucleus can be obtained and also in some cases the magnitude of the quadrupole interactions.

In the magnetic materials investigated so far, the iron atoms occupy equivalent lattice positions and the local fields at the iron nuclei are characterized by a single set of parameters. In the present investigation, a study has been made of the local fields in a ferrimagnetic material in which the iron atoms occupy two nonequivalent sets of positions. It was thought that this might result in a difference in the effective magnetic fields at the iron nuclei in the two sites. The ferrimagnetic materials studied were the iron garnets (stoichiometric formula 5 $Fe_2O_3\cdot3M_2O_3$, where M indicates a rare earth ion or yttrium). The magnetic properties of these materials have been studied intensively in recent years.[6] Pauthenet has shown that in order to explain these properties it is necessary to assume that the two iron sublattices in this structure have opposite and unequal magnetizations. The garnets have a body-centered cubic structure, space group O_h^{10}, the unit cell containing 96 oxygen ions in the general lattice positions, with 16 Fe^{3+} ions in the *a* special positions (octahedral sites) and 24 Fe^{3+} ions situated in the *d* special positions (tetrahedral sites). These constitute the two iron sublattices. The yttrium or rare earth ions occupy the 24 *c* dodecahedral sites. The unit cell edge is about 12 A.

Two representative garnets of the above type were studied, yttrium iron garnet and dysprosium iron garnet. The yttrium ion is diamagnetic, whereas the dysprosium ion is strongly paramagnetic. It is known that in these garnets there is an exchange field which tends to align the rare earth ions relative to the magnetization of the iron ions. Although this exchange interaction is known to be small relative to the dominant exchange interaction, which occurs between the two iron sublattices (10^5 oe compared to 6×10^6 oe),[7] it was thought of interest to see whether this could give rise to a difference in the effective field at corresponding iron nuclei for the yttrium and dysprosium garnets, respectively, at a given temperature.

Since the magnetization of the garnets is a function of temperature[6] it was also considered interesting to try to correlate the effective fields at the nucleus with temperature.

EXPERIMENTAL

In these experiments the absorption of the 14.4-kev gamma ray of Fe^{57m} bound in stainless steel was measured in polycrystalline garnet absorbers, containing iron enriched in Fe^{57}, as a function of the relative velocity between source and absorber. A stainless steel source containing Co^{57} has already been shown to give a relatively narrow unsplit emission line.[3,4] Such a source can be used very effectively to explore the absorption spectrum of an absorber containing Fe^{57}. A large argon-filled proportional counter was used to detect the 14.4-kev radiation and provided a better resolution of this radiation against background than a thin

† Supported in part by the U. S. Air Force, Air Research and Development Command through its European Office.
[1] R. L. Mössbauer, Z. Physik, 151, 124 (1958).
[2] S. S. Hanna, J. Heberle, C. Littlejohn, G. J. Perlow, R. S. Preston, and D. H. Vincent, Phys. Rev. Letters 4, 177 (1960).
[3] G. K. Wertheim, Phys. Rev. Letters 4, 403 (1960).
[4] O. C. Kistner and A. W. Sunyar, Phys. Rev. Letters 4, 412 (1960).
[5] G. DePasquali, H. Frauenfelder, S. Margulies, and R. N. Peacock, Phys. Rev. Letters 4, 71 (1960).
[6] R. Pauthenet, Ann. Phys. 3, 424 (1958).
[7] P.-G. de Gennes, C. Kittel, and A. M. Portis, Phys. Rev. 116, 323 (1959).

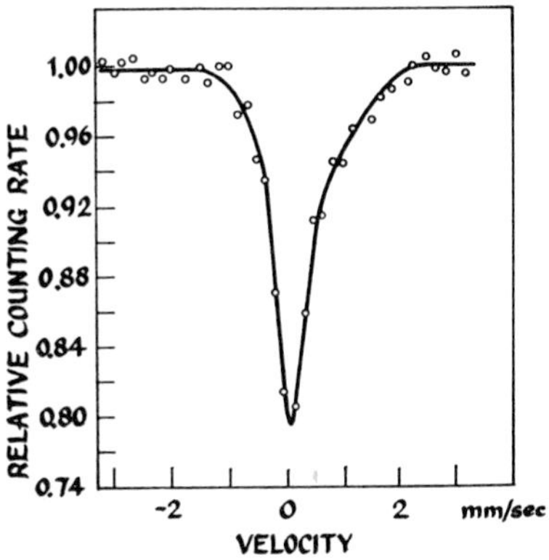

FIG. 1. The absorption by stainless steel of the 14.4-kev gamma ray emitted in the decay of Fe^{57m} embedded in stainless steel, as a function of relative velocity between source and absorber.

NaI(Tl) scintillation counter. As absorbers, two types of garnets were used in this work, yttrium iron garnet and dysprosium iron garnet. These were synthesized from Y_2O_3 or Dy_2O_3 and Fe_2O_3, containing iron enriched in Fe^{57} (70%) in order to maximize the Mössbauer absorption relative to competing processes. X-ray photographs taken by Mr. Kallman of this laboratory showed a unique crystal structure for the samples. The samples were ground fine, spread out to an average thickness of about 10 mg/cm^2 and held rigidly between thin Lucite disks, and in this form used as absorbers.

At first, the Doppler shift between source and absorber was provided by a mechanical device[8] consisting of a uniformly rotating eccentric wheel driving a carriage bearing the source, whose speed could be varied via a coupling. Later an instrument was developed which enabled the counting rate to be automatically recorded as a function of the relative velocity,[9] and the final results presented here were carried out in this way. The source was mounted on a loudspeaker membrane and vibrated sinusoidally at 65 cycles/sec. The amplitude of the output of the pulse-height selector, channelled on the 14.4-kev peak recorded in the proportional counter, was modulated in appropriate phase with the sinusoidal motion, so that the modulated part of the amplitude would be proportional to the source velocity at the time of emission of the corresponding photon. The spectrum of modulated pulses was displayed on the first 128 channels of a 256-channel pulse-height analyzer. As a consequence of the harmonic motion, the time the source spends in each velocity channel is itself a function of velocity. In order to obtain the true spectrum of counting rate as a function of velocity, the spectrum recorded on the analyzer was normalized in the following way. The output pulses from an independent scintillation counter and radioactive source were treated in an identical fashion as described above for the pulses from the proportional counter and displayed on the second half of the multichannel analyzer. The output of the two counters were alternately switched every half-minute into the single-channel analyzer equipped with modulated output and the two spectra stored in the two halves of the analyzer. Identical counting rates were arranged in order to insure similar counting losses in the two halves of the multichannel analyzer. The normalized spectrum was obtained by dividing the number in a given channel of the first half of the analyzer by the number in the corresponding channel in the second half. This method of normalization ensured good stability over long periods of time against drift in the electronic instrumentation. In practice, a scale of velocities was established by using as a calibration the absorption spectrum of antiferromagnetic Fe_2O_3 and relying on the velocity assignments to the peaks in the Zeeman pattern obtained by Kistner and Sunyar[4] and as confirmed, also, by measurements in this laboratory, using the mechanical device providing uniform relative velocity mentioned at the beginning of this section. In both the latter measurements the relative velocities were measured directly. A typical absorption spectrum of Fe_2O_3, using Co^{57} embedded in stainless steel, is shown in Fig. 2. Figure 1 shows the results obtained using a stainless steel absorber with the same source and confirms that an unsplit emission line is indeed obtained. The width of the absorption line is about four times the natural linewidth. Assuming an emission and absorption line of the same shape in the stainless steel source and stainless steel absorber, respectively, one concludes that the width of the emission line is about twice the natural width.

Measurements were carried out for both types of garnet absorbers at room temperature and also at the temperature of liquid air. The latter experiments were carried out with the garnet absorbers immersed in liquid air contained in a Styrofoam container.

RESULTS AND DISCUSSION

Figures 3 and 4 show the results obtained with the yttrium garnet absorber at room and liquid air temperatures, respectively. These spectra should be compared with the spectrum obtained with antiferromagnetic Fe_2O_3 shown in Fig. 2. The latter spectrum has already been investigated by Kistner and Sunyar[4] and analyzed in terms of a Zeeman splitting of the nuclear levels produced by a single magnetic field at the iron nucleus (5.15×10^5 oe) somewhat modified by a quad-

[8] S. Ofer, P. Avivi, R. Bauminger, A. Marinov, and S. G. Cohen, Phys. Rev. **120**, 406 (1960).

[9] The instrument used was similar to a device constructed recently by Dr. E. Sunyar of Brookhaven National Laboratory. We are indebted to him for information concerning his instrument, particularly the electronic circuits.

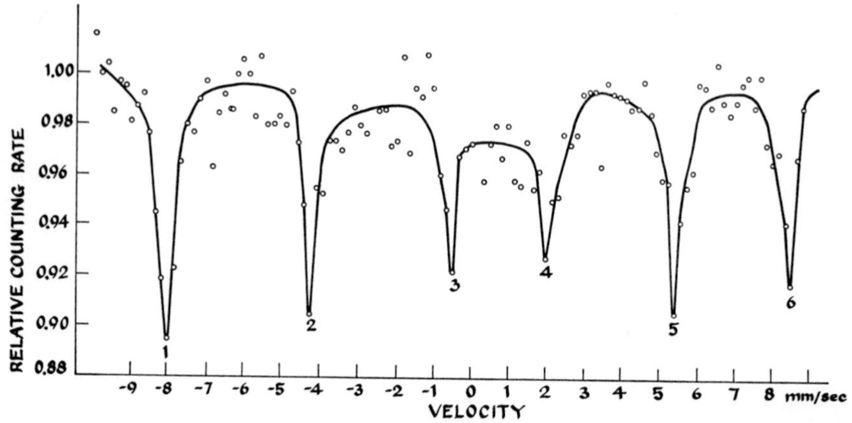

FIG. 2. The absorption at room temperature by Fe_2O_3 of the 14.4-kev gamma ray emitted in the decay of Fe^{57m} embedded in stainless steel, as a function of relative velocity between source and absorber.

rupole interaction of the Fe^{57} nucleus with a finite electric field gradient at the nucleus.

It is seen that there is an essential difference between the garnet spectra and the Fe_2O_3 spectrum, the garnet spectra consisting of a series of doublets, but otherwise resembling the Fe_2O_3 spectrum. An actual splitting is not apparent in the lines close to zero velocity (i.e., for the two "3" and "4" lines in Fig. 3 and for the three "2", "3" and "4" lines in Fig. 4) but these lines are wider than would be expected assuming a single field. This pattern in the garnets is in fact exactly that to be expected if the conjecture mentioned in the Introduction is correct, namely, that the iron nuclei situated in the two different lattice sites experience local fields which are appreciably different. One would then expect to obtain a superposition of two patterns, whose intensities are in the ratio of 3:2 (ratio of iron atoms in the two nonequivalent sites) and each resembling in shape that of Fe_2O_3 to a first approximation, but characterized by spacings determined by different parameters. The spectra have been analyzed in accordance with this interpretation.

In the cases when the doublets are resolved, the stronger component is assigned to the *d* sites (which are more numerous than the *a* sites in the ratio 3:2) and are labeled *d* in the figures, and the weaker component is assigned to the *a* sites. For the spectrum taken at room temperatures (Fig. 3) the positions of the four resolved lines "1*d*," "2*d*," "5*d*," and "6*d*" were used to calculate the four parameters determining

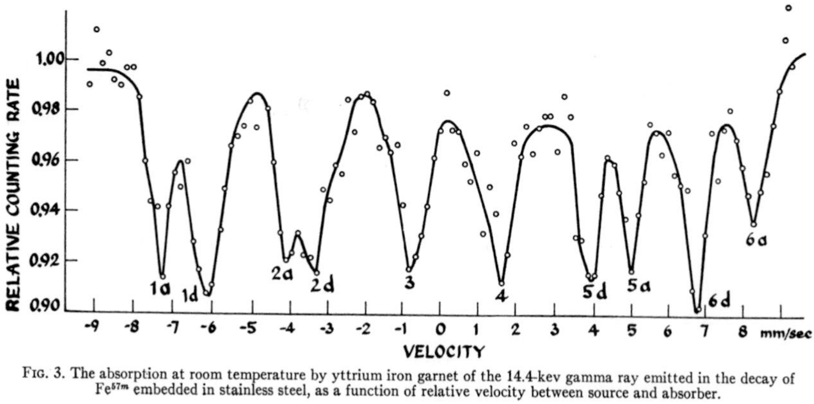

FIG. 3. The absorption at room temperature by yttrium iron garnet of the 14.4-kev gamma ray emitted in the decay of Fe^{57m} embedded in stainless steel, as a function of relative velocity between source and absorber.

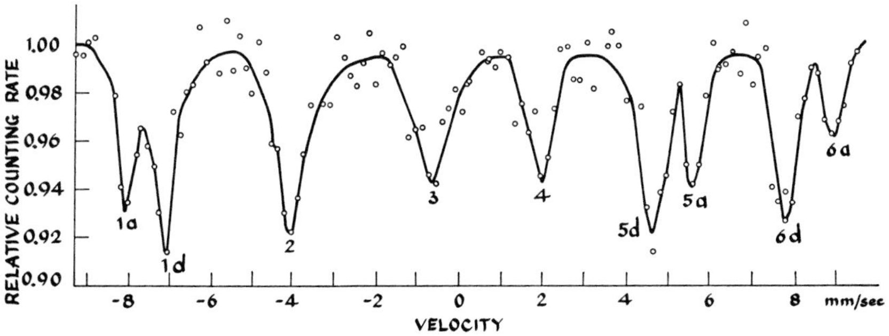

FIG. 4. The absorption at liquid air temperature by yttrium iron garnet of the 14.4-kev gamma ray emitted in the decay of Fe^{57m} embedded in stainless steel, as a function of relative velocity between source and absorber.

the Zeeman pattern of the iron nuclei in the *d* sites, and the positions of the four corresponding *a* lines to calculate the parameters of the nuclei at the *a* sites. As described in the work of Kistner and Sunyar,[4] the Zeeman spectrum is characterized by four parameters and these are uniquely determined by the position of four peaks. The parameters are, in the notation of Kistner and Sunyar: g_0 and g_1, the magnetic splitting parameters for the $\frac{1}{2}$ and $\frac{3}{2}$ nuclear levels, respectively; ΔE, the shift between the center of gravity of the absorption lines and the emission lines of Fe^{57} in stainless steel; and ϵ, the quadrupole interaction parameter, shifting only the substates belonging to the upper $\frac{3}{2}$ level. When the parameters were found in this way, the expected positions of the lines "3*a*" and "3*d*," "4*a*" and "4*d*" were calculated, and found to be in very good agreement with the position of the experimentally unresolved lines "3" and "4," thus demonstrating the consistency of the analysis. Moreover, the values of g_0/g_1 (equal to the ratio of the nuclear *g* factors in the $\frac{1}{2}$ and $\frac{3}{2}$ states) obtained are in satisfactory agreement with the value obtained by Hanna *et al.*[2] and Kistner and Sunyar.[4]

In the analysis of the spectrum taken at liquid air temperature (Fig. 4) in which only three clearly resolved doublets are seen, the four characteristic parameters for each site were calculated, assuming a value of 1.77 for g_0/g_1 and using the position of the three resolved lines appropriate to each lattice site, i.e., "1*d*," "5*d*," and "6*d*" for the *d* sites, and "1*a*," "5*a*," and "6*a*" for the *a* sites. As in the previous example, the expected positions of the remaining lines were calculated from these parameters thus obtained and found to be in good agreement with the position of the observed unresolved peaks "2," "3," and "4."

The spectra obtained with the dysprosium garnet absorber are not shown since they so closely resemble those obtained with yttrium garnet at the same temperature. They were analyzed in a similar way. The final values of the characteristic parameters g_0, g_1, ΔE, and ϵ for the two sites in the various experiments are given in Tables I and II. Table I, showing the results obtained at room temperatures, also shows the values of g_0/g_1 obtained directly from the experiments in each case. The value of the effective magnetic field at the nucleus, H_{eff}, in each case was calculated from the value obtained for g_0 using a value[10] of $+(0.0903 \pm 0.0007)$ nm for the magnetic moment of the nuclear ground state of Fe^{57}. The values of H_{eff}, determined in this way, are given in Tables I and II.

The results demonstrate that the *a* and *d* sites are indeed characterized by considerably different values of H_{eff}. Thus the values obtained for H_{eff} at room temperature are 3.9×10^5 oe at the *d* sites and 4.85×10^5

TABLE I. Results of analysis of measurements on yttrium and dysprosium iron garnets at room temperature.

	$Y_3Fe_5O_{12}$ (yttrium iron garnet) at 300°K		$Dy_3Fe_5O_{12}$ (dysprosium iron garnet) at 300°K	
	Strong spectrum *d* sites	Weak spectrum *a* sites	Strong spectrum *d* sites	Weak spectrum *a* sites
g_0 (cm/sec)	0.46±0.02	0.58±0.02	0.460±0.025	0.580±0.025
g_1 (cm/sec)	0.270±0.015	0.325±0.015	0.275±0.020	0.325±0.020
ΔE (cm/sec)	0.035±0.010	0.055±0.010	0.05±0.01	0.06±0.01
ϵ (cm/sec)	0.00±0.01	0.00±0.01	0.00±0.01	0.00±0.01
g_0/g_1	1.7±0.1	1.8±0.1	1.7±0.1	1.75±0.1
H_{eff} (oe)	$(3.90\pm0.1)\times10^5$	$(4.85\pm0.15)\times10^5$	$(3.95\pm0.15)\times10^5$	$(4.85\pm0.20)\times10^5$

[10] G. W. Ludwig and H. H. Woodbury, Phys. Rev. **117**, 1286 (1960).

TABLE II. Results of analysis of measurements on yttrium and dysprosium garnets at liquid air temperature.

	$Y_3Fe_5O_{12}$ (yttrium iron garnet) at 85°K		$Dy_3Fe_5O_{12}$ (dysprosium iron garnet) at 85°K	
	Strong spectrum *d* sites	Weak spectrum *a* sites	Strong spectrum *d* sites	Weak spectrum *a* sites
g_0 (cm/sec)	0.550±0.015	0.635±0.015	0.545±0.020	0.64±0.02
g_1 (cm/sec)	0.31±0.01	0.36±0.01	0.310±0.015	0.360±0.015
ΔE (cm/sec)	0.04±0.01	0.06±0.01	0.030±0.015	0.060±0.015
ϵ (cm/sec)	0.00±0.01	−0.010±0.01	0.00±0.015	−0.010±0.015
H_{eff} (oe)	$(4.60\pm0.15)\times10^5$	$(5.35\pm0.15)\times10^5$	$(4.6\pm0.2)\times10^5$	$(5.4\pm0.2)\times10^5$

oe at the *a* sites. The results at liquid air temperature give higher values for H_{eff}, but still different for the two sites -4.6×10^5 oe and 5.35 oe for the *d* and *a* sites, respectively.

Nagle *et al.*[11] have recently shown that in ferromagnetic iron, H_{eff}, which has a well-defined value for temperatures below the Curie temperature, shows the same functional dependence on the temperature as the relative saturation magnetization M_s, from temperatures at which the magnetization is almost saturated up to the Curie temperature. This remarkably simple result seems to demand that the fluctuations in the value of the nuclear field at a particular iron nucleus must take place in a time short compared to the Larmor precession period of the nucleus in the magnetic field produced by the extranuclear electrons.

These fluctuations may be expected to follow the fluctuations of the magnetic moment of the extranuclear electrons. The temperature dependence of the expectation value of the extranuclear moment in the direction of magnetization will then determine the temperature dependence of both the microscopic H_{eff} at the nucleus and the macroscopic magnetization. It is of interest to test these ideas in the case of the garnets and to see whether the values of H_{eff} at different temperatures are proportional to the values of the partial spontaneous magnetizations of the appropriate sublattice. The partial magnetizations cannot of course be directly measured for ferrimagnetic materials. Pauthenet, however, starting from the experimental results for the relative saturation magnetization of the garnets as a function of temperature, and using the Néel two-sublattice model,[12] has calculated the partial spontaneous magnetization for yttrium ion garnet as a function of temperature for the two iron sublattices.[13]

Table III shows a comparison between the ratio of the values of H_{eff} at 85°K and 300°K in yttrium iron garnet for the *a* and *d* sites and the corresponding ratio of the spontaneous magnetization per ion (m) as calculated by Pauthenet.[6]

The agreement is seen to be quite good and suggests that in this case, also, H_{eff} follows the variation in magnetization. It should be pointed out that the calculations of Pauthenet, based on the Néel model, indicate that at liquid air temperatures the partial magnetizations of the *a* and *d* lattices should both be very close indeed to saturation, corresponding to a value of 5 μ_B per ferric ion. Nevertheless, the values of H_{eff} remain different for the *a* and *d* sites. Assuming saturation really occurs at liquid air temperature, this behavior implies a difference in the extranuclear electronic configurations determining the nuclear field in the two sites.

As seen from the results in Tables I and II, no significant difference in the values of H_{eff} and the other parameters between the corresponding sites in yttrium and dysprosium garnets has been detected. The local fields at the corresponding sites in the two garnets cannot differ by more than a few percent. This is not unreasonable in view of the relatively small value of the exchange interaction acting between the rare earth ions and the ferric ions.

It is not to be expected that a reliable value of the quadrupole interaction can be obtained from measurements on polycrystalline materials, since the shift in the sublevels due to the quadrupole interaction is a function of the angle between the magnetic field and the direction of the field gradients which are well defined with respect to the crystallographic axis. In fact, for the case of an axially symmetric field gradient and completely random orientation between the direction of magnetic field and the field gradient, the average quadrupole shift, to first order, would be zero, and only a line broadening would be produced. In ferromagnetic and ferrimagnetic materials the correlation which in general will exist between the orientation of a crystallite and the orientations of the domains within this crystallite may very well lead to an average value of the quadrupole shift different from zero. The present results show no evidence of an appreciable quadrupole shift, but in view of the above, little can be deduced

TABLE III. Comparison of ratio of value of H_{eff} at 85°K and at 300°K, with ratio of partial magnetizations at these temperatures as calculated by Pauthenet, for yttrium iron garnet.

	d sites	*a* sites
$H_{eff}(85°K)/H_{eff}(300°K)$	1.16	1.11
$m(85°K)/m(300°K)$	1.17	1.08

[11] D. E. Nagle, H. Fraunfelder, R. D. Taylor, D. R. F. Cochran, and B. T. Matthias, Phys. Rev. Letters 5, 364 (1960).
[12] L. Néel, Ann. Phys. 3, 137 (1948).
[13] See reference 6, Fig. 12 and p. 454.

concerning an upper limit for the quadrupole interaction at the iron nucleus.

Concerning the chemical shifts, there is no evidence of any temperature dependence. The values of the chemical shift however, do seem to be consistently greater at the *a* sites than the value at the *d* sites. Noting that H_{eff} is greater at the *a* sites than at the *d* sites, one might speculate on a possible correlation between chemical shift and the saturation value of H_{eff}. If an appreciable part of the chemical shift is due to an isotope shift, as has been suggested by Kistner and Sunyar,[4] such a correlation may arise since the isotope shift should certainly be influenced by changes in the value of *s* wave functions at the nucleus and it is possible that H_{eff} will also be influenced by these changes.

ACKNOWLEDGMENTS

The authors would like to thank M. Schieber of the department of electronics, the Weizmann Institute, for preparing the garnets, E. Sunyar of Brookhaven National Laboratory for information concerning electronic circuits, E. Segal for help in constructing the apparatus, and A. Mustachi for help in chemical problems.

ON THE USE OF THE MÖSSBAUER EFFECT FOR STUDYING LOCALIZED OSCILLATIONS OF ATOMS IN SOLIDS

S. V. MALEEV

Leningrad Physico-Technical Institute, Academy of Sciences, U.S.S.R.

Submitted to JETP editor June 29, 1960

J. Exptl. Theoret. Phys. (U.S.S.R.) **39**, 891-892 (September, 1960)

THE Mössbauer effect consists in the emission (or resonant absorption) by a nucleus in a solid of a γ quantum with an energy which is precisely equal to the energy of the transition, because of the fact that the recoil momentum is transferred to the crystal as a whole.

Usually the nucleus which radiates the γ quantum is formed by the decay of some other nucleus. As a result of this process, the nucleus can with a very high probability leave its place in the lattice and get stuck somewhere at an interstitial position. But, even if the nucleus does not move about, if it should change its atomic number as a result of the decay the forces holding it in the lattice will change. Thus the nucleus emitting the Mössbauer quantum must be a lattice defect.

On the other hand it is well known (cf. reference 1) that the spectrum of oscillations of a defect atom in a lattice consists of a continuous spectrum, coinciding with the spectrum of oscillations of the ideal lattice, and of discrete frequencies which do not coincide with any of the frequencies of normal vibrations of the atoms of the ideal lattice. Vibrations with such frequencies (localized oscillations) cannot propagate through the lattice over any sizeable distance.

At the same time there is a finite probability that in the emission of a γ quantum there is simultaneously emitted or absorbed (the latter, naturally, only for sufficiently high temperatures, $T \gtrsim \hbar\omega_L$, where ω_L is the frequency of the localized oscillation) a quantum of the localized oscillation. Thus, the spectrum of emitted γ quanta will consist of an unshifted line corresponding to the energy of the transition and of a continuous background corresponding to the emission and absorption simultaneously with the γ quantum of phonons from the continuous part of the spectrum of oscillations of the atom; on this background, there will be individual discrete peaks due to the emission and absorption of quanta of the localized oscillations.

These peaks can be observed in almost the same way as the unshifted line is observed. Namely, an absorber containing atoms in the ground state should be moved with such a velocity that the Doppler shift of its undisplaced absorption line will be equal to the frequency of the localized oscillation. One then will observe a stronger absorption than for neighboring frequencies. The velocity needed for this is obviously determined by the condition $\omega_L = v\omega/c$, where ω is the frequency of the γ line. If the energy of the transition is of the order of tens of kev, and $\hbar\omega_L \sim 0.01$ ev, $v \sim 10^3 - 10^4$ cm/sec. Such a velocity is not difficult to obtain by placing the absorber on the rim of a rotating disk.

[1] Maradudin, Mazur, Montroll, and Weiss, Revs. Modern Phys. **30**, 175 (1958).

Translated by M. Hamermesh

Polarization of Co^{57} in Fe Metal*

J. G. Dash,† R. D. Taylor, D. E. Nagle, P. P. Craig, and W. M. Visscher
Los Alamos Scientific Laboratory, University of California, Los Alamos, New Mexico

(Received December 16, 1960)

A study has been made of the effect of low temperatures on the resonant emission and absorption of 14.4-kev Mössbauer radiation from Fe^{57} in Fe metal. Analysis of intensity changes in the hyperfine spectrum is made in terms of the Zeeman level splittings of the ground states of Fe^{57} absorbing nuclei and of the ground states of Co^{57} parent nuclei. The theory for the temperature dependence is developed in terms of the properties of the Co^{57} decay and of the subsequent gamma transitions. Experiments were carried out with a source of Co^{57} nuclei in Fe metal at temperatures between 4.5° and 0.85°K. The experimental results, analyzed in terms of the theory, yield a value of the hyperfine magnetic field at the Co^{57} nuclei. Comparison of the result with other pertinent experimental values indicates that depolarization of the nuclei by the K-capture decay of Co^{57} is not evident in the present material.

I. INTRODUCTION

THE 14.4-kev gamma rays of Fe^{57} nuclei are known to have, in suitable crystals, a high proportion f of recoil-free, or "Mössbauer" radiation.[1–4] Interest in the Fe^{57} system is enhanced by the relatively narrow linewidths characteristic of the excited state (lifetime 10^{-7} sec) and the clearly resolvable hyperfine components of the Mössbauer pattern. Experiments with Fe crystal sources and absorbers are facilitated by the large value of f even at room temperature as a consequence of the high Debye characteristic temperature ($\Theta \simeq 420$°K) and the low nuclear recoil temperature ($T_R \simeq 40$°K). A source of Co^{57} nuclei dissolved in a Fe lattice at room temperature has $f \simeq 0.7$[1]; cooling the source to 0°K increases f to 0.92. This limit is achieved to within 0.1% by 20°K, and similar "saturation" obtains for the fraction f' of recoil-free absorption by an absorber of Fe^{57} in Fe metal. Further cooling will result in a negligible increase of f and f'; cryogenic studies of the system might appear unprofitable.

At sufficiently low temperatures, however, a redistribution of the populations of the Zeeman sublevels takes place, and the nuclei become polarized.[5] This polarization can be quantitatively studied through the effect upon the hyperfine Mössbauer spectrum. While nuclear polarization in ferromagnets has been observed before,[6] the present technique offers certain advantages. In this type of experiment the magnitude and sign of the magnetic field at the Co nucleus may be determined. The effects of the nuclear polarization are the concern of this paper.

II. Fe^{57} IN Fe METAL

The ground state of Co^{57}, with a half-life of 270 days, decays by K-electron capture and neutrino emission to the second excited state of Fe^{57}. The decay is probably an allowed transition, since its value of $\log ft=6$ lies

* Work performed under the auspices of the U. S. Atomic Energy Commission.
† Present address, University of Washington, Seattle, Washington.
[1] R. V. Pound and G. A. Rebka, Jr., Phys. Rev. Letters **3**, 554 (1959).
[2] J. P. Schiffer and W. Marshall, Phys. Rev. Letters **3**, 556 (1959).
[3] G. de Pasquali, H. Frauenfelder, S. Margulies, and R. N. Peacock, Phys. Rev. Letters **4**, 71 (1960).
[4] S. S. Hanna, J. Heberle, C. Littlejohn, G. J. Perlow, R. S. Preston, and and D. H. Vincent, Phys. Rev. Letters **4**, 177 (1960).
[5] J. G. Dash, R. D. Taylor, P. P. Craig, D. E. Nagle, D. R. F. Cochran, and W. E. Keller, Phys. Rev. Letters **5**, 152 (1960).
[6] M. J. Steenland and H. A. Tolhoek, *Progress in Low-Temperature Physics*, edited by C. J. Gorter (Interscience Publishers, Inc., New York, 1957), Vol. II, Chap. X, p. 292.

within the limits of log*ft* for known allowed transitions,[7] and this agrees with accepted spin assignments and considerations based on the shell model. The nuclear spin I_3 of Co^{57} is 7/2, and its magnetic moment μ_3 is 4.65 nm.[8] The second excited state of Fe^{57} has spin I_2 of 5/2 and a mean lifetime of about 9×10^{-9} sec.[9] This state decays, by emission of a 123-kev gamma ray, to the first excited state of Fe^{57}. A minor fraction (9%) of the decays involve a transition from the second excited state directly to the ground state, with the emission of a 137-kev gamma ray.[10] The multipolarity of the 123-kev radiation is 96% $M1$, 4% $E2$.[9,11] The first excited state has spin $I_1=3/2$, and moment μ_1 of 0.153 nm.[4] This state has a half-life of 1.1×10^{-7} sec, and decays by pure $M1$ emission of a 14.4-kev gamma ray, to the ground state of Fe^{57}. The spin of the ground state, I_0, is 1/2, and it has a moment μ_0 of 0.0903 nm.[12] Experiments on the Mössbauer effect have been used to obtain a detailed description of the first excited and ground states of Fe^{57} in Fe metal.[4] Results of this study, together with the properties of the higher states, are shown in Fig. 1. We also show the normal order of sublevels of Co^{57}, deduced from preliminary results[5] of the study reported here.

The hyperfine magnetic field H acting on equivalent nuclei in a ferromagnetic crystal has a single direction in space over the region of a ferromagnetic domain. Coupling between the nuclear magnetic moments and the hyperfine field removes the degeneracy of nuclear spin orientation and produces a set of equally spaced spin sublevels of energies $\Delta E_{hfs}=mg\mu_n H$, $-I\leq m\leq I$, where m is the magnetic quantum number, g is the nuclear gyromagnetic ratio, and μ_n is the nuclear magneton. In cubic Fe metal, all nuclei occupy equivalent lattice positions; hence, there is a single preferred direction in space and a single set of energy sublevels for the Fe nuclei in each ferromagnetic domain. An unmagnetized sample has its domains oriented in several directions, such that there is no net spatial polarization of the entire sample, but all of the nuclei (excepting those in the neighborhood of imperfections and impurities, and possibly those near domain walls) have the same hyperfine level splittings. The splittings of the first excited and ground states of Fe^{57} are greater than the linewidth of the 14.4-kev resonance radiation. Gamma-ray transitions between the 14.4-kev sublevels of magnetic quantum number m_j to the ground-state

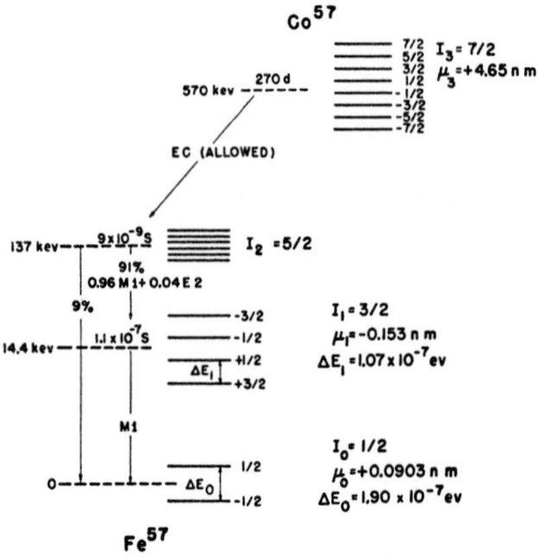

FIG. 1. Energy level diagram of Co^{57} and daughter nuclei.

sublevels m_k ($m_k=m_j$, $m_j\pm1$), therefore result in a gamma-ray spectrum of six hyperfine components. The relative intensity of the transition ($m_j\rightarrow m_k$) is proportional to the probability w_{jk} specified by the rules governing magnetic dipole radiation. Figure 2 is a schematic diagram of the radiation, similar to a diagram given by Hanna *et al.*[4] The radiation widths are suppressed, and relative intensities are appropriate to the case of unpolarized radiation from a source having no net magnetization.[12a] Positions of the line centers are given in terms of Doppler velocity shifts (positive velocity taken as increasing separation between source and detector) equivalent to shifts from the energy difference between degenerate excited and ground states. The m values of the upper and lower state sublevels are shown at the top and bottom of each line.

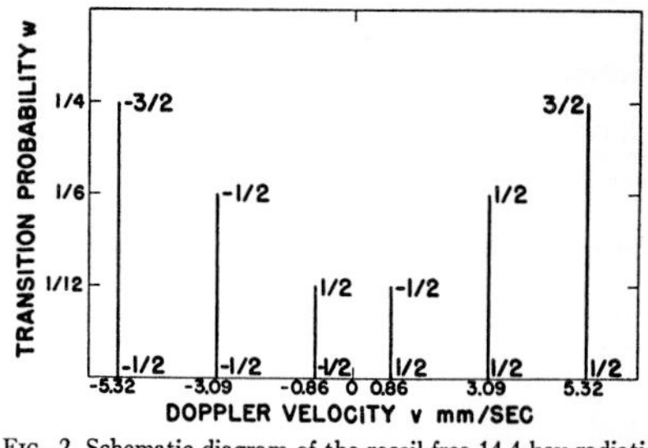

FIG. 2. Schematic diagram of the recoil-free 14.4-kev radiation from Fe^{57} in Fe metal. Individual linewidths are not shown. Relative transition probabilities are appropriate to the case of domains oriented at random. Energy displacements are in terms of Doppler velocity, positive velocity being taken as increasing separation between source and observer. Magnetic sublevel quantum numbers for the first excited and ground states are shown at top and bottom, respectively, of each line.

[7] B. L. Robinson and R. W. Fink, Revs. Modern Phys. **32**, 117 (1960).
[8] J. M. Baker, B. Bleaney, P. M. Llewellyn, and P. F. D. Shaw, Proc. Phys. Soc. (London) **A69**, 353 (1956).
[9] G. F. Pieper and N. P. Heydenburg, Phys. Rev. **107**, 1300 (1957).
[10] D. E. Alburger and M. A. Grace, Proc. Phys. Soc. (London) **A67**, 280 (1954).
[11] G. R. Bishop, M. A. Grace, C. E. Johnson, A. C. Knipper, H. R. Lemmer, J. Perez y Torba, and R. G. Scurlock, Phil. Mag. **46**, 951 (1955).
[12] G. W. Ludwig and H. H. Woodbury, Phys. Rev. **117**, 1286 (1960).

[12a] See "note added in proof."

An absorber of Fe^{57} in Fe metal has a similar hyperfine pattern of resonant cross sections. If Fig. 2 is translated over an identical pattern, the overlaps at velocity differences $v=v(\text{source})-v(\text{absorber})$ represent the absorption dips obtained when a source is moved relative to an absorber, resulting in a Mössbauer-type intensity pattern. As a result of chemical or temperature differences between source and absorber, the emission and absorption spectra are shifted relative to each other by a small Doppler velocity δv.[13,14] This shift is not essential to the present study, and the relative velocities v will be understood to represent the displacements from δv.

III. THEORY

Polarization and Depolarization

The intensity of the emission line $(m_j \rightarrow m_k)$ is proportional to the transition probability w_{jk} and to the population p_j of the sublevel at which the transition originates. We define W_{jk} as the normalized relative intensity

$$W_{jk}=p_j w_{jk}/\sum_{jk} p_j w_{jk}. \tag{1}$$

In thermal equilibrium the populations p_j are proportional to the Boltzmann factors of the nuclear sublevels. The nuclear spins of the first excited state of Fe^{57}, however, are not in thermal equilibrium. Gossard and Portis[15] have measured a spin relaxation time of 10^{-4} sec for Co^{59} nuclei in Co metal, and one may expect the relaxation time to increase as T^{-1} at lower temperatures.[16] The relaxation mechanisms for Co and Fe nuclei in Fe metal should be quite similar to those in the Co metal, and we may therefore treat the spin populations of the 14.4-kev state of Fe^{57} as unchanged during the 10^{-7} sec state lifetime. Since the lifetime of the second excited state is even shorter than 10^{-7} sec, the p_j of a source of 14.4-kev radiation are functions of the populations of sublevels in the 270-day Co^{57} parent. The equilibrium population p_l of the Co^{57} sublevel, in the case of pure magnetic hfs, is given by the Boltzmann factor:

$$p_l=C\exp(m_l\xi T^{-1}), \quad \text{where} \quad \xi=g\mu_n H k^{-1}; \tag{2}$$

m_l is the magnetic quantum member of the sublevel, T is the temperature, $g\mu_n$ is the moment of the Co^{57} nucleus, H is the hyperfine magnetic field at the nucleus, k is Boltzmann's constant, and C is a constant. A Co^{57} nucleus in the m_l sublevel decays to the m_j sublevel of the 14.4-kev state of Fe^{57} with a probability Q_{lj}. The matrix Q is the product of Clebsch-Gordan matrices for the two transitions preceding the arrival at the 14.4-kev state, and is presented in the Appendix. We can therefore obtain the p_j of the 14.4-kev state by summing contributions from the parent sublevels:

$$p_j=\text{const}\sum_l p_l Q_{lj}. \tag{3}$$

Substituting Eqs. (2) and (3) in Eq. (1), we obtain the relative intensity of an emission line $(m_j \rightarrow m_k)$ of a source,

$$W_{jk}=w_{jk}\sum_l e^{m_l\xi/T}Q_{lj}/\left(\sum_{jk} w_{jk}\sum_l e^{m_l\xi/T}Q_{lj}\right). \tag{4}$$

We have assumed that spin lattice relaxation causes negligible depolarization of the spins during the K capture and subsequent gamma emissions. A second possible mechanism for depolarization is due to perturbations by extranuclear fields resulting from K capture. A study of the angular distribution of the 123-kev radiation from partially aligned Co^{57} nuclei in a Tutton salt[11] indicated considerable depolarization of the second excited state, presumably as a result of the K-capture process. Depolarization to the extent observed in the Tutton salt would cause a marked decrease in the population asymmetries. We believe at the outset, however, that the large electron mobilities in the Fe metal provide a rapid extinction of the perturbing fields, making depolarization much smaller than in the salt.

Transmitted Intensities

We consider a resonance emission spectrum composed of several lines of Lorentzian shape, each line having the width Γ. The relative intensity of a line centered at energy E_{jk} is W_{jk}. When the source of radiation is moving away from the observer at speed v, the intensity distribution of the $(m_j \rightarrow m_k)$ line is given by

$$\mathcal{I}_{jk}(v)=\frac{I\Gamma/2\pi}{(E-E_{jk}+E_{jk}v/c)^2+\Gamma^2/4}, \tag{5}$$

where I is the total intensity,

$$I=\sum_{jk} W_{jk}\int_0^\infty \mathcal{I}_{jk}(v)dE. \tag{6}$$

The hyperfine emission spectrum of a source can be analyzed by filtering the radiation through an absorber containing ground-state nuclei: in the present case, Fe^{57}. Absorbing nuclei are excited from ground-state sublevels to sublevels of the first excited state, and the transitions $(m_{k'} \rightarrow m_{j'})$ have relative "intensities" $W_{k'j'}$, where the primed symbols represent the absorber. The hyperfine resonant absorption cross section is composed of lines of cross section $W_{k'j'}\sigma_{k'j'}$, where

$$\sigma_{k'j'}=\frac{\sigma\Gamma^2/4}{(E-E_{k'j'})^2+\Gamma^2/4}, \tag{7}$$

[13] R. V. Pound and G. A. Rebka, Jr., Phys. Rev. Letters 4, 274 (1960).
[14] B. D. Josephson, Phys. Rev. Letters 4, 341 (1960).
[15] A. C. Gossard and A. M. Portis, Phys. Rev. Letters 3, 164 (1959).
[16] G. E. Pake, in *Solid State Physics*, edited by F. Seitz and D. Turnbull (Academic Press, Inc., New York, 1956), Vol. 2.

and σ is the total resonant absorption cross section. If such an absorber is placed between a source of radiation as is represented by Eq. (5), the intensity transmitted at relative Doppler speed v is

$$I_t(v)=\sum_{jk} W_{jk}\int_0^\infty \mathcal{g}_{jk}(v) \times\exp[-naf' \sum_{k'j'} W_{k'j'}\sigma_{k'j'}]dE, \quad (8)$$

where n is the total number of atoms/cm² in the absorber, a is the abundance of the isotope which absorbs resonantly, and f' is the fraction of recoil-free resonant absorptions.[17]

The overlap integral of Eq. (8) is implicitly limited to the case of unpolarized spectra obtained with unmagnetized sources and absorbers. In the event of a net magnetization it is necessary to take account of the relative orientations of the magnetic fields acting on the source and absorber nuclei. We will, however, limit this treatment to the case of unpolarized radiation, such as is represented in Fig. 2. The integral in Eq. (8) can be solved in closed form for two special cases: either perfect overlap of emission and absorption lines, or for no overlap. The latter case is equivalent to no resonant absorption, the transmitted intensity then being given by Eq. (6). In the case of perfect overlap, when an emission line energy E_{jk} is Doppler shifted so that $E_{jk}(1-v/c)=E_{k'j'}$, the transmitted jk line intensity $I_t(jk)$ can be written

$$I_t(jk)=\frac{I}{\pi}W_{jk}\int_{-\infty}^{\infty}\frac{dy}{1+y^2}\exp\left[\frac{-W_{k'j'}x}{1+y^2}\right], \quad (9)$$

where $y=2(E-E_{k'j'})/\Gamma$, and $x=naf'\sigma$. The solution of Eq. (9) is

$$I_t(jk)=IW_{jk}J_0(iW_{k'j'}x/2)\exp(-W_{k'j'}x/2), \quad (10)$$

where J_0 is the Bessel function of zeroth order. We shall assume that the 14.4-kev spectrum given in Fig. 2 represents both the emission spectrum of the source and the absorption pattern of the absorber. The overlap, or Mössbauer, pattern of such a source-absorber combination has several discrete Doppler speeds V at which the transmitted intensity due to all emission lines can be expressed in terms of the two special cases given above. Although the Lorentzian form of the lines vanishes only at infinity, a separation of 5Γ between source and absorption line energies is sufficient to reduce the resonant absorption to less than 1% of that at perfect overlap. We shall adopt this separation as a practical criterion for the absence of overlap. There are then four speeds V at which we can evaluate the transmitted intensity with good accuracy: These speeds are 2.23, 6.18, 8.41, and 10.46 mm/sec. The overlap and no-overlap contributions can be distinguished by a function Δ_V having the properties:

$$\Delta_V=1, \quad \text{when} \quad E_{jk}(1-V/c)=E_{k'j'},$$
$$\Delta_V=0, \quad \text{when} \quad |E_{jk}(1-V/c)-E_{k'j'}|>5\Gamma. \quad (11)$$

The intensity transmitted at one of these discrete speeds can then be obtained by summing the contributions of overlapping and nonoverlapping lines:

$$I_t(V)=I\sum_{jkk'j'} W_{jk} \times\{1-\Delta_V[1-J_0(iW_{k'j'}x/2)\exp(-W_{k'j'}x/2)]\}. \quad (12)$$

The hyperfine radiation is, in practice, associated with a broad background of nonresonant gamma rays, and the absorber has a certain amount of nonresonant absorption. The nonresonant background to the Mössbauer pattern can be formally eliminated by comparing transmitted intensities at speed V with the intensity transmitted at high speed. The results of our experiment are expressed as a ratio,

$$R(V)\equiv[I_\infty-I_t(V)]/[I_\infty-I_t(-V)], \quad (13)$$

where I_∞ is the intensity transmitted at speeds high enough so that no lines overlap, and $I_t(V)$ and $I_t(-V)$ are the intensities transmitted at $+V$ and $-V$, respectively. The explicit dependence of $R(V)$ on the relative intensities of source and absorber lines is obtained by substituting Eq. (12) in Eq. (13):

$$R(V)=\sum_{jkk'j'}\Delta_V W_{jk}K_{k'j'}(x)/\sum_{jkk'j'}\Delta_{-V}W_{jk}K_{k'j'}(x), \quad (14)$$

where

$$K_{k'j'}(x)=1-J_0(iW_{k'j'}x/2)\exp(-W_{k'j'}x/2).$$

We wish to obtain the explicit dependence of $R(V)$ on the temperature of the source or of the absorber. Each case will be treated separately in the following sections.

Cold Source

We assume the absorber to be sufficiently warm so that we can neglect differences between sublevel populations in the absorber: $W_{k'j'}=w_{k'j'}/\sum_{k'j'}w_{k'j'}$. The temperature dependence of $R(V)$ then arises from the differences in Boltzmann factors of the Co^{57} sublevels and their influence on relative line intensities, Eq. (4). Before making the indicated substitution for W_{jk} in Eq. (14), we note a symmetry property of the hyperfine spectrum, Fig. 2: If emission line (j,k) overlaps absorption line (k',j') at relative velocity V, then $(-j,-k)$ overlaps $(-k',-j')$ at velocity $-V$. Furthermore, the transition probabilities of symmetric lines are equal:

$$w_{jk}=w_{-j-k}, \quad \text{and} \quad w_{k'j'}=w_{-k'-j'}.$$

Making use of these relations, substituting Eq. (4) in

[17] P. P. Craig, J. G. Dash, A. D. McGuire, D. Nagle, and R. D. Reiswig, Phys. Rev. Letters 3, 221 (1959).

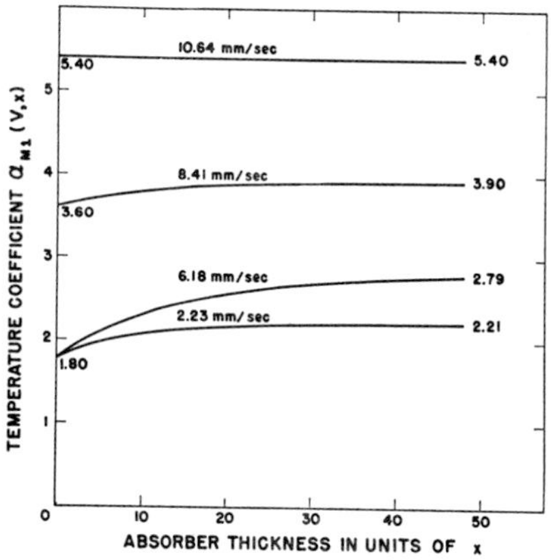

FIG. 3. Calculated temperature coefficients of several relative absorption-emission velocities as a function of the thickness parameter x.

Eq. (14) yields

$$R(V)=\frac{\sum_{jkk'j'}\Delta_V K_{k'j'}(x)w_{jk}\sum_l e^{m_l\xi/T}Q_{lj}}{\sum_{jkk'j'}\Delta_V K_{k'j'}(x)w_{jk}\sum_l e^{m_l\xi/T}Q_{l-j}}=\frac{\sum_{jkk'j'}\Delta_V K_{k'j'}(x)w_{jk}\sum_l e^{m_l\xi/T}Q_{lj}}{\sum_{jkk'j'}\Delta_V K_{k'j'}(x)w_{jk}\sum_l e^{-m_l\xi/T}Q_{lj}},\quad(15)$$

since $Q_{lj}=Q_{-l-j}$. Equation (15) takes a simple form at relatively high temperatures, when $\xi/T\ll 1$. Expanding the Boltzmann factors to first order in ξ/T, we obtain the high-temperature approximation,

$$R(V)=1+\alpha(V,x)\xi T^{-1},\quad(16)$$

where

$$\alpha(V,x)=\frac{2\sum_{jkk'j'}\Delta_V K_{k'j'}(x)w_{jk}\sum_l m_l Q_{lj}}{\sum_{jkk'j'}\Delta_V K_{k'j'}(x)w_{jk}\sum_l Q_{lj}}.\quad(17)$$

The decay from the first excited state to the ground state of Fe^{57} is pure $M1$. There is, however, a mixture of $M1$ and $E2$ gamma rays in the decay from the second to first excited states. If we assume that the mixture is incoherent, as for the unpolarized spectra from unmagnetized sources, the temperature coefficient will have a similar mixture:

$$R(V)=1+[0.96\alpha_{M1}(V,t)+0.04\alpha_{E2}(V,t)]\xi T^{-1},\quad(18)$$

where α_{M1} and α_{E2} are the coefficients corresponding to Eq. (17) with the proper matrix elements Q_{lj} for $M1$ and $E2$ radiation, respectively.

The temperature coefficient $\alpha_{M1}(V,x)$ for each speed V is shown as a function of the thickness parameter in Fig. 3. Coefficients $\alpha_{E2}(V,x)$ are approximately one-half to one-third of the corresponding factor for the $M1$ radiation: The coefficient representing all of the transitions can therefore be estimated as 98% of the $\alpha_{M1}(V,x)$.

Cold Absorber

The temperature dependence of $R(V)$ for a warm source and a cold absorber is related to the splitting of the ground-state levels of Fe^{57} in the absorber, and is independent of the hfs of the ground state of Co^{57}. Therefore, this case does not depend on the matrix elements Q_{lj}, and the analysis is accordingly simpler. Also, no depolarization or coherence effects are present as considered above. Since we have not investigated this arrangement experimentally, we will only approximate the temperature dependence. The approximation considered is that of a thin absorber, $xW_{k'j'}/2\ll 1$. Expanding $K_{k'j'}(x)$ to first order in x, and expressing the relative strength $W_{k'j'}$ of an absorption line in terms of the population $p_{k'}$ of the ground-state sublevel,

$$K_{k'j'}(x)\simeq xW_{k'j'}/2=xp_{k'}w_{k'j'}/(2\sum_{k'j'}p_{k'}w_{k'j'}).\quad(19)$$

The most convenient overlap speeds for exploring the dependence of $R(V)$ on absorber temperature are those at $V=6.18$, 8.41, and 10.46 mm/sec. At these moderately strong absorption dips, all overlaps at $+V$ are due to absorption lines arising from the $+1/2$ ground-state sublevel, and all at $-V$ originate from the $-1/2$ sublevel. Equation (14) reduces, for these cases, to the particularly simple form:

$$R(V)=p_{\frac{1}{2}}/p_{-\frac{1}{2}}=\exp(\xi_0T^{-1}),\quad(20)$$

where $\xi_0 k$ is the energy splitting of the ground-state sublevels.

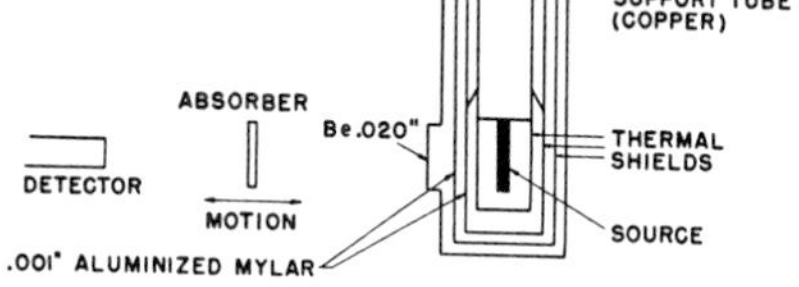

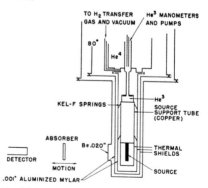

FIG. 4. Schematic diagram of the experimental arrangement.

IV. EXPERIMENTAL APPARATUS

A schematic diagram of the experimental arrangement is shown in Fig. 4. The cryostat has a somewhat unconventional design in that no liquid extends down to the height of the sample. The source is thermally protected by three concentric copper shields, the tops of which are maintained at liquid N_2, liquid He^4, and liquid He^3 temperatures. These features permit the 14-kev radiation to leave the cryostat with an attenuation due only to thin windows in the shields; namely, 0.001-in. Al at He^3 temperatures, 0.001-in. aluminized Mylar plastic at 1.4°K and 80°K, and 0.020-in. Be at room temperature. The source was connected directly to the He^3 reservoir via a heavy copper tube held rigidly in place within the He^4 shield by means of compressed leaf springs made of Kel-F plastic. The flange at the top of the He^4 shield was sealed to the He^4 reservoir by means of a Sn-In O-ring.

The desired temperature was reached and maintained by controlling the pumping rate on the He^3 bath. Temperatures were determined from the observed He^3 bath vapor pressures and a carbon resistance thermometer attached to the source holder.

The 10-millicurie source was prepared in the manner described by Pound and Rebka.[1] Co^{57} was plated from a $Co^{57}Cl_2$ solution on a 0.007-in. thick of Armco iron which was then annealed in vacuum for approximately one hour at 900°C to cause diffusion of the Co^{57} into the Fe lattice. The thin sheet was soft soldered to a copper holder for rigidity and good thermal contact.

Absorbing foils of Fe^{57} metal were prepared either by plating the enriched isotope on 0.1-mil Ni foil or by rolling sheets of the enriched Fe metal. The rolled foils were made by a technique used by Karasek of the Argonne National Laboratory.[18] A button of 78% Fe^{57}, 22% Fe^{56}, was rolled to approximately 1-mil thickness in successive stages during which the sheets were annealed several times. The 1-mil sheet was further reduced by "pack rolling" between ferrotype plates, to approximately 0.1 mil. The foil was clamped between thin sheets of Mylar plastic by a soft iron frame holder.

The detector consisted of a 1-mm thick NaI(Tl) crystal sealed to an RCA 6342 photomultiplier tube. Scintillation pulses corresponding to energies in the neighborhood of 14 kev were counted by means of a Franklin Model 358 amplifier and single-channel analyzer, a modified Berkeley Model 7161–3 counter and a digital recorder.

The absorber foils were mounted on a sliding carriage whose mean position was 20 cm in front of the scintillator crystal. A cable system drove the carriage at fixed linear speeds over a 6-cm horizontal path. This drive consisted of a 1/25-hp synchronous motor, worm gear speed reducers, and a 40-speed lathe gear box. Microswitches at each end of the carriage path reversed the motor, and after an initial absorber travel of about 1 cm, the microswitches automatically reset and started the counter. The timing interval on the counter could be preset to four significant figures, so that counting could be made over almost the same absorber path at any given speed. This procedure averaged the measured intensities over nearly the same path length for positive and negative velocities, and was found to be necessary because of a 1% difference in counting rates between the extremes of absorber travel. The gear box and three interchangeable worm gear reducers allowed a choice of 120 Doppler speeds, ranging from 0.0143 to 14.94 mm/sec at a motor speed of 1800 rpm. Intervals between the speed settings were adequate to explore the shape of the central absorption peak, but were in some cases too coarse to examine the details of other lines. We therefore used a vernier control on the speed by running the synchronous motor at power frequencies between 50 and 70 cps. The variable frequency power was generated by two audio oscillators and a power amplifier; the two oscillators were used alternately for positive and negative absorber velocities. This scheme made compensation possible for the small temperature and chemical shifts of the resonance patterns by setting the oscillators to different frequencies. The oscillator frequencies were measured and found to be stable to better than 0.1%. A 100-kc/sec crystal driven chronograph and optical gating system showed the absorber speeds to be uniform and stable to better than 0.03% over the whole length of travel when the motor was driven by the 60-cps power line. When two frequencies were used to drive the motor, the path length for the velocity corresponding to the lower drive frequency was slightly shorter because the preset timer on the counter was not alternated: The effect on the data is discussed in the next section. Unwanted relative motion of the source with respect to the absorber due to lateral vibration of the source within the cryostat was reduced by means of the Kel-F spacers. With this internal bracing, the assembly approached the rigidity of the outer casing of the cryostat; this in turn was fixed to the platform which supported the absorber carriage. Rigidity and good thermal isolation of the colder regions of the cryostat are somewhat incompatible; it was necessary to reach a compromise between the two extremes.

[18] S. S. Hanna (private communication).

Experimental Results

The absorbers used were a plated foil of 2 mg/cm² Fe^{57} and a rolled foil of 1.73 mg/cm² Fe^{57}. Although both foils had comparable resonance absorptions, the rolled foil was better in two respects; it had a narrower line and a smaller resonance pattern shift when both source and absorber were at room temperature. This shift was approximately 1.2×10^{-2} mm/sec, equivalent to a fractional resonant frequency difference between source and absorber of $\Delta\nu/\nu=4\times10^{-15}$, and could be accounted for by a difference between the characteristic Debye

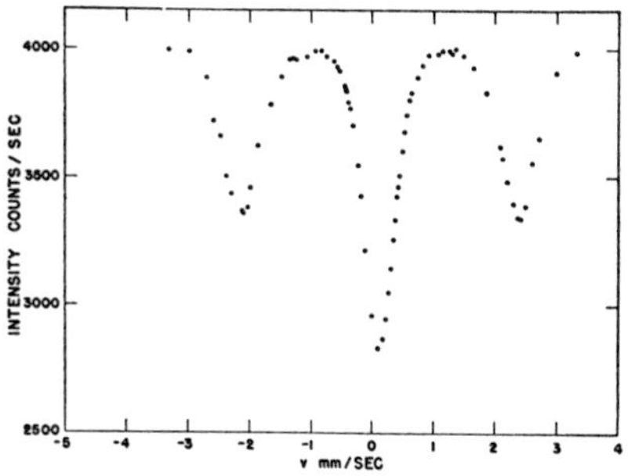

FIG. 5. Experimental overlap pattern of Fe^{57} in Fe metal, for Doppler speeds between 0 and 3 mm/sec. The source is Co^{57} in Fe metal at 4.5°K, and the resonant absorber is a 1.7-mg/cm² Fe^{57} rolled foil at room temperature. Intensities correspond to total counting rates of gamma rays having energies between 10 and 18 kev.

temperatures of source and absorber of 6°K.[19] The central absorption peak of the rolled foil had a width at half height of 0.42 mm/sec and a depth 53% (uncorrected for background) below the intensity at high velocities. This width is approximately two times that expected for a thin absorber, and corresponds closely to the width expected for the thick foil used. The first strong satellite absorption lines at 2.23 mm/sec were well resolved, and had the theoretical ratio, 0.57, of depth compared to the central peak. Upon cooling the source to low temperatures, the central resonance peak broadened to 0.60 mm/sec. The shift is in close agreement with that observed previously for an absorber at room temperature and a source at the temperature of liquid air.[13] The increased resonance width can be attributed to differences between the hfs of the source and absorber, due to the variation of hfs with temperature; this effect has been studied in more detail at higher temperatures,[20,21] and will not be discussed here. The resonance pattern obtained with the rolled foil and with the source at 4.5°K is shown in Fig. 5. Vibration associated with the accelerations at the ends of the absorber travel became excessive at higher speeds; consequently, the first strong satellite lines were judged most suitable for examining the intensity asymmetry at low temperatures.

Preliminary experiments[5] conducted with the present source required the application of a large external magnetic field in the plane of the source foil. An appreciable remanent magnetization of the source could possibly lead to errors in the present work if, in addition, the absorber were magnetized. The latter condition could result from the method of preparation of the absorber. A combination of the two circumstances would change the relative intensities of the absorption dips at the several source-absorber speeds V, as a result of the net polarization of individual spectral components.[4] To a first-order approximation, a net polarization does not influence the relative contributions of individual lines, and hence, the temperature dependence of $R(V)$. Nevertheless, an experimental check of the net polarization of the spectra was made; the absorber orientation was rotated by 90 degrees about an axis normal to its plane. This rotation caused no perceptible changes in transmitted intensities, ensuring that the spectrum of Fig. 2 was appropriate to the experiment.

Experimental values of R (2.23 mm/sec) for temperatures between 4.5° and 0.85°K are shown in Fig. 6. Data points were taken over a period of several hours for each temperature, in order to accumulate the necessary number of counts, $\sim 10^7$, for adequate statistics. That the line does not pass through 1.00 at $1/T=0$ is probably due to a geometry effect. The counting rate with the absorber placed at the extremes of the normal travel was shown to be slightly different; as also noted earlier the absorber path length was slightly different for positive and negative velocities in this particular experiment. A systematic 0.3% change in the counting rate at one of the satellites used in obtaining the ratio would shift the ordinate in Fig. 6 by 0.015.

The experimental slope, $dR/dT^{-1}=0.0313\pm0.0021$ obtained by a least squares analysis is directly proportional to the magnitude of the field H at the Co^{57} nuclei. In order to deduce H, it is necessary to evaluate the coefficients in Eq. (18) for the actual foil thickness.

The total resonance cross section is given by the formula[17]

$$\sigma=2\pi\lambda^2\frac{2I_1+1}{2I_0+1}\left(\frac{1}{1+\alpha}\right)=1.48\times10^{-18}\ \text{cm}^2, \quad (21)$$

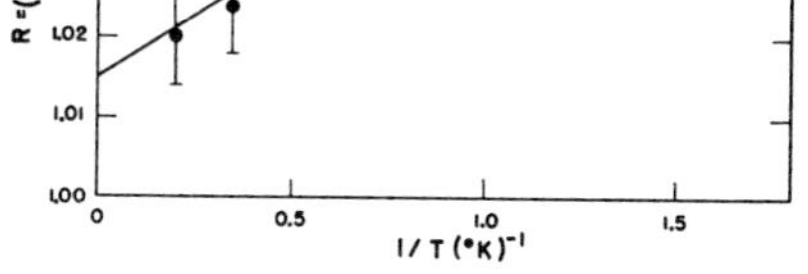

FIG. 6. Intensity ratio R for the 2.23-mm/sec resonant absorption dip at several temperatures between 4.5°K and 0.85°K.

[19] R. V. Pound and G. A. Rebka, Phys. Rev. Letters 4, 335 (1960).

[20] S. S. Hanna, Proceedings of the Allerton Park Conference on the Mössbauer Effect, University of Illinois, 1960 (unpublished), pp. 39–40; D. H. Vincent, R. S. Preston, J. Heberle, and S. S. Hanna, Bull. Am. Phys. Soc. 5, 428 (1960).

[21] D. E. Nagle, H. Frauenfelder, R. D. Taylor, D. R. F. Cochran, and B. T. Matthias, Phys. Rev. Letters 5, 364 (1960).

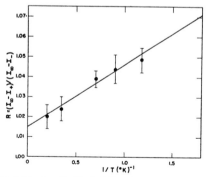

where $\lambda\!\!\!^{-}$ is $(2\pi)^{-1}$ times the wavelength of the 14.4-kev radiation, I_1 and I_0 are the spins of the excited and ground states, respectively, and[22] $\alpha=15$ is the internal conversion coefficient. The calculated thickness parameter for the 1.73-mg/cm^2 foil is $x=27$. The effective thickness for the absorption lines having the intensity factors $w_{k'j'}=1/12$, 1/6, and 1/4 which overlap in the 2.23-mm/sec resonance are therefore $xw_{k'j'}/2=1.13$, 2.26, and 3.39, respectively. The temperature coefficients are calculated to be

$$\alpha_{M1}(V=2.23\text{ mm/sec}, x=27)=2.19,$$
$$\alpha_{E2}(V=2.23\text{ mm/sec}, x=27)=1.13.$$

The resulting formula for the ratio of intensities is, by Eq. (18),

$$R(V)=1+2.15\xi T^{-1}. \qquad (22)$$

Comparison of Eq. (22) and the experimental value of $R(V)$ leads to the measured value of the Co^{57} level splitting,

$$\xi=(14.6\pm1.0)\times10^{-3}\text{°K}.$$

The hyperfine magnetic field H corresponding to this splitting is 300±20 kilogauss.[12a]

V. DISCUSSION

The hfs magnetic field H acting on Co nuclei at low concentrations in Fe metal has been measured previously by other methods. Table I lists the values obtained to date. All measurements were made at low temperatures. The experimental uncertainties in all of the determinations are probably within a factor of 2 of the 7% estimated for the present work. There is no evident disagreement among the several measurements. Since the earlier studies could not be subject to the depolarization mechanisms discussed earlier in this paper, it is apparent that depolarization does not play an important role in the present technique. It is clear that we have observed no major depolarization such as occurs for Co^{57} in a Tutton salt.[11] We can conclude that the perturbing fields which are considered to be responsible for the Tutton salt results arise after the K-capture decay of the Co^{57}, and are probably due, in the Tutton salt, to long-lived holes in the outer electron shells. These holes are filled rapidly by the conduction electrons of the metal, in times that are short compared to the 10^{-8}-sec lifetime of the 136-kev state of Fe^{57}.

TABLE I. Hyperfine field H at Co nuclei in Fe metal.

Reference	Method	H (kilogauss)
Present work		300
(23)	Specific heat	320
(24)	Specific heat	315
(25)	Gamma-ray (Co^{60}) anisotropy	350

Finally, we note that the magnitude of H for Co in Fe metal is much closer to the field value of 333 kilogauss for Fe in Fe metal[4] than to the value 219 kilogauss for Co in Co metal.[15] It is not surprising that for these materials the effect of environment appears to dominate those interactions which may be ascribed to the individual atoms. Co differs from Fe in that it has one additional 3d electron, which is probably accepted into the unfilled 3d band of the Fe metal, thus leaving the Co nucleus in an environment characteristic of the surrounding Fe.

ACKNOWLEDGMENTS

We gratefully acknowledge the contributions of several people. L. Wilets of the University of Washington helped us to clarify our understanding of details of the decay scheme. R. Keil provided the thin rolled absorbers, and J. M. Dickinson assisted in the preparation of samples. W. E. Keller and D. R. F. Cochran, who collaborated on the initial experiments, encouraged and assisted us in the present work. R. R. Rylander constructed portions of the apparatus, and R. Hanft assisted in many of the measurements.

APPENDIX

Here we calculate the coefficients Q_{lj} which were introduced in Eq. (3). Q_{lj} is the probability that, if the Co^{57} nucleus initially has magnetic quantum number m_l, the decay will proceed to the Fe^{57} first excited state with magnetic quantum number m_j. It depends, in addition to the spins of the nuclear states involved, upon the character of the K capture, and on the multipolarity of the γ ray emitted in the transition between the second and first excited states.[26] As has been discussed in the text, the K capture is almost certainly Gamow-Teller allowed, and we will calculate the coefficients for both of the possible multipolarities, namely, $M1$ and $E2$. In case the radiation is not pure, but, as is realized for this γ ray, is a mixture of $M1$ and $E2$, there will in general be interference between the two components. However, the interference term vanishes when averaged over angle, so that if the source is unmagnetized it will have no effect, and the result obtained by adding the two contributions [see Eq. (18)] is correct.

If we denote the wave functions of Co^{57} and the second and first excited states of Fe^{57} by $\psi_{7/2}^{m_l}$, $\psi_{5/2}^{m'}$, and $\psi_{3/2}^{m_j}$, respectively, then the cobalt decay may be

[22] H. R. Lemmer, O. J. A. Segaert, and M. A. Grace, Proc. Phys. Soc. (London) A68, 701 (1955).
[23] V. Arp, D. Edmonds, and R. Petersen, Phys. Rev. Letters 3, 212 (1959).
[24] N. Kurti, Suppl. J. Appl. Phys. 30, 2155 (1960).
[25] A. V. Kogan, V. D. Kul'kov, L. P. Nikitin, N. M. Reinov, I. A. Sokolov, and M. F. Stel'makh, J. Exptl. Theoret. Phys. (U.S.S.R.) 39, 47 (1960) [translation: Soviet Phys.—JETP 12(39), 34 (1961)].

[26] It also depends on depolarizing forces, if any, which act in the intermediate state. We calculate it on the assumption that there are none.

TABLE II. Q_{lj} for $L=1$ ($M1$ γ ray).

m_l \ m_j	3/2	1/2	−1/2	−3/2
7/2	1	0	0	0
5/2	4/7	3/7	0	0
3/2	2/7	4/7	1/7	0
1/2	4/35	18/35	12/35	1/35
−1/2	1/35	12/35	18/35	4/35
−3/2	0	1/7	4/7	2/7
−5/2	0	0	3/7	4/7
−7/2	0	0	0	1

TABLE III. Q_{lj} for $L=2$ ($E2$ γ ray).

m_l \ m_j	3/2	1/2	−1/2	−3/2
7/2	3/7	4/7	0	0
5/2	24/49	9/49	16/49	0
3/2	22/49	4/49	19/49	4/49
1/2	12/35	38/245	72/245	51/245
−1/2	51/245	72/245	38/245	12/35
−3/2	4/49	19/49	4/49	22/49
−5/2	0	16/49	9/49	24/49
−7/2	0	0	4/7	3/7

represented by

$$\psi_{7/2}{}^{m_l} \to \textstyle\sum_{m'} C(7/2, m_l|5/2, m'; 1, m_l-m') \times \psi_{5/2}{}^{m'} \chi_1{}^{m_l-m'}, \quad \text{(A1)}$$

where C is the usual Clebsch-Gordan coefficient and χ is a triplet S-wave function describing the emitted neutrino plus the absorbed electron. In turn, the decay of the second excited state is written

$$\psi_{5/2}{}^{m'} \to \sum_{m_j} C(5/2, m'|3/2, m_j; L, m'-m_j) \times \psi_{3/2}{}^{m_j} \gamma_L{}^{m'-m_j}, \quad \text{(A2)}$$

where γ_L represents the emitted γ ray of multipole order L. Upon substituting (A2) into (A1),

$$\psi_{7/2} \to \sum_{m_j} \sum_{m'} C(7/2, m_l|5/2 m'; 1, m_l-m') \times C(5/2, m'|3/2, m_j; L, m'-m_j) \times \chi_1{}^{m_l-m'} \gamma_L{}^{m'-m_j} \psi_{3/2}{}^{m_j},$$

we find that the sum of squares of the contributions to the coefficient of $\psi_{3/2}{}^{m_j}$ is

$$Q_{lj} = \textstyle\sum_{m'} |C(7/2, m_l|5/2, m'; 1, m_l-m') \times C(5/2, m'|3/2, m_j; L, m'-m_j)|^2.$$

The Clebsch-Gordan coefficients may be easily calculated, or found in tables, and the sum (which never contains more than 3 terms) evaluated numerically. The results are shown in Table II for $L=1$ (dipole γ ray), in Table III for $L=2$ (quadrupole γ ray).

Note added in proof. Recent examination of the hyperfine spectra of source and absorber by an unsplit absorber and source, respectively, has yielded relative intensities in the ratio 3:3.2:1, indicating that the samples were partially magnetized. Calculations based upon the revised spectrum increases the deduced value of the hyperfine field at Co^{57} nuclei to 375 kgauss. Further deviation of the actual intensity distribution from the distribution assumed in the text does not cause a further increase in the calculated field. Uncertainty in the intermediate magnetic history of the specimens prevents specifying the hyperfine field more precisely within the limits of 300 and 375 kgauss. Experiments now in progress should resolve the uncertainty in the near future.

COMMENTS AND CORRECTIONS

The authors of the papers listed below have requested that the following corrections to their papers be noted:

Diffusion des photons sur les atomes et les noyaux dans les cristaux, by C. Tzara • J. phys. radium, 22, 303 (1961)

205 2nd col., 4th line under head: For "[4]" read "[3]"
2nd col., 11th line under head: For "[5]" read "[4]"

206 1st col., 11th line: For "$dN(\omega)/\alpha\omega$" read "$dN(\omega)/d\omega$"
1st col., 13th line: For "(5)" read "[4]"

207 1st col., line above eq. (1): For "[6]" read "[5]"
Eq. (1): The numerator should read

$$\langle \{\beta_s\} | e^{iK_1u/\hbar} | \{n_s\}\rangle \{n_s\} 1 e^{iK_2u/\hbar} | \{\alpha_s\}\rangle$$

Last equation on page:
Numerator should start $1\langle \{$ etc.

208 1st col., eq. (3): Square the whole term in the first line of the equation
1st col.: Equation below (3) should read
$k_{is} = K_i \epsilon_s (2MN\hbar\omega_s)^{-1/2}$

Polarized Spectra and Hyperfine Structure in Fe^{57}, by S. S. Hanna et al. • Phys. Rev. Letters, 4, 177 (1960)

226 Figure 2: Reverse the signs of all the magnetic quantum numbers

227 Line 33: Sentence should read "Thus, the spacings between lines 1 and 2, 4 and 5, and 5 and 6 should be equal to the splitting of the *excited* state."

Temperature-Dependent Shift of γ Rays Emitted by a Solid, by B. D. Josephson • Phys. Rev. Letters, 4, 341 (1960)

252 1st col.: The last equation should read

$$\begin{aligned}\delta E &= \langle \delta H \rangle = \langle \delta (p_i^2/2m_i) \rangle \\ &= -\delta m_i \langle p_i^2/2m_i^2 \rangle \\ &= -(\delta m_i/m_i)T_i = (E/m_i c^2)T_i\end{aligned}$$

Recoilless Rayleigh Scattering in Solids, by C. Tzara and R. Barloutaud • Phys. Rev. Letters, 4, 405 (1960)

279 1st col.: Equation (1) should read

$$\varphi_T = \exp\left\{-\frac{3}{2}\frac{E_r}{k\theta}\left[1 + \frac{4}{x^2}\int_0^x \frac{u\,du}{e^u - 1}\right]\right\}$$

The Mössbauer Effect in Tin from 120°K to the Melting Point, by A. J. F. Boyle et al. • Proc. Phys. Soc. (London), 77, 129 (1961)

291 Eqs. (6), (7), and (8): A minus sign should precede the right-hand side of each equation

292 Eq. (10) should read

$$C_V = k\left\{1 + \frac{kT}{a}\left[15\left(\frac{b}{a}\right)^2 - 6\left(\frac{c}{a}\right)\right]\right\}$$